LIVING BUTTERFLIES
OF
SOUTHERN AFRICA

THE PRODUCTION OF THIS BOOK WAS MADE POSSIBLE
BY THE GENEROUS SUPPORT OF

FIRST NATIONAL BANK

Living Butterflies
of
Southern Africa

BIOLOGY, ECOLOGY AND CONSERVATION

VOLUME I

HESPERIIDAE, PAPILIONIDAE AND PIERIDAE OF SOUTH AFRICA

by
GRAHAM A. HENNING
STEPHEN F. HENNING
JOHN G. JOANNOU
STEPHEN E. WOODHALL

Umdaus Press
1997

UMDAUS PRESS
P.O. BOX 11059
0028 HATFIELD
SOUTH AFRICA

REGISTRATION NO. 94/06389/07

FIRST PUBLISHED 1997

COPYRIGHT© GRAHAM A HENNING, STEPHEN F HENNING,
JOHN G JOANNOU & STEPHEN E WOODHALL 1997

EDITED BY ROGER DIXON AND FRANCOIS STEFFENS

DESIGN BY TERSIA VAN RENSEN

REPRODUCTION BY STUDIO SCAN, PRETORIA

PRINTED BY TIEN WAH PRESS (PTE) LTD, SINGAPORE

ISBN 1-919766-01-4 (SPONSORS' EDITION)
ISBN 1-919766-02-2 (COLLECTORS' EDITION)
ISBN 1-919766-03-0 (STANDARD EDITION)

IN MEMORY OF

ROBERT DUNDONALD PARÉ

1946 – 1995

CONTENTS

Contents

Contents

Contents

INTRODUCTION

I am extremely fortunate to have been exposed to beautifully presented natural history books all my life, and, for more than thirty years, I have been an avid collector of those much needed records of all living things that surround us and share our fragile world. Without these records, which are at once educational, and glorious to behold, future generations would be deprived of a literary and visual 'archive' of the flora and fauna of both the past and present. I trust that the interest and dedication of those few who promote the successful publication of such 'archives' will ensure that our natural treasures remain in the present instead of being relegated to the past.

I deem it an honour to be writing this introduction to the first volume of the five volume series entitled *Living Butterflies of Southern Africa*. I have to admit however to a somewhat limited knowledge in the field of entomology; my involvement in this publication has indeed opened a new door and will, I hope, educate me in a previously 'shadowy' subject. The first thing that stimulated my interest in this book was the depiction of living subjects, not dried, lifeless examples of a former glory which was experienced too briefly. One can only marvel at the patience and skill of the photographers who captured these 'living moments' for posterity.

As a result of man's increasing impact in Africa, many species of our flora and fauna are threatened with extinction. The widespread intrusion of 'First World greed', with its all-encompassing technological power, probably 'guarantees' that a great number of species which are largely habitat-specific will lose the battle for survival and become extinct. An example of this, currently ongoing, is the plight of the Brenton Blue Butterfly – *Orachrysons niobe* (Trimen), and the battle to save it from sure extinction at its last known colony/locality on earth. With the assurance that future 'developments' should give necessary thought to the environment and all those creatures great and small that survive in it, we may succeed in preserving what little is left for future generations.

So often have I stressed the importance of the support given by the corporate world in making possible the publication of books such as this. It is therefore most gratifying to know that this support is also provided by private individuals. In this context I should like to mention the publisher Umdaus Press, whose members display such admirable commitment and dedication. They share a common interest in natural history, in particular, succulent plants, and a desire to conserve and promote knowledge of South African succulent plants. Although the subject of butterflies is slightly out of their field of expertise, the members of Umdaus Press were so impressed by the photographs and text of *Living Butterflies of Southern Africa* that the whole project became irresistible. The nettle was grasped and the process of production commenced, even though they knew that the publication would be a major drain on financial resources. So committed were these men to publish this work that they were prepared to make considerable sacrifices, both financial and personal. These actions show extreme dedication to the cause of conservation and the pursuit of knowledge and must surely be saluted by all those who share an interest in the preservation of what little is left.

This dedicated team comprises Professor Francois Steffens, Head of the Department of Statistics at UNISA, Kotie Retief, a former lecturer in mathematics at the University of Pretoria, Paul Brink an attorney and lecturer in law at UNISA, Roger Dixon, a retired curator of the Geological Survey Museum, Pretoria, and now a forensic scientist with the South African Police Service. Last, but certainly not least, Alex Fick, a civil engineer and avid collector of natural history books.

The work which has resulted is a vindication of their decision to back this mammoth project. It fills an important gap in the knowledge and content of previous works on butterflies and will surely establish the publishing success of Umdaus Press and those who run it. Their future plans will no doubt be as exciting. I will certainly monitor and support their endeavours in any way possible. Such dedication needs to be rewarded, and I have no doubt that it will be so.

With their wish to conserve our butterfly heritage the authors have been inspired to produce this series of books which emphasises butterflies as living organisms. There are currently about 884 described species of butterfly in Southern Africa, belonging to five families. The Southern African subregion covers the entire geographical area south of the Kunene, Okavango and Zambesi rivers – the ecologically diverse countries of South Africa, Lesotho, Swaziland, Botswana, Namibia, Moçambique and Zimbabwe. The work is divided into five volumes, the first four covering South Africa, Lesotho and Swaziland, and the fifth volume dealing with Botswana, Namibia, Moçambique and Zimbabwe, as well as with species not included in previous volumes.

The magnitude of the task of producing this series of books is beyond the scope of a single individual, and as such, has led to the combining of the talents of the four authors. John Joannou is a leading photographer of lepidoptera. He actively promotes these insects in South Africa, advising local government on lepidopteran matters and lecturing to the public on the subject. He is an expert in rearing butterflies with many new life history discoveries to his credit and he has also discovered the butterfly *Aloeides barbarae*. The brothers, Graham and Stephen Henning are the recognised authorities on southern African butterflies and have been studying them since 1961. They have led the initiative in the conservation of these insects, jointly working towards the establishment of the first Entomological Reserve in Africa at Ruimsig, Gauteng. They have also authored the *South African Red Data Book* on butterflies and are currently involved in the campaign to save the Brenton Blue. Stephen and Graham have published over 100 scientific works on these wonderful creatures and have been responsible for the major butterfly publications of recent years. The fourth author, Stephen Woodhall is not only an expert photographer, but a keen and gifted artist. Stephen's enthusiasm, in promoting butterflies to the general public is well known. He regularly produces articles for journals and magazines, is consulted on the production of television programmes and lectures widely to interested groups. All four authors are active members of the Lepidopterists' Society of Africa. They have all at some time, served on its council, with Stephen and Graham Henning currently holding the posts of President and Secretary respectively. It is no wonder that with this vast reservoir of talent to draw from, such a magnificent book has been produced.

This series of books has been written in such a way that even I, with my limited knowledge of the subject, can easily understand. All aspects of butterfly life are covered, including their requirements for survival, and we are given an insight into the enormous and fascinating world of insects generally. In these pages the interaction between butterflies and their food plants and predators, their cooperation with ants to their mutual benefit and their relationship with their specific environments all reveal a world unbelievably complex and astounding. The importance of habitat will play a major role in any environmentalist's perception of the fundamental right to survive for many species of butterfly. It is hoped that this knowledge and its significance will engender a new respect for butterflies and all the smaller denizens of our planet. Butterflies can indeed be found anywhere, provided that their natural habitat is preserved. The possibilities for enrichment are endless for those with an enquiring mind and a fascination for nature in all its glory.

May we all gain the knowledge and have the wisdom to preserve what rightfully shares our world. The members of Umdaus Press should be honoured and given the support they so richly deserve in order to enable them to continue with their endeavours to create these much-needed archives for the sake of future generations. The authors are also to be warmly congratulated on a superb work of scholarship and dedication.

STEVE BALES
Group Art Custodian
FIRST NATIONAL BANK GROUP
Johannesburg, June 1997

FOREWORD

It is my pleasure to contribute this foreword to this magnificent book on the butterflies of Southern Africa. Virtually all the species, and the early stages of most, are illustrated in good colour photographs of living specimens. That this has been possible is eloquent testimony to the enthusiasm, skill and perseverance of the many lepidopterists in South Africa. That all these photographs have been assembled in a single book is also testimony to the organisational skills of the many people associated with the project. Nowhere else in Africa – and in few places elsewhere in the World – could such a book have been assembled.

Do we need yet another book on the butterflies of Southern Africa? More has been written about butterflies of the region than about those of the rest of the continent combined. The roll call of honour is a long one. As far back as 1857 an obscure Swedish country vicar, Wallengren, put together what was effectively the first regional list of butterflies from Africa. Trimen remains a giant of the African butterfly literature. Pinhey, van Son, Swanepoel, Pennington, Murray, Clarke & Dickson, Quickelberge, Vári, Migdoll and the Hennings have bequeathed us books summarising a wealth of experience.

But books beget books – and that is how it should be. They distil the information from the scientific journals which is not readily available – or even intelligible – to the lay person, the enthusiast, or the conservationist. Without the baseline of an up-to-date and authoritative book, all but the specialist have no yardstick against which to judge their own observations and experience, to challenge received wisdom, and to advance our knowledge of butterflies. But not only of butterflies, for butterflies are more than just that. They are one of the best understood major arthropod groups and can be used as indicators for more general research into ecology, biogeography, and a host of other interesting topics.

This book, too, will beget books. There is still so much to be done. Butterflies are excellent subjects for a wide range of research into subjects such as population ecology, mimicry, behaviour, chemistry, communication, genetics, evolution – the list is endless. Such research has hardly begun in southern Africa. So, please let it flower in the decades to come.

The book appears at a propitious time. Its preparation spans the period when South Africa was transformed from the status of international pariah to a potential powerhouse for regional, even continental, development. I am currently ploughing a rather lonely furrow with my research into a book on the Butterflies of West Africa – origins, natural history, diversity and conservation. How I wish I could have marshalled some of the talent, experience and enthusiasm of South African lepidopterists to help me in that task. So, please let us see the unrivalled resources of South African - lepidopterology contribute elsewhere on the continent as well.

But I digress. I was asked to endorse the present book, not to ruminate about the future. It is a wonderful book, from a long and honourable tradition. Everyone involved in its production deserves our thanks and our congratulations.

TORBEN B. LARSEN
London, June 1997

PREFACE

Why a new Butterfly Book?
Recent years have seen a greater awareness in the conservation of butterflies. We are getting away from the old "descriptive" natural history that was concerned only with naming things and describing them. We are now beginning to recognise the great importance, as well as interest, of studying the living butterfly in the field. The life history, habits, behaviour and the inter-relationships of the butterfly with other organisms around it are all important when one wishes to conserve this unique heritage.

We have dealt with each species in as much detail as possible. This being the case it was impossible to include it all in one book of manageable size. Also one very large book would be beyond the price range of most people. Therefore we have decided to produce the work in five volumes and spread the cost over a number of years. The first four volumes will cover South Africa, Lesotho and Swaziland, and the fifth volume will cover Namibia, Botswana, Zimbabwe and Moçambique, and will include only species not already dealt with.

Volume 1 will include the Hesperiidae (93 species), Papilionidae (15 species) and Pieridae (48 species).

Volume 2 Nymphalidae: Satyrinae (67 species), Charaxinae (24 species), Nymphalinae (46 species), Acraeinae (33 species), Danainae (6 species), Libytheinae (1 species).

Volume 3 Lycaenidae: Theclinae (164 species).

Volume 4 Lycaenidae: Lipteninae (16 species), Liphyrinae (1 species), Miletinae (27 species), Lycaeninae (2 species) and Polyommatinae (120 species).

Volume 5 (Namibia, Botswana, Zimbabwe, Moçambique) Hesperiidae (43 species), Papilionidae (2 species), Pieridae (12 species), Lycaenidae (79 species), Nymphalidae (71 species).

Anyone who has paused a moment to watch a butterfly, to wonder perhaps what its name might be; anyone who has collected a few scruffy specimens in a shoe box or obtained a degree in Entomology; in short, anyone with any interest at all in nature and her mysteries, will know how much there is to learn and discover, and with what excitement these discoveries can be made.

This book has been written to supplement the literature already available on the subject, treating a completely different aspect of lepidopterology than any book before it. Previous authors dealt mainly with taxonomy and collecting. The earliest book on Southern African butterflies was *Rhopalocera Africae Australis* by Roland Trimen, published between 1862 and 1866 in two parts. Trimen followed this up between 1887 and 1889 with his magnificent three-volume work *South African Butterflies*, which remained the standard reference work on the butterflies of the subregion for the next sixty years.

The next comprehensive work covering South African butterflies appeared only in 1953. *Butterflies of South Africa: Where, when and how they fly* was written by David Swanepoel.

Dr Georges van Son, at about the same time, commenced a comprehensive taxonomic work, *The Butterflies of Southern Africa* which was to be published in four volumes over the next thirty years. In 1949 volume 1 was published covering the Pieridae and Papilionidae; 1955, volume 2, Nymphalidae: Danainae and Satyrinae; 1963, volume 3, Nymphalidae: Acraeinae; 1979, volume 4, Nymphalidae: Nymphalinae.

The most recent publication to cover the whole of the Southern African subregion is the second edition of *Pennington's Butterflies of Southern Africa*, revised and updated by G. A. Henning, E. L. Pringle and J. B. Ball in 1994. However, all these books tend to emphasise collecting and the taxonomic study of butterflies. A turning point was the publication by the CSIR of the *South African Red Data Book – Butterflies* by S. F. and G. A. Henning in 1989. With our new and increased awareness of the environment and our wish to conserve our butterfly heritage we have been inspired to produce a book that emphasises butterflies as living organisms.

THE AUTHORS

ACKNOWLEDGEMENTS

First of all we would like to thank our wives Mercedes Henning, Eileen Henning, Barbara Joannou and Jayne Woodhall for their help and patience over the many months during which they have been ignored while we worked on this book. We would also like to thank Mercedes Henning for reading part of the manuscript and for her constructive comments.

Our special thanks to Mr Bill Henning for reading the manuscript at various stages during its development.

We are most grateful to Mr Ivan Bampton who has made available to us all his extensive observations and notes on the habits and early stages of butterflies.

Mr Rob Paré † and Mr Ian Mullin have also made available to us all their observations on distribution, habits and early stages of many species. Rob Paré's excellent photographs have also greatly enhanced the book.

We are grateful to Dr A.J.M. Claassens who made available his excellent photographs and his observations on the habits and early stages of various species from the Cape and to Dr J.B. Ball for his photography and advice on various matters, as well as for making available his observations on the habits and early stages of many species from the Cape.

Our thanks also to Mr Douglas Clark for allowing us to use some of the magnificent paintings of his father, Mr Gowan Clark.

Thanks are due also to the following for their help in various ways including observations on the habits and early stages of several species: Mr S.C. Collins, Mr H.C. Ficq, Dr J.H. Greyling, Mr A. Heath, Mr S. Joubert, Mr J. C. McMaster, Mr R. Oberprieler, Dr T.B. Larsen, Mr A. Mayer, Mr N.K. Owen-Johnston, Mr E.L. Pringle, Mr H.E. Selb, Mr W. Steele, Mr R. Swart, Mr D. Upshon, Mr R.T. Warren and Dr M.C. Williams.

Finally we would like to thank Mr Koos de Wet and Mrs L. Boyd of the Transvaal Nature Conservation Department for their views on the conservation of butterflies.

BUTTERFLY
BIOLOGY AND ECOLOGY

BUTTERFLY SYSTEMATICS AND NOMENCLATURE

Butterflies belong to the insect order Lepidoptera. They are in turn placed in the suborder Ditrysia which includes about 98% of the species of Lepidoptera. The Ditrysia in turn are divided up into 17 superfamilies. Butterflies form two of these superfamilies, the Hesperioidea with one family and the Papilionoidea with 5 families.

Some authors, such as Brock (1971), treat them as a single superfamily and Ackery (1984) also feels they form a monophyletic group.

Within the Papilionoidea four families, namely the Papilionidae, Pieridae, Nymphalidae, Riodinidae and Lycaenidae, are recognised. At the subfamily level there is good agreement within the Papilionidae, Pieridae and Lycaenidae. However, the Nymphalidae remain only unconvincingly resolved (Ackery, 1984).

The arrangement and classification of butterfly families and subfamilies adopted in this work is that of Ackery (1984) and Ackery et. al (1995). He based this mainly on the works of Evans (1937, 1949), Ehrlich (1958), Eliot (1973) and Kristensen (1976).

LIFE CYCLE, MORPHOLOGY AND TERMINOLOGY

The life cycle of a butterfly, like that of many other insects, is completed in four stages, namely the egg or ovum, the larva or caterpillar, the pupa or chrysalis and the adult or imago (plural: imagines). The transformation of the larva via the pupal stage into the imago is called complete metamorphosis. Each stage in this life-cycle can be used in the identification and classification of butterflies.

DISTINGUISHING FEATURES OF BUTTERFLIES

The following are the most obvious features used by taxonomists in grouping butterflies into families and subfamilies. Often more than one feature is characteristic of the same group or family.

Adult

Wings. Although the general shape of the wings is of some help in classifying butterflies, it is their veins in particular which, due to their definite and constant arrangement, are very useful guides in allocating species to the various families, subfamilies, genera and even species.

Legs. All butterflies have six legs, that is one pair on each thoracic segment, but there is considerable difference in the degree of development of the first pair. All three pairs of legs are well developed in some families, e.g. in the Papilionidae and Pieridae, but in others such as in the Nymphalidae the first pair is poorly developed.

Egg

In some families the eggs are almost spherical and in others they are elongated and tall. Eggs may be smooth, ribbed or delicately sculptured.

Larva

The general appearance of the larvae is often characteristic of the family to which they belong. In some families they are thin and cylindrical, in others they are short and squat. Some kinds are hairy, others are smooth and still others have protuberances or other distinguishing external features which are helpful in placing a larva in its correct family or subfamily.

Pupa

Not only their external structural features, but also the manner in which they are attached to a support are indicative of the family to which the pupae belong. Some pupae are attached by cremastral hooks only and others have added support of a silken girdle around their middle. However, the pupae of some species lie freely on the ground between debris or just below the surface, and those lycaenid larvae which usually occur in ants' nests also pupate among the ants in their nests.

ADULT

The adult butterfly is divided into an easily distinguishable head, thorax and abdomen. Most of the body and appendages are covered with a layer of highly modified flattened hairs known as scales.

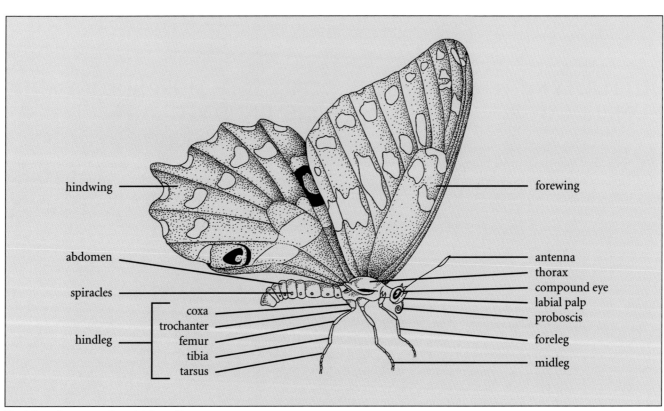

Fig. 1 General structure of an adult butterfly

Head

On either side of the head is a pair of large globular or *compound eyes*, made up of hundreds of facets called *ommatidia*. A pair of long segmented *antennae* arise between the eyes. The large basal segment of each antenna is called the scape, the smaller second segment the pedicel, while the remaining segments make up the flagellum. In the butterflies the flagellum gradually or abruptly thickens towards its tip, forming a club. Behind the bases of the antennae are a pair of sensory organs known as *chaetosemata*, each made up of a series of somewhat radiating hairs. The mouth-parts are greatly reduced except for the maxillae which are highly modified to form a median suctorial *proboscis* or *haustellum* and a pair of upturned three-segmented *labial palpi*.

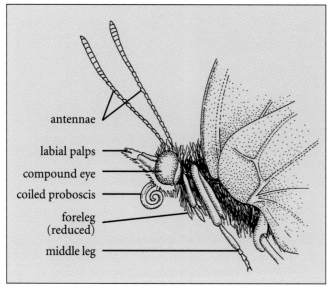

antennae

labial palps

compound eye

coiled proboscis

foreleg
(reduced)

middle leg

Fig. 2 Head and thorax of a nymphalid butterfly

Legs

The legs consist of five main segments, coxa, trochanter, femur, tibia and tarsus. The tarsi are normally five-segmented with a pair of apical claws. The forelegs are fully developed for walking in the Hesperiidae, Papilionidae and Pieridae, but are reduced to various degrees, at least in the males, in the Nymphalidae and Lycaenidae. This reduction usually involves a loss of the terminal claws and reduction in size and number of the tarsal segments. In most Nymphalidae segments of the tarsus are fused to form one elongate segment without claws. The tibia of the foreleg in the Hesperiidae and Papilionidae bears a moveable lobe known as the *epiphysis*. This structure usually has a marginal comb of hairs or bristles thought to be used to clean the antennae and haustellum. The mid- and hindlegs usually have the tibia and tarsi spiny above and below. The paired tarsal claws of the mid- and hindlegs are usually simple hooks, but throughout the Pieridae all the claws are bifid (Common & Waterhouse, 1972).

Wings

Adult butterflies have two pairs of fully developed wings. The wings are membranous and both surfaces are usually clothed with overlapping, usually broad, flattened scales. Each scale has a short stem which is inserted in a minute socket on the wing membrane. The surface of each scale bears many fine longitudinal ridges or striae which often produce iridescent colours. Pigments are usually present within the scale. In males of some groups specialised scales (androconia) help to diffuse scents (pheromones) secreted by associated glands that are scattered over the wings, or which occur in well-defined sex brands or patches.

The sides of the triangular butterfly wing are referred to as the costa (leading edge), the outer margin (termen) and the inner margin (hind margin). Each angle is also named: the base (near-

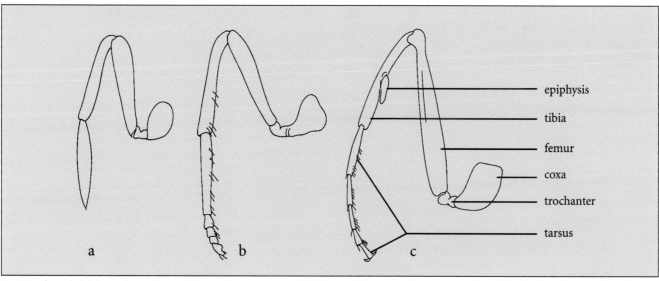

epiphysis

tibia

femur

coxa

trochanter

tarsus

Fig. 3 Forelegs of adult butterflies. a: Reduced foreleg of a male nymphalid; b: Reduced foreleg of a female nymphalid; c: Fully developed foreleg of *Papilio* sp. with epiphysis on tibia

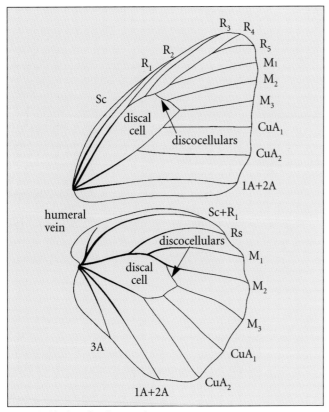

Fig. 4 Pierid wings showing venation

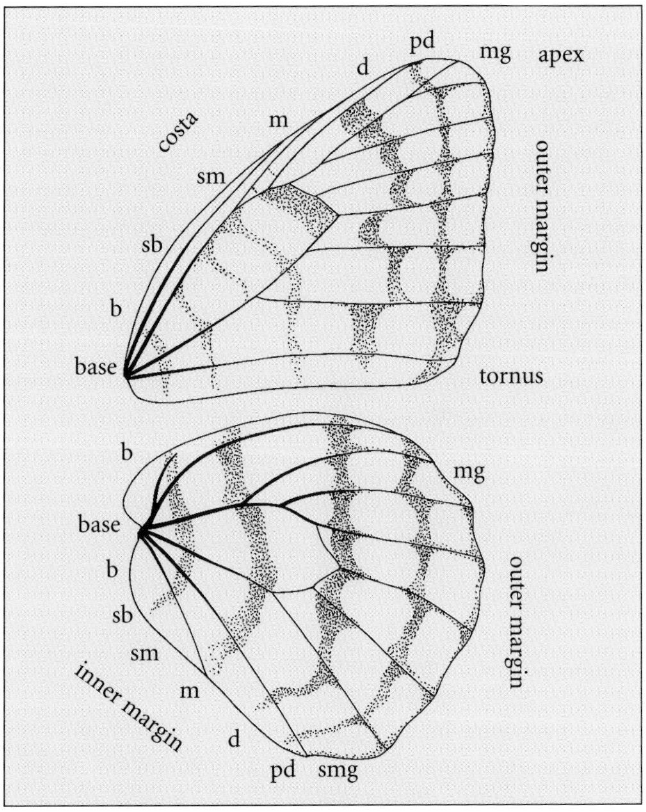

Fig. 5 Pierid wings showing generalised pattern. b – basal striae; sb – subbasal striae; sm – submedian striae; m – median striae; d – discal striae; pd – postdiscal striae; smg – submarginal striae; mg – marginal striae

est the body), the apex (outer forward angle), and the tornus or anal angle (outer posterior angle). Various regions of the wings are identified to these areas: costal (along the costa), subcostal (near the costa), apical (at the apex), subapical (near the apex), basal (at the base). The disc is the central area of the wing. The dorsal (upper) surface of the wing is called the upperside and the ventral (lower) surface the underside.

In the Keys the following abbreviations are used – UFW: upperside forewing; UHW: upperside hindwing; LFW: underside forewing; LHW: underside hindwing.

The wings are traversed by a series of hollow tubes called veins. Blood circulates through the veins although much of the space in them is usually occupied by tracheae. These veins follow a characteristic basic pattern which includes five sets of longitudinal veins. These are the subcosta (Sc), radius (R), media (M), cubitus (Cu) and anal veins (A). The subcostal vein is unbranched and terminates on the costa. Branching of the radial vein differs in fore- and hindwings. The forewings usually have five radial branches (R_1-R_5). The hindwing has only a two-branched radial vein, the radial sector (Rs) and R_1 which is entirely fused with the subcostal vein forming a composite vein Sc+R_1. The radial vein forms the anterior margin of an area known as the discal cell, or often simply the 'cell', while the anterior branch of the cubital vein (CuA) marks the posterior border. The distal end of this cell is usually formed by weak transverse veins called discocellulars, when it is said to be closed. If one or more of the discocellulars are absent, the discal cell is said

to be open. The basal sections of the median vein have been lost in butterflies, and for this reason the three branches (M_1, M_2 and M_3) usually begin at the discocellulars. There are two main branches of the cubital vein, the anterior CuA and the posterior CuP, but the latter has been almost entirely lost in butterflies, being found only in the forewing of Papilionidae. CuA also has two branches CuA_1 and CuA_2. In butterflies there are two anal veins (2A and 3A) on the hindwings and one (2A) on the forewing. An additional small vein, the humeral vein (precostal spur), is present near the base of the hindwing, running towards the costa (after Common & Waterhouse, 1972).

The membranous spaces between the veins are known as 'cells' or 'areas' and take the name of the vein directly in front of it. Thus the cell (or area) between veins M_1 and M_2 is called cell (or area) M_1, and that between Sc+R_1 and Rs is called cell (or area) M_1, and that between Sc+R_1 and Rs is called cell (or area) Sc+R_1.

The generalised pattern of the wings (fig. 5) consists of a series of usually well-defined lines, stripes or spots running approximately at right angles to the veins. These markings are designated as follows:- basal (b), subbasal (sb), submedian (sm), median (m), discal (d), postdiscal (pd), submarginal (smg) and marginal (mg). The interspaces or areas between these markings are designated from the base to outer margin as basal, subbasal, submedian, median, discal, postdiscal, submarginal and marginal. The interspace receives its name from the line at its distal side.

The forewing length is taken by measuring from the centre of the mesonotum of the thorax to the apex of the forewing.

Abdomen

The abdomen has ten segments, the last two or three being modified to accommodate the external genital organs. Each segment consists of a strongly sclerosed dorsal plate, the tergum, and a similar ventral plate, the sternum, joined laterally by a membranous pleural area where the spiracles are located.

Genitalia

The genitalia of both sexes consist of two systems: the primary internal, membranous structures and the secondary, external, mostly sclerosed, structures. The external genital structures are modified from the original ninth and tenth abdominal segments and are extensively used in taxonomy – particularly those of the male because they are easier to dissect and usually have good distinguishing characters for study.

Male genitalia

The internal genitalia consist of two fused testes, each with its own duct, the v*as deferens*. These two vasa deferentia join posteriorly to form a median ejaculatory duct. Just anterior to their union an *accessory gland* opens into each vas deferens, supplying the material with which the spermatophore is formed. The ejaculatory duct continues posteriorly, entering the sclerosed *aedeagus* through which it passes to the outside (Clench, 1975).

Accessory to these primary reproductive organs is a complex of external sclerosed structures, the *genital capsule*. This is of extreme taxonomic importance and is usually what is meant when the term "male genitalia" is used in such contexts. At the base of the capsule is a sclerosed ring, the modified ninth segment, comprising the dorsal *tegumen*, the lateral and ventral *vinculum* and a midventral anterior process, the *saccus*. Dorsally the *uncus*, the modified tenth tergite, is fixed to the posterior edge of the tegumen, forming a sort of hood. On either side at its base arises the modified tenth sternite, the *gnathos*. It is less chitinised than the uncus. The anal opening lies just beneath the uncus, flanked by the gnathi. On the ventral part of the capsule, articulating with the posterior edge of the vinculum, are the paired *valvae* which serve to hold the sexes together during copulation. These are derived from the primitive styli of the ninth segment. The valvae sometimes bear internal projections, ridges or spines, and are generally clothed with hairs and scales. Between the bases of the valvae there often arises a median structure formed from the posterior part of the ninth sternite, the *furca* or *juxta*. This structure serves to guide and support the aedeagus during copulation. The end of the abdomen is closed by a terminal membrane, the diaphragm, which is provided with two openings for the anus and aedeagus. The aedeagus is a sclerosed tube through which the eversible penis or *vesica* passes, and projects backwards through the diaphragm between the bases of the valvae. When everted the vesica often bears on its outer surface one or more strongly sclerosed spines known as *cornuti*.

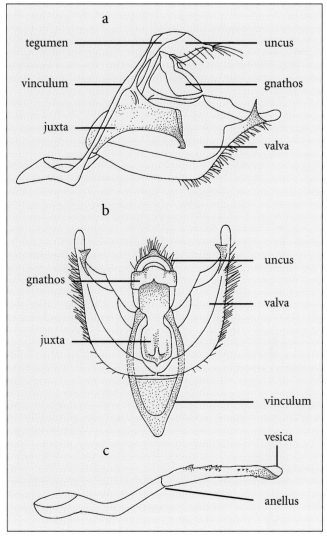

Fig. 6 Structure of male genitalia: a: Lateral view, with left valva and aedeagus removed, of *Charaxes phaeus* Hewitson (Nymphalidae); b: Ventral view, with aedeagus removed; c: Aedeagus (after S.F. Henning, 1989a)

13

Female genitalia

As in the male it consists of two basic internal complexes which may be called the *primary genitalia*, for egg production and delivery, and the *bursa copulatrix*, for sperm reception and storage. Each has a separate opening to the outside. The primary genitalia consists of two ovaries, each consisting of a set of long tubules in which the eggs form and move down. The tubules of each ovary unite to form a single *lateral oviduct*, and the two lateral oviducts in turn unite into a single median (or common) oviduct. Two *accessory glands* enter here, providing the adhesive material with which the eggs are attached during oviposition. The median oviduct then passes via a section known as the *vestibulum*, to the outside (*ostium oviductus*) between the sclerosed *papillae anales* (highly modified tenth and ninth segments), just ventral to the anus.

The *bursa copulatrix* consists of the mating or copulatory opening called the *ostium bursae*, between the seventh and eighth sternites which is partially or wholly bordered by sclerosed plates or *sterigma*. The seventh and eighth sternites also undergo some modifications in connection with the opening. The duct, called the *ductus bursae*, leads anteriorly into the abdomen from the ostium to a strong membranous sac, the *corpus bursae*, in which the sperm received during copulation is stored. The posterior part of the ductus bursae is often expanded and strongly sclerosed and has been called the *antrum*. The sperm is passed to the female enclosed in an elongated sac, the *spermatophore*, and this sac must be ruptured by the female to release the sperm. In the corpus bursae walls are sclerosed plates or *signa* which appear to aid in the rupturing of the spermatophores. Between the two complexes is a connecting tubule, the *ductus seminalis*, leading from the ductus bursae to the vestibulum. Sperm released from the spermatophore leave the corpus bursae, move down this tubule to a storage sac called the *spermatheca*, where they remain until egg-laying is due to

begin. As each egg moves down the oviduct and vagina, passing the opening to the spermatheca, a motile sperm penetrates the minute micropyle to fertilise the egg.

EARLY STAGES

Egg

After mating, the female butterfly deposits fertilised eggs, usually on the larval food plants. Some species such as the Garden Acraea, *Acraea horta* (Nymphalidae: Acraeinae), and the Dotted Border, *Mylothris agathina* (Pieridae), produce batches of up to 80 eggs, sometimes more, but often fewer, on the same leaf.

However, most species lay their eggs singly, usually on separate leaves or other parts of the food plant. The eggs are glued to the food plant by a sticky secretion which soon hardens. They are often attached to the underside of leaves where they are, at least to some extent, protected against extreme climatic conditions, such as torrential rain and the heat of the summer sun. Some species, such as the Autumn Brown, *Dira clytus*, and many other members of the subfamily Satyrinae lay their eggs in flight, scattering them among the grasses on which their larvae feed, or they land on a blade of grass before dropping their eggs.

Some lycaenid butterflies, whose larvae are associated with ants from an early stage, lay their eggs in places where ants are likely to find them, or the freshly emerged larvae, and carry them to their nest or specially constructed shelters, where the larvae will be protected and in return supply the ants with their sweet secretions. In deciding where exactly to oviposit, the females of these butterflies may well be guided by *pheromones*, chemical messenger substances, laid down by ants on their trails.

Butterfly eggs are small, but when seen under a microscope or

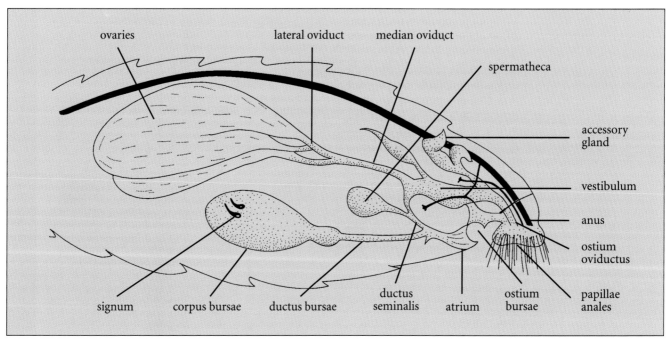

Fig. 7 Female genital structure of generalised butterfly (After Klots, 1970)

even under a magnifying glass they are beautiful objects. Some are smooth and reminiscent of dew drops, others are ribbed, pitted, fluted, sculptured or patterned. They all have a small opening, called the *micropyle*, in the centre of the upper surface. Through the micropyle one of the many sperm cells received by the female during mating must enter the egg cell and join with its nucleus before the egg is laid. It is also through this opening that the developing embryo obtains air to breathe.

The incubation period lasts from three to four days, but depending on the species may take as long as three weeks. Factors essential for the developing embryo are oxygen, moisture and warmth, all of which under normal conditions, are provided by the natural environment.

Parasites are the most efficient agents in controlling the number of offspring produced by insects, including butterflies. Small parasitic wasps and flies oviposit in the freshly laid eggs and after hatching inside the host eggs the parasite larvae devour the contents of the eggs and eventually pupate in them. The young adults of the parasites emerge from the host eggs by eating a hole in the side of the egg shells, unlike the larvae of butterflies which eat their way out of the top of the eggs.

Freshly laid *Charaxes* egg

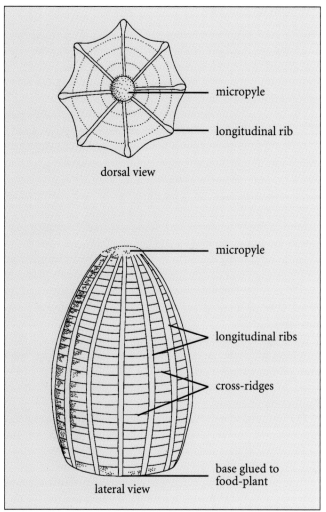

Fig. 8 The general features of an egg of a butterfly of the family Pieridae

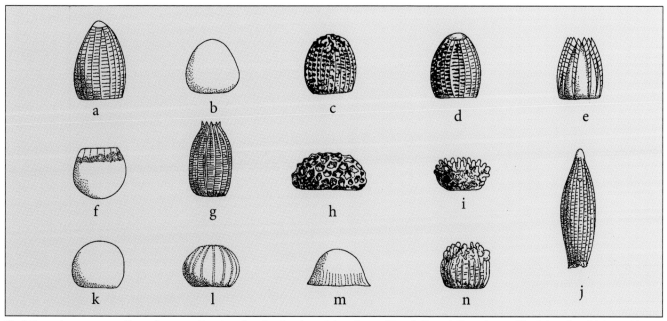

Fig. 9 General appearances of butterfly eggs. a: Danainae; b and c: Satyrinae; d: Acraeinae; e: Nymphalinae; f: Charaxinae; g: Libytheinae; h and i: Lycaenidae; j: Pieridae; k: Papilionidae; l, m and n: Hesperiidae

Caterpillar or larva

From a few days before hatching, the dark head of the young larva inside the egg shell is visible beneath the micropyle. The tiny head is provided with specially adapted mouth-parts which enable the larva to gnaw through the micropylar end of the egg shell. The emergence of the larva from its egg shell is known as *eclosion*.

The larvae of many species devour the discarded egg shell or part of it, thus providing themselves with sufficient energy to crawl to a favourable position on a leaf or another part of the food plant. This readily available first meal is of particular importance in species in which the eggs are not laid directly on the food plant or on a part of the food plant not suitable for consumption, such as a dried up leaf or on bark.

Most butterfly larvae are herbivorous, i.e. plant-eating or phytophagous, but the larvae of a number of species of the family Lycaenidae are carnivorous either from an early stage or from a later, critical stage in their development. Carnivorous butterfly larvae are usually associated with ants and in some instances they feed on ant brood. Other species will feed on plant bugs such as coccids and jassids (Homoptera).

Some lycaenid larvae turn cannibalistic when they come into close proximity with other larvae of the same species, or, perhaps when they come into contact with them. This phenomenon has been observed by several lepidopterists, including ourselves, at least in larvae reared in captivity.

The larvae of some butterflies protect themselves against parasites and predators such as praying mantids (fig. 10) and spiders, and perhaps against unfavourable weather conditions, by constructing shelters from leaves. They hide in these shelters when at rest and emerge from them, often only partially, to feed. Common examples of leaf-shelter builders are the larvae of the *Vanessa cardui* (Nymphalidae) and those of many skippers (Hesperiidae). The larvae of the Skippers eject their droppings from the anus with such force that they land a considerable distance away from their shelters. In this way they not only keep their shelters clean, but also avoid an accumulation of droppings from building up near their hiding place and thus prevent drawing the attention of potential predators to their whereabouts. In contrast, the larvae of *Vanessa cardui* 'disgrace' themselves by fouling their hide-outs with their own droppings.

The protection enjoyed by certain lycaenid larvae in ants' nests, or in shelters specially built for them by certain ants, has already been alluded to under the discussion of the fertilised egg and is also discussed later.

The larvae of *Lampides boeticus* (Lycaenidae) feed on the seeds inside the pods of leguminous plants. Here they may also be visited by ants and thus are well protected against predators and parasites. The larvae of *Capys alphaeus* (Lycaenidae) are not popular with *Protea* growers because they feed on the reproductive organs and developing seeds inside *Protea* heads where they are relatively safe from parasites and predators (fig. 11). Proteas thus affected cannot develop into perfect flowers. The larvae of Henning's Black-eye *Gonatomyrina henningi* (Lycaenidae) and other closely-related species burrow into the thick leaves of cotyledons and other thick-leafed succulents where they feed between the upper and lower surfaces until ready to pupate.

Fig. 10 A praying mantid grasping a pierid butterfly

1st instar larva of *Charaxes jahlusa*

2nd instar larva of *Charaxes candiope*

Larval Structure

Although butterfly larvae vary considerably in size, shape, colour and body covering, their basic structure is the same and the three body regions of a typical insect, namely head, thorax and abdomen, are easily discernable.

The head is a rounded sclerosed capsule or shield which bears three pairs of simple eyes (not compound eyes such as found in the adult) on each side of the head. The simple eyes, also referred to as *ocelli* (singular: ocellus) or *stemmata* (singular: stemma) are believed to be able to distinguish merely between light and dark and seem of little use during this stage of the life-cycle of a butterfly. Other senses such as touch, taste and smell are more important and ensure that the larvae feed on the correct food-plant and react to danger. Just above and a little below the ocelli are the bases of the small three-segmented antennae. Above the mouth there is a median hinged plate known as the *labrum*, and on each side there is a pair of strong dentate *mandibles* and a pair of maxillae, while ventrally there is a further hinged plate called the *labium*. Both mandible and labrum carry paired palpi. The mandibles are used in biting off bits of food.

Butterfly larvae, like moth larvae, manufacture silk which they use for various purposes. The silk is produced by modified salivary glands and is spun in place by the highly adapted labium (lower lip) which functions as a spinneret. The uses of the silk are as follows:

- Butterfly larvae spin a mat of silk on which the tiny claws of the legs and the hooks or crochets of the prolegs can hold tight between feeding times and during periods of rest, especially prior to moulting and pupation.
- The larvae of some species, such as *Vanessa cardui* and many of the Skippers, as mentioned earlier, use silk to draw the edges of leaves together to form shelters. Prior to pupation some Skipper larvae also form shelters this way, but may use more than one leaf to accommodate the pupa inside. Shelters, especially those destined for pupae are usually lined with silk, but cocoons like those found in many moths are not formed. However cocoons and leaf-shelters have the same protective purpose.

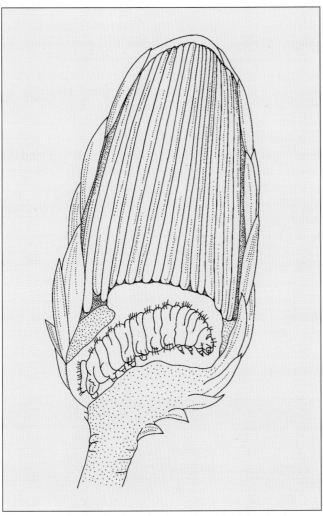

Fig. 11 Longitudinal section through a *Protea* flower-head showing the position of the *Capys alphaeus* final instar larva

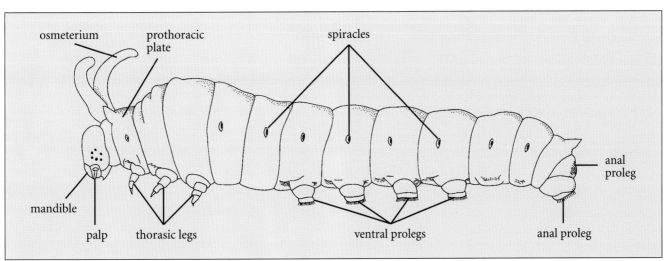

Fig. 12 Structure of larva of *Papilio demodocus*

17

- The larvae of most butterflies spin a mat of silk to which the posterior end of the pupa becomes firmly attached. In addition many larvae spin a delicate girdle of silk to support the pupa around its middle.
- When disturbed some butterfly larvae, such as those of the Dotted Borders (*Mylothris* species), lower themselves from the leaf on which they are feeding to another position or even onto the ground, dangling from a silken thread which they spin while descending. Thus they escape.

The thorax is comprised of the first three segments behind the head. Each one of the thoracic segments bears a pair of segmented legs which end in single claws. There is also a pair of spiracles on the first segment.

The abdomen is made up of ten segments. The abdominal segments three, four, five and six each bear a pair of fleshy unsegmented false legs or *prolegs* which are provided with tiny claws or hooks, called *crochets.*

The prolegs support the long sluggish body of the larva. They are particularly important in locomotion during which they function as legs and hold onto the food plant while the anterior part of the body is raised, as happens especially during feeding. In typical larvae the last segment ends in a pair of *claspers* or anal prolegs which are used to hold tightly to the food plant, so that the larva is not easily shaken off in the wind or removed from its substrate by predators.

In many larvae of the family Lycaenidae, specialised secretory cells are found in the skin and in addition a honey-gland and tubercles may be found on the seventh and eighth abdominal segments respectively. The secretory cells and the more advanced structures play an important role in ant-association and will be referred to again under "*Myrmecophily*".

The first eight abdominal segments bear a pair of *spiracles* each. These are tiny openings leading to the respiratory tubes through which breathing takes place.

The skin of the larvae bears hair-like structures, called *setae*, the size and number of which vary from species to species. In some they are small, but in others they are prominent features. In addition some larvae bear spined protuberances which may be branched or simple.

3rd instar larva of *Charaxes candiope*

4th instar larva of *Charaxes candiope*

Final instar larva of *Charaxes candiope*

Moulting or Ecdysis

The skin or cuticle of the early stages of insects such as butterflies and moths is made up of *chitin*, a non-living substance manufactured by underlying live tissue. The skin, therefore, cannot grow but, when newly formed, allows for a certain degree of stretching. A larva must moult i.e. cast its skin which has become too tight, in order to grow. At intervals which, depending on the species and climatic conditions, last from a few days to a week or two, the existing cuticle is shed and replaced by a newly formed, fresh one. This is still soft and pliable, allowing the larva to increase in size. The stage of a larva between two moults is called an *instar*. Most larvae moult four or five times, some more often, before reaching their maximum size and maturity. The final moult results in the formation of the pupa in which metamorphosis into the adult butterfly takes place.

Prior to moulting the larva ceases to feed, spins a thin pad of silk on which it secures itself with its legs and prolegs and in this contracted state waits for a few days for its new cuticle to be completed. The old cuticle then splits at its anterior end and while the old cuticle with its discarded head capsule shrinks and is shed, the next instar larva with a fresh stretchable cuticle emerges. The larvae of some species devour the cast skin.

Moulting is controlled by the interaction of several hormones and allows not only for growth to take place but also for changes in the body covering, colour, distribution of setae and even the formation of new structures such as a honey-gland and/or tubercles in those lycaenid larvae in which these organs are not present from the first instar. In some species the larvae change their behaviour and

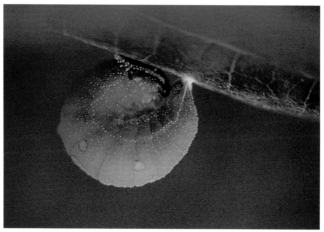

Charaxes candiope larva preparing to moult to pupa

even their diet in the new instar. The larvae of *Acraea horta* are gregarious at first but in later instars they become solitary. In certain ant-associated lycaenids the larvae are phytophagous until the third instar. During this third instar they are picked up by their host ants and carried into their nests. During their first moult inside the ants' nest they lose the honey-gland and become carnivorous, feeding on ant brood (eggs, larvae, pupae). This change in diet must involve adaptations of the digestive system, including certain digestive enzymes.

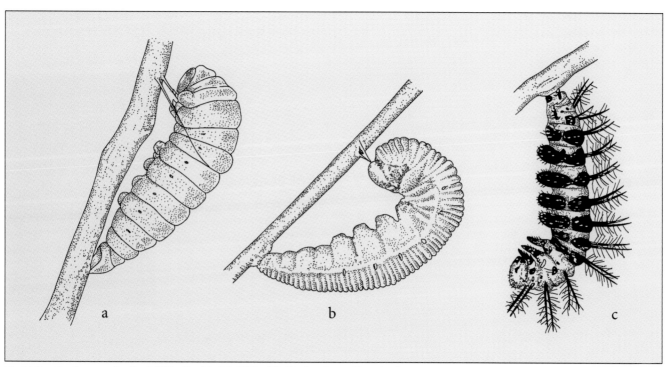

Fig. 13 Pupating larvae. a: Swallowtail (Papilionidae); b: White (Pieridae); c: *Acraea* (Acraeinae)

Pupa

Under favourable conditions butterfly larvae reach maturity within three to four weeks. The fully grown final instar larva moults for the last time to form a pupa. In most species pupation takes place on or near the food plant, but some larvae desert the food plant prior to pupation and after finding a suitable place on another plant, a tree trunk, a blade of grass, some debris, or on man-made structures such as a wall or a fence, they complete pupation. Prior to pupation most larvae spin a silken support from which they are suspended by the claspers, either in a slanting, upright position with the aid of a girdle, or head downwards. In this position they rest for a few days, lose their bright colours and assume a humped shape (fig. 13). The larval skin begins to split down the centre of the humped thorax and the skin is slowly shed down the body by the vigorous undulating movements of the pupa.

The pupae of the Nymphalinae, Charaxinae, Acraeinae and most Satyrinae are suspended upside down from their support by structures called *cremastral hooks* located on their tail end and these are embedded in a mat of silk which is spun on the support by the larva.

The pupae of most Lycaenidae, Papilionidae and Pieridae are attached by means of a cremaster as well as by a girdle spun around the middle to provide extra support. It has already been mentioned that the pupae of many Skippers are protected in a shelter constructed by the pupating larvae. In lycaenids in which the larvae live in ants' nests pupation takes place in the hosts' nests. Adults emerging from such pupae must of necessity find their way out before wing expansion takes place.

Pupae often adopt the colour which matches their environment and many are therefore green or at least have a green ground colour. Some pupae resemble part of their larval food plant, assuming the shape of a short branch, resembling a piece of bark or having markings which render them difficult to distinguish from their immediate surroundings, e.g. a leaf.

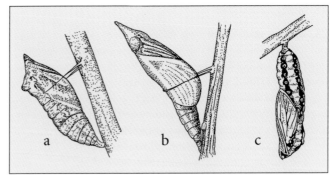

Fig 14 Typical pupae. a: Swallowtail (Papilionidae); b: White (Pieridae); c: *Acraea* (Acraeinae)

The pupae of the Acraeinae are usually situated in exposed positions where their bright colours and bold markings warn potential predators of their poisonous properties. The pupae formed by larvae which live in sheltered positions, such as the larvae of many satyrines, are inconspicuous in colour, usually brown, matching the colour of the soil and debris among which they occur at the roots of the grasses on which the larvae feed.

The duration of the pupal stage varies in different species, but most butterflies of average size metamorphose inside the pupal shell within three or four weeks. In species below average size emergence usually takes place within two weeks or ten days as in the small Sooty Blue, *Zizeeria knysna* (Lycaenidae). During the colder winter months emergence can be delayed and pupae may hibernate for one or more months, but in summer multibrooded species complete their life-cycle several times. Some species such as certain satyrines and lycaenids have a short flight period and usually have one or two broods a year, i.e. they usually hibernate, and pupate in early spring. Alternatively they aestivate during the dry summer months, when their larval food plants die, and they start feeding again, reach maturity and pupate in late summer or autumn. These then produce the autumn brood of adults which start the cycle again.

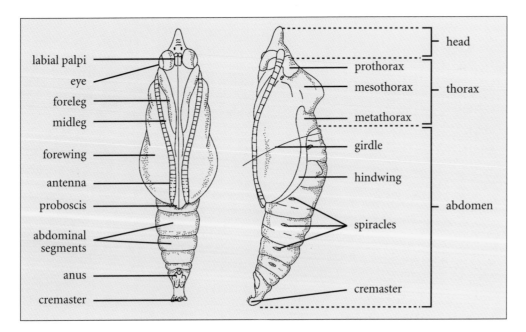

Pupa of *Charaxes candiope*

Fig. 15 Structure of a pupa, ventral (left) and lateral views (right)

Eclosion

As the *imago* or adult forms inside the pupa the general features and colours of the butterfly become visible through the transparent shell. The shell then bursts along the sutures at its anterior end, allowing the imago to escape head first, from its narrow confinement. The emergence of the imago, known as *eclosion*, often takes place at night or in the early morning. The vulnerable, helpless imago hangs upside down from its support to allow its crumpled wings to be easily inflated. It ejects from its anus the *meconium*, i.e. the waste products (uric acid) accumulated during metamorphosis. These wastes appear in the form of a thick liquid, often dirty red in colour.

Wing expansion is achieved by the butterfly pumping a liquid, called *haemolymph*, into the soft wing veins. The veins, once stretched out to their full capacity, slowly harden and begin to support the wings which start to move apart and later repeatedly open and close. Eventually the wings are able to support the butterfly in its first flight in the sun and the imago commences its rather short adult existence, usually only of a few weeks duration in most species.

Fully expanded upperside of *Charaxes druceanus*

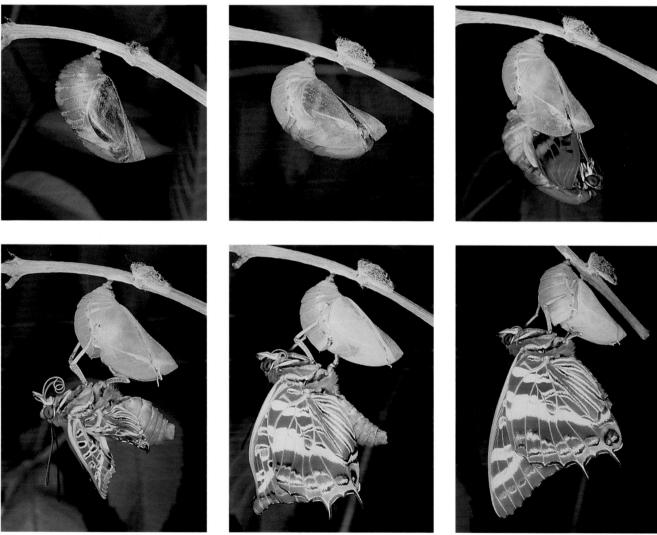

Eclosion of *Charaxes druceanus*

BEHAVIOUR AND HABITS

Every action of a butterfly, even the most insignificant, is concerned with some aspect of its behaviour. What behaviour we are actually observing is not always apparent and cannot always be easily interpreted. All aspects of the behaviour of butterflies are adapted, in one way or another, to enable them to find food and mates, to avoid or to endure adverse climatic conditions and to avoid attacks by predators.

TEMPERATURE AND FLIGHT

Flight is impossible in butterflies unless the temperature of the flight muscles is high enough. Butterflies are poikilothermic which means their body temperature varies with that of their environment. They thus derive most of their heat from the sun. They are active only as long as they can absorb sufficient radiant heat from the sun. If the sun is obscured they will almost immediately come to rest. Measurements have shown that the temperature of the thorax drops rapidly when flight ceases. In the absence of radiant heat, flight is not possible in most species of butterflies at temperatures below about 20°C (Common & Waterhouse, 1972). If air temperatures are too low for flight an increase in thoracic temperature can be produced by vibrating their wings or basking in the sun. The heat of the sun is received through the wings in which blood circulates. The efficiency of the wings as heat receptors is improved by modifications in their shape, colour and pattern, and particularly by the behaviour of the butterfly under varying temperatures.

Butterflies usually sun themselves with their wings spread, especially in the early morning and after heavy rain. They orientate themselves towards the sun, enabling the upperside or underside of the wings to receive the maximum amount of heat. The veins of the wings receive and transfer most of the heat obtained from the sun to other parts of the body. The veins of the wings are often pigmented with black which presumably facilitates heat absorption, as matt black surfaces absorb and radiate heat more quickly than smooth pale surfaces. Most butterflies sunning themselves avoid strong wind, as cooling occurs more rapidly in moving air currents. Heat-loss is achieved mainly by seeking shade or resting with wings closed and orientating themselves parallel to the sun's rays.

In flight the wings act as an aerofoil (like an aircraft wing) which generates lift and thrust during both the upward and downward strokes. The wing tip traces a roughly elliptical or figure of eight closed path relative to the insect. The flight is a result of the uneven airflow generated by the movement of the wings. An important feature is the production and shedding of vortices (whirlwinds) of moving air. In a vortex a mass of air (or fluid) rotates in a ring about a centre line. We have all seen how a small whirlwind lifts up leaves and carries them away. In insects the vortex rings provide them with lift and momentum. In flight the movement of the wings causes the circulation of air around the aerofoil surface. This circulating air is shed from the wing as a vortex when the wings reverse direction or change shape and inclination (see fig. 17). The flying insect can be supported and propelled forwards by the reaction force resulting from the downward-shed vortex rings (Barnes *et al.*, 1988).

Fig. 16 *Papilio euphranor*, a rare endemic swallowtail in flight

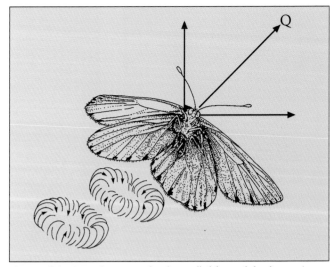

Fig. 17 A flying insect is supported and propelled forwards by the reaction force Q resulting from the downward-shed vortex rings

Colotis antevippe gavisa in flight

Circulation is often induced when the wings are clapped together and then flung apart. The anterior stiffened edges are first to be pulled away from each other and air rushes in to the low pressure space developing between the wings. Thus a circulation of air is established around the wing. The downwards movement of the wing accelerates the air, giving lift and thrust (fig. 18).

Once the moving air has maximum velocity no further work can be done by the wings until the vortex is shed, which may occur when the wings change direction of movement at the bottom of the wing stroke (Barnes *et al.*, 1988).

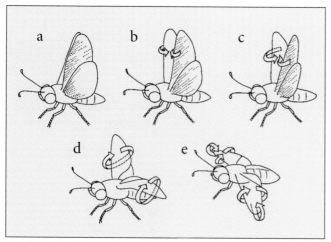

Fig. 18 The clap/fling mechanism for vortex generation. a: At the top of the stroke the wings are clapped together; b: The wings are flung apart, the stiffened leading edges being separated first, thus establishing a circulation of air around the wing; c: Downward movement of the wing accelerates the air; work is done and the reaction force generated has components giving lift and thrust (after Weis-Fogh, 1975)

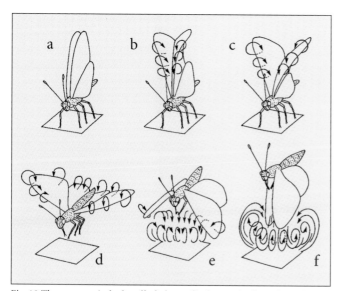

Fig. 19 The near-vertical take off of a butterfly also results from the induced and downward shedding of a vortex (after Kingsolver, 1985). a: The wings held together in the up position; b, c: As they move apart, circulation is induced over the leading edges of the wings; d: Acceleration of the mass of circulating air induces lift and the butterfly loses contact with the ground; e, f: As the wings reach the bottom of the stroke, the circulating air is shed from the wing surface as a vortex ring with downward momentum

FEEDING

Nearly all the food utilised by each butterfly in its entire life cycle is consumed by the larva. An outstanding feature of butterfly and moth larvae is that their mouth-parts, which are of the biting kind, are completely different from those of the adult. The adults possess sucking mouth-parts and feed mainly on nectar and other liquids. In butterflies and other insects with similar life cycles the larval and adult stages do not compete for food. The advantage of this situation is obvious.

The larval food of butterflies is usually plant material and can consist of leaves, seeds and flowers of a wide range of species from different families. The larvae of some lycaenids are predatory on other insects, either from the first instar, or at a later stage.

Adult butterflies possess sucking mouth-parts and require only the sugars and water of nectar or fermenting juices for survival. Butterflies are attracted to suitable food sources primarily by odour or colour. Flowers are the principal food source of most butterflies. Some species such as the *Charaxes* generally feed on fermenting fruit or sap and animal droppings, especially those of carnivores. In hot weather a number of species seek moisture from damp ground.

Charaxes zoolina zoolina feeding on tree sap

Thestor basutus capeneri larva eating scale bug (*Pulvinaria* species – Hemiptera)

Food plant preferences

Female butterflies will normally oviposit on a plant only when presented with certain specific stimuli. These stimuli are offered only by a limited number of plant species in a particular environment. Other factors affecting oviposition are suitable temperatures, the colour and texture of the leaf, direct sunlight or, occasionally, shade. In addition the odour of the plant helps the female orientate towards it. When the female lands on a plant and investigates the surface, the appropriate chemical stimulation of the *chemoreceptors* (sense organs) on the antennae, legs and tip of abdomen results in an egg being laid (Common & Waterhouse, 1972).

The larvae will feed only on a particular plant if its sense organs receive the correct chemical stimuli. The most important larval chemoreceptors occur on the maxillary palps but others occur on the antennae and the beginning of the digestive tract. The presence of the same chemical stimuli which cause the female to lay, determines whether or not a larva will feed on the plant.

These stimuli are alkaloids or essential oils which arose during the plants' evolution to protect them from various herbivorous animals. Some of the phytophagous insects, however, evolved simultaneously and developed protective mechanisms against toxic substances and actually use them to identify their host plant. This adaptation has, in turn, restricted the range of plants that can be used by these insects (Common & Waterhouse, 1972).

Charaxes jahlusa rex feeding on baboon droppings

Various species sucking on damp sand at Lapalala Wilderness

COURTSHIP AND MATING

The most important function of adult butterflies is the continuation of the species. All their behaviour is geared towards this end. Each species has a particular type of behaviour so that males and females are able to locate or find each other. Having achieved this, a specific courtship ritual takes place to ensure that the prospective mate which has been found belongs to the same species and is receptive to mating. Only at the completion of courtship will mating take place.

Although various aspects of sexual behaviour of a number of butterflies have been studied, only a surprisingly small number of species have had their entire courtship patterns observed and described. The females of many species tend to remain in the general vicinity of the larval food plants, and males presumably seek out these areas for courtship. On the other hand, males of the Lycaenidae in particular, but other families too, often gather on nearby rises or hilltops which they 'stake out' a little territory which they protect, and the females come up to these hilltops to find a mate. Visual recognition of the female by the male is of great importance in bringing the sexes together, but not much is known about just how important the visual, tactile, chemical and acoustic stimuli are, relative to each other, in bringing the sexes of one species together. Entire courtships ending in mating are rarely seen at close quarters in nature, and there has been little experimentation in the field or in large cages.

Mate-locating and territoriality

Mate-locating behaviour is defined as behaviour which brings the sexes together for mating. It includes the methods used to find mates, the location of mating, and the time of day of initiation of mating (Scott, 1974).

Chemoreception is known to be very important in the long-distance location of females by males in moths, and in the courtship of moths and butterflies. It may possibly prove to be important in the location of females by males in the Acraeinae as well. For most butterflies, however, the maximum distance of attraction is limited by sight, while chemoreception is important only within a few metres of the females by the release of pheromones from hair pencils, androconial scales and so on.

There are two main types of mate-locating behaviour in butterflies. The first is *perching behaviour* which is defined as a mate-locating method in which males sit at characteristic sites and dart out at passing objects in search of females. The females generally fly to these sites to mate, then they depart. The second is *patrolling behaviour*, a mate-locating method in which males fly almost constantly in search of females.

Movement, size, wing colour, wing pattern and odour are stimuli which can be transmitted during sexual communication in the approach of a male to a female. Perching males are highly attracted to moving objects, whereas patrolling males often are attracted to motionless objects resembling females in some way. Perching species usually mate in limited areas of habitat, often during only part of the day, whereas patrolling species usually mate throughout the habitat at any time of day.

Territoriality is usually exhibited by males which perch or patrol in a particular beat or area. They will investigate and challenge not only other males of the same species which enter the territory but other appropriately sized flying insects as well. The resident male most frequently succeeds in his challenge. Virgin females entering a territory are at once pursued and courtship commenced. In the case of many Hesperiidae and Lycaenidae a particular male will have a favoured perch or perches in its territory on which it will settle, often returning after an encounter to the exact spot from which it launched itself. If the individual is caught it may be replaced within minutes or hours by another individual of the same or a different species. Surprisingly, the new individual may rest on or near the same twig as its predecessor. Evidently there are certain particularly favoured spots in any small area of habitat and these are occupied in preference to others. On the other hand, in some species (e.g. *Papilio demodocus*) the males patrol for long periods and perch only briefly. The males seldom engage in feeding activities while they are perching or patrolling. Since they appear only as the day warms up, they probably go nectar-gathering before initiating their territorial behaviour.

Aphnaeus hutchinsoni perching

Both perching and patrolling species also exhibit other types of behaviour which help the sexes to locate each other. The most noticeable is hill-topping behaviour in which males of low-density species fly to the summits of hills and there show perching or patrolling behaviour. In these species the males ascend to the hill-tops to be in a conspicuous spot so that the newly emerged females know where to find them. Otherwise the female might fly for kilometres without finding a mate if they tend to be sparsely scattered. So the female goes up to the top of the hill, very soon gets fertilised and goes away again and almost never returns (Scott, 1968).

Most of the non-hilltopping species, especially the weak fliers, spend their entire lives, except for brief forays in search of mud or flowers for nourishment, around stands of the food plant, and therefore have a built-in mechanism for bringing the sexes together. Often the sexes are limited both to food plant and to certain areas of the environment such as marshes, rockslides or forests, which may or may not be the only locations of the food plant. The behaviour of these species usually limits them to these areas so that mating is possible with 'random' flight by both sexes or by patrolling of the area by males.

In some species the males occupy small areas along the bottom of a gully or gorge, presumably for mating purposes. Males may occupy an area for some time, but this behaviour may not be territorial since the males may wander to another gully and show the same behaviour. A group of butterflies which demonstrate this behaviour are the lycaenids of the genus *Poecilmitis*. The males of rainforest species usually show perching and patrolling behaviour in forest clearings, roads or along the outskirts of the woods.

Hilltopping

Hilltopping is defined as a behaviour pattern of certain insects in which males fly to the summits of hills and, when there, remain on the summit and show perching (territorial) or patrolling behaviour (Scott, 1968).

Hilltopping low-density species have many behavioural traits in common. They do not congregate about the food plant but instead tend to be large, strong-flying, solitary species. When an adult specimen of these low-density species emerges from the pupa it will be unlikely to find a member of the opposite sex in the near vicinity. If unable to find a mate it will ascend to the highest topographic point where it will find other members of the species who will also have ascended to the peaks to mate. The males, who will mate more than once, tend to congregate around these high points waiting for females. A high proportion of females mate only once or twice in their lives, therefore many will ascend to the summit shortly after emerging, and once mated will never return. This is why females are seldom observed on the summits, as they are there only long enough to mate. Courtship usually lasts only 2-3 minutes and once in copulation they are usually out of sight in the grass or in a tree, often downhill from the summit. So chances are very slight that you will see a female. This gives rise to the impression that only the males are hilltopping. *Charaxes jasius saturnus* is a good example of a low-density species which shows hilltopping behaviour. It is an extremely common butterfly in the bushveld of Southern Africa but is regarded as a low-density species as its food plants are scattered throughout the bush and the females range widely, laying their eggs wherever they find a suitable tree.

During hilltopping the males may either perch on a shrub, tree or patch of ground (e.g. *Iolaus trimeni*) or patrol on the summit (as in *Papilio demodocus*). The behaviour of hilltopping species is not fundamentally different from that of other species; hilltopping behaviour occurs when these activities are transferred to a hilltop. Perching males may well remain on a hilltop for several days.

The males, which usually emerge before the females, visually orientate and fly to the hilltops where each will stake out a little territory which he will defend against challengers of his own species (or even other species if they look similar). The females, when they emerge, also fly to the hilltops, mating occurs, and then the females leave to lay their eggs and almost never return. Nearly all females found flying on the hilltops will be virgins searching for mates. Usually there is no food plant to lay their eggs on up on the hilltops, nor is there much nectar to feed on. This means that the males must feed further down in the valleys before coming up to the hilltops. Species differ in their time of arrival on a hilltop and may stay until quite late in the afternoon. Certain hilltops are consistently favoured over others nearby but no one knows yet why some seem more preferable than others.

It appears that hilltopping behaviour is effective only for low-density species, because at high densities on hilltops interference between males prevents mating with females and the number of hilltops is limited. If a species is common, only a small proportion of the males can occupy a hilltop, so that most males will be forced into non-hilltop situations. As the population density rises, the probability that a female will meet a male before reaching a hilltop therefore increases, so that hilltopping is less important for commoner species. The few males on hilltops could not possibly inseminate all the females in a common species, so that most matings will occur with males which remain at the breeding site or which are between the breeding site and the hilltop. Because hilltopping is less useful for common species, selection should eliminate the hilltopping response since males which remain at the breeding sites will contribute more genes to the next generation.

Hilltopping species are, then, generally large, fast-flying, solitary species with more widely scattered and less abundant food plants than non-hilltopping species, which tend to be small, weak-flying, colonial species with common or clumped food plants.

Courtship and pheromones

There is a tremendous diversity of courtship behaviour. In patrolling species, the two sexes may meet during flight or the flying male may meet a female at rest. In perching species, the female flies near the male, who then pursues her. Subsequent events may be divided into aerial events and ground events although in some species identical activities may occur in the air and on the ground or on a plant. In the aerial phase, which is omitted altogether in some species, the two sexes often merely flutter about each other, or fly in stereotyped patterns, or one or both sexes may perform specialised acts for transferring pheromones. The aerial flights usually result in the female alighting, whereupon the receptive females of some species usually become inactive until copulation occurs. Unreceptive females of some species may flap their wings or fly a special pattern (*rejection dances*), or adopt a special *rejection posture*. After the female alights, the male may continue to fly about the female, or may land, whereupon one or both sexes may still flutter their wings, and the male may perform complicated manoeuvres with his wings, antennae, or legs. Copulation may then occur, or various courtship events may then be repeated.

Sex-related pheromones of one or both sexes are important in the courtship of most species, although only in the Danainae have these pheromones been chemically identified. These pheromones are substances, produced by one individual, that influence the sexual behaviour of members of the opposite sex of the same species. It is well-known, for example, that the virgin females of many moth species produce a powerful and specific sex pheromone that is capable of attracting her specific mate from distances of hundreds if not thousands of metres. In some species of moth, when the male gets close to the female he releases an aphrodisiac pheromone which brings about mating. Amongst butterflies it is usually the male, rather than the female, that possesses scent organs. These may be highly modified scales or pouches on either the fore- or hindwings, or special little structures on the abdomen. *Sex brands*, which are formed of these specially modified scales and which also produce scents, occur in many butterfly species.

The most highly developed male scent organs are found in the Danainae. These organs are the paired hair-pencils (they look like pencils made up of lots of little hairs in a cylinder). These pencils can be pushed out from the tip of the abdomen and release a pheromone during courtship. In some species the hair-pencils are covered with fine dust-like particles which shower forth as a rain of scented particles when the hair-pencils shoot out. There are also conspicuous wing glands which, with the hair-pencils, produce pheromones that are characteristic for each species so that the butterflies can seek out and identify their own species from all the others. Some of these pheromones can even be detected by the human nose.

Stride (1958) watched the courtship of *Danaus chrysippus* and he noticed that, while the female normally flies in a leisurely manner, during courtship she adopts a rapid, rather jerky flight. On overtaking the female, the male flies above, hair-pencilling the front part of the female every time an opportunity presents itself. Within a short time, the female settles with the male beside her facing in the same direction. Then the male bends his abdomen sideways to reach the female and join with her. If, during mating, flight becomes necessary, the male flies carrying the female with him, not as in some other butterflies where the female is the active partner and carries the male. In most other species, the pheromone is used only when the butterfly is one or two metres, but not further away, from its partner. Female pheromones evoke the male pursuing response and cause continued courtship, while the male pheromone may cause the female to land and accept the male. It is not unusual to find two or three males trying fervently to mate with the same receptive female, probably in response to her pheromone.

Mating

To initiate copulation the males of almost all butterfly species grasp the female from a position slightly behind her while facing the same direction as the female and bending his abdomen right or left 180 degrees to grasp her abdomen. Then the male moves sideways until the partners face opposite directions.

The pair remain at the mating site, where they may separately or together bask in the sun by opening their wings, or may fly if disturbed. If disturbed, whichever of the sexes carries the other will fly off, carrying the other behind. In species in which only one sex carries the other, the active sex usually positions itself above the other, with its wings outside of those of the other, and is more likely to walk during copulation. The inactive sex remains in a state of immobility known as *catalepsis*.

Spialia spio mating
(Photo A.J.M. Claassens)

At the end of copulation in *Precis* the female kicks and turns until the male is broken off; then the male flies away. In other species the male initiates uncoupling. Apparently only in the Danainae is there a postnuptial flight (the male always carrying the female a short distance).

Copulation lasts from about one half to three hours depending on the species, and occasionally overnight. Copulation is longer at lower temperature and if the male has recently mated. Males can mate five times or more during their life span, whereas the number of matings per female varies between species from only once to an average of three.

In some species a large structure known as the *sphragis* is deposited by the male in the copulatory opening of the female, thus preventing further mating. Among South African butterflies a sphragis is known in the Acraeinae and Danainae (*Amauris*). In all the species with a large sphragis, many similarities exist, including the absence of courtship, powerful odour (pheromones) of adults of both sexes, and strong attraction of males to virgins. The male captures the female without any courtship in the Acraeinae and the females produce an attracting pheromone. It appears that the large sphragis serves to inhibit the emission of the female pheromone. The male of these species can easily detect whether the female is virgin or mated by physically detecting the sphragis (or because of pheromones) and he can therefore mate immediately without wasting time courting. In other butterflies, determining the receptivity of the female may not be so easy, and one function of courtship is to increase the female's receptivity so that mating can occur.

Females can mate the first day of adult life in almost all species, although they may mate more readily after a day or two. In contrast, males usually mate only after several days. Males often develop distinctive odours (male pheromones) only after a few days. Females of perching species often must fly to the mating site, so may be older than patrolling species at first mating. The difference between the sexes in minimum age of mating is due to several reasons. Males almost always take the active role in mate-locating, so must be capable of stronger flight, and so must wait a few days before actively perching or patrolling. It is also advantageous to fertilise the females as soon as possible in the usual pre-oviposition period so that the time for oviposition is not reduced.

MIGRATION

The migration of butterflies is a phenomenon familiar to many people in Southern Africa. The periodic migration of *Belenois aurota* is perhaps the only time most people notice butterflies at all. Considerable research has been conducted overseas on the causes of migration and how the butterflies orientate themselves. Very little has been undertaken in Southern Africa apart from observing the swarms. Migration may be defined as the deliberate movement of a group of individuals to or from a specific area out of their normal environment. It is usually found in species breeding in high latitudes which can be colonised only during the warmer months of the year, or those found in seasonal rainfall areas which are rendered periodically uninhabitable by drought.

Vanessa cardui, a common migrant

True migration, where there is a mass movement of a population to a warmer climate to overwinter, and subsequent return the following season to breed, is not found in Southern African insects. This is of course due to the absence of extreme climatic conditions.

In butterflies the only well documented case is that of the American Monarch, *Danaus plexippus*, in northern America which flies south from Canada and the northern United States to southern California or Mexico. They overwinter in enormous colonies in particular trees. They are in diapause for most of this time. How they find these particular trees is a somewhat contentious issue. It has been suggested that they orientate by means of the sun or navigate by means of polarised light. Recently, however, it has been demonstrated that there is magnetic material consisting mainly of grains of super-paramagnetic magnetite in the head and thorax of adult monarchs. It has also been found that the principal overwintering site in Mexico is characterised by a major magnetic anomaly. Bringing these two factors together it appears, then, that the monarchs probably migrate by means of the earth's magnetic field and can locate particular areas by anomalies in the field.

It has also been demonstrated that migrating females are generally in a state of reproductive diapause (sexually immature). They also have large fat bodies in their abdomens which may constitute 20% of their body mass, providing the migrant with the energy to undertake the long journey.

Another major migrant found throughout the world is the Painted Lady, *Vanessa cardui*. During the summer months individuals spread out and disperse towards the poles (higher latitudes) where they establish temporary breeding populations in normally inhospitable habitats. These temporary breeding populations are usually wiped out during the cold winter months. The areas are recolonised the next year from the stable permanent population in the warmer lower latitudes. *V. cardui* occurs in South Africa. Migrations have been recorded in spring or early summer down the KwaZulu-Natal coast and up to the Cape Peninsula from the northerly direction. These migrations are normally small, possibly due to the absence of extreme climatic conditions. In the northern hemisphere where unfavourable conditions occur, this species migrates in enormous numbers, usually into Europe from the Mediterranean area northwards and in North America from the southern states northwards. The direction of flight is away from the equator which indicates that orientation is possibly by the earth's magnetic field, i.e., they are flying towards the magnetic poles.

The most well-known Southern African migrant is the Brown-veined White, *Belenois aurota*. It migrates from the Karoo and Northern Cape in a north-easterly direction across the Free State, Gauteng, North-West Province, Northern Province and Mpumalanga, into Moçambique and KwaZulu-Natal, then usually turning northwards. In exceptional years specimens have been recorded migrating into the Eastern Cape. Occasionally some migrants even reach the southern extreme of the Western Cape where they normally do not occur. In May 1980 large numbers were seen all over Cape Town and neighbouring suburbs.

These migrations of *Belenois aurota* appear to be the result of population explosions in their breeding areas in the Karoo. This species feeds on the plants *Boscia oleoides* and *Maerua caffra*. The number of larvae feeding on the plants builds up over spring and early summer and eventually defoliates entire trees of the host species. Under such circumstances the scene is set for a migration to occur. The larvae are under stress due to overcrowding and the lack of food. Over two thousand larvae have been recorded from one small tree. The adults from these overcrowded populations are often nearly a third smaller than normal and occasionally have reduced sex organs (20% of a small sample collected during one of the April migrations on the Witwatersrand). The undersized adults start making their appearance in mid-summer, from the end of November to the end of January, with a seldom recorded second migration at the end of March/April.

The migrating specimens set off in a north-easterly direction and do not deviate from this course, flying over obstacles and not around them. They fly all day from early morning until sunset and rest only to feed on flowers or take in water from a mud patch or damp place along a stream. At night they settle in masses on bushes or tall grass.

These migrations may reach a considerable sizes, one estimate in East Africa in 1926 was about 36 million insects passing per mile (1,6 km) of front each day. Another more recent estimate by one of the authors, J. Joannou, in January 1986 at Krugersdorp in the Gauteng Province put the number at five million butterflies over a five kilometre front per day. Some migrations over this part of South Africa occur almost continuously for up to two months. Most of these migrating individuals remain on the move until they die from exhaustion and wear and tear. Large numbers fly out to sea over the Moçambique Channel and the corpses can be observed washed up in the surf.

These large migrations of *Belenois aurota* often induce secondary migrants to accompany them. Species which are induced to migrate usually also belong to the pierid family and include the genera *Colotis*, *Dixeia*, *Eurema* and *Colias*. The well-known *Catopsilia florella* is a migrant in its own right and may be seen migrating on its own or with other induced species (see Larsen, 1992a). The subfamily Acraeinae is also represented by several species of the genus *Acraea*. Strong-flying nymphalines such as *Vanessa cardui* and *Junonia hierta cebrene* also take part. The family Lycaenidae has also been recorded in East Africa, represented by the genera *Syntarucus* and *Azanus*.

Other insect groups have also been recorded. One of the authors,

S.F. Henning (1987d), observed that a migration of *Belenois aurota* in January 1986 was accompanied by a large number of dragonflies of the species *Pantala flavescens*. This is a large species which is a temporary pool breeder. When these temporary pools dry up the newly-emerged adults must migrate to new areas to search for water. They fly persistently upwards, so as to allow themselves to be lifted and then carried by the wind at considerable heights and over long distances. The convergence of wind-currents is an essential feature in the production of large-scale precipitation of rain, therefore the migrating dragonflies are automatically delivered by winds to the right place at the right time (Corbet, 1983).

PREDATORS AND PARASITES

Predators

Not one stage in the life-cycle of butterflies is free from attack by predators. Insectivorous mice, birds, lizards, chameleons, small and juvenile snakes and even certain monkeys prey on the larvae, pupae and adult butterflies. Invertebrate predators, such as spiders, praying mantids and robberflies or assassin flies and other preying insects also eat the larvae, pupae and adults (fig. 10). Certain wasps, including the Common Paper Wasp, *Polistes smithii* and the Large Paper Wasp, *Belonogaster junceus*, carry butterfly and moth larvae to their nests and feed them to their own larvae. Some invertebrate predators probably also feed on butterfly eggs.

Parasites (Parasitoids)

Nothing is known about parasites attacking adult butterflies, but eggs, larvae and pupae are heavily parasitised by certain wasps (Hymenoptera) and flies (Diptera). Among the wasp families the most common butterfly parasites are the Ichneumonidae, the Braconidae and the usually tiny Chalcidoidea. The dipteran parasites usually belong to the family Tachinidae or Bristle Flies. In distinguishing between wasps and flies it should be remembered that

Crab spider eating *Aloeides thyra* (Photo A.J.M. Claassens)

Crematogaster ants eating *Charaxes* larva

Praying mantis eating *Catopsilia florella* (Photo A.J.M. Claassens)

wasps possess four wings and flies have only two wings.

Much of this parasitism of insects by insects is of a special type, which results in the death of the host and the total consumption of its internal tissues, in contrast to most other kinds of parasitism, in which it is advantageous to the parasite for the host to survive. It is, in effect, midway between predation and true parasitism, and organisms that exhibit it are known as parasitoids. Usually only the larval stages are parasitic (Norris, 1970).

The general appearance of the Ichneumonidae, Braconidae and Chalcidoidea as well as the Tachinidae is shown in fig. 21. Note that the Tachinidae resemble ordinary Houseflies, but that they are more hairy.

Eggs are usually parasitised by tiny Chalcidoidea, while larvae and pupae are attacked by the other, larger parasites. All these parasites feed and develop inside their hosts, but avoid destroying their vital organs until they themselves are fully grown and ready to pupate. Prior to pupation parasitic larvae leave their host larvae to pupate outside. The parasitic larvae of eggs and pupae, after having consumed the contents of their host, pupate inside the egg or pupal shell, thus ensuring themselves of extra protection.

Several parasites will be discussed under various species of butterfly dealt with in this work. Best known in this regard are perhaps the parasites of the Garden Acraea (*Acraea horta*), whose early stages are heavily parasitised. Parasitism, cruel as it may seem, is nature's way of maintaining an ecological equilibrium or balance. In the case of butterflies that means keeping a balance between the available number of food plants (the producers of food) and the butterfly offspring (the consumers). If left unchecked the consumers, mainly the larval stage, would soon exhaust all food supply and in doing so eat themselves out of existence.

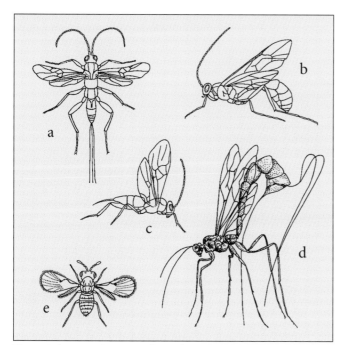

Fig. 20 Various parasitic wasps of butterflies. a: *Orgilus* sp. female (Ichneumonidae); b: Ichneumonid sp. (Ichneumonidae); c: *Apanteles* sp. female (Braconidae); d: Ichneumonid female laying an egg; e: *Trichogramma* sp. (Trichogrammatidae)

Fig. 21 Parasitic fly belonging to the family Tachinidae

Braconid wasp larvae spinning cocoons after emerging from an *Acraea anacreon* larva

Ichneumonid wasp emerged from pupa of *Capys disjunctus*

PROTECTION AND DEFENCE

The balance of nature would not be served, nor could it be maintained if the predators and parasites were allowed to kill indiscriminately and without being checked themselves by protective and defence mechanisms operating among their prey. Moreover, some predators are preyed upon by other, usually larger predators and even parasites have their own parasites. Some of these mechanisms, operating in butterflies, are discussed below.

Unpalatability

In contrast to many butterflies which are palatable in all four stages of their life-cycle, the Danainae and Acraeinae have developed distasteful and even poisonous properties which deter at least vertebrate predators. These butterflies are not only unpalatable, but they display bright red, yellow and black warning colours on their wings which combined with their slow, often gliding flight advertise their distastefulness. Potential predators which have attempted to eat these species, will recognise them by their brilliant, gaudy colours and leisurely flight and avoid them rather than being tempted again. Unpalatable butterflies obtain their distasteful properties from the poisons present in their larval food plants which render not only the larvae and pupae unpalatable, but also the adults in which the poisonous properties are retained, especially in the wings. In some poisonous species the warning colours are also displayed by their larvae and pupae.

Camouflage

Many palatable butterflies make use of camouflage in order to escape the attention of predators. Camouflage is achieved by colour, patterns and markings as well as shape, not only of the wings of the adults but also with regard to the larvae and pupae. The caterpillars of many palatable species are green, or at least their ground colour is a shade of green, which together with other markings render them indistinguishable from the leaves on which they feed.

The young black and white caterpillars of the swallowtail but-

Iolaus silarus silarus on shiny leaves of *Englerophytum magalismontanum*

terflies resemble bird droppings stuck to leaves and would look most unattractive to insectivorous birds searching for juicy caterpillars. Some caterpillars rest on the leaves of their food plants in such a manner and position that their colour and markings resemble their immediate surroundings. Likewise many pupae are green or they have other cryptic colours which match their surroundings. Some pupae resemble the bark against which they are attached, others imitate short branches.

Although the pupating larvae of a swallowtail butterfly have the same colour generally, they are able to determine which colour would best suit their defenceless pupae. In a light environment the pupae of *Papilio demodocus* are usually light green, grey or yellowish-brown or even orange in colour, but in dark surroundings or against a dark background they usually are dark grey or almost black. The pupae of *Stugeta bowkeri* not only resemble in outline a piece of bark to which they are attached, but their colour also matches the colour of the bark or the lichen growing on the bark.

Active defence mechanisms

Adult butterflies on the wing have little to fear from insectivorous birds. They are capable of a very erratic and fast flight when alarmed and can dodge a pursuer with a surprising degree of agility. Many species, especially amongst the brilliantly coloured Lycaenids, have a blue or violaceous blue sheen on the wings which, depending upon the angle at which the wings are moved against the rays of the sun, makes it difficult to follow them in flight.

Butterflies have adopted various methods of confusing a predator when they are at rest. The wing shape and underside markings of species such as *Junonia archesia* and *Junonia octavia sesamus* are such that, when they settle with closed wings on rocks or on the ground between twigs and leaves, they resemble dead leaves. Thus camouflaged they are hardly distinguishable from their surroundings, but when disturbed make off at great speed to settle in similar surroundings elsewhere.

Many butterflies have bright 'eye'-spots which, when the wings are opened and closed repeatedly, either frighten predators, or encourage them to strike at the false eyes rather than at the butterflies'

Melanitis leda among dead leaves

bodies. A butterfly is none the worse for losing part of its wings and often specimens are seen with a piece of the wing or wings missing, obviously torn off with force by a bird or lizard.

In many species belonging to the family Lycaenidae the eye-spots on the hindwings are associated with hair-like projections or tail-like appendages, as well as lines and other markings directed towards the eye-spots (fig. 22).

When these butterflies are at rest they usually hold their wings closed and while keeping their antennae motionless rub their hindwings together. In this way the impression is created that their hindwings are their head-end with the moving tails representing antennae and the false eye-spots resembling large eyes. A lizard lurking for a moving prey is tempted to strike at these wings, allowing the insect to escape almost unharmed.

The adults and larvae of the Acraeinae produce an orange-yellow liquid when handled. This liquid is poisonous to vertebrate animals.

The larvae of many butterflies drop from the place where they are resting or feeding as soon as they are touched. In the debris below the food plant they are hard to detect. The larvae of many satyrids (Browns) which feed on grasses display this escape behaviour and once they have dropped remain motionless for a long time.

Pupae of butterflies which are attached to a substrate by means of a cremaster and a girdle, execute vigorous, jerky movements when touched. This behaviour may well frighten would-be predators or parasitic wasps or flies intending to oviposit on them. The unexpected sudden movements may even discourage small insectivorous birds from attacking such pupae.

The larvae of the Swallowtail butterflies possess a brightly coloured, eversible, forked organ, called an *osmeterium*, situated just behind the head. The osmeterium is shot out when the caterpillar is disturbed and produces a volatile liquid with an unpleasant, strong acrid smell. When persistently interfered with, the larva bends its anterior end backwards or sideways to direct the osmeterium menacingly towards the attacker. The anterior segments swell and together with the osmeterium resemble the head of a snake.

The larvae of many skippers (Hesperiidae) hide from predators and parasites in tubes formed by 'sewing' the edges of leaves of the food plant together with the aid of silk secreted from the mouth. They crawl out of their shelter, usually only at night, to feed from the edge of the leaf and withdraw immediately into safety when disturbed. Some species even pupate inside a closed shelter formed by drawing several leaves together, again using silk.

The larvae of some ant-associated Lycaenidae spend part of their larval and their entire pupal stage in an ants' nest, or the larvae emerge from the ants' nest only at night to feed. Such larvae gain protection against predators and parasites. See also under Myrmecophily.

Iolaus diametra natalica (dorsal view) showing false head

Fig. 22 *Iolaus diametra natalica* male underside showing false head pattern on wings

Melanitis leda flashing warning eye-spots

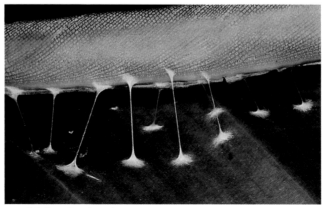

Larval shelter of *Moltena fiara*

Mimicry

Many insects which enjoy protection against predators by being poisonous, or possessing warning colours, a sting or other devices, are mimicked by other insects. These insects are sometimes completely unrelated and are themselves not poisonous or dangerous in other ways and thus by mimicry derive a measure of protection against potential foes. Some mimics resemble their models so closely that it is difficult to separate the fraud from the model. Thus some hover flies and day-flying moths resemble bees or even wasps, but do not possess stings. They move about on flowers among the nectar- and pollen-gathering bees, and predators, not being able to distinguish between the dangerous models and the harmless mimics, leave them alone.

Some Robber flies resemble certain Carpenter bees so closely that the latter are unaware of their deceit. The mimics may even position themselves next to the nest entrance of a female Carpenter bee and when she emerges from the nest is pounced upon, killed and devoured. Note that in this particular case the mimic imitates its own prey.

One can distinguish between two kinds of mimicry. In Batesian mimicry, named after the English naturalist Bates, a palatable species mimics an unpalatable one; only the mimic benefits. In Müllerian mimicry, named after the Brazilian naturalist Müller, an unpalatable species resembles another unpalatable species and both benefit.

It is thought that a predator, after catching a number of individuals of an unpalatable butterfly, 'learns' that they are distasteful and recognising the species by its flaunting colours and leisurely flight, will eventually leave it alone. It will also avoid the mimics, which of course must fly in the same locality as their models. In Müllerian mimicry the two look-alikes both 'teach' a predator that they are unpalatable and in that way, by sharing the initial losses, each species will suffer less in loss of numbers.

For example if the African Monarch, *Danaus chrysippus* (Danainae) were to lose a hundred individuals before a predator species realises that it is distasteful, it would be advantageous for another unpalatable species flying in the same locality to look like the Monarch. The two look-alikes may lose, say, only about 50 individuals each before they are both left alone.

In Batesian mimicry it is sometimes only the female, the more important reproductive form, which mimics an unpalatable species, a good example being the female Diadem (*Hypolimnas misippus*) which mimics the African Monarch (*Danaus chrysippus*). The male

Hypolimnas misippus, the Batesian mimic of *Danaus chrysippus*

Danaus chrysippus, the unpalatable model for many mimics

Diadem which does not resemble the female at all, does not imitate another species. However, black and white is also a common warning pattern and *H. misippus* could itself be unpalatable.

How successful species are in safeguarding themselves by 'sailing under false colours' is difficult to assess, but judging by the common occurrence of mimicry in all its forms one can only conclude that the deceit must be rewarding. Although one can easily understand the advantage of mimicry to certain species, it is by no means easy to comprehend how it came about. It is certain that it must have developed through a long and intricate evolutionary process.

Acraea encedon, the Müllerian mimic of *Danaus chrysippus*

Papilio echerioides, the Batesian mimic of *Amauris echeria*

The unpalatable model, *Amauris echeria*

ZOOGEOGRAPHY

This is intended to be only a brief outline of the zoogeography of Southern African butterflies. For a more comprehensive account on African butterflies in general the article by Carcasson (1964) and the book by Owen (1971) are recommended. For a more comprehensive account on the zoogeography of Southern African butterflies and the Cape floral region in particular the excellent work by Cottrell (1978) is recommended.

The Southern African subregion lies roughly between latitudes 15° S and 35° S. By 135 million years B.P., the southern tip of Africa looked very much in outline as it does today. Since that time uplift and erosion have led to the appearance of the Interior Plateau separated from the Marginal Zone by the great divide known as the Great Escarpment. The Interior Plateau is the southern tip of the great African Plateau, and its altitude varies from a minimum of slightly under 900 m a.s.l. in the Kalahari Desert, to almost 3500 m a.s.l. in the Lesotho Highlands. Here, the thick Karoo sediments of the Carboniferous to Triassic ages were covered in the Jurassic by thick lava flows, which, on cooling to a hard layer of basalt, protected the underlying softer rocks from weathering, giving rise to the high mountains of Southern Africa.

The Marginal Zone, between the Great Escarpment and the coast, varies in width from 60 km in the west to 240 km in the east. Its elevation varies from sea-level to a maximum of 2300 m a.s.l. in the Swartberg Range south of the Great Escarpment. In turn, the Great Escarpment is composed of several distinct mountain ranges, giving Southern Africa a characteristic and varied topography.

Off the coast, the northward flowing Benguela Current flows up the west coast, and the southward flowing warm Agulhas Current flows down the east coast. These flow patterns, along with topography and global wind patterns, influence the area's rainfall regimes. There are three distinct rainfall regions in Southern Africa: summer, winter and all-season rainfall areas.

VEGETATION TYPES

As one moves further away from the equator on the African continent the rainfall gradually decreases, the annual dry seasons become longer and seasonal and daily temperature oscillations become increasingly pronounced until one encounters conditions of extreme aridity at about 20° S. With the gradual desiccation the equatorial forest gives way to deciduous woodland of decreasing density, then to wooded steppe, open steppe, scrub and eventually desert. Beyond the desert areas there is moderate winter rainfall together with a well defined cool season, giving rise to a vegetation of evergreen shrubs and trees with small, leathery leaves – the Cape Macchia or Fynbos. The extreme desert conditions in Southern Africa are limited to a narrow coastal strip in Namibia.

This transition from equatorial forest to desert is slow and irregular, no doubt due to the great prevalence of maritime climatic influences and to the great central plateau, with its almost uniform cover of deciduous woodland. The transition from desert (Kalahari) to Mediterranean-type vegetation (Cape Macchia) includes a large area with a very characteristic vegetation of low-

The floodplains of Maputaland, KwaZulu-Natal, South Africa

growing succulent plants and bushes (Karoo). In the eastern part of Africa the typical succession of vegetation is strongly modified by the plateau. Equatorial conditions are limited to a narrow coastal belt which however extends further south than on the west coast, due to the effect of the warm Moçambique Current and of the southeast monsoon. In this narrow belt there are many small relics of equatorial forest, isolated from one another and forming a complex mosaic with deciduous woodland and savannah. These forests frequently extend to the eastern escarpment of the plateau where the moist winds from the Indian Ocean are forced to condense their water content. Beyond the escarpment lies a vast table-land of savannah and steppe with scattered areas of highland forest at higher elevations and subalpine grassland and moorland on the higher mountains, above the tree line.

Evergreen forest can be separated into two types, lowland and montane. Near the equator montane forest is confined to land higher than 1600 metres, but at higher latitudes it extends progressively to lower altitudes, to the point where it exists at sea level (Knysna).

Lowland evergreen forest

Lowland evergreen forest is developed only in areas with at least 1500 mm of rain well distributed throughout the year. This forest is richer in biomass and in plant species than any other vegetation type in Africa. It forms a dense stand of many species of trees, with a continuous canopy often between 20 m and 30 m above the ground. From this other trees emerge but rarely exceed 60 m in height. Typically the trees have pale, smooth trunks which are relatively thin and are unbranched for most of their height. The trees support a wealth of lianas and their branches are loaded with epiphytes (Moreau, 1966).

Lowland forest in the Pungwe Valley, Zimbabwe

Montane forests of Mariepskop, Mpumalanga, South Africa

Montane or highland forest

Montane or highland forest resembles lowland forest but is composed of different species and does not grow as tall or as dense. The trees are mostly broad-leaved. It is interesting to note that the highland forest, though confined to scattered mountains, is surprisingly uniform in botanical composition. It occurs from northern Ethiopia to South Africa, but at progressively lower altitudes as one proceeds further from the equator. The Knysna Forest in the Western Cape, for example, though situated at sea level, is homologous and similar to forest areas occurring in Kenya and Uganda above 2 000 metres.

Associated with highland forest is highland grassveld which is a major habitat of many of the rarer species of Lycaenidae in Southern Africa. As the forest shrinks so the grassland spreads, and vice versa. However, recent evidence appears to indicate that the montane grassland may, in part, be due to activities of man over the past 8 000 years.

Secondary forest

Much of the primary rainforests of Africa have been destroyed, the big trees removed and the land cultivated. Large tracts of rainforests have been replaced by secondary forest which differs from undisturbed primary forest in having a dense tangle of undergrowth in which especially quick-growing but short-lived tree species have a temporary advantage. These trees never attain the height of the trees of climax forest and are eventually replaced by them.

Wooded savannah or moist woodlands

Wooded savannah or moist woodlands are terms which cover the greatest areas of Africa on the periphery of the lowland forest, where rainfall exceeds 800 mm a year but where the dry season is severe. The dominant vegetation of savannah is grass but trees are usually present. In the higher rainfall areas the grass is tall and thick while the accompanying trees are small and sparse, probably due to the extremely severe fires induced by the thick growth of grass. In the lower rainfall areas the grass is not as thick and the trees are taller and predominantly leguminous. In Southern Africa this area extends into Zimbabwe and Moçambique as a continuation of the great block of miombo, dominated by *Brachystegia* and *Julbernardia* spp., that covers Africa almost from the Atlantic to the Indian Ocean between latitudes 7° and 17° S (Moreau, 1966).

Dry woodlands and wooded steppe

Dry woodlands and wooded steppe occur in a belt outside the preceding woodland type with rainfall between 300 mm and 800 mm. It is found in the hotter and drier river valleys of Zimbabwe and extends southwards and westwards over most of the northern parts of South Africa, Botswana and north-western Namibia. The most widespread trees are *Acacia* species but at the lower latitudes, where the rainfall is not as limited, there is considerable admixture of broad-leaved trees and baobabs (Moreau, 1966). In South Africa these are commonly known as bushveld areas.

In some savannah, woodland or bushveld areas gallery forest extends along the rivers.

Desert and subdesert

Desert and subdesert in Southern Africa is found in a narrow strip from the Angolan border through Namibia to the lower reaches of the Orange River. The main vegetation of the subdesert consists of low perennial plants, often bushy, with a few *Acacia* trees in favourable spots. The grasses are ephemeral; fire is no longer a factor, but the soil is bare for most of the year, since any herbage, on drying, is removed by harvester termites and wind. In the true desert plants are solitary, few indeed and far between, with very large areas which are completely barren (Moreau, 1966).

Macchia

Macchia is the term employed to cover the vegetation found at the extremity of the continent, in the Western Cape Province. The vegetation of this region is characteristically sclerophyllous and is also known as fynbos. A transitional zone of this type of vegetation is found at high altitude along the Drakensberg into Mpumalanga.

Cape macchia on the mountains above Muizenberg, Western Cape Province, South Africa

Dry bushveld at Lapalala Wilderness, Northern Province, South Africa

Brachystegia woodland at Christon Bank, Zimbabwe

Kalahari sandveld at Hotazel, near Kuruman, Northern Cape Province, South Africa

35

AFROTROPICAL FAUNISTIC REGIONS

Carcasson (1964) pointed out that any serious study of African butterflies will show that a natural biogeographic classification must be based on habitat rather than on semi-arbitrary geographic barriers. He suggested the following geographic divisions for the Lepidoptera of the Afrotropical region.

1. Sylvan sub-region, comprising all evergreen forests on the continent
2. Sub-region of open formations, comprising all open plant associations, excluding subalpine moorland and grassland in the tropics and the areas included in the Cape sub-region
3. Cape sub-region, comprising the areas of winter rainfall in the Western Cape, the Karoo and high level grassland (highveld) in South Africa and Zimbabwe, as well as the Namib desert
4. Malagasy sub-region, comprising Madagascar, the Comoro Islands, the Seychelles and the Mascarenes
5. Special habitats, such as montane grassland and moorland in the tropics, high level swamps, low level swamps and littoral sand dunes

The sub-regions which occur in Southern Africa are as follows:

Sylvan sub-region

This should be divided into the Lowland Forest Division and the Highland Forest Division. The dividing line between the two is around 1 600 m at the equator, progressively descending to sea level at 33° S (Knysna Forest). There is naturally a wide zone of vertical overlap between the two divisions, particularly at the equator, where highland species do not normally descend below 1 000 metres and lowland species do not rise above 2 000 metres. The 1 000 metre overlap becomes narrower as the distance from the equator increases and disappears altogether in KwaZulu-Natal, where lowland forest elements are absent beyond 30° S, even at sea level. A few widespread and highly adaptable species, such as *Charaxes candiope, Protogonomorpha parhassus aethiops, Junonia terea, J. tugela* and *Anthene lemnos*, occur at all levels.

Lowland forest division

The greatest density of butterfly species occurs in this division. It supplies optimum conditions for insect life and evolution. A perpetually warm and moist climate with appreciable seasonal checks encourages abundant plant life and permits numerous annual broods and consequent rapid evolution. Where conditions are optimal, comparatively unspecialised species can thrive and large numbers of individuals are not necessary for survival, since there is little risk of sudden disasters, such as the prolonged droughts of arid areas.

In Southern Africa the Eastern lowland forest sub-division extends through Moçambique to as far south as Zululand. At present this is not a continuous belt, but a long series of scattered relics, usually in areas of better drainage near the coast and on the lower slopes of the eastern escarpment. The butterfly fauna of this area, although much poorer than that of the western equatorial forests, shows unmistakable affinities with the western forest fauna. Most of the species in the eastern forests are endemic species, or very distinct subspecies representing genera which are much better developed in the western forests of Africa.

Riverine forest along the Pungwe River, Zimbabwe

The impoverishment of the eastern forests must have been due to their extreme fragmentation and reduction during the arid ice-age periods and to the small area of the forest refuges.

Some endemic species of the eastern lowland forest found in Southern Africa are: *Graphium polistratus, G. colonna, G. junodi, Euxanthe wakefieldi, Charaxes violetta, Euryphura achlys, Cymothoe coranus, Euphaedra neophron, Neptis goochii, Hypolimnas deceptor, Acraea rabbaiae, A. satis, A. igola, Hyalites conradti, Pentila tropicalis, Deudorix dariaves* and *Axiocerses punicea.*

Highland forest division

As was pointed out earlier, the forest and its fauna change as the altitude increases. The number of butterfly species decreases, but most of the high-altitude species are closely related to those of the lowland forest. The lower limit of the highland forest is near 1 600 metres at the equator and varies with latitude and climate. At present the highland forest consists of fragments scattered over most of Africa. The butterfly fauna of these forest patches is surprisingly uniform, suggesting that at one time they formed part of a single forest area.

During the Miocene (7 million years before present) the area was at a low altitude with an equable climate – most of the subcontinent was covered by evergreen forest. In the east upwarping of the low mountains to become the Drakensberg escarpment was causing the evolution of cool-adapted montane (highland) forests and hence butterflies. In the middle Miocene the aridification of western Southern Africa began to intensify due to the growth of the Antarctic ice cap and the stronger Benguela current. At the end of the Miocene major uplift (about 1 800 m) raised the montane forest and fragmented it. Aridification eradicated the large lowland forests that gave it birth. Since then, glacial/interglacial cycles have caused localised speciation, but the majority of their butterflies are related at subspecies level, for example *Charaxes xiphares* and *Papilio ophidicephalus.*

The butterfly fauna of the highland forest is so uniform that major subdivisions are impossible, and the limits suggested should have the same status as the zones of the lowland forest. Carcasson (1964) divides this area into 6 zones, two of which extend into Southern Africa.

The first of these is the Tanzania-Malawi Zone which includes the highland forests from south-east Kenya to the mountains of Malawi, Moçambique and of the eastern border of Zimbabwe. Much of the highland forest in this zone is along the broken edge of the eastern tableland from the Usambara Mountains in north Tanzania to Chirinda Forest in Zimbabwe. This long, interrupted escarpment may have carried very considerable areas of highland forest in the comparatively recent past, which would account for the richness of its fauna, despite present fragmentation and reduction. The highland forests in Zimbabwe are considerably poorer than the remainder of the zone and include one species typical of the adjoining South African Zone (*Cymothoe alcimeda*). There are, however, a number of endemic butterflies in the Zimbabwean forests such as *Cymothoe vumbui*, *Mylothris carcassoni*, *Mimacraea neokoton* and *Charaxes alpinus*.

The South African Zone has the majority of its forest relics situated on the eastern escarpment of Mpumalanga and KwaZulu-Natal and on the eastern and southern seaboard. One or two of the coastal forests in KwaZulu-Natal retain a tropical character and are included in the Eastern Lowland Forest Division. The Knysna Forest in the Western Cape, however, must be regarded as montane, although it is situated at sea level. There are a few endemic species in this zone: *Papilio euphranor*, *Mylothris trimenia*, *Paralethe dendrophilus*, *Charaxes karkloof*, *C. marieps* and *Bowkeria phosphor*.

Some species of the South African Highland Forest Zone are represented by several distinct subspecies, such as *Papilio ophidicephalus*, *Paralethe dendrophilus*, *Charaxes xiphares* and *C. druceanus*.

The South African forest fauna suggests that forests have not covered any significant portion of the country at least since the Miocene and that the present Cape fauna may have occupied a more extensive area in the past.

The South African forest butterflies are nearly all of tropical origin, with the exception of *Paralethe dendrophilus* and *Bowkeria phosphor*, which are elements of the Cape fauna and may have entered the forest from the adjoining open formations.

Montane grassveld

This vegetation type is closely associated with highland forest. As the climatic conditions change and the forest expands and contracts so the converse happens with the grassveld. Many important Lycaenidae genera inhabit highland grassveld such as the *Aloeides* in the Aphnaeini (Theclinae) and the *Orachrysops* and *Lepidochrysops* in the Polyommatinae. Relic populations on mountain tops are found from the Western Cape through to Inyanga in Zimbabwe. There are also many endemic Satyrinae (Nymphalidae) which inhabit highland grassveld, including the genera *Dira*, *Dingana*, *Pseudonympha* and *Stygionympha*.

Dune forest at the Ntafufu river mouth, Eastern Cape Province, South Africa

The montane grasslands of the Golden Gate Highlands National Park, Free State Province, South Africa

Sub-region of open formations

This sub-region includes a great variety of vegetation types, in fact all formations other than closed canopy evergreen forest and montane grassland and moorland, and extends to about 25° S. Carcasson (1964) divides this subregion into northern and southern divisions, the latter one concerning us here.

The Southern Division is an enormous area, comprising all the open formations excluding grassland above 2 000 metres from the northern division to the Namib and Karoo. This area is further subdivided into three zones, all of which occur in the Southern African Subregion.

Eastern Zone

The Eastern Zone comprises all the open formations in Southern Africa on the east coast from the Zambezi River to KwaZulu-Natal. Its western boundaries are the eastern escarpment of Zimbabwe and the foothills of the Drakensberg in KwaZulu-Natal. The Eastern Zone enjoys a climate which is mostly moist, with short dry seasons, except towards its southern extremity, where the dry season becomes longer. This zone does not rise above 1 000 metres and includes a great variety of open formations from tall, dense deciduous woodland to semi-arid *Acacia-Commiphora* scrub, occasionally with *Adansonia*, particularly between the mouths of the Rovuma River and Quelimane, and south of Beira. In the moister areas north of Delagoa Bay it includes a good deal of *Brachystegia, Julbernardia, Afzelia* and *Oxytenanthera*, and *Hyphaene* in areas of poor drainage.

The Eastern Zone shares a great many butterfly species with the Zambesian Zone, but has a few endemic species such as *Colotis erone* and *Leptomyrina hirundo*.

Zambesian Zone

The Zambesian Zone in Southern Africa extends only into Mashonaland, Zimbabwe and is bordered in the east by the Eastern Zone, and in the west and south by the Kalahari Zone.

This zone is the richest in species. It is comprises mostly of a high plateau, between 1 100 and 1 600 metres in altitude. Soils are mainly sandy and acid, and much of the vegetation is deciduous woodland of varying density. The dominant trees are numerous species of *Brachystegia* and *Julbernardia*, together with *Uapaca, Monotes, Parinari* and with *Cryptosepalum pseudotaxis, Guibourtia coleosperma* and *Marqueisia*. The rainfall is abundant but there is a long dry season. The hot dry valleys of the Limpopo and lower Zambezi with their characteristic *Colophospermum mopane* woodland, connect the Eastern Zone with the Kalahari Zone.

There are numerous endemic butterfly species from the Zambesian Zone in our area and the genus *Acraea* is particularly well represented. Species characteristic of the Zambesian Zone are:

Bicyclus angulosus selousi	*Cnodontes penningtoni*
Henotesia simonsii	*Liptena homeyeri*
Physcaeneura pione	*Deloneura sheppardi*
Charaxes bohemani	*Iolaus (Epamera) australis*
C. penricei penricei	*I. (E.) violacea*
C. guderiana guderiana	*Aphnaeus marshalli*
C. fulgurata	*A. erikssoni*
C. manica	*Lepidochrysops solwezii*
Neptis jordani	*L. chloauges*
Junonia touhilimasa	*L. gigantea*
J. artaxia	*L. longifalces*
J. actia	*Sarangesa astrigera*
Acraea omrora	*Teniorhinus harona*
A. atolmis	*Fresna nyassae*
A. atergatis	*Platylesches shona*
A. axina	

Kalahari Zone

The Kalahari Zone is much drier than the Zambesian Zone and includes parts of Matabeleland and the Northern Province, the Northern Cape, the North-West Province, Botswana and the western half of Namibia. It is bordered by the Zambesian Zone in the north, by the Eastern Zone in the east, by the Cape Grassland and Karoo Zones in the South, and by the Namib desert in the west (Carcasson, 1964).

Most of this zone consists of subdesert steppe with scattered *Acacia* and with *Euclea, Commiphora, Combretum, Terminalia, Boscia, Tamarix* and *Cadaba* in the more favoured areas and along dry river beds. Many of the more xerophilous butterflies occur in the Kalahari Zone. In the South, where the Karoo vegetation begins, the tropical xerophilous species are gradually replaced by Cape floral elements and in the extremely arid Namib desert to the west, plant, and hence butterflies, disappear almost completely.

There are a few endemic species of tropical origin:

Colotis lais	*Iolaus (Epamera) obscura*
Acraea hypoleuca	*Spindasis modesta*
A. onerata	*Anthene lindae*
A. brainei	*Sarangesa gaerdesi*

The Cape Sub-region

The Cape sub-region consists of all Southern Africa excluding the Kalahari, the eastern coastal belt and the forests, but including the restricted areas of montane grassland in Zimbabwe. It is further subdivided into four zones.

The **Namib desert**, which is the extremely arid coastal belt of Namibia, the **Karoo**, which is a vast area characterised by low-growing succulent vegetation, the **winter rainfall areas** of the Western Cape, which are typified by the fynbos and the **high-level grasslands** which occupy much of the plateau of the Free State, KwaZulu-Natal and Mpumalanga, as well as the mountains of the Western and Eastern Cape and small montane areas in the eastern districts of Zimbabwe. The butterfly fauna of the Cape sub-region has a high percentage of endemic genera and species, particularly in the families Nymphalidae (Satyrinae) and Lycaenidae and is associated with a very rich and probably ancient flora.

The presence of many closely related butterflies of limited and frequently allopatric distribution suggests extreme proliferation from limited stocks of great antiquity. The hot dry bush areas and the forests of South Africa are inhabited by impoverished butter-

Typical karoo habitat of the Roggeveld Escarpment, Northern Cape Province, South Africa

fly faunas of tropical character. On the other hand in the mountains, on the grassland, in the Karoo and fynbos, the endemic South African genera appear to be doing well.

There is also good reason to believe that the Cape fauna may have occupied a much greater area in the past than at present, because some of the typically South African genera are represented in the montane grasslands of tropical Africa. For example, the genus *Aloeides* with 46 species in South Africa, is represented by three species (2 endemic) in the highlands of Zambia and East Africa. The genus *Capys* which, although poor in species in South Africa, must be regarded as typically South African because it is always associated with plants of the genus *Protea*, occurs in many of the mountains of tropical Africa, including the Cameroons and Nigeria. The butterfly genus *Lepidochrysops*, although present in montane grassland and in wooded savannah all over Africa, has an exceptionally high concentration of species (mostly endemic) in South Africa. There are 112 known species of this genus, of which 57 are endemic to the Cape sub-region. The 27 known species of *Thestor* are confined to South Africa, except *T. basutus* which also occurs in the montane grasslands of Zimbabwe.

The Lycaenid genera *Durbania* (2 species), *Durbaniella* (1 species), *Durbaniopsis* (1 species), *Poecilmitis* (49 species), *Phasis* (4 species) and *Oxychaeta* (1 species) are also endemic. There are also many endemic species in the subfamily Satyrinae of the Nymphalidae: *Aeropetes tulbaghia* Linnaeus (monotypic genus) occurs throughout the South African mountains and on the eastern border of Zimbabwe, but does not cross the Zambezi. The genera *Dira* (4 species), *Dingana* (7 species), *Serradinga* (3 species), *Tarsocera* (7 species), *Torynesis* (5 species) are solely South African and do not even penetrate Zimbabwe. The genus *Neita* has 4 species in Southern Africa, and one endemic in the grasslands of East Africa. The monotypic genera *Cassionympha* and *Melampias* are South African endemics. The genus *Stygionympha* has 8 species endemic to South Africa and one which has penetrated Zimbabwe. *Pseudonympha* has 22 species of which 19 are South African endemics, 2 are endemic to Zimbabwe and one occurs in the Northern Province and in Zimbabwe. The genus *Coenyra* consists of 3 species confined to South Africa.

Other species endemic to the Cape Sub-region are:

Tarucus thespis	*K. lepenula*
T. bowkeri	*Spialia agylla*
Cacyreus marshalli	*S. nanus*
C. dicksoni	*S. sataspes*
Harpendyreus notoba	*Alenia sandaster*
H. tsomo	*A. namaqua*
H. noquasa	*Metisella metis*
Spindasis namaqua	*M. malgacha*
Lycaena orus	*M. aegipan*
Charaxes pelias	*M. meninx*
Acraea horta	*M. syrinx*
Kedestes chaca	*Tsitana tulbagha*
K. barberae	*T. dicksoni*

Special habitats

Swamps

Some Southern African butterflies are dependent on swamp plants and therefore occur only in the vicinity of swamps. Some examples include: *Eurema hapale* which is found in high level swampy areas in tropical Africa; *Mashuna mashuna* occurs in high level swamps in Mashonaland, Zimbabwe; *Junonia ceryne* also found in high level swamps; and *Hyalites rahira* in swamps between 1 600 – 2 100 metres in Southern and East Africa. *Eicochrysops hippocrates* occurs near streams throughout Africa; *Cupidopsis cissus* is found in wet meadows throughout Africa; *Metisella meninx* occurs in wet meadows in South Africa; and *Borbo micans* is found in areas of swampy vegetation.

Littoral sand dunes

Many of the common species of dry areas occasionally frequent this type of habitat, but only one appears to be confined to it: *Colotis eunoma* (Pieridae), which is associated with littoral sand dunes on the East African coast, from Kenya to Moçambique.

The wetlands of Verlorenvallei near Dullstroom, Mpumalanga Province, South Africa

BREEDING BUTTERFLIES

The breeding or rearing of butterflies in captivity has become very popular in recent times. This is an important development as until recently the life histories of comparatively few species were known. With increasing urbanisation and agriculture in Southern Africa more species of butterflies are coming under threat. Conservation measures for these species can be considered only if we know their habitat requirements and host plants and this is achieved only by breeding them. The following are a few hints for the breeding of butterflies.

LARVAL FOOD PLANTS

For successful breeding of butterflies it is essential to know which food plant a species uses. Some species are very selective and will accept only one particular plant species, while others have more catholic tastes and will accept several different, usually related species. The food plants of most of the common butterflies are well-known and hence can be simply looked up either in the present work, or in other butterfly books which list the food plants of the various species of butterflies they deal with.

When caterpillars or eggs are found in the wild, the food plant is of course established at the same time and may be identified by comparing the leaves and flowers with illustrations in books, or by asking the help of a lepidopterist who is familiar with food plants. Sometimes it will be necessary to consult an expert on plants.

If one wishes to breed a butterfly species of which the food plant is unknown, a female of that species should be watched to observe on what plant she oviposits. She may have to be followed for a considerable time before she obliges and lays her eggs, usually one at a time, on separate leaves or buds of a plant. Having established on which plant she has oviposited she should be captured, taken home, and put in a large jar, box or cage with a sprig or two of the food plant.

The food plant is absolutely necessary to ensure that females lay in captivity as it is the chemicals in the plant which stimulate laying. If the butterfly is in an airtight container the food plant will remain fresh for a few days. In a more open netting cage the food plant should be placed in a small bottle or tube of water to keep it fresh. It is still better to have the food plant growing in a small pot and to place this inside the cage for the female to lay on.

WHERE TO FIND EARLY STAGES

Eggs are usually easy to find in nature. They are often yellow, pale green or white and in most species are simply laid on the leaves on which the newly emerged caterpillar will feed. If the caterpillars feed on flowers, the eggs will be found on the outsides of the flower buds. Those feeding on seeds will have their eggs laid on the outside of a young fruit or pod.

The caterpillars or larvae can usually be found on the food plants by observing characteristic half-eaten leaves and twigs. The larvae of species feeding on the seeds of leguminous plants can be found by looking for holes in the pods. Larvae collected at random in the wild may prove to be parasitised by small wasps or flies.

Pupae are very rarely found in the wild as they are usually very well camouflaged. They can be found on twigs, tree trunks, leaves or inside seed pods. The presence of a parasitoid can upset the larva's instinct to hide, therefore pupae of normally hard-to-find species found in the open often produce wasps or flies.

BRINGING HOME LIVE MATERIAL

Before one can breed insects one first has to obtain living material from the wild. When bringing home insects one has to have glass or plastic vials, jars or boxes or some similar containers. These can be of various sizes depending on the size of the insect being collected.

Conditions in these containers are completely different to life on a leaf, where the caterpillar, pupa or egg is usually in the shade and cooled by the wind. The adult butterfly will also sit in the shade of a tree to cool down. Bottles and vials are particularly prone to heating by the sun and most insects will die in a few minutes if exposed to the sun in a jar or a box. Therefore as soon as possible after collecting, the jars or boxes containing the insects should be placed in a shady or cool place. Travelling in a car also poses problems of overheating. The best way of transporting live specimens is in a polystyrene cool-box, since it is both cool and dark. Most insects become less active in the dark (if they are normally active during the day) and cool down, and this prevents them (particularly the adults) from damaging themselves.

When placing an insect in a container it is important to bear in mind the size of the insect in relation to its container. A large final instar caterpillar will suffer in a small jar but a small first instar or egg in the same container will remain quite healthy. If the container is of reasonable size for the insect, one need not worry about punching ventilation holes in the lid.

Leaf feeding larvae should always be provided with food, as they will often continue to feed in the dark of the box. Pupae should be transported between layers of cotton wool to prevent them from bouncing about and being damaged.

BUTTERFLY REARING AT HOME

Having got the live specimens home, they must be looked after with great care. Caterpillar cages or boxes must be kept clean of droppings and the larvae supplied daily with fresh food unless they are kept on growing plants. When fresh foliage is provided larvae should not be forced off old leaves but these should be cut off and left in the container among the new leaves. Overcrowding and excessive dampness may cause disease and must be avoided in larval containers. Moisture which occasionally collects along the sides of airtight boxes should be dried off as soon as possible. Organisms attacking the early stages of butterflies are certain viruses and fungi. When breeding in captivity fungi are the common cause of death among caterpillars reared in a very humid environment, e.g. a tightly closed small jar.

When breeding butterflies it is always best to rear them in an environment which is as close as possible to that of the species in nature. Specimens bred in unsuitable conditions are often stunted and much smaller than they would normally be found in nature. One of the best methods is to rear larvae on their food plants growing in a pot. A mosquito-netting cage can be placed over the plant to prevent the caterpillars escaping or predators entering. Alternatively a potted plant can be placed inside a wire-mesh cage or a wire frame bent over a potted plant and covered with nylon stocking, net curtain or other fine mesh. Some people use large glass "aquaria" instead of netting cages. This eliminates all possibility of the larvae escaping and the humidity can be kept higher than in the netting cages. The air of the highveld is often too dry for caterpillars which come from the coast or rainforests.

If by chance the food plant is growing in the garden, the larvae can be sleeved on this plant. By sleeving we mean placing the larvae on a branch of the food plant and covering the whole branch with a bag of mosquito netting or other suitable material and tying the open end tightly around the base of the branch. The caterpillars are then in a perfectly natural environment in the garden on their food plants and protected from predators and deterred from escaping by the netting bag completely covering the branch. However, care must be taken not to enclose any potential predators inside the bag. Each branch must be carefully searched to remove spiders, preying mantises and other dangers before the larvae are sealed onto it.

The larvae often spin a silk thread or pad across a leaf for security. When replacing leaves in a container it is therefore advisable to avoid pushing or jolting the larvae off the old ones; merely discard untenanted leaves. When about to moult, the larvae stop feeding and will cling to their silk pads. The symptoms are recognizable by the impression of the future head bulging largely behind the small existing head and separated from it by a temporary neck. If disturbed at this stage the larvae will not be able to moult properly and they will die. Larvae about to pupate may also become irritable, jerking from side to side but without clinging to foliage. Sometimes at this stage they have to start wandering around searching for a pupation site. When they find one they will spin a silk pad on which the pupa will be attached and supported.

Once a caterpillar has pupated it can be transferred to a container provided with dead twigs, lined with mosquito netting or any other rough material up which an emerging butterfly can climb to spread its wings.

EGG LAYING IN CAPTIVITY

It is sometimes possible to induce a gravid female to lay eggs in captivity. The females can be kept in netting cages or in large containers such as large plastic ice-cream boxes. The containers or cages should be provided with fresh or living food plants to induce the female to lay. The adult female, however, feeds on nectar in nature and this should be provided. Some people provide sugar or honey water on a tight wad of cotton wool or a sponge which is soaked in the solution and held in a small bowl (a tin lid or watch glass often suits the purpose well). Others just place the soaked cotton wool on top of the netting cage and the butterfly can suck through the netting. These methods are not always successful as the butterfly occasionally gets stuck to the cotton wool or just does not feed. To make sure that the female does feed and to eliminate the

sticky cotton wool from the container the butterfly can be fed manually. The butterfly is gently lifted out of her cage onto a saucer, containing cotton wool soaked in sugar or honey water. The female is then persuaded to sip a little of the sugar solution by drawing out her proboscis into it with a pin (fig. 23). The females should be fed once a day. In these artificial conditions the butterflies often take a few days to settle down. After that they will start laying. Some females have been kept in captivity for up to six weeks, often laying a hundred or more eggs.

All the eggs and the newly emerged larvae should be kept in small containers. The first meal of the young larva is often its egg-shell. As the larvae get larger they can be introduced into larger containers or placed in sleeves in the garden.

THE FATE OF THE NEWLY BRED ADULT

Once a perfect adult butterfly is reared one must decide what to do with it. It can be killed and mounted for a collection. In this case the best way to kill the specimen without damaging it is to put the container with the butterfly into the freezer for at least two hours. The specimen will then die without being handled at all and is ready to be set. It is very important to allow the freshly emerged butterfly to dry its wings properly. Premature killing nearly always results in crinkling of the wings when they dry out. Wings can be regarded as dry as soon as the butterfly starts making definite attempts to fly.

These newly emerged adults are also perfect for photography. Not only are the specimens immaculate but they are also not very active as their wings are still soft. They can be easily posed on a

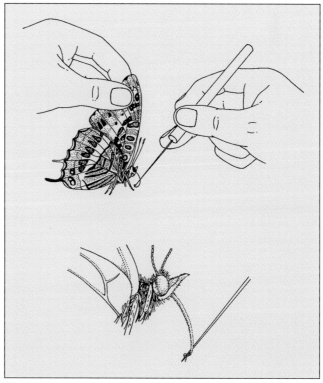

Fig. 23 Persuading a female *Charaxes jasius saturnus* to feed by drawing out her proboscis with a pin onto cotton wool soaked with a sugar solution

branch or twig for the perfect photograph.

If a common species is bred and the food plants happen to be growing in the garden, the newly emerged butterflies may be released in the hope that they will establish a permanent breeding colony there.

Any excess specimens should be released back into the natural habitat from which they came.

ANT-ASSOCIATED LARVAE

Certain butterfly larvae belonging to the family Lycaenidae can be bred only in association with ants. The ants are often required to keep the honey-gland of the lycaenid larva clean, otherwise they tend to develop a fungal infection and die.

If the larvae are totally phytophagous, some of the host ants may simply be added to the container with the butterfly larvae and their food plant. Small test tubes of sugar water and water should also be placed in the container for the ants.

If the larvae are predacious on ant brood, they should be kept in a formicarium with their host ants. A formicarium consists of an ant nest placed in or attached to a large arena or foraging area.

Most of the life-histories of predacious and phytophagous myrmecophilous lycaenid larvae are still either completely unknown or only partially known. Anyone interested in breeding and describing the early stages of these butterflies will make a major contribution towards their conservation, because one cannot conserve species with such complicated life-cycles, until their basic requirements such as food plants, host ants and other environmental factors are known.

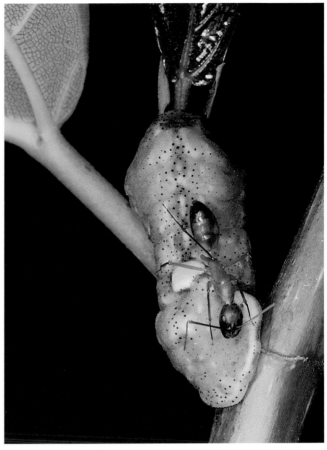

Camponotus maculatus ant attending *Myrina silenus ficedula* larva

Aphnaeus hutchinsoni larva living in *Crematogaster* ant nest

BREEDING IN GENERAL

In many multi-brooded species the life-cycle from egg to adult is completed in about two to three months, but other species have only one brood a year and the complete cycle may require up to 10 or 11 months. Many species which have a close association with ants fall in the latter category and demand much patience and attention when bred in captivity. Moreover, the ants kept in captivity with the early stages of the butterflies associated with them must be kept happy and healthy in order to ensure normal behaviour in the ant colony as well as between the butterfly larvae and the host ants. Anybody who wishes to breed ant-associated species of this kind should be well aware of what they are letting themselves in for!

Other species, such as many browns (Satyrinae) are also single-brooded and rearing them from egg to adult also takes about ten months or more. Most larvae of browns feed on grasses and the females of many species simply scatter the eggs in flight or settle on a blade so that the eggs land in the grass below. Females readily oviposit in captivity when kept together with potted grass in the manner described above.

PARASITES (PARASITOIDS)

Probably all species of butterfly have their parasites. Often 90% or more of the eggs, larvae and pupae collected in the wild are parasitised. Most butterfly parasites are wasps (Hymenoptera), but also some flies (Diptera), belonging to the family Tachinidae, may be parasitic.

Adult butterflies are not known to be parasitised but the eggs, larvae and pupae all have their specialised parasites. Remarkably little is known about parasitism of butterflies and, in fact, if parasites are bred, they should be preserved together with a record of the host, for further study. One may then have something even more interesting than the butterfly itself, since so little may be known of the parasites' highly specialised behaviour.

For example, some tachinids lay their tiny eggs on the food plant of the host caterpillar, and these eggs hatch only when they are swallowed (unsuspectingly) with the food of the caterpillar. Other tachinids place living larvae on or near the caterpillar. Once inside the caterpillar, they start to eat it from inside. To obtain oxygen, the tachinid will sometimes push its spiracle-bearing posterior through the skin of the caterpillar to the outside. Other tachinids connect up with one of the main tracheae within the host.

KEEPING RECORDS

When breeding butterflies, most people keep records and notes about each stage. The life histories of a number of Southern African species are still unknown and if one managed to breed a previously unrecorded species the observation could probably be published. A good way to keep a record is to photograph each stage. If the egg, larva, pupa or adult is posed in natural surroundings and the photograph comes out well, it may be suitable for publication in an article or a book. Factors which should be recorded for each stage are size, colour and duration. One should also make notes on any unusual behaviour shown by any of the stages. If the specimens

are parasitised, a record of the parasitoid should be made, including the stage of the life cycle during which it was parasitising and other details.

The early stages may also be recorded by preserving examples in 70% alcohol or some other liquid preservative. Unfortunately all liquid preservatives cause some colour change in the preserved specimen, so a note should also be kept of their true colours. A data label giving name, locality where found, date and further detail which might be of interest, in waterproof ink or pencil should be included in the bottle to complete the records. Hatched eggs and pupal cases can be stuck onto a piece of cardboard pinned in the collection and provided with a label carrying all relevant data. There are also methods available to preserve caterpillars by blow-drying or freeze-drying.

Further information regarding breeding butterflies may be obtained from the following publications: Migdoll (1987) – general; Williams (1985,1986) – general; Woodhall (Editor, 1992) – general; Claassens (1974) and Claassens and Dickson (1977, 1980) – ant-associated species; Skaife (1961) – keeping ants in captivity.

CONSERVATION

One might ask whether collecting insects as a hobby is not in direct conflict with the presently growing awareness of conservation. In answering that question it may be stated categorically that, in the case of the vast majority of South African butterflies and moths, collecting does no harm whatsoever. As a 'predator' of butterflies, man is undoubtedly the most inefficient and definitely less harmful than any of the many natural predators that harass and kill these insects, not only in the adult stage, but also during all other stages of their life cycle. Butterflies and indeed other insects have survived the predatory, parasitic and even chemical onslaught waged against them from time immemorial and they still fulfill their part in pollination and many food-chains without any danger of becoming extinct.

COLLECTING

The subject of collecting has been a bone of contention for many years both here and abroad. It is often mentioned as one of the chief threats to insect populations, although there are no documented cases of extinction or even local extirpations of insect populations due to indiscriminate collecting from anywhere in the world (Pyle & Opler, 1975; Pyle *et al.*, 1981). Some ecologists, conservationists and lepidopterists think that intensive collecting may, in some rare cases, be deleterious to a species and could possibly accelerate its extinction. This could only happen if, due to habitat destruction, the species had already been decimated and finally reduced to a few specimens. In a low density population reproduction is already difficult and a small colony, thus affected, struggles to survive. Once a colony has reached that critical situation and intensive collecting does occur it may well hasten the end. Fortunately it is often discovered that isolated populations of such rare species still occur in other places, either in the same general area or elsewhere in suitable habitats. However, nowhere in the world has it been proven that intensive collecting has caused the extinction of a species. The prime cause is habitat destruction and this must be prevented at all costs.

Natural predators of insects, including butterflies, include most kinds of living things. There are many insectivorous mammals, birds and reptiles, fish and spiders. Even some plants eat insects. Some of the major enemies are insects which prey on, or are parasitic upon, other insects. The early developmental stages of insects are one of nature's main food resources. One female butterfly will often lay up to five hundred eggs, of which only two are required to reach adulthood for the population to remain constant, the remainder may be consumed at various stages. Man as a butterfly collector is a very inefficient predator compared with insectivores. Butterfly populations have amazing recuperative powers, as long as they have the correct habitat in which to live (after S.F. & G.A. Henning, 1989).

HABITAT DESTRUCTION AND ALIENS

Overseas studies (see Pyle *et al.*, 1981) have established that the major or only cause in the loss or decline of insect populations throughout the world is habitat destruction. Unfortunately habitat destruction cannot always be avoided as it is necessary to satisfy the insatiable demands for housing, food, transport, industry and so many more facets of human activities which require much space. Expansion of cities, building of new cities, conversion of natural vegetation into agricultural land, and the provision of recreational areas to accommodate the needs of the, alas, ever increasing human population are visible manifestations of habitat destruction which, whether defendable or not, are carried out daily and for everyone to see. The building of large dams and the draining of marshes and vleis and other wetlands are regarded as projects of the greatest importance and advantage to the one species,

Homo sapiens. However, these interventions in nature have changed and even destroyed many habitats of specialised plants and animals, including insects depending on such plants.

Alien vegetation has invaded and even destroyed large tracts of natural flora, a process which is extremely difficult to reverse and very expensive to control on a large scale. Alien vegetation usually is unsuitable as food for indigenous fauna, including our butterflies and moths. The establishment of plant invaders in existing plant communities upsets the delicate balances which operate between competing plant communities. This usually results in the dominance of the invader species over the indigenous, usually multi-species, plant communities. The success of plant invaders may be seen all around us and is due to a great extent to the absence of natural enemies of these species. Indigenous plants have to cope with many enemies such as viruses, bacteria, fungi, insects and grazing animals.

When an ecosystem has changed, either due to habitat destruction or by invasive green cancers, it is usually no longer suitable for the fauna associated with the original plant communities and even ants, certain species of which are host to myrmecophilous lycaenid butterfly larvae and pupae.

In Southern Africa the butterflies most at risk are the myrmecophilous (ant associated) Lycaenidae. These species are often quite local and rare as they require the presence of host ants as well as optimal climatic conditions. Being thus confined to a limited area, often no larger than a tennis court, these species are particularly vulnerable to any disturbance of their preferred habitat. Thus the building of a house, the construction of a road or the ploughing of a field could lead to the extinction of a rare species confined to a single locality (S.F. & G.A. Henning, 1989).

Let us now consider some habitat changes and impacts associated with man's activities that have resulted in significant extinctions or declines of insect and related populations.

Cities are often situated in locations favourable to commerce or

Montane grasslands over-planted with pine near Haenertsburg, Northern Province, South Africa

agriculture. Sites at the confluences of major rivers, near major embayments, or along coastlines are favoured. In South Africa, urbanisation and agriculture conversion on the sandveld, to the north of Cape Town, has brought the endemic butterfly *Oxychaeta dicksoni* to the verge of extinction. Along the south coast of KwaZulu-Natal, urbanisation has destroyed much of the natural habitat and in Durban itself several good localities have been destroyed including the type locality of *Aloeides penningtoni*.

The draining of wetlands or the lowering of water tables has destroyed or threatens to destroy many habitats of marsh-adapted insect communities. On the Witwatersrand the draining of marshes and vleis has resulted in the loss of several colonies of the skipper *Metisella meninx*.

Conversion of natural habitats for agricultural purposes, particularly for planting food and fibre crops, is one of the most extensive land uses and has resulted in the greatest loss of native insect populations. For example, agricultural conversion in the Free State and the North-West Province has apparently resulted in the destruction of colonies of *Aloeides dentatis maseruna*.

Although often cited as a major factor responsible for loss of insect populations, five decades of wide use of organic pesticides have not resulted in the extinction of any insect, except for the possible loss of some ectoparasites and symbionts of birds of prey which have undergone drastic population declines due to pesticide residues and direct poisoning.

In South Africa the introduction of exotic plants, especially from Australia, has had a serious effect on butterfly populations over the past 40-50 years. The coastal, or near-coastal, belt to the north of Cape Town is a prime example. Endemic lycaenid butterflies such as *Poecilmitis brooksi brooksi* and *P. pan* have largely disappeared from many areas in which they were once relatively abundant.

ARGENTINE ANTS

Another harmful, often overlooked, alien active in habitats of many butterflies is the introduced Argentine Ant, *Iridomyrmex humilis*, regarded as the most pernicious ant in the world. This little species was first discovered in this country in Cape Town in the early years of this century. It is believed that it was introduced during the Anglo-Boer war, some time about the year 1900, and that the pest arrived in Cape Town in fodder imported from Argentina for the British Cavalry, but there is no evidence for or against this theory. It has since spread far inland and in northerly and easterly directions. It appears to have been first recorded in Johannesburg in the 1970's. However, little is known about the true distribution of this destructive creature in South Africa, but people are well aware of its harmful activities wherever it establishes itself. Apart from doing harm in many other respects, it drives away our indigenous ants by harassing them, killing them and taking over their nests and food supplies.

They even interfere with termite mounds. Dr S.H. Skaife (1955), referring to the Black-mound Termite (*Amitermes atlanticus*), wrote: "In those parts of the Cape, where that pernicious pest, the Argentine ant, *I. humilis*, has established itself you will not find any young termitaries at all, because the ants seek out the termites and destroy them (the author is referring to young queens and males

attempting the start of new colonies), only old, well-guarded mounds can persist in the presence of these destructive little creatures."

We cannot refrain from quoting the following paragraph from the same publication: "The mounds also disappear from ground that is being cultivated or built on; they are found only on raw, untouched veld, and there they are destroyed by veld fires. The result of all this is that the Black-mound Termite is getting scarcer year by year and one has to go higher and higher up the mountains to find their nests."

These remarks, written many years ago, represent a famous naturalist's early warnings against habitat destruction and the perils caused by the Argentine Ants.

The Argentine Ants make life difficult also for those much larger than themselves such as the Spotted Sugar Ant (*Camponotus maculatus*) and the Black Marsh Ant (*Camponotus niveosetosus*). The small Black Sugar Ant (*Acantholepis capensis*) is absolutely defenceless against this intruder. These and other ants play an important role in the life cycles of various lycaenid butterflies and hence they are necessary components of the ecosystems in which these butterflies occur (see Myrmecophily).

It is doubtful whether the spread of the Argentine Ant can be stopped or even controlled in those areas where they have established themselves already. In one's own garden it is advisable to look out for them. Their nests, if found, should be destroyed because these ants tend plant lice and scale insects for the sake of their sweet secretions and in doing so encourage them to flourish. The ants also drive away predacious ladybirds and other natural enemies of these pests, thus allowing the pests to multiply unchecked.

By killing indigenous ants, the Argentine Ants adversely affect the butterfly fauna and that of other insects and the organisms depending on them in yet another way. Many ants, including the species which act as hosts to lycaenid butterfly larvae, are agents in dispersal of elaiosome-bearing seeds. These seeds have fleshy, oily structures attached to them which contain powerful ant attractants. The ants laboriously collect these seeds and take them to their underground nests, in the safety of which they consume the elaiosomes. The seeds without the elaiosomes, but still viable, are either left lying in the ants' nests or they are carried to the surface and dumped outside the nests on the ants' middens. In both situations the seeds are more likely to germinate. The seeds are thus widely dispersed and those left behind in the ants' nests are protected against seed-eating birds, rats and mice.

Among the fynbos plants there are many with elaiosome-bearing seeds which depend on indigenous ants for dispersal. Seed dispersal by ants is known as myrmecochory and the seeds which are adapted to attract ants for the sake of dispersal are known as myrmecochores.

When their seeds are not dispersed by ants, the plants depending on this method of seed dispersal become rarer and eventually disappear completely. The disappearance from an area of certain plants adversely affects certain insects, including butterflies, whose larvae feed on these plants. The Argentine Ant thus not only causes the disappearance of ants associated with butterflies and hence the butterflies themselves, but also of those larval food plants of which the seeds are dispersed by the indigenous ants.

The Argentine Ants play no part in seed dispersal because, although they eat elaiosomes, they do not collect and transport seeds. Instead they leave them lying about under the parent plants, where they are easily found and eaten by birds and small mammals. For further information on the Argentine Ant and the importance of seed dispersal by ants we recommend the studies by Slingsby (1982) and Slingsby & Bond (1981).

CONSERVATION MEASURES

When a species has been reduced to one or very few populations, it should be protected against any further unfavourable influences such as discussed above. It is usually the serious and attentive butterfly collectors who, in the first place, become aware of the rarity of a species and it is often through them that the appropriate authorities are informed and advised. In the *South African Red Data Book – Butterflies*, 1989, published by the Council for Scientific and Industrial Research, S. F. & G. A. Henning have listed and reviewed 141 species of South African butterfly for which some degree of threat has been established or is suspected. This important publication should have a profound influence on the thinking and attitude of the authorities concerned with conservation and who, quite understandably, are concerned in the first place with flora and the larger members of our fauna such as fish, reptiles, birds and mammals. The long list of threatened species of butterfly is in sharp contrast to the short lists, if any, of butterflies thus far protected by legislation in the various provinces. A number of threatened species occur in Nature Reserves and are thus, at least to some extent and in a general way, protected. One threatened species, *Aloeides dentatis dentatis* (Swierstra) is very special in that it has its own Nature Reserve, namely the Ruimsig Entomological Reserve, which was proclaimed by the Roodepoort City Council with the aim of protecting this rare species.

Although one would not expect all threatened species or even all endangered species to receive such preferential treatment it is of vital importance that, when a species, even if only an insect, has become endangered, its last few surviving populations should be protected by legislation and the colony or colonies monitored carefully by qualified entomologists or lepidopterists. The Lepidopterists' Society of Southern Africa has conservation of butterflies and moths as one of its main aims and is actively involved in various conservation projects. This society was also involved in the establishment of the Ruimsig Entomological Reserve mentioned above.

Recently, a very important new development in conservation has occurred, in the establishment of the South African Natural Heritage Programme. This scheme, started by the Department of Environmental Affairs in 1985, aims to establish natural areas, known as Natural Heritage Sites, in private or public ownership, thus encouraging landowners to participate actively in Nature Conservation. By safeguarding threatened or unique ecosystems or individual species of plants or animals, including butterflies and other rare or endangered insects, and also in some instances by protecting features of outstanding beauty or historical value occurring on their property, land owners contribute positively to conservation of our natural assets, without losing ownership rights.

There is an increasing interest in this programme which is fast

Information board at the Ruimsig Entomological Reserve

becoming one of the most important participation projects in Nature Conservation. In fact, during 1989 the hundredth South African Natural Heritage site was registered. The breeding locality of the rare *Poecilmitis aureus* at Heidelberg in Gauteng is one of these registered heritage sites. The larvae of *P. aureus* are associated with *Crematogaster* or Cocktail ants while remaining phytophagous. The breeding location of *P. aureus*, also known as the Heidelberg Copper, is a koppie situated within the SANDF Heidelberg Training Area. The Defence Force has undertaken not to use the koppie for military operations and, of course, the site is protected from development and the public. The locality of another rare butterfly, *Erikssonia acraeina*, in the Waterberg mountains west of Nylstroom in the Northern Province is a proposed Natural Heritage site. The larvae of this species are closely associated with ants, although they remain phytophagous.

FIRE

Veld and mountain fires by their very nature are destructive, although if they occur only very occasionally they are apparently advantageous to at least a number of plants making up the Cape fynbos. When they occur less than 10 to 15 years apart they can do great harm to flora and fauna. However, usually the indigenous vegetation manages to re-establish itself from roots and seeds left unaffected by the heat and, together with the flora, the fauna slowly returns. When mountain fires destroy the vegetation and fauna of the same area too frequently the damage is much greater if not irreparable. It takes much longer for such a destroyed ecosystem to rebuild itself almost from the pioneer stage.

Butterflies are particularly vulnerable to fires occurring during their main breeding season, because they affect the reproductive adults as well as their eggs, larvae and pupae on the food plants. Fortunately larvae and pupae which at the time of the fire are in underground ants' nests usually are not adversely affected. It is quite normal to see newly emerged adult ant-associated lycaenids flying about burnt vegetation and settling on dead twigs and blackened soil. The same may, of course, be said of the ants themselves, i.e. of those species which nest predominantly underground.

Fires may have been a contributory cause in the disappearance of *Poecilmitis nigricans* in the Cape Peninsula. Possibly too-frequent mountain fires during the actual flight-period of *Argyrocupha malagrida malagrida* has also led to its decline in recent times.

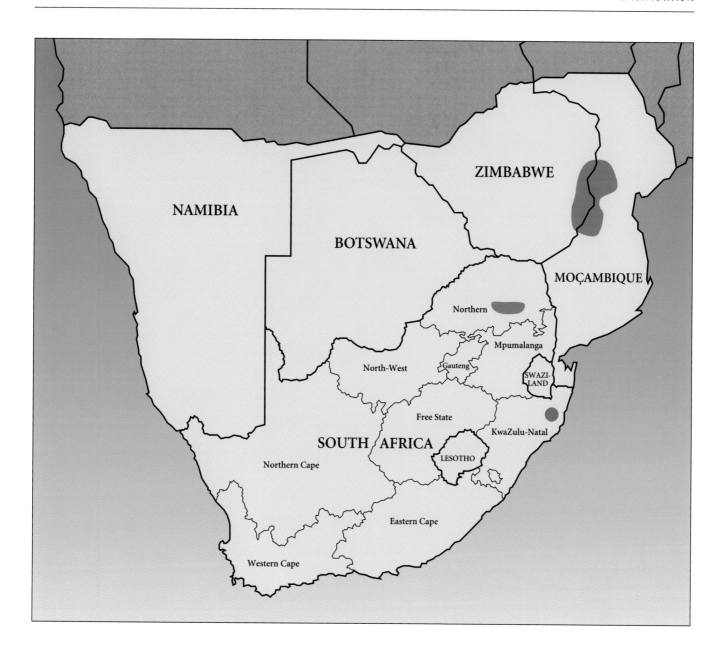

KEY TO THE DISTRIBUTION MAPS

The Southern African subregion consists of South Africa, Lesotho, Swaziland, Namibia, Botswana, Zimbabwe and Moçambique south of the Zambezi River.

This is an ecologically diverse region but does represent a zoo-geographic zone. The thick lines delineate the countries while the thin lines outline the South African provinces.

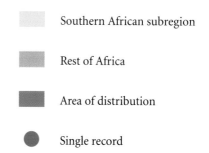

Southern African subregion

Rest of Africa

Area of distribution

Single record

Moltena fiara male underside

Facing page: *Colotis regina* female upperside

CLASSIFICATION AND REVIEWS OF SPECIES

ORDER LEPIDOPTERA AND SUBORDER DITRYSIA

Butterflies belong to the order Lepidoptera, forming two superfamilies, the Hesperioidea and Papilionoidea, in the suborder Ditrysia.

The Papilionoidea and Hesperioidea are characterised by the antennae being clubbed or dilated, the absence of a frenulum and by the humeral lobe of the hindwing being greatly developed (see fig. 24). In other Lepidoptera (moths) the antennae are not clubbed or dilated except in infrequent cases, and in such instances a frenulum is present. The frenulum plus retinaculum is the prevalent wing-coupling apparatus in moths. It is found in the male and consists of a single composite bristle arising from the humeral angle of the hindwing, held beneath the forewing by a hook-like retinaculum at the base of the subcostal vein. In butterflies and some moths the frenulum is lost and so-called amplexiform coupling occurs. The enlarged humeral lobe of the hindwing is maintained against the stiffened base of the forewing, thus ensuring synchronous action of the two wings.

The Papilionoidea consist of four families and the Hesperioidea of one family in Southern Africa.

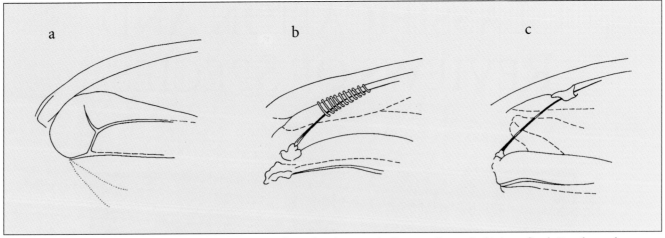

Fig. 24 Ventral view of wing-bases showing wing-coupling in butterflies and moths. a: Amplexiform coupling method in butterflies; b: Frenulum and retinaculum as a series of hooks as found in moths of the superfamily Nepticuloidea; c: Frenulum and retinaculum as a membranous hook as found in the moth family Oecophoridae

---

KEY TO THE SUPERFAMILIES

1. Antennae set widely apart at base; veins arising separately from discal cell in both wings, thus peripheral veins are never stalked .... Hesperioidea

   Antennae set close together at base; at least some of the peripheral veins of the wings stalked .... Papilionoidea

SUPERFAMILY HESPERIOIDEA

Hesperioids are small to medium-sized, stout butterflies. Ocelli are absent and chaetosemata present. The antennae are widely separated at the base and the flagellum gradually thickens apically to form a club which often ends in a hook. The haustellum is naked, maxillary palpi are absent and the labial palpi are ascending and more or less rough-haired. In both fore- and hindwings the veins arise separately from the discal cell so that none of them is stalked. The forewing is without a retinaculum and the hindwing is without a frenulum. Eggs are of the upright type, smooth or with vertical ribs. Larvae are without obvious primary setae, but with fine short hair. Their crochets are multiordinal, in a circle. Pupae may be found in the larval shelters, attached by the cremaster and usually by a central silken girdle.

The Hesperioidea differ from the Papilionoidea in having the antennae set widely apart at the base and the peripheral veins of both wings not being stalked.

The Hesperioidea include only two families, the Hesperiidae and the Megathymidae, the latter confined to the New World.

FAMILY HESPERIIDAE

The skippers are small to medium-sized butterflies with thick bodies and relatively short wings. The head is very broad with prominent, smooth eyes, and antennae widely separated at the base. Towards the tips the antennae are gradually thickened to form a club that is usually strongly curved or hooked. The wing patterns are usually sombre, often consisting of yellow, white or hyaline spots on a brownish-black ground colour. A few species are brightly coloured. All three pairs of legs are fully developed for walking.

The eggs are usually hemispherical, in their general shape, with a micropylar depression above. The surface may be smooth, slightly roughened or, more frequently, with vertical ribs. They are deposited singly on, or close to, the food plants.

The larvae have a prominent head, usually of characteristic shape, and a body that tapers towards each end. The skin may be smooth or finely spinulose. The larvae feed mainly at night and hide during the day in a shelter of some kind.

This is often formed by means of the margins of the leaves of the food plant being folded over, or two or more leaves being drawn together, with silk. Sometimes the larvae shelter in a curled-up dead leaf, near the base of the plant.

The pupae are elongate, more or less cylindrical in shape, or with the abdomen tapering posteriorly. Sometimes the surface of the pupa is partly clothed in short, dense, erect hairs. In most species a white waxy powder may cover the pupa and the inside of the shelter. Pupation usually occurs in a shelter of some kind, previously prepared by the larva and lined with silk. The pupa is attached to the silk lining of the shelter by the cremaster, and often by a silken girdle. A large number of Southern African hesperiid larvae feed on monocotyledons, especially grasses (Poaceae). Others feed on dicotyledons such as the Sterculiaceae.

There are 136 species of Hesperiidae in Southern Africa belonging to and comprising 3 subfamilies. In South Africa there are 92 species belonging to 30 genera and representing each of the 3 subfamilies.

A fertile, coloured *Fresna nyassae* egg, a typical example for the Hesperiidae (Photo R. Paré)

A freshly laid *Coeliades pisistratus* egg, a typical example for the Hesperiidae

Larval shelter of *Coeliades pisistratus* on *Sphedamnocarpus pruriens*

KEY TO THE SUBFAMILIES OF HESPERIIDAE

1. Palpi with 2nd segment erect, 3rd, long, thin, porrect; antennal club long, curved; thorax and legs very hairy .... Coeliadinae

   Palpi and antennae otherwise; if thorax and legs hairy then 3rd antennal joint short, stout 2

2. Forewing with origin of M_2 nearer that of M_1 than of M_3; wings held flat in repose; or hind tibiae fringed, and then with cubitus and M_3 of hindwing collinear .... Pyrginae

   Forewing with M_2 rising centrally, or, more usually nearer M_3 than M_1; wings held erect in repose .... Hesperiinae

---

SUBFAMILY COELIADINAE

Medium or large skippers with relatively broad wings and short stout bodies. They have a rapid jerky flight and rest with their wings held erect.

The adults may be recognised by their unusual labial palpi. The second segment is stout and is held erect and close to the face, but compared with other skippers the third segment is long and slender and projects forwards. The antennae are short, less than half the length of the costa of the forewing, with a slender club and sharp-pointed, slender, curved apiculus. The hindwing is distinctly lobed and is sometimes produced at the anal angle. Vein M_2 is tubular and arises nearer M_1 than M_3, but terminates about midway between M_1 and M_3. The males sometimes have a sex-brand on the forewing.

There is only one genus, *Coeliades* Hübner, in Southern Africa.

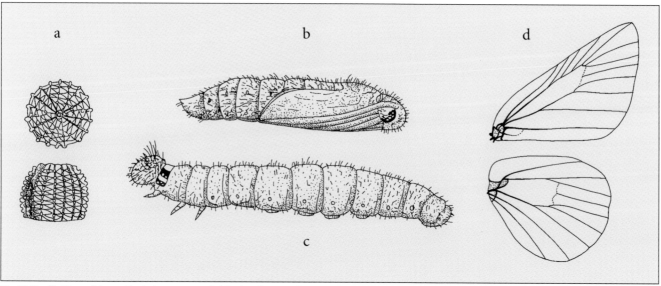

Fig. 25 Family Hesperiidae. a: Typical egg – top and side view; b: Typical pupa; c: Typical final instar larva; d: Typical wing-shape and venation (after S.F. & G.A. Henning, 1989)

Genus *Coeliades* Hübner

Coeliades Hübner, 1818. *Zuträge Samml. exot. Schmetterl.*
1: 31. Type species: *Papilio forestan* Stoll, 1782, by selection
by Hemming (1935, *Trans. R. ent. Soc. Lond.* **83**: 436).

A genus of large, robust skippers, with thick bodies. Anal angle of hindwing drawn out into a short broad tail. The larvae are brightly coloured and feed on dicotyledons.

Eggs domed and ribbed. Larvae with light and dark transverse bands; heads white to red with black spots. Pupae white with small dark spines anteriorly. Food plants Malpighiaceae, Asclepiadaceae, Euphorbiaceae, Papilionoideae, Rosaceae, Combretaceae, Solanaceae, Geraniaceae, Malvaceae, Connaraceae and Lecythidaceae.

In Southern Africa there are five species in this genus. They are large butterflies with similar sexes in each case.

KEY TO THE SPECIES OF *Coeliades*

1. LHW without white band 2

   LHW with white band 4

2. Wings above and below plain brown; cilia of hindwing white
   .... *C. libeon*

   UHW with orange hair; LHW with orange-red patches near anal angle and an orange fringe 3

3. LHW orange-red patch does not project towards margin; in male genitalia distal portion of valve quadrangular .... *C. keithloa*

   LHW orange-red patch projects towards margin; in male genitalia distal portion of valve not quadrangular .... *C. lorenzo*

4. Discal band of LHW immaculate .... *C. forestan*

   Discal band of LHW with one or more black spots 4

5. Discal band of LHW with a single black spot in CuA2
   .... *C. anchises*

   Discal band of LHW with several black spots .... *C. pisistratus*

Coeliades anchises (Gerstaecker)

ONE-PIP POLICEMAN

Ismene anchises Gerstaecker, 1871. *Arch. Naturgesch.* **37**: 358.

There are two subspecies, of which only the nominate occurs in Southern Africa and the eastern side of Africa. The subspecies *jucunda* (Butler, 1881) is found in Oman, Arabia and Socotra.

Coeliades anchises anchises (Gerstaecker)

Ismene anchises Gerstaecker, 1871. *Arch. Naturgesch.* **37**: 358. Type locality: Zanzibar.

IDENTIFICATION

Adult. The largest of the hesperiids in Southern Africa. Male. Upperside: uniform dark grey. Underside: forewing uniform grey. Hindwing has a small white patch with a single black spot posteriorly. Female. Similar to male but has rounder wings and a stouter abdomen.

Forewing lengths: male 25-32 mm; female 31-33 mm.

Early stages. Final instar larva: orange-red to dark reddish-brown with bright white transverse bands, the head is orange-red (S.F. & G.A. Henning, 1989: 151). The egg and pupa are apparently unrecorded.

Coeliades anchises anchises male underside

HABITAT AND ECOLOGY

The habitat in which specimens have been recorded varies widely, from bushveld to lush riverine and coastal forest. This adds credence to the possibility of it being a migrant. No actual migration has ever been recorded in Southern Africa but it has apparently been recorded in migrations in East Africa. One record observes that a collector, while on the deck of an ocean liner about 160 kilometres out to sea, was astonished to see a specimen of *C. anchises* slowly circling around him before flying off over the sea. Single records exist from riverine forest in the KwaZulu-Natal midlands and Mpumalanga, bushveld areas of northern KwaZulu-Natal and Northern Province. Pennington (1978) records a number of worn specimens feeding on flowers in the KwaZulu-Natal coastal bush and Swanepoel (1953) records it regularly from Mokeetsi in the Northern Province and found it plentiful one year near Potgietersrus in dry thornveld. Specimens are also regularly recorded in Durban, KwaZulu-Natal, so apparently they breed there. Dr E.C.G. Pinhey (1949) records only two, taken separately, along the eastern border of Zimbabwe. They have been recorded feeding on flowers and at damp places.

C. anchises males show hilltopping behaviour early in the morning and remain there until the afternoon. The males establish territories which they vigorously defend against intruders, darting off their perches at great speed to chase other butterflies and even other insects. The perch is usually a leaf of a low tree or bush but they sometimes select the lower branches of bigger trees. They also fly at dusk, at which time their dark colour and swift flight make them difficult to observe.

The females fly at random in the bush in search of suitable food plants on which to lay. The larvae live in the rolled-up leaves of the food plant. When feeding the larva never eats all of the leaf but stops about halfway down and then moves on to the next leaf. Pupation takes place in an elaborate shelter constructed from the leaves of the food plant (S.F. & G.A. Henning, 1989: 151).

C. anchises is on the wing from October to May.

LARVAL FOOD PLANTS

Triaspis glaucophylla (Malpighiaceae) and *Dregea angolensis* (Asclepiadaceae).

DISTRIBUTION

South Africa, KwaZulu-Natal midlands to Mpumalanga and Northern Province and the eastern border of Zimbabwe and Moçambique. The species is widely distributed through East Africa to Arabia. Some of the South African records are: KwaZulu-Natal: Umgeni valley, Umhlanga Rocks, Umkomaas, Manguzi forest and Makhathini flats. Mpumalanga and Northern Province: Mokeetsi, Bellevue, Potgietersrus, Buffelsberg, Mariepskop, Blyderivierspoort and Pongola.

CONSERVATION

There is evidence that *C. anchises* does breed in Southern Africa but none of the populations are stable. Perhaps temporary populations are created by migrants. Swanepoel (1953) records females laying eggs at Potgietersrus and specimens recorded in the Blyderivierspoort Nature Reserve were freshly hatched. The paucity of Southern African records would be strange if it were a resident, as in East Africa and Arabia the species is considered quite common.

Although the species is considered to be rare in Southern Africa, there appear to be no threats to its existence in our area. Specimens have been recorded in Blyderivierspoort Nature Reserve and in the Manguzi forest which was under the control of the KwaZulu-Natal Bureau of Natural Resources.

This species is classified as rare by S.F. & G.A. Henning (1989:150) in the *South African Red Data Book – Butterflies*.

Coeliades anchises jucunda final instar larva (Photo: T.B. Larsen)

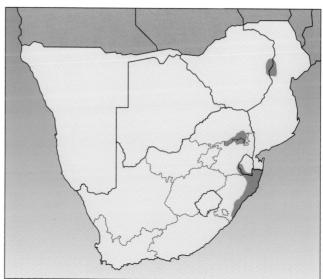

Distribution map of *Coeliades anchises*

Coeliades libeon male underside

Coeliades libeon (Druce)

SPOTLESS POLICEMAN

Ismene libeon Druce, 1875. *Proc. zool. Soc. Lond.* **1875**: 416.
Type locality: Angola.

IDENTIFICATION

Adult. Recognisable by its total lack of markings. Male. Upperside: uniform brown. Underside: brown, becoming paler on the hindwing submarginal area. Female. Similar to male but usually larger with a stouter abdomen.

There is a smaller form *brussauxi* Mabille (1890, *Bull. Soc. ent. Fr.* (6) iv: 221) with more rounded wings.

Forewing lengths: male 21-24 mm; female 22,5-25 mm.

Early stages. Egg: unrecorded. Final instar larva: lemon-yellow with black chequering. It attains a length of about 30 mm (Paré, 1988, pers. comm.) Pupa: 19-20 mm, greenish-white in colour.

HABITAT AND ECOLOGY

C. libeon is well-known as a migrant, having been recorded migrating regularly in eastern and central Africa and in Zimbabwe by Pennington in 1957. It was recorded in numbers at Pietersburg by Swanepoel in January one year and never seen again. It is normally a forest species but it was recorded in the desert along the Skeleton Coast of Namibia. *C. libeon* is alert and wary, with a swift and elusive flight. It has been recorded feeding on flowers and sucking at damp patches along the banks of streams. Specimens have also been recorded congregating at dusk with their congeners to feed at flowers along the forest edge.

There appear to be no records of males showing hilltopping behaviour and they appear to establish their territories in the vicinity of the food plants.

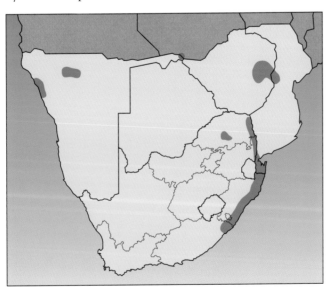

Distribution map of *Coeliades libeon*

The females fly at random in search of suitable food plants on which to lay. The female lays her eggs singly on the leaves of the food plant. The larva bends the side of a leaf over, and secures it with silk to form a shelter in which it lives. It crawls out at intervals to feed. It usually feeds on fresh new growth. Pupation occurs within a shelter formed by binding leaves together (Paré, 1988, pers. comm.).

This species is on the wing throughout the year.

LARVAL FOOD PLANTS

Drypetes gerrardii (Euphorbiaceae); *Craibia brevicaudata* ssp. *baptistarum*; *Millettia* sp. and *Cassia* sp. (Papilionoideae).

DISTRIBUTION

Widespread throughout sub-Saharan Africa. In Southern Africa it is found in Namibia, Zimbabwe and Moçambique. It is a marginal species in South Africa, being sporadically recorded from the Northern Province and Mpumalanga and KwaZulu-Natal, but occasionally as far south as Port St. Johns in the Eastern Cape.

CONSERVATION

A relatively scarce species being recorded fairly regularly in Zimbabwe and Moçambique. It is a migrant which at times establishes itself temporarily in South Africa. It is not under any immediate threat. It has been recorded from the Manguzi Forest which was under the protection of the KwaZulu-Natal Bureau of Natural Resources, as well as in the Kruger National Park. It has been classified as indeterminate by S.F. & G.A. Henning (1989:150) in the *South African Red Data Book – Butterflies*.

Coeliades forestan forestan final instar larva

Coeliades forestan (Stoll)

STRIPED POLICEMAN

Papilio plebeius urbicola forestan Stoll, 1782. *Uitl. Kapellen* **4**: 210.

There are two subspecies, the nominate race being found on mainland Africa, while the subspecies *arbogastes* Guenée is restricted to Madagascar and other Indian Ocean islands.

Coeliades forestan forestan (Stoll)

Papilio plebeius urbicola forestan Stoll, 1782. *Uitl. Kapellen* **4**: 210. Type locality: "Bengal Coast" = *patria falsa*.

IDENTIFICATION

Adult. A large species. Male. Upperside: forewing dark brown or grey-brown; hindwing pale yellow, with very broad brown costal border extending along outer margin and into the strongly lobed anal angle; cilia around anal lobe orange. Underside: forewing brown; hindwing brown with broad white median band broken at vein 2A. Female. Similar to male but rather darker in colour, especially on the hindwing.

Forewing lengths: male 20-25 mm; female 25-29 mm.

Early stages. Egg: yellowish-white; diameter 0,8 mm, height 0,5 mm; with 15 to 17 longitudinal ribs, breaking into a series of beads near the micropyle and cross-braced by 25-32 very thin ribs. The surface is covered with rows of small indentations. Final instar larva: Pinhey (1949) records it as bluish-white with black transverse bands.

  Murray (1932), however, records it as being pale yellow marked by broad bars of reddish-lake across the segments, with three fine lines of the same colour between the broader markings. There are distinct spots of the same colour along the sides and above the legs.

Coeliades forestan forestan pupa

Coeliades forestan forestan male underside

Head orange with two rows of black spots. It attains a length of about 40 mm. Pupa: 22-23 mm long; greenish in colour, marked with blackish spots and covered with a white chalky powder.

HABITAT AND ECOLOGY

This species is usually found along the edges of rainforest and coastal bush and savannah areas. It has, however, also been recorded in the grassveld of southern Gauteng and eastern Free State, feeding at flowers. *C. forestan* has a fast irregular flight, skipping about the trees, sometimes at a great height, but more often from one to two metres above the ground. It can often be observed sucking at mud and frequently feeding at flowers.

  The males show hilltopping behaviour but never appear to remain on the peaks for very long. Swanepoel (1953) observed that they are on the wing as early as 06:00. In general, it is more frequently seen in the early morning or the late afternoon, even flying at dusk.

  The female is usually observed flying at random in the bush, searching for suitable food plants on which to lay. Eggs are laid singly on a leaf or young shoot of the food plant. The egg hatches after about 9 days. At first the young larva forms a shelter by cutting two adjacent ovals out of the leaf and joining them together. The older larva bends the edge of a leaf over and sews it with silk to form a shelter in which it lives. It crawls out at intervals to feed. The larval stage lasts some 21 days. Pupation takes place in the final larval shelter. The pupal stage lasts some 21 days (Clark, 1978: 206).

C. forestan flies throughout the year but is scarcer in winter. In the colder areas it flies from September to April.

LARVAL FOOD PLANTS

Combretum bracteosum, C. apiculatum, Quisqualis sp., *Terminalia* sp. (Combretaceae); *Parinari curatellifolia* (Chrysobalanaceae); *Solanum mauritianum* (Solanaceae); *Millettia sutherlandi, Robinia pseudoacacia, Lonchocarpus capassa, Canavalia* sp., *Cassia* sp., *Crotalaria* sp., *Phaseolus* sp., *Indigofera* sp., *Sesbania* sp. (Papilionoideae); *Sphedamnocarpus pruriens* subsp. *galphimiifolius* (Malpighiaceae); *Geranium* sp. (Geraniaceae); *Gossypium* sp. (Malvaceae); *Dregea* sp. (Asclepiadaceae).

DISTRIBUTION

South Africa, along the edges of rainforest and coastal bush in the Eastern Cape and KwaZulu-Natal and inland and northwards to the savannah areas of the Free State, Northern Cape, Gauteng, North-West Province, Mpumalanga and Northern Province, Botswana, northern Namibia, Zimbabwe, Lesotho, Swaziland, Moçambique to most of tropical Africa south of the Sahara.

CONSERVATION

C. forestan is widespread and relatively common, consequently it is under no threat.

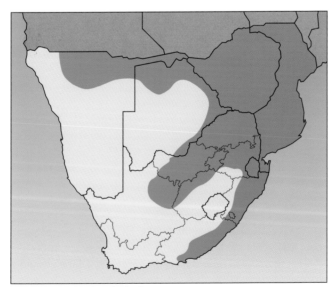

Distribution map of *Coeliades forestan*

Coeliades pisistratus (Fabricius)

TWO-PIP POLICEMAN

Hesperia pisistratus Fabricius, 1793. *Syst. Ent.* **3**: 345. Type locality: "America" = *patria falsa.*

IDENTIFICATION

Adult. A large species. Male. Upperside: forewing dark brown or greyish-brown; hindwing pale yellow, with very broad costal border extending along outer margin and into the strongly lobed anal angle; orange cilia around anal lobe. Underside: Forewing brown; hindwing brown with white band which narrows towards the costa and broadens to about vein CuA$_2$, where it more or less terminates; discal area of hindwing with a row of three or four black spots. Female. Similar to male but larger with a stouter abdomen.

Forewing lengths: male 25-30 mm; female 29-33 mm.

Early stages. Egg: very pale creamy-white with a waxy appearance, darkening through yellow to pink and finally grey; diameter 0,8 mm, height 0,5 mm; prominently ribbed with eighteen vertices of which twelve reach the top of the egg; all stop slightly short of micropyle; cross-ribbing extremely fine and invisible to the naked eye, there being 15-20 cross-ribs with a tiny protuberance where each crosses the vertices. Larva: first instar pale cream, darkening to whitish-yellow with a yellow head; body bluntly tapered at both ends; grows from 1,5 mm on hatching to 4,5 mm in four days. Second instar yellow-cream with dark brown transverse bands stretching laterally as far as the spiracles; head yellow with double transverse row of dark brown spots in characteristic pattern; grows to 11 mm in seven days. Third instar dark maroon-brown fading to maroon ventrally; spiracles conspicuously yellow; each segment with a white transverse dorso-lateral band posteriorly above spiracles; in segments one to three it is simple and in segments four to ten it carries two thin black parallel transverse dorso-lateral lines within it; these segments also carry a white dorso-lateral spot above the spiracles; white bands on segments eleven to thirteen are invaded by

Coeliades pisistratus male underside

Coeliades pisistratus final instar larva

Coeliades pisistratus pupa

bright yellow; head yellow with same spotting as second instar; grows to 18 mm in five days. Fourth instar very similar to third but ground colour deeper black; spiracles white; transverse bands stretch down as far as ventral surface; grows to 30 mm in seven days. Fifth (final) instar identical to fourth except for much deeper black ground colour and wider transverse bands; grows to 45 mm in fifteen days.

Pupa: 23-24 mm long; bluish-white dorsally with pinkish-white wing-cases and ventral appendages; a prominent blunt black protuberance projects from head and each wing-base; whole pupa coated in waxy white, slightly iridescent powder (from eggs collected from Hornsnek, Magaliesberg Mountains, east of Pretoria by S.E. Woodhall).

HABITAT AND ECOLOGY

C. pisistratus inhabits the edges of rainforests, coastal bush and savannah areas. It has a fast irregular flight, skipping about the trees, sometimes at a great height, but more often from one to two metres above the ground. It is often observed feeding at flowers and occasionally sucking at mud.

The males show hilltopping behaviour although they do not remain on the peaks for long periods. They also establish their territories lower down around favourite trees. Here they patrol backwards and forwards over the restricted area of their territories, often circling around the tree or neighbouring trees, but quickly returning to their territory. They often return to the same territory day after day.

The females are usually observed in the vicinity of their food plants. Here they can be seen flitting in and out among the branches and leaves of the food plant and those of nearby trees or shrubs.

Having found a suitable food plant the female will circle and hover about it, alighting very quickly to lay single eggs on the very tips of the youngest shoots. The egg hatches after about 10 days. On emergence the young larvae make a distinctive shelter by cutting a "V"-shaped notch in a young leaf, so that the tip of the "V" sits astride the mid-rib and the leaf-tip is pulled down over the leaf and anchored to its base using strands of silk. The larva uses the leaf-tip as a "parasol" whilst sitting on the base of the leaf. Second to fourth instar larvae stitch two leaves together by their edges and shelter within. Final instar larvae make an untidy shelter of several leaves held together by random silk strands. Some older larvae live in the rolled-up leaves of the food plant. The larval stage lasts some 38 days. Pupation takes place in the final larval shelter. The pupa is supported by the cremaster and a silken girdle. The pupal stage lasts some 28 days.

In the warmer parts *C. pisistratus* is on the wing throughout the year, being scarcer in winter. In colder areas it flies from October to May.

LARVAL FOOD PLANTS

Triaspis macropteron, Sphedamnocarpus pruriens, Acridocarpus sp. (Malpighiaceae); *Indigofera* sp. (Papilionoideae); *Dregea* sp. (Asclepiadaceae); *Combretum* sp. (Combretaceae).

DISTRIBUTION

South Africa, in KwaZulu-Natal, Free State, Northern Cape, North-West Province, Gauteng, Mpumalanga and Northern Province, Lesotho, Swaziland, Botswana, northern Namibia, Zimbabwe, Moçambique and northwards over most of Africa south of the Sahara.

CONSERVATION

C. pisistratus is a common and widespread species and is under no threat.

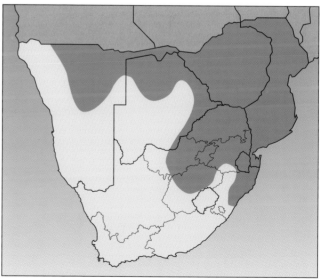

Distribution map of *Coeliades pisistratus*

Coeliades keithloa (Wallengren)

RED-TAB POLICEMAN

Rhapalocampa keithloa Wallengren, 1857. *K. svenska Vetensk-Akad. Handl.* (N.F.) **2**(4): 48. Type locality: Kaffraria.

IDENTIFICATION

Adult. Male. Upperside: forewing dull ochreous-brown; hindwing brown with basal orange scaling from base to submarginal area, leaving a broad costal and narrow marginal border; cilia orange. Underside: brown, tinged with bronzed green. Hindwing with an orange-red mark, divided by a black transverse black streak; cilia orange. Female. Similar to male but larger with a stouter abdomen.

Forewing lengths: male 26-29 mm; female 28-29 mm.

Early stages. Egg: white; diameter 1,0 mm, height 0,75 mm; with some 20 longitudinal ribs, breaking up into small beads near micropyle: between the ribs there are rows of small indentations. Larva: final instar slate grey with black or reddish-lake bands across the segments, four elongate spots being surrounded by black, the division of the segments is also marked with a black line; there is occasionally a dorsal band of orange from head to tail; the head is large, orange in colour, marked with two rows of black spots; lower part of segments and legs are reddish-lake (Murray, 1932). The larva attains a length of 46 mm. Pupa: 24 mm long; white, pale green to brown, covered with a white chalky powder.

HABITAT AND ECOLOGY

C. keithloa is confined mainly to certain coastal forests from Port St. Johns northwards into KwaZulu-Natal where the food plants grow principally in the shade of the canopy. It flies rapidly from early dawn till dusk along the edges of bush, searching for suitable flowers on which to feed. It occasionally settles on the flower but more often hovers to feed. It can be seen sucking at mud. Its flight is swift and irregular.

The males establish territories around the trees and shrubs along forest edges or in glades where they can be found patrolling up and down. Bowker (in Trimen, 1887) observed the possible mating behaviour of *C. keithloa*: "The female darts away from a flowering tree the species frequents and settles on the ground, closely followed by the male; after a little she rises slowly, keeping her wings constantly fluttering, while the male circles around her, and when they reach about a yard (metre) above the ground, off they go to the flowers of the tree for a drink, but soon return to go through the same evolution."

Coeliades keithloa male underside

Coeliades keithloa male upperside

Coeliades keithloa pupa

Coeliades keithloa final instar larva

The females are usually observed flying about the undergrowth in search of suitable food plants on which to lay. Eggs are laid singly on the leaf of the food plant. The egg takes some 7 days to hatch. The whole larval stage is spent within a shelter which is formed by the larva drawing the edges of the long leaves of their food plant together with silk. The larva forages for food from this shelter. The larval stage lasts some 84 days. Pupation takes place within the final larval shelter. The pupal stage lasts some 16 days (Clark, 1978: 208).

C. keithloa flies throughout the year, although it is much scarcer during winter.

LARVAL FOOD PLANTS

Barringtonia racemosa (Lecythidaceae); *Acridocarpus natalitius, A. zanzibaricus, A. glaucescens* (Malpighiaceae); *Dregea* sp. (Asclepiadaceae); *Combretum* sp. (Combretaceae); *Byrsocarpus* sp. (Connaraceae).

DISTRIBUTION

South Africa, in coastal forests from Port St. Johns northwards along the KwaZulu-Natal Coast as far north as Eshowe. There are odd records from Port Elizabeth and King William's Town.

TAXONOMY

The following species (*C. lorenzo*) has been separated from *C. keithloa* by genitalia and life history. Similarly the East African races should no longer be included under this species: *C. menelik* (Ungemach 1932), *C. kenya* Evans 1937, *C. merua* Evans 1947.

CONSERVATION

Although *C. keithloa* is not a common species it has a wide distribution and consequently is under no immediate threat.

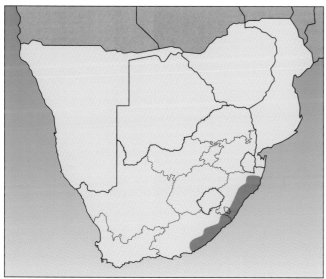

Distribution map of *Coeliades keithloa*

Coeliades lorenzo Evans stat. n.

LORENZO RED-TAB POLICEMAN

Coeliades keithloa lorenzo Evans, 1946. *Ann. Mag. nat. Hist.* (11) **13**: 641. Type locality: Lourenço Marques (Maputo), Moçambique.

IDENTIFICATION

Adult. Similar to *C. keithloa* but upperside ground colour is paler and underside has an extended tornal red area extending towards the outer margin along the veins. These characters do, however, vary and the only positive means of identification is the male genitalia where the shape of the valves are distinctive (Evans, *loc. cit.* (11) **13**: 642). Also depicted by G.A. Henning *et. al*, 1994: 310.

Forewing lengths: male 26-29 mm; female 28-29 mm.

Early stages. Egg: unrecorded. Larva: final (putative fifth) instar with ground colour velvety black, fading to maroon ventrally; first eleven segments each with two white transverse dorsal bands, the anterior one being unbroken and the posterior one broken in middle of dorsum and extending laterally almost as far as the spiracle; on segments twelve and thirteen only one white band present, the posterior one; in addition segments four to thirteen have two orange-yellow transverse dorsal bands anterior of the white bands; spiracles white. The larva attains a length of 40 mm. Pupa: 20 mm long; ground colour pinkish-white totally obscured by a bluish-white powder; adult appendages a slightly darker pink (recorded from final instar larvae collected at Tembe Elephant Park, Maputaland, KwaZulu-Natal by S.E. Woodhall).

Coeliades lorenzo male underside

Coeliades lorenzo final instar larva

HABITAT AND ECOLOGY

C. lorenzo is confined mainly to certain coastal forests from Zulu-land northwards into Moçambique where the food plants grow principally in the shade of the canopy. It flies rapidly from early dawn till dusk along the edges of bush searching for suitable flowers on which to feed. It occasionally settles on the flower but more often hovers to feed. It can at times be seen sucking at mud. Its flight is swift and irregular.

The males establish their territories around the trees and shrubs along forest edges or in glades where they can be found patrolling to and fro.

The females are usually observed flying about the undergrowth in search of suitable food plants on which to lay. Eggs are laid singly on a leaf of the food plant. The final instar larvae spend the daylight hours in untidy shelters made of several of the thin leaves of the food plant spun together with silk strands which show no distinctive pattern. Pupation takes place within the final instar shelter. The pupa is suspended from the walls of the shelter by the cremaster and a silken girdle.

C. lorenzo flies throughout the year, although it is much scarcer during winter.

LARVAL FOOD PLANTS

Acridocarpus natalitius var. *linearifolius* (Malpighiaceae).

DISTRIBUTION

South Africa, from Manguzi Forest and Tembe, northern KwaZu-lu-Natal and extending into Moçambique; and also recorded sporadically from Mpumalanga in the Kruger National Park, Wolkberg and Swadini in the Blyderivierspoort Nature Reserve.

TAXONOMY

This species has been separated from *C. keithloa* due to differences in the genitalia and larvae.

CONSERVATION

Although *C. lorenzo* is not a common species it has a fairly wide distribution and consequently is under no threat. It has also been recorded in the Kruger National Park.

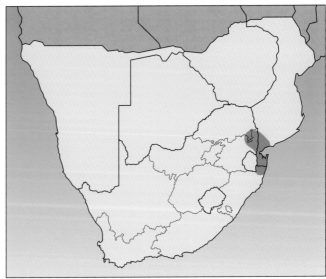

Distribution map of *Coeliades lorenzo*

SUBFAMILY PYRGINAE

Small to large and robust skippers, with broad wings which are expanded flat when the insect is at rest. They fly rapidly and feed freely at flowers. Some fly only in strong sunshine, whereas others are active only at twilight.

They differ from the Coeliadinae, in that the labial palpi are held erect and the third segment is short, stout and porrect. The antennae are moderately long to long, and the apiculus may be gently curved or hooked. Vein M_2 of the hindwing may be tubular or absent or almost entirely lost.

The larvae are brightly coloured or uniformly whitish in colour, with a large head. They are found in shelters formed by joining or folding leaves of the dicotyledonous food plants. The pupae are found in similar shelters.

There are 13 genera in Southern Africa, namely *Celaenorrhinus* Hübner (1819: 106); *Calleagris* Aurivillius (1925: 571); *Tagiades* Hübner (1919: 108); *Eagris* Guenée (1862: 19); *Eretis* Mabille (1891: lxxi); *Sarangesa* Moore (1881: 176); *Netrobalane* Mabille (1904: 76); *Caprona* Wallengren (1857: 51); *Leucochitonea* Wallengren (1857: 52); *Abantis* Hopffer (1855: 643); *Spialia* Swinhoe (1912: 99); *Gomalia* Moore (1879: 144) and *Alenia* Evans (1935: 409).

Genus *Celaenorrhinus* Hübner

Celaenorrhinus Hübner, 1819. *Verz. bek. Schmett.* (7): 106. Type species: *Papilio eligius* Stoll, 1781, by selection by Scudder (1875, *Proc. amer. Acad. Arts Sci.*, Boston **10**: 137).

Fairly large skippers with broad wings and narrow bodies. They all exhibit black or dark brown ground colour on the upperside with numerous, often large yellow, or rarely white spots on the forewing and often also on the hindwing. Forewing with M_2 rising centrally between M_1 and M_3, R_1 separate. Hindwing with vein CuA_2 far behind centre of the cell. CuA_1 from the posterior angle, M_2 distinct. Antennal club bent down in centre with a long sharp point. Apical segment of palpi short coniform or knob-shaped. Male with a hair-pencil on hind tibiae.

Eggs domed and ribbed. Larvae greenish with longitudinal stripes. Heads dark and pronounced dorsally. Pupa greenish with small pointed appendage anteriorly. Food plants Acanthaceae.

There are three species in Southern Africa, namely *C. galenus, C. mokeezi* and *C. bettoni*. Only *C. mokeezi* occurs in South Africa.

KEY TO THE GENERA OF THE PYRGINAE

1. Forewing with origin of M_2 nearer that of M_1, wings held flat in repose 2

   Forewing with M_2 central at origin, facies very distinct, blackish with many white or creamy spots 11

2. Antennal club pointed, body shorter than hindwing 3

   Antennal club blunt, body as long as dorsum of hindwing; female with an anal tuft 8

3. Hindwing with vein 2A much shorter than CuA_2 .... *Celaenorrhinus*

   Hindwing with vein 2A about as long as CuA_2 4

4. Antennal club evenly bent in middle where thickest 5

   Antennal club bent beyond the middle, distal to the thickest part 7

5. Third palpal joint longer than second; female lacking anal tuft .... *Calleagris*

   Third joint of palpi shorter than second; female with anal tuft 6

6. Hind tibiae of male lack hairpencil; forewing with 2A curved .... *Tagiades*

   Male hind tibiae with hairpencil; forewing with straight 2A .... *Eagris*

7. Forewing outer margin excavate in area CuA_2; hindwing outer margin excavate in areas 3A and $Sc+R_1$ .... *Eretis*

   Outer margins more or less even; hindwing sinuous at most .... *Sarangesa*

8. Forewing outer margin convex at M_2 and M_3, often excavate at CuA_2; hindwing produced in M_3 9

   Outer margin even; hindwing roundly produced at 3A 10

9. Male lacks hairpencil between forelegs; forewing with vein M_3 rising nearer CuA_1 .... *Netrobalane*

   Male with a black hairpencil between forelegs; forewing with M_3 midway between CuA_1 and M_2 at origin .... *Caprona*

10. Male with a black hairpencil between forelegs; forewing with vein M_3 rising centrally between CuA_1 and M_2 .... *Leucochitonea*

    Male lacks hairpencil between forelegs; forewing with M_3 nearer CuA_1 at base .... *Abantis*

11. Hindwing with outer margin sinuous, produced at 2A; markings mottled green and grey .... *Gomalia*

    Hindwing with outer margin regular; blackish to dark brown with pale spots 12

12. Antennal club rounded with tip not bent over; end of forewing cell inclined; hindwing with vein 2A not short and not declined at its origin .... *Spialia*

    Antennal club flattened to a thin oval disc with its tip bent over; end of forewing cell not inclined; hindwing with vein 2A very short and slightly decurved at its origin .... *Alenia*

Celaenorrhinus mokeezi (Wallengren)

LARGE SPRITE

Pterygospidea mokeezi Wallengren, 1857. *K. svenska Vetensk-Akad. Handl.* (N.F.) **2**(4): 54.

An endemic Southern African species commonly found through many of our eastern forests. There are two subspecies, both of which occur in South Africa.

Celaenorrhinus mokeezi mokeezi male upperside

Celaenorrhinus mokeezi mokeezi (Wallengren)

Pterygospidea mokeezi Wallengren, 1857. *K. svenska Vetensk-Akad. Handl.* (N.F.) **2**(4): 54. Type locality: Kaffraria.

IDENTIFICATION

Adult. Male. Upperside: brown, coated with yellow hairs; forewing with oblique orange bar across middle and a short subapical bar; hindwing with orange central spot and traces of faint submarginal spots. Underside: very similar to upperside. Female. Similar to male but larger with rounder wings.

Forewing lengths: male 19-22 mm; female 22,5-25,5 mm.

Early stages. Egg: white; diameter 0,9 mm, height 0,65 mm; with 25 longitudinal ribs composed of small moles arranged as if to meet staggered cross-bracing. Larva: first instar white with dorsal area greenish-grey and laterally pinkish-brown. Second instar greyish-green with a dark grey head; third to final instar green with dark dorsal line running length of body and white dorso-lateral and lateral longitudinal lines; head of final instar brown and pointed dorsally; maximum length attained 28 mm. Pupa: 23 mm long; green in colour and generally covered with white powder (Clark, 1978: 210).

DISTRIBUTION

South Africa, from the Amatolas and East London in the Eastern Cape Province to the forests of the KwaZulu-Natal Midlands.

Celaenorrhinus mokeezi mokeezi final instar larva
(After G.C. Clark 1978)

Celaenorrhinus mokeezi mokeezi pupa
(After G.C. Clark 1978)

Celaenorrhinus mokeezi mokeezi female upperside

Celaenorrhinus mokeezi separata
male upperside

Celaenorrhinus mokeezi separata (Strand)

Apallaga separata Strand, 1911. *Ent. Rdsch.*: 28. Type locality: Delagoa Bay. Type in Berlin Museum.

IDENTIFICATION

Adult. Differs from nominate race in having an additional small spot in area M_2 of the forewing and a large distinct series of submarginal spots on the hindwing.

Forewing lengths: male 20,5-22,3 mm; female 22-24 mm.

DISTRIBUTION

South Africa, from KwaZulu-Natal, Mpumalanga, Northern Province, Swaziland and Moçambique.

HABITAT AND ECOLOGY

A forest species being particularly fond of dense rainforest where lianas and mosses dangle from the trees. They fly rapidly about open glades and clearings in the forest. They settle on the upper or undersides of leaves of low plants along the edges of forest clearings or roads with their wings spread flat. At times they feed on small pink blooms and other flowers in the undergrowth. Although they often venture into the sunlight, shady places seem to be more to their liking.

The males usually establish their territories under the trees where they can be seen fluttering about in the sunbeams falling through the leaves. They actively chase off all intruders.

The females fly at random in the undergrowth in search of suitable food plants on which to lay. Eggs are laid singly on the leaves of the food plant. The egg hatches after some ten days and the newly emerged larva does not eat the shell. It cuts an elliptical slot in a leaf and folds the piece over to form a purse-like shelter in which it lives, crawling out at intervals to feed. It moults inside the shelter. The duration of the larval stage is about 43 days. Pupation takes place within leaves bound together by the final instar larva. The pupal stage lasts some 21 days (Clark, 1978:210).

C. mokeezi is on the wing from November to May, being most common in February to March, with occasional specimens being seen as late as July.

LARVAL FOOD PLANTS

Isoglossa woodii (Acanthaceae).

CONSERVATION

This species is fairly widespread and common and is under no immediate threat.

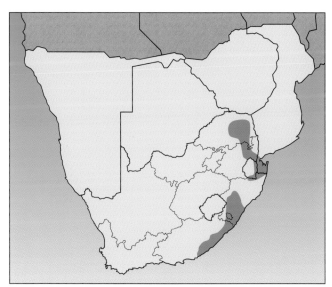

Distribution map of *Celaenorrhinus mokeezi*

63

Genus *Tagiades* Hübner

Tagiades Hübner, 1819. *Verz. bek. Schmett.* (7): 108. Type species: *Papilio japetus* Stoll, 1781, by selection by Butler (1870, *Ent. mon. Mag.* **7**: 99).

Relatively large skippers with broad wings and a narrow body. The adults fly very rapidly in bright sunshine, usually at the margins of rainforest, and rest with wings extended flat. The antennae are long and the apical segments of the labial palpi are very small. The hindwing is evenly rounded and vein M₂ is absent. The wings are usually brownish-black in colour, the forewing with small hyaline spots. The hindwing underside for its greatest part is white.

Egg domed and ribbed. The stout greenish to brown larvae feed on species of Dioscoreaceae. The head of the larva is pronounced dorsally. The pupa is mottled brown and white with a small point anteriorly. Food plants Dioscoreaceae.

There is only one species in Southern Africa.

Tagiades flesus (Fabricius)

CLOUDED FLAT

Papilio flesus Fabricius, 1781. *Species Insect.* **2**: 155. Type locality: West Africa. Type male in Natural History Museum, London (coll. Banks).

IDENTIFICATION

Adult. Male. Upperside: dark brown with bluish-grey suffusion on the outer part of the hindwing; forewing with transparent hyaline patches on the outer half. Underside: forewing similar to upperside; hindwing almost completely white, with a brown band along the costa and black dots on the outer half of the wing. The abdomen is dark brown above and white below. Female. Similar to the male but tends to have larger hyaline patches on the forewing. The wet-season form tends to be darker than the dry-season form.

Forewing lengths: male 16-22 mm; female 20-23 mm.

Tagiades flesus male upperside

Tagiades flesus male underside

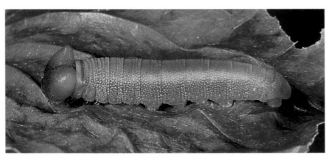

Tagiades flesus final instar larva

Early stages. Egg: pale yellow-cream; diameter 0,85 mm, height 0,65 mm; with 16 longitudinal ribs and 34 staggered cross-braces; the surface is covered with minute indentations. Larva: first instar reddish in colour and remains so until the final instar when its colour changes to pale green with a brown head; there are five larval instars; maximum length 28 mm. Pupa: about 20 mm long; greyish-brown in colour with white markings below and dusted with white powder (Clark, 1978: 212).

Tagiades flesus pupa

HABITAT AND ECOLOGY

This is a very common species in most wooded areas, both bush and rainforest. It has a fast erratic flight, often settling, usually on the underside of a leaf or twig. It can frequently be found flying rapidly, and dodging around trees, along the edges of forest or along roads. It has the habit of settling abruptly on the undersides of leaves, apparently disappearing into 'thin air' in the process. It is very conspicuous on the wing because of its white hindwings. This species is seldom observed feeding at flowers.

The males establish territories along the roads or forest margins and return to the same places day after day. They frequently settle on the leaves and dart off at intervals to chase off intruders.

The females fly about the undergrowth in search of suitable food plants on which to lay. They lay their eggs singly on the upper surface of a leaf of the food plant. The eggs take about 7 days to hatch. For protection the larva cuts an elliptical trench on a leaf and folds the cut portion over to form a shelter which is held in place by silk. It lives in this shelter, emerging only to feed or to make a new shelter when it outgrows the existing one. The duration of the larval stage is about 39 days. The larva eventually pupates within the final larval shelter. The pupal stage lasts some 21 days (Clark, 1978: 212).

This species is on the wing throughout the year.

LARVAL FOOD PLANTS

The Wild Yam, *Dioscorea cotinifolia* (Dioscoreaceae).

DISTRIBUTION

South Africa, from Somerset East in the Eastern Cape Province, along the coast into KwaZulu-Natal, and northwards into Mpumalanga and Northern Province, northern Botswana, Swaziland, Zimbabwe and Moçambique. From here it spreads northwards over Africa reaching Gambia in the west and Ethiopia in the east.

CONSERVATION

This is a widespread and common species and is under no threat.

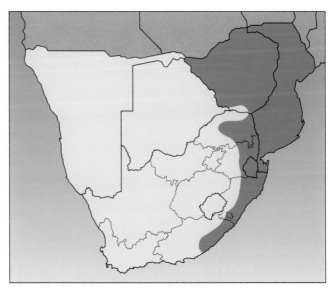

Distribution map of *Tagiades flesus*

Genus *Eagris* Guenée

Eagris Guenée, 1862. In Maillard, *Notes sur l' Ile de la Réunion* 2. Annexe G: 19. Type species: *Thymele sabadius* Boisduval, 1833, by monotypy.

Medium-sized broad-winged skippers. Forewing with vein CuA_2 arising near the base of the cell; M_2 somewhat nearer to M_1 than to M_3; R_1 is quite separate. Hindwing with vein CuA_2 a little behind centre of the cell, M_2 distinct. Outer margin of hindwing emarginated between vein M_1 and M_3. Male forewing with a costal fold and hind tibiae with hair-pencils. Female abdomen with a tuft of hair at end.

Early stages similar to *Tagiades*.

Food plants Tiliaceae, Sterculiaceae, Erythroxylaceae, Violaceae and Rhamnaceae.

There is only one species in Southern Africa.

Eagris nottoana (Wallengren)

RUFOUS-WINGED FLAT

Pterygospidea nottoana Wallengren, 1857. *K. svenska Vetensk-Akad. Handl.* (N.F.) **2**(4): 54.

There are two subspecies in Southern Africa, and a third on Madagascar.

Eagris nottoana nottoana (Wallengren)

Pterygospidea nottoana Wallengren, 1857. *K. svenska Vetensk-Akad. Handl.* (N.F.) **2**(4) 54. Type locality: Kaffraria.

IDENTIFICATION

Adult. Male. Upperside: dark reddish-brown with a row of faintly marked darker spots and minute hyaline dots on costa near apex of forewing. Underside: similar to upperside but paler without prominent dark marking on the forewing. Female. Upperside: similar to male but ground colour brown with larger dark spots and an irregular, oblique hyaline band across middle of forewing. Underside: forewing as on upperside without dark marking. Hindwing, almost completely white with a brown band along the costa and black dots on the outer half of the wing – it is in fact rather similar to that of *T. flesus*.

Forewing lengths: male 17-19 mm; female 20-21 mm.

DISTRIBUTION

South Africa, in the coastal forests of the Eastern Cape, KwaZulu-Natal, northwards into Mpumalanga and Northern Province, Swaziland, Moçambique and inland into Mashonaland in Zimbabwe and hence into East Africa.

Eagris nottoana nottoana male

Eagris nottoana nottoana female

Eagris nottoana knysna Evans

Eagris nottoana knysna Evans, 1946. *Ann. Mag. nat. Hist.* (11)**13**: 643. Type locality: Knysna, Western Cape Province.

IDENTIFICATION

Adult. Male. Similar to nominate subspecies. Female. Similar to nominate female but lacks the white hindwing underside.

Forewing lengths: male 17-18 mm; female 18,5-20 mm.

Early stages. Egg: pale white at first, changing to green; diameter 0,9 mm, height 0,8 mm; with 12-13 white longitudinal ribs. Larva: first to third instars reddish-brown with a black head; fourth instar olive-green with cream dorso-lateral lines and a black head; final instar with body green with anterior and posterior segments white, first eight abdominal segments with a distinct row of yellow dorso-lateral spots, head reddish-brown; maximum length 27,8 mm. Pupa: 12-13 mm long; yellowish-brown with darker brown marking and mottled with white; wing-cases white (Clark, 1978: 214).

DISTRIBUTION

South Africa, from East London in the Eastern Cape to Knysna and George in the Western Cape.

HABITAT AND ECOLOGY

E. nottoana is mainly a coastal forest species in South Africa, but extends inland north of the Limpopo river where it may also be encountered in dense riverine forest. It has a rapid flight. Both sexes may be observed feeding at flowers.

The males establish territories usually around a particular bush. They often perch with expanded wings on the leaves, sometimes on the undersurfaces.

The females are less often recorded, possibly due to their remarkable resemblance to the more common *T. flesus*. They lay their eggs singly on the surface of a leaf of the food plant and cover it with abdominal scales. The eggs hatch after 7 to 10 days. The newly emerged larva does not eat the empty shell. The larva constructs a purse-like shelter or simply binds some leaves together. The larval stage lasts some 50-60 days. The larva moults and pupates inside the shelter. The pupal stage lasts some 11 to 20 days (Clark, 1978: 214).

E. nottoana is on the wing throughout the year, but is more common from August to May.

LARVAL FOOD PLANTS

Grewia occidentalis (Tiliaceae); *Dombeya cymosa* (Sterculiaceae); *Erythroxylum emarginatum* (Erythroxylaceae); *Rinorea arborea* (Violaceae) (Paré, pers. comm.); *Scutia myrtina* (Rhamnaceae).

CONSERVATION

E. nottoana is not a very common species, however it is quite widely distributed and is consequently under no immediate threat.

Eagris nottoana knysna final instar larva (After G.C. Clark 1978)

Eagris nottoana nottoana pupa (Photo: R. Paré)

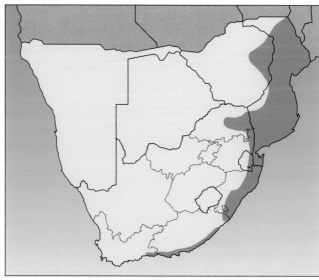

Distribution map of *Eagris nottoana*

Genus *Calleagris* Aurivillius

Calleagris Aurivillius, 1925. *Macrolep. of World* **13**: 571. Type-species: *Antigonus jamesoni* Sharpe, 1890, by monotypy.

Medium-sized to large skippers. Apical segment of palpi long and porrect. Forewing with vein CuA_2 arising before centre of cell, CuA_1 near the posterior angle, M_2 midway between M_1 and M_3, R_1 is widely separated from Sc. Hindwing outer margin rounded off, but deeply emarginated between veins M_1 and M_3, M_2 distinct. Male forewing without a costal fold, but hind tibiae with a hair pencil.

Early stages appear to be unrecorded.

There are two species in Southern Africa.

KEY TO THE SPECIES OF *CALLEAGRIS*

1. Forewing with small hyaline spots usually only in CuA_1, end of cell and subapically in R_2-R_4; UFW and LFW with dark ochreous irroration between postdiscal spots and inner margin .... *C. kobela*

   Forewing with large hyaline spots in CuA_1 and M_3, at end of cell and subapically in R_2-R_4; UFW and LHW with no or little irroration of dark ochreous between discal spots and inner margin .... *C. krooni*

Calleagris kobela (Trimen)

MRS RAVEN'S FLAT

Nisoniades kobela Trimen, 1864. *Trans. ent. Soc. Lond.* (3) **2**: 180. Type locality: Bashee River, Eastern Cape Province.

IDENTIFICATION

Adult. Male. Upperside: dark brown with darker spotting; forewing with small hyaline spots usually only in CuA_1, end of cell and subapically in R_2-R_4 and dark ochreous irroration between postdiscal spots and inner margin. Underside: dark brown with similar markings to upperside; hindwing with dark ochreous irroration between postdiscal spots and inner margin. Female. Similar to male but paler and hyaline marking larger and better developed.

Forewing lengths: male 19-20,5 mm; female 20-21 mm.

Early stages. Unrecorded.

HABITAT AND ECOLOGY

C. kobela is an inhabitant of thick evergreen forest. They are quite wary, rising instantly when disturbed, flitting about for a few seconds before alighting on another plant. Their flight is not very fast. Both sexes can be observed feeding at flowers.

Calleagris kobela male upperside

The males establish territories around the edges of the forests, along roads, settling on the underside of leaves of low plants with their wings expanded. The females are less often observed than the males as they fly at random in the undergrowth in search of suitable food plants on which to lay.

This species is on the wing from November to May, the best months for observation being February and March.

LARVAL FOOD PLANTS

Unrecorded.

DISTRIBUTION

South Africa, from Somerset East in the Eastern Cape to Kwa-Zulu-Natal.

CONSERVATION

C. kobela is relatively widespread and is under no immediate threat.

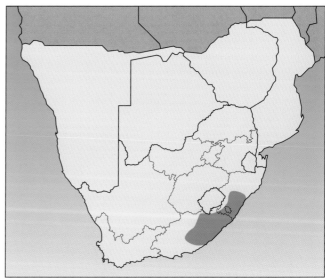

Distribution map of *Calleagris kobela*

Calleagris krooni Vári

KROON'S FLAT

Calleagris krooni Vári, 1974. *Ann. Transv. Mus.* **29**: 10. Type locality: Mariepskop, Mpumalanga. Holotype male in Transvaal Museum.

IDENTIFICATION

Adult. Male. Upperside: dark brown with darker spotting and large hyaline spots and no dark ochreous irroration on forewing. Underside: dark brown with similar markings to upperside and with little to no irroration of dark ochreous between discal spots and inner margin. Female. Similar to male but paler and markings better developed.

Forewing lengths: male 20-22 mm; female 22-24 mm.

Early stages. Unrecorded.

HABITAT AND ECOLOGY

C. krooni is an inhabitant of thick evergreen forest along the eastern slopes of the Drakensberg in Mpumalanga. Its flight is not particularly fast. Both sexes can be observed feeding at flowers.

The males establish territories along the edges of the forests, in clearings and along roads. They can usually be found perching on the leaves of low plants with expanded wings. In the morning they can be observed vigorously chasing intruding butterflies out of their territories. The females are less often observed than the males and fly at random, searching for suitable food plants on which to lay.

This species is on the wing from November to May, being commoner in the late summer months.

LARVAL FOOD PLANTS

Unrecorded.

DISTRIBUTION

South Africa, along the eastern slopes of the Drakensberg in Mpumalanga, from Mariepskop to Blyfstaanhoogte.

CONSERVATION

C. krooni is restricted to certain localities, however it is relatively widespread and is apparently under no immediate threat.

Calleagris krooni male upperside

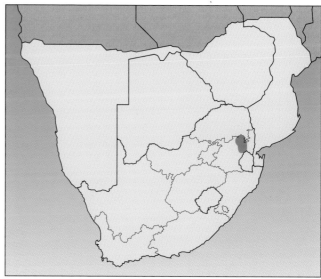

Distribution map of *Calleagris krooni*

Genus *Eretis* Mabille

Eretis Mabille, 1891. *Bull. Soc. ent. Belg.* **35**: 71. Type-species: *Eretis melania* Mabille, 1871, by monotypy.

Small skippers with broad dark wings, often silky or finely dusted with white. They are characterised by a slight indentation in the middle of the hindwing outer margin. Forewing usually with small hyaline spots, but hindwing without these markings. All settle with wings flat.

Egg, ribs large and well-sculptured. Larva greyish brown, head black and covered with fine filamentous setae. Pupa greenish, blunt anteriorly. Proboscis tube extends beyond end of abdomen. Food plants Acanthaceae.

There are three species in Southern Africa of which two occur in the Republic of South Africa.

KEY TO THE SPECIES OF *ERETIS*

1. Underside hindwing red with dark markings, forelegs white
.... *E. djaelaelae*

   Underside hindwing red only at ends of cells; forelegs brown
.... *E. umbra*

Typical habitat of the genus *Eretis*

Eretis djaelaelae (Wallengren)

MARBLED ELF

Pterygospidea djaelaelae Wallengren, 1857. *K. svenska Vetensk-Akad. Handl.* (N.F.) **2**(4): 54. Type locality: Kaffraria.

IDENTIFICATION

Adult. Similar to *E. umbra* but is larger, has less rounded wings, larger hyaline spots and white forelegs. Male. Upperside: a mottled purplish-brown with silky sheen; forewing with a few fine hyaline dots across middle and near apex except for some brown markings. Female. Similar to male but has a larger, rounder abdomen.

Forewing lengths: male 14,5-16 mm; female 16-16,5 mm.

Early stages. Egg: yellow when laid, changing to red; diameter 0,8 mm; height 0,5 mm; with 14-16 upright ribs, only half of them reaching the micropyle, and some 10 cross-ribs. Larva: first instar reddish-brown in colour; after the first moult the larva becomes greyish-brown and remains so until the final instar; head black spotted with white; maximum length attained is 16-17 mm. Pupa: length 11,5-13,5 mm; dull greenish-grey in colour (Clark, 1978: 216).

HABITAT AND ECOLOGY

A common bushveld or woodland species only rarely venturing into open grassland. *E. djaelaelae* can be found flying anywhere about the bushveld, feeding at flowers or skipping about in the shade of trees. They often settle on the ground or low plants with expanded wings. Occasionally one can be observed drinking at damp places or fresh cow-dung.

   The males often establish territories around a low shrub or bush and can be observed fluttering about the area for hours. They perch on low plants and the ground and chase off any intruders which encroach into their territories.

   The females are less often observed as they fly at random through the bush searching for suitable food plants on which to lay. They lay their eggs singly on a leaf or bud-cluster. The egg takes about 8 days to hatch. The larva constructs a shelter by binding leaves together and lives concealed in it, emerging only to feed. The larval

Eretis djaelaelae final instar larva (After G.C. Clark 1978)

Eretis djaelaelae pupa (After G.C. Clark 1978)

Eretis djaelaelae male underside showing white forelegs

stage lasts some 140 days depending on climatic conditions. Moulting and pupation takes place within the shelter. The pupal stage lasts from 10 to 11 days. They are parasitised by *Apanteles* species (Hymenoptera) (Clark, 1978: 216).

In the warmer parts of Southern Africa this species is on the wing throughout the year, however, in the cooler areas it is usually found from August to April/May.

LARVAL FOOD PLANTS

Phaulopsis imbricata, Chaetacanthus setiger, Dyschoriste sp., *Justica protracta* and *Justica* sp. (Acanthaceae).

DISTRIBUTION

South Africa, from the Eastern Cape, KwaZulu-Natal, Gauteng, Mpumalanga and Northern Province, into Swaziland, Moçambique, Zimbabwe and Tropical Africa.

CONSERVATION

This is a widespread and common species and is under no threat.

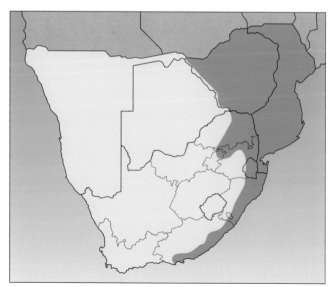

Distribution map of *Eretis djaelaelae*

Eretis umbra (Trimen)

SMALL MARBLED ELF

Nisoniades umbra Trimen, 1862. *Trans. ent. Soc. Lond.* (3)**1**: 289.

There are two subspecies in Southern Africa of which the nominate is found in South Africa. The subspecies *nox* Neave occurs in Zimbabwe and Moçambique. The species is also found in East Africa.

Eretis umbra umbra (Trimen)

Nisoniades umbra Trimen, 1862. *Trans. ent. Soc. Lond.* (3)**1**: 289. Type locality: Plettenberg Bay, Western Cape Province. Type male in Natural History Museum, London.

IDENTIFICATION

Adult. Similar to *E. djaelaelae* but smaller, has more rounded wings, smaller hyaline spots and brown forelegs. Male. Upperside: a mottled purplish-brown with a silky sheen; forewing with a few fine hyaline dots across the middle and near apex. Underside: brown, red only at ends of cells. Female. Similar to male but has a rounder abdomen.

Forewing lengths: male 13,8 – 15 mm; female 15-17 mm.

Early stages. Unrecorded.

Eretis umbra umbra male underside showing unmarked legs

Eretis umbra umbra male upperside

HABITAT AND ECOLOGY

Eretis umbra usually inhabits open grassland and bushveld areas. They often settle on the ground or low plants with expanded wings. They can be observed feeding at flowers or skipping about in the shade of trees. Occasionally they can be seen at muddy places or at fresh cow-dung.

The males often establish territories around a particular bush and can be observed skipping around the area for hours. At times they perch on a low plant or on the ground. The females are less often observed as they fly at random through the bush looking for suitable plants on which to lay. They lay their eggs singly on the leaf buds of the food plant. The female holds its wings erect during egg-laying, and will fuss about a particular plant for a while before selecting an oviposition site on the underside of a leaf-bud. Further observations on the life history are not available.

This species is on the wing throughout the year, however, in the cooler areas it is usually found from August to May.

LARVAL FOOD PLANTS

Chaetacanthus setiger, Phaulopsis sp., *Dyschoriste* sp., *Justica* sp., *Asystasia schimperi* (Acanthaceae).

DISTRIBUTION

South Africa, from as far west as Mossel Bay in the Western Cape to the Eastern and Northern Cape, Free State, KwaZulu-Natal, Gauteng, North-West Province, Mpumalanga and Northern Province, into Swaziland.

CONSERVATION

This is a fairly widespread and common species and is under no threat.

Distribution map of *Eretis umbra*

Genus *Sarangesa* Moore

Sarangesa Moore, 1881. *Lepid. Ceylon* **1**: 176. Type species: *Sarangesa albicilia* Moore, 1881, by monotypy.

Medium-sized skippers which show seasonal dimorphism. While some like to settle in the sunshine like other butterflies, others prefer shaded spots such as hollows, excavations, steep banks of streams, aardvark holes and beneath leafy trees. Palpi short, inconspicuous, porrect. Antennal club obtuse beyond middle, pointed. Wing outline even or slightly excavate on the forewing in area CuA$_2$. Hind tibiae with a hair pencil or fringed.

Egg domed with well-sculptured ribs. Larva brown to green with longitudinal stripes, head dark brown with fine branched setae. Pupa obtuse, proboscis tube extends as far as mid-abdomen.

Food plants Acanthaceae.

There are seven species in Southern Africa, of which four occur in the Republic of South Africa.

KEY TO THE SPECIES OF *SARANGESA*

1 UFW and LFW with small markings; underside bright ochreous yellow .... *S. phidyle*

Large spots on both of these areas; underside brown with variable orange markings 2

2. UFW with two spots in CuA$_2$; antenna with white patch below club .... *S. seineri*

UFW lacking pale spots in CuA$_2$; antenna without white patch 3

3. UHW with a hyaline cell spot .... *S. motozi*

UHW lacking a cell spot .... *S. ruona*

Sarangesa phidyle form *varia* male upperside

Sarangesa phidyle (Walker)

SMALL ELFIN

Cyclopides phidyle Walker, 1870. *Entomologist* **5**: 56. Type locality: Hor Tamanib.

IDENTIFICATION

Adult. Male. Upperside: forewing ochreous-brown with three small hyaline subapical spots and three large ones across centre of wing, darker brown patches subapically and across middle of wing; hindwing mottled brown with ochreous. Underside: with characteristic bright ochreous-yellow ground colour and brown markings. Female. Similar to male, but with a rounder abdomen.

The dry-season form *varia* Evans (1937, *Cat. Afr. Hesper.* : 43) differs from the nominate wet-season form in having smaller hyaline spots and more pronounced dark patches on the forewing upperside.

Forewing lengths: male 12-18 mm; female 12-18 mm.

Early stages. Egg: pinkish-white when laid, changing later to red; diameter 0,8 mm, height 0,5 mm; with 16 longitudinal ribs, only 7 of which reach the micropyle; five cross-ribs extend part of the way down the side and then become incomplete. Larva: first instar reddish in colour on emergence; after first moult it becomes brown and remains so until the fourth instar when it changes to greyish-green; the final (fifth) instar is greenish-white with a dark longitudinal dorsal green line, flanked on either side by a white dorsolateral line, head brown mottled with white and yellowish hairs; maximum length 20 mm. Pupa: 16 mm long; pale greyish-green in colour and covered with a white powder (Clark, 1978: 218).

Sarangesa phidyle final instar larva (After G.C. Clark 1978)

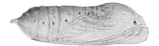

Sarangesa phidyle pupa (After G.C. Clark 1978)

HABITAT AND ECOLOGY

S. phidyle is a common bushveld species, most often observed on hillsides and in dense riverine forest. It settles on rock faces and on bare ground. Its flight is fast and darting. In most arid and hot areas the species tends to roost in little caves or under overhanging rocks including aardvark burrows. Little groups of both sexes of up to twenty are often found. At times they can be observed feeding at flowers. They are also attracted to damp patches on the ground along streams where they can be observed drinking from the sand.

Sarangesa phidyle male upperside

The males usually establish territories in the shade of trees where they can often be found day after day. Here they flit about, skipping or zig-zagging from one plant to another or perching on the ground or rocks, rarely on leaves, with expanded wings. They fly quite fast at times, in particular when chasing other males out of their territories, or when they themselves are chased by other butterflies. They always fly near the ground, occasionally resting in patches of sunlight.

The females frequent the same places as the males where they search for suitable food plants on which to lay. Eggs are laid singly on the underside of the leaf of the food plant. The eggs take about 13 days to hatch. The discarded shell is not eaten. The larva cuts a rough circle in a leaf and bends the cut portion over and secures it with silk to form a purse-like shelter, in which it lives. It feeds on the surface of the leaf within this shelter. Later, it binds leaves together, and tends to approach the ground more closely with each change of shelter. The larval stage lasts some 10-11 weeks. It eventually pupates within a shelter made of leaves bound together. The pupal stage lasts from 15-23 days (Clark, 1978: 218).

This species is on the wing throughout the year, but is scarcer during the winter.

LARVAL FOOD PLANTS

Peristrophe hensii, Barleria sp. (Acanthaceae).

DISTRIBUTION

South Africa, from the Eastern Cape Province, through KwaZulu-Natal, Mpumalanga and Northern Province, into Moçambique, Zimbabwe, northern Botswana and northern Namibia, and on into most of the Afrotropical Region.

CONSERVATION

S. phidyle is a widespread and common species and is under no threat.

Sarangesa motozi (Wallengren)

FOREST ELFIN

Pterygospidea motozi Wallengren, 1857. *K. svenska Vetensk-Akad. Handl.* (N.F.) **2**(4): 53. Type locality: Kaffraria.

IDENTIFICATION

Adult. Male. Upperside: brown slightly mottled in appearance, sometimes clothed with yellow hairs; with faint darker bands; forewing with a few hyaline spots across the middle and three small squarish dots near apex; hindwing, unlike most *Sarangesa*, with a round hyaline central spot at end of cell. Cilia chequered brown and white. Underside: brown mottled with small orange patches, particularly near outer margin of hindwing. Female. Similar to male but slightly larger with outer margins of wings more rounded.

There is a dry-season form *pertusa* Mabille (1891, *Bull. Soc. ent. Belg.* **35**: 68) which is more variegated with reduced pale spots.

Forewing lengths: male 16-17 mm; female 16-18 mm.

Early stages. Egg: pure white when first laid, changing to red as development proceeds; diameter 0,8 mm, height 0,6 mm; with 12 to 14 white longitudinal ribs, only 7 to 8 of which reach the micropyle. Larva: first instar yellow to reddish in colour with a black head; second instar brown with a black head; third instar more yellowish-brown; fourth instar greyish-green; final (fifth) instar green with a darker longitudinal stripe dorsally, flanked on either side by white dorsolateral longitudinal lines, head brown with short yellow to white hairs; maximum length 21 mm. Pupa: 17 mm long; green in colour (Clark, 1978: 220).

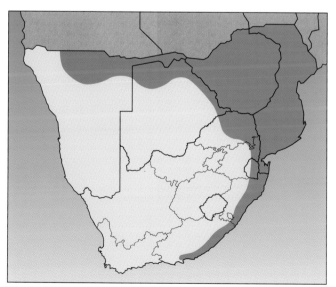

Distribution map of *Sarangesa phidyle*

Sarangesa motozi female upperside

HABITAT AND ECOLOGY

S. motozi is an inhabitant of dense woodland or evergreen forest. It is often found in shady places under trees although it often ventures out into the warm sunlight. It is often found sheltering in holes in the ground. Wood (in Gifford, 1965) records hundreds from a warthog hole. Both sexes are also frequent visitors to damp patches.

The males usually establish territories in the shade of trees along the fringes, or on the tracks in the forests. Occasionally they can be found in dry river beds overshadowed by trees or even in the shade of a solitary tree, far from others. The males may return to the same territory for several days on end. The resident male chases all intruding males rapidly out of its territory. These pursuits can often be sustained for long periods as the two males dart about in the speckled sunlight under the trees. However, the males can usually be observed patrolling rapidly around their territories, zig-zagging and skipping in any direction, or circling vigorously about under the trees. They always perch close to or on the ground with expanded wings until they retire to rest under a leaf.

The females are found in the same areas as the males where they search for suitable food plants on which to lay. Eggs are laid singly on a leaf of the food plant. The egg hatches after about 11 days and the discarded shell is not eaten. The larva bites round a small portion of a leaf, without completing the circle, bends this part over and secures it with silk to form a shelter in which it spends its early instars. It later joins together a few leaves to form a shelter. When lying dormant the larva turns its head sideways, to the fifth segment. Moulting and pupation takes place within the shelters produced by the larva. The larval stage lasts some 40 days. The adult emerges from the pupa after some 26 days (Clark, 1978: 220).

This species is on the wing throughout the year, but is scarcer in winter.

LARVAL FOOD PLANTS

Peristrophe hensii, *Justica* sp., *Barleria* sp. (Acanthaceae).

DISTRIBUTION

South Africa, from the Eastern Cape Province, KwaZulu-Natal, Mpumalanga and Northern Province and into northern Botswana, Swaziland, Zimbabwe, Moçambique and into East Africa.

CONSERVATION

This is a widespread and common species and is under no threat.

Sarangesa motozi final instar larva (After G.C. Clark 1978)

Sarangesa motozi pupa (After G.C. Clark 1978)

Sarangesa motozi female form *pertusa* upperside

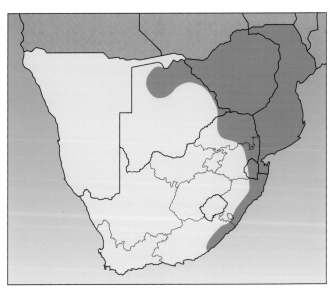

Distribution map of *Sarangesa motozi*

Sarangesa seineri Strand

DARK ELFIN

Sarangesa seineri Strand, 1909. *Arch. Naturgesch.* **75**(1): 383.

There are two subspecies in Southern Africa, both of which occur in the Republic of South Africa.

Sarangesa seineri seineri Strand

Sarangesa seineri Strand, 1909. *Arch. Naturgesch.* **75**(1): 383. Type locality: Livingstone, Zambia. Female type in Berlin Museum.

IDENTIFICATION

Adult. The white patch on the antenna below the club is peculiar to this species. Male. Upperside: mottled greyish-brown; forewing with a few hyaline spots across the middle and three small spots near apex; hindwing mottled greyish-brown. Underside: brown mottled with diffuse orange patches, particularly on the hindwing and inner margin of the forewing. Female. Similar to the male but has a larger, rounder abdomen.

Forewing lengths: male 12-19 mm; female 18,5-21,5 mm.

DISTRIBUTION

South Africa, from the Northern Province and Mpumalanga, northern North-West Province, into Botswana, northern Namibia, Zimbabwe, Moçambique and East Africa.

Sarangesa seineri seineri male upperside

Sarangesa seineri durbana Evans

Sarangesa seineri durbana Evans, 1937. *Cat. Afr. Hesper.*: 44. Type locality: Durban, KwaZulu-Natal. Type male in British Museum.

IDENTIFICATION

Adult. Similar to but differs from the nominate subspecies in having a much browner hindwing underside.

Forewing lengths: male 17-18,3 mm; female 18,5-20,3 mm.

DISTRIBUTION

South Africa, being confined to KwaZulu-Natal and adjacent areas of Mpumalanga and Swaziland.

Early stages. Egg: pure white when first laid, changing to pink as development proceeds; diameter 0,8 mm, height 0,6 mm, domed in shape. Larva: first instar creamy-white, becoming pale yellow with a black head; grows from 1,5 mm on hatching to 5 mm in five days; second instar pale yellow, darkening to pale orange with a black head; grows to 8 mm in six days; third instar similar in appearance, growing to 12 mm in seven days; fourth instar translucent green with darker dorsal line and thin white dorso-lateral and lateral lines from head to tail, head shiny black with tiny black papillae; growing to 18 mm in seven days; fifth (final) instar similar to fourth, growing to 25 mm in twelve days. Pupa: 18 mm long; whitish bluegreen in colour; translucent in appearance (from eggs collected at Makhathini Flats, Maputaland, KwaZulu-Natal by S. E. Woodhall).

HABITAT AND ECOLOGY

S. seineri is found mainly in woodland, bushveld and savannah country. It is often present on steep hillsides, but may also be found in dry river beds. It often settles in shady places of rocks and aardvark holes. *S. seineri* is often found on muddy places along streams and occasionally at flowers.

The males establish territories in the shade of large trees where they can often be observed flying close to the ground. They always perch close to or on the ground with expanded wings, often on the underside of a leaf.

The females are scarcer but frequent the same places as the males, searching for suitable food plants on which to lay. Eggs are laid singly on a leaf of the food plant about a third of the way down from the tip. The egg hatches after about 11 days. First to third instar larvae cut a long oval, approximately twice the larval length, from the edge of a leaf and fold it over the underside, securing it with silk for use as a shelter. Older specimens fold the entire leaf over, binding the edges together with short silk strands. Moulting and pupation take place within the shelters produced by the larva. The larval stage lasts some 37 days. Pupation takes place in final larval shelter and the pupa is unattached. The adult emerges from the pupa after some 14 days.

It is on the wing throughout the year but is scarcer in winter.

LARVAL FOOD PLANTS

Peristrophe hensii (Acanthaceae).

CONSERVATION

S. seineri is a relatively uncommon species, however it is widely distributed and under no threat.

Sarangesa seineri seineri final instar larva

Sarangesa seineri seineri pupa

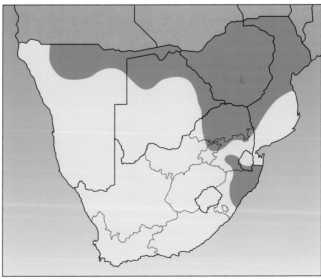

Distribution map of *Sarangesa seineri*

Sarangesa ruona Evans

RUONA ELFIN

Sarangesa ruona Evans, 1937. *Cat. Afr. Hesper.*: 45. Type locality: Ruo Valley, Malawi. Type male in Natural History Museum, London.

IDENTIFICATION

Adult. Male. Upperside: dull ochreous-brown with faint darker bands; forewing with a few hyaline spots across the middle and three small dots near apex; hindwing without hyaline cell spot. Underside: brown with hindwing and outer marginal area of forewing with yellow-orange markings. Female. Similar to the male, but with a rounder abdomen.

Forewing lengths: male 15-18,5 mm; female 19-20 mm.

Early stages. Unrecorded.

HABITAT AND ECOLOGY

This species is found in sub-montane and riverine forest. Here it can be observed flying about the thick bush, exclusively in the shade of trees.

The males establish territories in the undergrowth under the shade of the trees, where they can be found perching on small plants, with wings held flat. They also congregate during the day in holes in banks or culverts under roads.

The female is scarcer but frequents the same places as the male, searching for suitable food plants on which to lay.

S. ruona is on the wing from September to May.

LARVAL FOOD PLANTS

Unrecorded.

DISTRIBUTION

A marginal species in South Africa, having been recorded from Louis Trichardt to Pafuri and Satara in the Northern Province; and from Mhlosinga in KwaZulu-Natal. Also in Zimbabwe, Moçambique and Malawi.

CONSERVATION

S. ruona has been recorded as a rare species by S.F. & G.A. Henning in the *South African Red Data Book – Butterflies* (1989). It is a marginal species, the northern areas of South Africa being the southernmost limit of its range. It is more widely distributed in Zimbabwe, Moçambique and Malawi. In South Africa it does not appear to be under any immediate threat as it has been recorded in the Kruger National Park.

Sarangesa ruona male upperside

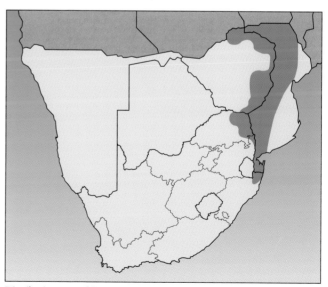

Distribution map of *Sarangesa ruona*

Genus *Netrobalane* Mabille

Netrobalane Mabille, 1903. *Genera Insect.* **17** : 76. Type species: *Caprona canopus* Trimen, 1864, by monotypy.

Medium-sized species with white ground colour and brown or black markings and grey hyaline spots. Male without thoracic hair pencil between forelegs.

Egg domed, slightly ribbed. Larva green with white pubescence; head dark, covered with long filamentous setae. Pupa white with bifid, black, anterior process. Food plants Sterculiaceae, Malvaceae and Tiliaceae.

There is only one species in Southern Africa.

Netrobalane canopus (Trimen)

BUFF-TIPPED SKIPPER

Caprona canopus Trimen, 1864. *Trans. ent. Soc. Lond.* (3) **2**: 180. Type locality: Kaffraria. Holotype in Natural History Museum, London.

IDENTIFICATION

Adult. Male. Forewing angled below apex. Upperside: thinly white-scaled with underside marking faintly showing; forewing base and outer half reddish-brown with a small group of subapical hyaline spots; hindwing dark brown at base, extending irregularly down inner margin with extensive hyaline patches in mid-wing. Underside: creamy-brown, shading to reddish-brown towards forewing apex; hindwing with a prominent black spot near anal angle. Female. Similar to male but larger with a stouter abdomen.

Forewing lengths: male 12-21 mm; female 19-22 mm.

Netrobalane canopus female upperside

Early stages. Egg: pale watery yellow, changing to pale salmon as development proceeds; diameter 0,85 mm, height 0,7 mm; with 20 longitudinal ribs, cross-braced by some 28 very fine ribs, which are very close at the base. Larva: first instar ochre-yellow with a broad reddish-brown stripe along the sides; after the first moult the larva becomes greenish with whitish spots; fifth (final) instar larva yellowish-green with white spots and a black hairy head; maximum length 26 mm. Pupa: 18 to 21 mm long; white with small black markings (Clark, 1978: 222).

HABITAT AND ECOLOGY

N. canopus is an inhabitant of wooded areas, both bush and rainforest. It is not a rapid flier, but has a rather fluttering motion on the wing. It frequently visits flowers. It usually alights with wings expanded on the upperside of a leaf, but has also been observed to settle on the underside. When at rest it strongly resembles a bird dropping.

The males usually select a low tree or bush as a territory. Here they perch on an isolated twig or branch from which they dart out and chase off intruding butterflies. Colonel Bowker observed that, while in flight, this butterfly made a sharp clicking or buzzing sound. Trimen (1887) believed that it is possible that this sound is peculiar to the male when courting the female. The males also regularly show hilltopping behaviour, ascending to the peaks where they establish their territories. They often occupy the same perch for days.

The females frequent the same areas as the males, flying at random in search of suitable food plants on which to lay. Eggs are laid singly on the surface of the leaf and covers them with abdominal scales. The eggs take some 13 days to hatch. The young larva bites round most of a small portion of a leaf and folds over this oval-shaped piece, and then secures it to form a purse-like shelter. It feeds on the surface of the leaf within the shelter, but as it grows it constructs larger shelters and finally binds leaves together. The larval stage lasts some 46 days. Moulting and pupation take place within the shelter. The pupal stage lasts 13 days (Clark, 1978: 222).

N. canopus is on the wing throughout the year.

LARVAL FOOD PLANTS

Grewia occidentalis, G. similis, G. flavescens (Tiliaceae); *Dombeya cymosa, D. calantha* (Sterculiaceae); *Pavonia burchellii* (Malvaceae).

DISTRIBUTION

South Africa, from the Eastern Cape, KwaZulu-Natal and Mpumalanga and Northern Province, Swaziland, Moçambique, Zimbabwe and northwards throughout the Afrotropical Region.

CONSERVATION

N. canopus is a widespread species and is under no immediate threat.

Netrobalane canopus final instar larva (Photo: R.G. Oberprieler)

Netrobalane canopus pupa (After G.C. Clark 1978)

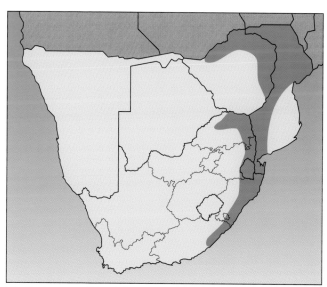

Distribution map of *Netrobalane canopus*

Genus *Caprona* Wallengren

Caprona Wallengren, 1857. *K. svenska VetenskAkad. Handl.* (N.F.) **2**(4): 51.

Type species: *Caprona pillaana* Wallengren, 1857, by monotypy. Medium-sized species with a grey ground colour. Forewing with distinct, sharply defined hyaline spots; posterior margin more or less emarginated; vein M_2 arising distinctly nearer to M_1 than M_3. Hindwing without distinct hyaline spots; margin at the end of vein CuA_1 distinctly angled. Male with a very long black hair-pencil under the thorax between the forelegs.

Egg unrecorded. Larva off-white with dense covering of small setae emanating from small white tubercles. Head black with long setae. Pupa white. Food plants Sterculiaceae and Tiliaceae.

There are two species in Southern Africa, only one of which occurs in South Africa.

Typical habitat of *Caprona pillaana*

Caprona pillaana fourth instar larva

Caprona pillaana Wallengren

RAGGED SKIPPER

Caprona pillaana Wallengren, 1857. *K. svenska VetenskAkad. Handl.* (N.F.) **2**(4): 51. Type locality: Kaffraria. Type in Natural History Museum, London.

IDENTIFICATION

Adult. Male. Upperside: ground colour from pale to dark brown; forewing with four subapical dots and an irregular discal band of hyaline spots. Hindwing with discal grey markings and angled in middle of margin. Both wings with a marginal whitish line. There is slight seasonal variation. Female. Similar to male, but larger with a stouter abdomen.

Forewing lengths: male 15,5-18,5 mm; female 20-22 mm.

Early stages. Eggs unrecorded. Larva: final instar cylindrical, off-white in colour and densely covered with half millimetre long setae; the setae arise from small white tubercles giving the larva a granular appearance; each segment bears a pair of very small black dots, one on either side of the dorsal mid-line; the dorsally bilobed head is black and densely covered with setae of approximately two millimetres long, those dorsally on apices black, giving the appearance of two black spots when viewed from above, while those below are white; an ill-defined band of grey setae bisect the head laterally, giving the appearance of a stripe across the face. The larva attains a length of 25 mm. Pupa: 20 mm long; cylindrical and white in colour, covered with a waxy powdery bloom (Paré, pers. comm.).

HABITAT AND ECOLOGY

C. pillaana is typically an inhabitant of dry bushveld areas, but is also found in woodland and the fringes of riverine gallery forest. It is a fairly rapid flier and readily comes to flowers. Swanepoel (1953) recorded 4 to 10 specimens on some sunny days in August, feeding on flowers at Munnik in the Northern Province; while Pennington (1978) saw 7 coming to red flowers in the Tugela Valley in KwaZulu-Natal. They are also attracted to mud along streams.

The males show strong hilltopping behaviour and can most often be seen flying about the tops of little hills or ridges in the bushveld. They usually select a territory around a tree some distance from where the usual butterfly hilltopping takes place. Here they can be seen patrolling rapidly or sometimes in a leisurely manner about their territories.

The females fly at random in the bush searching for suitable food plants on which to lay. The female lays her eggs singly on the surface of the leaf of the food plant. The larva spends its entire life in a shelter constructed from leaves of the food plant, and emerges to feed only at night. The larval stage lasts some 42 days. Pupation occurs within the shelter which consists of two leaves stitched together. The pupa is held in place by a Y-shaped girdle. It is attached to the uppermost leaf by its cremaster and further supported in the fork

Caprona pillaana male upperside

of the Y. The two arms and the foot of the Y are stitched to the roof and floor of the shelter respectively, further strengthening the structure. The pupal stage lasts some 10 days (Paré, pers. comm.).

This species is on the wing throughout the year, the spring or late winter brood differing slightly from the summer brood.

LARVAL FOOD PLANTS

Dombeya rotundifolia, D. burgessiae, Sterculia quinqueloba (Sterculiaceae); *Grewia flava, G. monticola* (Tiliaceae).

DISTRIBUTION

South Africa from the Northern Cape, Free State, KwaZulu-Natal, North-West Province, Gauteng, Northern Province and Mpumalanga into Botswana, Zimbabwe, Swaziland, Moçambique to tropical Africa.

CONSERVATION

C. pillaana is a local but widespread species and is consequently under no threat.

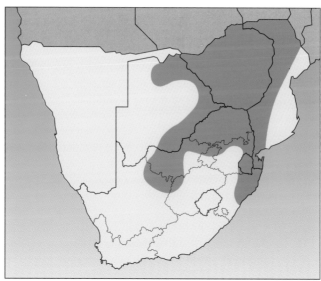

Distribution map of *Caprona pillaana*

Genus *Leucochitonea* Wallengren

Leucochitonea Wallengren, 1857. *K. svenska VetenskAkad. Handl.* (N.F.) **2**(4): 52. Type species: *Leucochitonea levubu* Wallengren, 1857, by selection by Wallengren (1858, *Ofvers. K. VetenskAkad. Forh.* **15**: 82).

Medium-sized species with white wings and black markings. Differs from *Abantis* in the facies and the presence of a black hair pencil on the thorax between the forelegs, as in *Caprona*, from which it differs in the regular outline of the wings (Evans, 1937: 50).

Early stages unrecorded. Food plants Tiliaceae.

There is only one species in Southern Africa.

Leucochitonea levubu male upperside

Leucochitonea levubu Wallengren

WHITE CLOAKED SKIPPER

Leucochitonea levubu Wallengren, 1857. *K. svenska Vetensk-Akad. Handl.* (N.F.) **2**(4): 2. Type locality: Kaffraria. Type in the Natural History Museum, London.

IDENTIFICATION

Adult. Male. Upperside: white with black margins, the apical and marginal bands of the forewing relieved by white dots; veins partially blackened. Underside: similar to upperside but has a black border to the basal half of the hindwing costal margin and heavier black markings towards the anal angle of the hindwing. Female. Similar to the male but larger with a stouter abdomen.

Forewing lengths: male 20-21 mm; female 21,5-23 mm.

Early stages. Unrecorded.

HABITAT AND ECOLOGY

L. levubu is an inhabitant of bushveld. Its flight is usually rather leisurely unless disturbed or chasing other butterflies. It is often observed feeding at flowers and is only occasionally attracted to muddy spots.

The males show strong hilltopping behaviour and are regular visitors to the tops of little hills and ridges in the bushveld. They usually select a low tree or bush as a perch site. From here they dart off every now and then to chase off intruders. Occasionally they establish their territories on the flats where they show similar behaviour as on the hilltops. The males occupy the same territories for many hours.

The females are usually found on the slopes of hills or on the flats where they apparently search for suitable plants on which to lay. The females are most often observed feeding at flowers.

This species is on the wing from November to April.

LARVAL FOOD PLANTS

Grewia flava (Tiliaceae).

DISTRIBUTION

South Africa, from the Northern Cape, Free State, Gauteng and North-West Province into the Northern Province and Mpumalanga and southeast to the eastern side of the Lebombo Mountains in KwaZulu-Natal and into Swaziland, Moçambique, Zimbabwe, Botswana and northern Namibia.

CONSERVATION

L. levubu is a fairly widespread species and is under no threat.

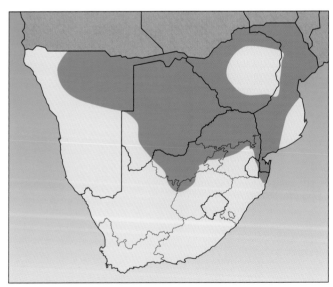

Distribution map of *Leucochitonea levubu*

Genus *Abantis* Hopffer

Abantis Hopffer, 1855. *Mber. dt. Akad. Wiss. Berl.* **1855**: 643. Type species: *Abantis tettensis* Hopffer, 1855, by monotypy.

Medium-sized, very colourful, robust skippers. Forewing with vein M_2 arising centrally between M_1 and M_3; posterior margin straight. The outer margin of hindwing is rounded off or straight at vein CuA_2. Females are characterised by the rounded tuft of hairs at the tip of the abdomen.

Egg domed with fine ribs. Larva pale with dorsal marks and small setae; head dark with long setae, being longest dorsally. Pupa white with dark bifid anterior process.

Food plants Malvaceae, Sterculiaceae, Annonaceae, Sapindaceae, Euphorbiaceae, Papilionoideae and Tiliaceae.

There are six species in Southern Africa, four of which are found in South Africa.

KEY TO THE SPECIES OF *ABANTIS*

1. UFW bright yellow with 4 large black patches .... *A. bicolor*

   UFW black, grey or ochreous with white or hyaline markings 2

2. UHW with disc brownish-ochreous with dark veins .... *A. venosa*

   UHW with disc white or whitish-ochreous 3

3. UHW whitish-ochreous on disc with black spots .... *A. tettensis*

   UHW disc white with black veins .... *A. paradisea*

Abantis tettensis Hopffer

SPOTTED VELVET SKIPPER

Abantis tettensis Hopffer, 1855. *Mber. dt. Akad. Wiss. Berl.* **1855**: 643. Type locality: Moçambique. Type in Berlin Museum.

IDENTIFICATION

Adult. Male. Upperside: blackish-brown; forewing with a row of five long and narrow whitish subapical spots, a curved band across middle and a basal stripe along inner margin; hindwing with whitish-ochreous disc with black spots. Underside: pinkish-brown; forewing with markings as on upperside; hindwing spotted with black and a narrow yellow-spotted black outer marginal border. Female. Similar to male but hindwing underside pale orange.

Forewing lengths: male 17-20 mm; female 20,5-22 mm.

Early stages. Egg: not recorded. Larva: greenish-white, very similar to *C. pillaana*, but headshield dark reddish. Pupa: reddish-brown with large forked snout-like appendage (R. Paré, pers. comm.).

Abantis tettensis male underside

Abantis tettensis male upperside

HABITAT AND ECOLOGY

A. tettensis is an inhabitant of woodland and bushveld areas. It is a fast flier when disturbed. It is occasionally encountered while feeding at flowers or at damp, muddy spots along streams.

The males show hilltopping behaviour, ascending to the top of koppies and ridges in the bushveld to establish their territories. Here they perch on a leaf on the low branches of trees, low trees, shrubs or even at times on the stems of grass. They occasionally patrol their territories, slowly circling around. Any intruder is actively pursued and chased out. They remain in their chosen spots for hours.

The female is much rarer than the male and flies at random in the bush in search of suitable plants on which to lay. The larva constructs a very robust shelter and is very long-lived, from December to the following September. The species appears to have only one brood per year. Pupation is in the shelter. The pupal stage lasts from 12-14 days (Paré, pers. comm.).

This species is on the wing from November until April.

LARVAL FOOD PLANTS

Grewia flava and *G. monticola* (Tiliaceae).

DISTRIBUTION

South Africa, from the Northern Cape, Free State, North-West Province, Gauteng, KwaZulu-Natal, Northern Province and Mpumalanga, Namibia, Botswana, Zimbabwe and Moçambique.

CONSERVATION

A. tettensis is a widespread species and is under no threat.

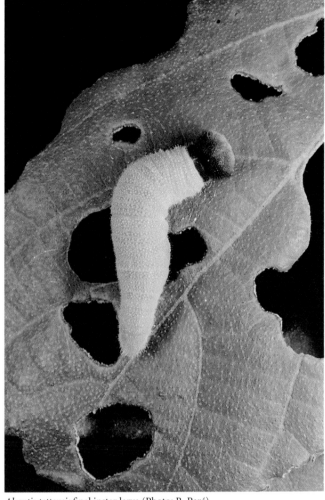

Abantis tettensis final instar larva (Photo: R. Paré)

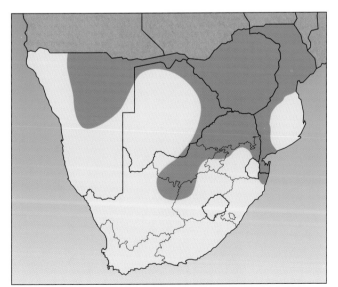

Distribution map of *Abantis tettensis*

Abantis tettensis pupa (Photo: R. Paré)

Abantis bicolor (Trimen)

BICOLOURED SKIPPER

Leucochitonea bicolor Trimen, 1864. *Trans. ent. Soc. Lond.*
3 (2) : 180. Type locality: Kaffraria. Type in Natural History
Museum, London.

IDENTIFICATION

Adult. Male. Upperside: golden-yellow with black margins; forewing
with four large black patches. Underside: deep yellow with only a
very narrow black edging; hindwing with a short black submarginal
line above the anal angle. Female. Ground colour is not as bright
as male but is otherwise similar with a rounder wing-shape.

Forewing lengths: male 18-19 mm; female 22-23 mm.

Early Stages. Unrecorded.

HABITAT AND ECOLOGY

A. bicolor is an inhabitant of lush coastal bush. It is alert and swift
on the wing. Recorded in numbers in the Ngoye Forest in northern KwaZulu-Natal in April 1952 while feeding on white *Scabiosa*
flowers. Most of those observed were females sitting with wings
open.

The males show hilltopping behaviour. The males usually establish their territories around the upper branches of trees on hilltops along the coast. They select perches on prominent twigs or
branches a few metres within the fringe of the bush and defend their
territory against any intruders, and fly off at speed around the
trees but return in a minute or so. They usually sit with their wings
open and flat. Occasionally the males establish their territories
along the edges of the forests where they perch two to three metres
above the ground.

It is double brooded, the first brood in summer being quite
sparse but the autumn brood can be quite plentiful in good years.
The best time to see *A. bicolor* is during April and May.

Abantis bicolor male upperside

LARVAL FOOD PLANTS

Unrecorded.

DISTRIBUTION

Endemic to South Africa, being found from the Eastern Cape to
KwaZulu-Natal.

CONSERVATION

A. bicolor has disappeared from many of its original haunts, such
as Durban, and has been classified as rare by S.F. & G.A. Henning
in the *South African Red Data Book – Butterflies* (1989). It does, however, inhabit some fairly inaccessible forests along the Wild Coast
and is not uncommon at Port St Johns. It is also found in the
Ngoye Forest, which is under the control of the KwaZulu-Natal Bureau of Natural Resources.

Abantis bicolor male underside

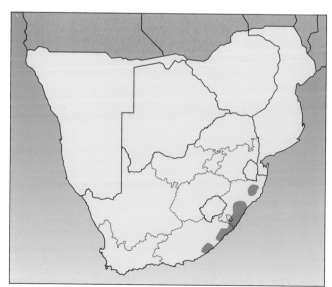

Distribution map of *Abantis bicolor*

Abantis paradisea (Butler)

PARADISE SKIPPER

Leucochitonea paradisea Butler, 1870. *Trans. ent. Soc. Lond.*
1870: 499. Type locality: Port Natal. Type in Natural History
Museum, London.

IDENTIFICATION

Adult. Male. Upperside: ground colour black, forewing with numerous hyaline spots which, in basal area, are tinged with yellow;
hindwing with a yellow and white band, traversed by black veins and
broad black margin. Underside: with markings as on upperside but
whiter. Thorax speckled with red and pale bluish-grey; abdomen
with red bands. Female. Similar to male but larger with rounder
wings.

Forewing lengths: male 19-21,5 mm; female 21,5-26 mm.

Early stages. Egg: watery-yellow; diameter 0,1 mm, height 0,65 mm;
with 20 longitudinal ribs and some 35 concentric rows of indentations. Larva: first instar ochre with a broad reddish lateral band;
second instar similar but ground colour becomes greener; third instar reddish-brown with a pair of yellow and black dorso-lateral spots
on the anterior margin of abdominal segments I-VII; fourth instar
similar but ground colour green; fifth (final) instar similar but
greenish-white with a brown prothoracic shield and a black head
with long ochre-coloured hair; maximum length some 31 mm.
Pupa: 21 mm long; white in colour with a brown bifid projection
from head and three brown protuberances from anterior margin
of thorax resembling eyes (Clark, 1978 : 224).

HABITAT AND ECOLOGY

A. paradisea is an inhabitant of open bush country, wooded or partially wooded places. It is a fast flying species when disturbed but
otherwise skips slowly about. It is often encountered feeding at low
flowers and occasionally at muddy places.

The males exhibit hilltopping behaviour, ascending to the tops
of koppies and ridges where they establish their territories. They usually select a perch along the lower branches of trees or on small trees
or shrubs. From here they leisurely patrol around the surrounding
trees, returning to the same perch. They vigorously chase all intruders out of their territories. Occasionally the males select a
perch site along the slopes of the hills instead of on their peaks.

The females can be encountered anywhere searching for suitable
food plants on which to oviposit. The females lay their eggs singly
on a leaf, covering them with abdominal scales. These are 'pasted'
on to the egg in a regular formation and gives it a symmetrical frill
round the base which perfectly camouflages the egg. The egg hatches after 8 days. The larva bites an elliptical incision in a leaf, leaving a small portion 'uncut', and then draws the outer portion over
the adjoining surface of the leaf, and secures it with silk to form a
shelter. The larva feeds on the surface of the leaf within this shelter. When too large for this shelter, it draws the edge of a leaf over

Abantis paradisea male upperside

Abantis paradisea female underside

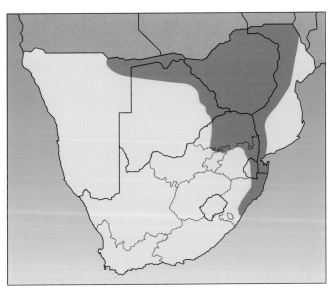

Distribution map of *Abantis paradisea*

Abantis paradisea final instar larva

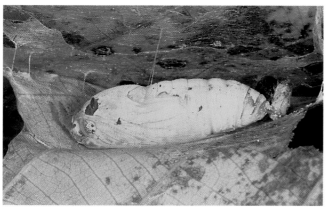

Abantis paradisea pupa

and makes a larger shelter for itself. Later still, it draws two leaves together, and it pupates between these leaves. The larval stage takes some 59 days while the pupal stage lasts 21 days. The larva is parasitised by flies (Diptera) *Thecocarcelia* sp. (Clark, 1978 : 224).

This species is on the wing throughout the year, being more plentiful from August to October.

LARVAL FOOD PLANTS

Hibiscus tiliaceus (Malvaceae), *Cola natalensis* (Sterculiaceae); *Xylopia parviflora*, *Annona* spp. (Annonaceae); *Bridelia cathartica*, *B. micrantha*, *Pseudolachnostylis maprouneifolia* (Euphorbiaceae); *Lonchocarpus capassa* (Papilionoidea); *Lecaniodiscus fraxinifolius* (Sapindaceae).

DISTRIBUTION

South Africa from KwaZulu-Natal, Mpumalanga and Northern Province, Swaziland, Botswana, northern Namibia, Zimbabwe, Moçambique and northwards into East Africa.

CONSERVATION

A. paradisea is a widespread and fairly common species and is under no threat.

Abantis venosa Trimen

VEINED SKIPPER

Abantis venosa Trimen, 1889. *S. Afr. Butterfl.* **3** : 339. Type locality: Transvaal. Type in Natural History Museum, London.

IDENTIFICATION

Adult. Male. Upperside: ground colour yellowish or gingery-brown with clearly-marked blackened veins; forewing with three large conjoined discal hyaline spots, a small spot beyond them and three oblong subapical spots. Underside: hindwing white with a black border. Female. Similar to male, but with a more rounded wing shape.

The normal dry-season form is form *umvulensis* (Sharpe, 1890. *Ann. Mag. nat. Hist.* **6**(6) : 348). This is of a lighter colour and has no dark border to the hindwing below.

Forewing lengths: male 17-21,5 mm; female 21-22,5 mm.

Early stages. Egg: unrecorded. Larva: final instar off-white with clusters of yellow spots laterally on each segment; prothoracic plate brown; head black with white hairs. Pupa: unrecorded.

Abantis venosa male upperside

89

Abantis venosa final instar larva (Photo: R. Paré)

HABITAT AND ECOLOGY

A. venosa is an inhabitant of open woodland and bushveld country. This species usually skips about slowly unless disturbed, then they display quite a turn of speed. They are occasionally met with feeding at flowers.

The males show hilltopping behaviour and can be encountered on nearly every koppie in the lowveld of Mpumalanga during the summer. The males generally select low branches of trees as perch sites. From here they dart out and chase off intruders. Occasionally they establish territories on the flats or slopes of hills.

The females fly at random through the bush in search of suitable food plants on which to lay. The larval shelter is typical of the group.

This species is on the wing throughout the year.

LARVAL FOOD PLANTS

Pterocarpus rotundifolius, P. brenanii (Papilionoideae).

DISTRIBUTION

South Africa from False Bay in KwaZulu-Natal, through Swaziland and Mpumalanga and Northern Province to Zimbabwe, Moçambique and into East Africa.

CONSERVATION

A. venosa is a widespread species and is under no threat.

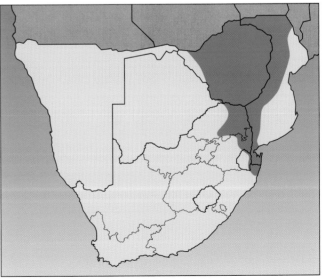

Distribution map of *Abantis venosa*

Genus *Spialia* Swinhoe

Spialia Swinhoe, 1912. *Lepid. Indica* **12** : 99. Type species: *Hesperia galba* Fabricius, 1793, by original designation.

A large genus of small blackish skippers speckled with opaque white spots. Border and cilia of hindwing entire or almost entire. Forewing on both sides with numerous white, not transparent, spots; generally two white dots in discal cell. Cilia white with dark spots at the ends of the veins. The same basic arrangement of spotting occurs in all members of the genus. The species differ from each other in the loss of certain spots and in the size and development. One of the more readily used features to distinguish the species is the shape and extent of the white band on the hindwing, particularly on the underside.

The basic colour and arrangement of spotting is as follows (after De Jong, 1978). In principle, each internervular space has three spots, viz., a basal, median and submarginal spot. In addition, there is a basal cell spot, central cell spot and a discocellular spot covering the discocellular veins. The markings may be very reduced, all basal spots may be absent and there are no submarginal spots in areas R_3 to Sc. In area CuA_2 of the forewing the spots can often be seen divided into an upper and lower part. Moreover, in this area the median spot is double, being divided into an inner and outer spot, which in turn may be divided into an upper and lower part. So there may be four median spots in area CuA_2 of the forewing, the relative development of which is important in the distinction of some species. In *Spialia* one of these spots is always absent.

The markings of the hindwing are simpler than those of the forewing. The median spots on the underside of the hindwing are usually fused together and to the discocellular spot to form a more or less regular band (the median band) parallel to the outer margin. In a few species these spots are separate and in a few others the band is not parallel to the outer margin.

Egg domed with finely sculptured, sometimes sinuate, ribs. The larvae have a stout body, slightly tapering anteriorly, sparsely coated with short fine hairs and a head of moderate size. Head dark with very long setae and dorsally with extremely long, sometimes ribbon-like, setae. Pupae dark greyish brown, anteriorly blunt. Food plants Sterculiaceae, Tiliaceae and Malvaceae.

There are 14 species in Southern Africa, all of which are found in South Africa.

KEY TO THE SPECIES OF *SPIALIA*

1. UFW with central cell spot closer to discocellular spot than to basal cell spot; basal spots in areas R_1 and R_2 usually well developed (lying over the central cell spot); male with costal fold (*asterodia* group) 2

    UFW with central cell spot not closer to discocellular spot than to basal spot, or basal cell spot absent, no spots in area R_1 and R_2 3

2. LHW median band with irregular edges, parallel to the series of basal spots; fringes not conspicuously spotted on underside .... *S. asterodia*

    LHW median band very irregular, along vein CuA_2 pointing basad and reaching series of basal spots; fringes conspicuously chequered black and white on underside .... *S. agylla*

3. Submarginal spots M_1 and M_2 of hindwing not in line with other submarginal spots, being placed more basad; male with costal fold (*colotes* group) 4

    Submarginal spots M_1 and M_2 of hindwing in line with other submarginal spots; male without costal fold 5

4. UHW and LHW with central median band composed of separate spots .... *S. colotes*

    UHW and LHW with central median spots fused into a continuous unbroken band .... *S. confusa*

5. LHW with median spot Rs absent or very small, not connecting the large central spot to one of the spots in Sc+R_1 6

    LHW with median spot Rs present, connecting the central spot (in areas M_1 and M_2) with one of the spots in area Sc+R_1 8

6. LHW with median spots 3A – M_1, basal cell spot and basal spot 3A shining white, median spots 3A and CuA_1 entirely fused, no spot between median and submarginal spots in area 3A (*dromus* group) .... *S. paula*

    LHW with all spots plain white 7

7. UFW with no light spot at base of costa; LHW with a spot between median and submarginal spots in area 3A, inner spot in area Sc+R_1 usually narrow and irregular, submarginal spot 3A double, the upper part out of line, median spot 3A usually not joined to median spot CuA_1 (*sertorius* group) .... *S. mafa*

    UFW usually with a light spot at base of costa; LHW with a spot between median and submarginal spots in area 3A, inner spot in area Sc+R_1 usually large and rounded, submarginal spot 3A usually single, median spot 3A joined to median spot CuA_1 (*spio* group) .... *S. spio*

8. UFW without basal cell spot, at most some white scales forming a small dash against cubitus (*delagoae* group) 9

    UFW with basal spot present in cell 12

9. LHW with basal cell spot; UHW with median spot Rs present 10

    LHW without basal cell spot; UHW with median spot Rs absent or at most vaguely indicated 11

10. LHW with submarginal spots absent; median band slightly winding .... *S. sataspes*

    LHW with submarginal spots present; median band straight. .... *S. depauperata*
    Continued overleaf

KEY TO THE SPECIES OF *SPIALIA*
(continued)

11. LHW with median band winding .... *S. nanus*

    LHW with median band straight .... *S. delagoae*

12. UFW outer median spots in CuA$_2$ forming a bar from vein 1A-2A to vein CuA$_2$; upper inner median spot absent and lower one usually smaller than one of the outer median spots; mid-tibiae spined (*spio* group) .... *S. diomus*

    UFW with lower spot in outer median row of CuA$_2$ absent; lower inner median spot as large as or larger than lower median spot, which may be absent; mid-tibiae without spines, except for the apical pair (as in all other species of the genus) (*dromus* group) 13

13. UHW median spots incomplete, only CuA$_1$ and M$_1$ – M$_2$ present and of the submarginal spots only CuA$_1$ and M$_3$ well-developed, sometimes also M$_2$ and M$_1$ present as vague dots, very rarely a few white scales at place of submarginal spots in CuA$_2$; LHW median band straight, outer margin finely dentate (spots slightly extended towards outer margin along veins) and this margin ground colour darker .... *S. secessus*

    UHW median spots and usually also submarginal spots better developed; LHW median band more or less curved, outer margin not finely dentate nor contrasted by darkening of ground colour .... *S. dromus*

Spialia nanus (Trimen)

DWARF SANDMAN

Pyrgus nanus Trimen, 1889. *S. Afr. Butterfl.* **3** : 290. Type locality: Cape Town. Type in Natural History Museum, London.

IDENTIFICATION

Adult. Male. Without costal fold. Upperside: ground colour blackish-brown with small white spots. Forewing with normal spotting except basal spot and spots in R$_1$ and R$_2$ absent. Hindwing basic spotting except median spot in Rs absent: submarginal spots M$_1$ and M$_2$ in line with other submarginal spots. Underside: ground colour variegated ochre and brown with white spots and patches. Forewing as on upperside. Hindwing with a continuous very winding median band of spots from end of area R$_3$ through a double curve to about middle of distal part of area CuA$_2$; basal cell spot absent. Female. Similar to male but with a stouter abdomen.

Forewing lengths: male 8,5 – 11,5 mm; female 11,5-13 mm.

Early stages. Egg: creamy-white at first, changing to pale green;

Spialia nanus male underside

diameter 0,7 mm, height 0,5 mm; with 17 to 21 heavy irregular longitudinal ribs, only some 5 of which reach the micropyle, and 16 to 18 very thin cross-ribs. Larva: First instar white with a black head. Second and subsequent instars pale green. Final instar slightly more yellowish with a black white-haired head. It attains a length of some 17 mm. Pupa: 11 mm long; white in colour and covered with white powder (Clark, 1978 : 226).

HABITAT AND ECOLOGY

S. nanus is an inhabitant of karoid type vegetation, however it extends into the Western Cape. It can be found on the flats, among the Karoo bushes, along the slopes of hills and mountains, settling here and there on the ground or feeding at flowers. Its flight is rather rapid and close to the ground.

The males establish territories on the flats or hillsides. They settle on the ground or on stones, flying up and chasing off any intruders that encroach on their territories. They occasionally flit around their territories before settling again.

The females can be encountered anywhere in the area searching for suitable plants on which to lay. Eggs are laid singly among young buds on the food plant. The eggs take some 12 days to hatch. The young larvae at first shelter in a partly open, very young leaf, and feed on the inner surface. Later they construct a shelter by binding leaves together. In this they live, moult and pupate. The larval stages last some 57-65 days. The final instar shelter is usually near the ground and it is in here that the larva finally pupates. The pupal stage lasts some 12 days (Clark, 1978 : 226).

The butterfly is on the wing from August to April, the heaviest emergence being in September to October and March to April.

LARVAL FOOD PLANTS

Hermannia diffusa., H. incana, H. comosa, H. cuneifolia and *H. pulverata* (Sterculiaceae); *Hibiscus aethiopicus* (Malvaceae).

DISTRIBUTION

South Africa from the Western Cape, western portions of the Eastern Cape, large areas of the Karoo, northwards into the Northern Cape, Free State and southern Namibia.

CONSERVATION

This is a widespread species and is under no threat.

Spialia nanus final instar larva (Photo: A.J.M. Claassens)

Spialia nanus pupa (After G.C. Clark 1978)

Spialia nanus male upperside

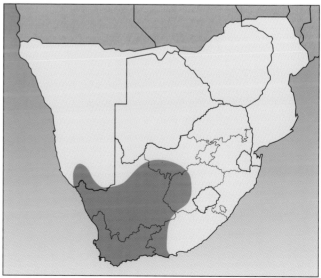

Distribution map of *Spialia nanus*

Spialia delagoae (Trimen)

DELAGOA SANDMAN

Pyrgus delagoae Trimen, 1898. *Trans. R. ent. Soc. Lond.* **1898** : 15. Type locality: Delagoa Bay, Moçambique. Type in the South African Museum, Cape Town.

IDENTIFICATION

Adult. Easily identified by its straight, light hindwing underside median band. Male. Upperside: ground colour blackish-brown with small white spots. Forewing normal spotting without a basal cell spot and no spots in R_1 and R_2. Hindwing submarginal spots in M_1 and M_2 in line with other submarginal spots, median spot in Rs absent. Underside: ground colour variegated ochre and brown with white spots and patches. Hindwing with basal cell spot absent, median band straight. Female. Similar to male but larger with rounder wings.

Forewing lengths: male 9,9 – 11,6 mm. female 11,5-13,5 mm.

Early stages. Unrecorded.

HABITAT AND ECOLOGY

S. delagoae is an inhabitant of bushveld areas. It usually flies close to the ground in short grass. Specimens can occasionally be observed feeding at flowers, or sucking at mud along a stream. Swanepoel (1953) records it feeding from fresh baboon dung littering the road.

The males show hilltopping behaviour although they are seldom found on the actual peak of a hill, ridge or koppie. They usually settle on the ground or a stone from which they chase off intruders from their territory.

The female is scarcer but frequents the same places as the male where she flies at random in search of food plants.

The species is on the wing throughout the year in more northern areas but in South Africa it is most abundant in February-March and August-September.

Spialia delagoae male upperside

LARVAL FOOD PLANTS

Unrecorded.

DISTRIBUTION

South Africa in the North-West Province, Northern Province and Mpumalanga, KwaZulu-Natal, northwards into Namibia, Botswana, Zimbabwe, Swaziland and Moçambique. It also occurs in Angola, Zambia, Kenya and Uganda.

CONSERVATION

S. delagoae is a fairly common widely spread species and is under no threat.

Spialia delagoae male underside

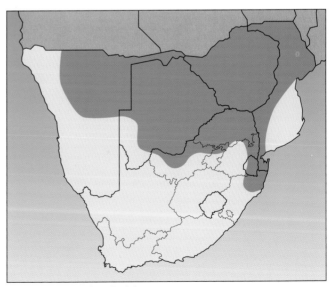

Distribution map of *Spialia delagoae*

Spialia sataspes (Trimen)

BOLAND SANDMAN

Pyrgus sataspes Trimen, 1864. *Trans. ent. Soc. Lond.* (3) **2** : 178. Type locality: Plettenberg Bay, Western Cape Province. Type in Natural History Museum, London.

IDENTIFICATION

Adult. The main differentiating character is the absence of sub-marginal spots on the underside of the hindwing. Male. Upperside: ground colour blackish-brown with basic white spots except for: forewing basal cell spot and spots in areas R_1 and R_2 which are absent. Hindwing with submarginal spots M_1 and M_2 in line with submarginal spots; median spot Rs present. Underside: ground colour variegated ochre and brown with white spots and patches. Forewing with white spotting as on upperside. Hindwing ground colour tawny with a yellowish-white median band with a straight distal edge; basal cell spot present, submarginal spots absent. Costal fold absent. Female. Similar to male but larger with rounder wings.

Forewing lengths: male 10-12,5 mm; female 12-13,5 mm.

Early stages. Egg: whitish; diameter 0,75 mm, height 0,55 mm; with 20 heavy, irregular, longitudinal ribs only some 6 to 7 of which reach the micropyle; there are some 25 very thin cross-ribs. Larva: First instar greenish-white with a black head; instars 2 to 4 more green; final instar greenish-white with reddish-brown and white prothoracic shield and a black head with white setae. It attains a length of some 18 mm. Pupa: 11 mm long; greenish-grey in colour (Clark, 1978 : 228).

HABITAT AND ECOLOGY

S. sataspes appears to be confined to the coastal or near coastal areas of the Western and Eastern Cape Provinces where it inhabits mainly open grassy areas. The species does not appear to penetrate the drier areas of the Karoo. It is usually found along the slopes – particularly the lower – of mountains and only occasionally on the flats. They may also inhabit some of the highest parts of the mountains but do not show hilltopping behaviour. They are readily attracted to flowers and are often encountered feeding on them.

The males usually establish territories on the slopes where they appear to prefer to perch on stems of grass and low shrubs rather than on the ground. They flit about their particular areas for hours on end, venturing every now and then to those of their neighbours, which leads to them being chased back by the resident male. In some places the territories are far apart, in others as many as six may occupy an area not larger than 30 square metres.

The female lays the eggs singly and conceals them in young shoots. The eggs take some 11 days to hatch. The young larvae feed on the surface of very young, half-opened leaves. Later, they bind more mature leaves together to form a shelter, and feed on the surface of the leaf within this shelter, but they may crawl out and feed on adjacent leaves. Moulting and pupation take place within these

Spialia sataspes male underside

Spialia sataspes male upperside

shelters. The larval stage lasts some 53 days. The pupal shelter is generally made of dry leaves near the ground. The pupal stage lasts 16-20 days (Clark, 1978 : 228).

This species is on the wing from September to March.

LARVAL FOOD PLANTS

Hermannia spp. (Sterculiaceae); *Pavonia burchellii* and *Hibiscus aethiopicus* (Malvaceae).

DISTRIBUTION

South Africa, being confined to the Western, Northern and Eastern Cape Provinces, from the Cape Peninsula to Grahamstown.

CONSERVATION

Although rather restricted in distribution, *S. sataspes* does not appear to be under any threat.

Spialia sataspes final instar larva (After G.C. Clark 1978)

Spialia sataspes pupa (After G.C. Clark 1978)

Spialia depauperata (Strand)

WANDERING SANDMAN

Hesperia ferax var. *depauperata* Strand, 1911. *Mitt. zool. Mus. Berl.* **5** (2) : 304.

There are two subspecies, only one of which is found in Southern Africa. The nominate subspecies occurs in East Africa.

Spialia depauperata australis De Jong

Spialia depauperata australis De Jong, 1978. *Tijdschr. Ent.* **121** : 105. Type locality: Muden, KwaZulu-Natal. Type in Natural History Museum, London.

IDENTIFICATION

Adult. Male. Upperside: ground colour blackish-brown with medium-sized white spots. Forewing with basic spotting, except for basal cell spot and spots in areas R_1 and R_2 which are absent. Hindwing with submarginal spots M_1 and M_2 in line with other submarginal spots, median spot Rs present. Underside: ground colour greyish-brown with white spots and patches. Forewing with white spotting as on upperside. Hindwing with a broadish straight white median band tapering from costa posteriorly; basal cell spot and submarginal line present. Costal fold absent. Female. Similar to male but larger with rounder wings.

Forewing lengths: male 10,8-12,9 mm; female 14,5-15,3 mm.

Early stages. Unrecorded.

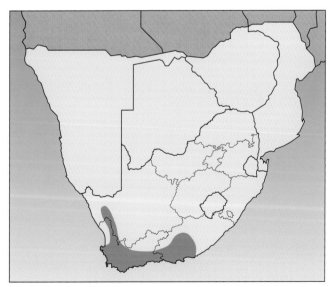

Distribution map of *Spialia sataspes*

Spialia depauperata australis male upperside

HABITAT AND ECOLOGY

S. depauperata australis is an inhabitant of open montane habitats and bushveld areas. It flies low among the grass on grassy hillsides and *Acacia* thorn trees. The species is often found feeding at flowers or sucking at muddy patches.

The males do not show hilltopping behaviour and establish territories in the vicinity of their food plants. They usually select a spot on the ground from which they dart off every now and then to chase off intruders.

The female frequents the same places as the male but flies at random, searching for suitable food plants on which to lay.

This species is on the wing from August to April.

LARVAL FOOD PLANTS

Melhania sp. (Sterculiaceae).

DISTRIBUTION

South Africa from KwaZulu-Natal and the Northern Province and Mpumalanga, Swaziland, Botswana, northwards into Zimbabwe and Moçambique.

CONSERVATION

S. depauperata australis is a relatively widespread species and is under no threat.

Spialia depauperata australis male underside

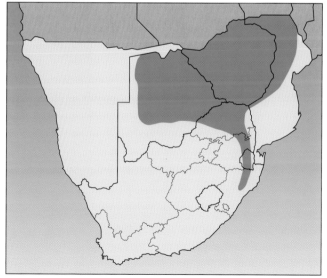

Distribution map of *Spialia depauperata*

Spialia asterodia (Trimen)

ASTERODIA SANDMAN

Pyrgus asterodia Trimen, 1864. *Trans. ent. Soc. Lond.* (3)
2 : 178. Type locality: Plettenberg Bay, Western Cape
Province. Type in the Natural History Museum, London.

IDENTIFICATION

Adult. Male. Upperside: ground colour blackish-brown with medium-sized white spotting. Forewing with central cell spot closer to discocellular spot than to basal spot; basal spots in areas R_1 and R_2 fairly well developed. Hindwing with median band broadest in Rs to M_3. Underside: median band with irregular edges parallel to the series of basal spots. Fringes not conspicuously spotted on underside. Costal fold present. Female. Similar to male but larger with rounder wings.

Forewing lengths: male 9,8-12,5 mm; female 12,8-14 mm.

Early stages. Egg: pale blue-green; diameter 0,6 mm, height 0,5 mm; with fine white ribbing consisting of 18-20 longitudinal ribs, only 8 or 9 of which reach the micropyle; these are crossed by 20-23 fine ribs. Larva: first three instars greenish-white with a black head; fourth instar reddish-brown; final (fifth) instar greyish-brown with a reddish-brown prothoracic shield, head black and hairy. It attains a length of 17 mm. Pupa: 13 mm long; greyish-green in colour (Clark, 1978 : 230).

Spialia asterodia male upperside

joining leaves together. With increased growth large shelters are constructed, the last generally near the ground. The larval stage lasts some 86 days. Moulting and pupation take place within these shelters. The species usually hibernates during the pupal period, which sometimes occurs among dead leaves joined together near the roots of the plant. If no hibernation takes place the pupal stage lasts about 20 days. The species is occasionally parasitised in the larval stage by flies belonging to the Tachinidae (Clark, 1978 : 230).

This species is on the wing from August to March.

HABITAT AND ECOLOGY

S. asterodia is generally an inhabitant of grassy hillsides, and often occurs at considerable altitudes ascending the Drakensberg to a height of more than 3000 metres. It is seldom seen in the bushveld or in the Karoo. It is particularly fond of flowers and is often encountered feeding at them. It seldom visits muddy places.

On hot sunny days the males occasionally show hilltopping behaviour although they more often establish territories on the slopes. The males select a spot on the ground from which they dart off to chase away any intruders. The same specimens have been observed to frequent the same territory for hours or even days.

The females are scarcer than the males and frequent the same places in search of food plants. Eggs are laid singly among young leaf buds. The eggs hatch after some 11 days. On emergence the young larva starts feeding on the inner surface of a very young, still folded leaf. It later constructs a shelter by

Spialia asterodia male underside

LARVAL FOOD PLANTS

Hermannia diffusa, H. incana (Sterculiaceae); *Pavonia burchellii* and *Hibiscus* sp. (Malvaceae).

DISTRIBUTION

South Africa, from the Western, Northern and Eastern Cape Provinces, into KwaZulu-Natal, Free State, North-West Province, Gauteng, Northern Province and Mpumalanga, Lesotho, Swaziland and northwards into Moçambique and Zimbabwe.

CONSERVATION

S. asterodia is a widespread species and is under no threat.

Spialia asterodia final instar larva (After G.C. Clark 1978)

Spialia asterodia pupa (After G.C. Clark 1978)

Spialia agylla (Trimen)

GRASSVELD SANDMAN

Pyrgus agylla Trimen, 1889. *S. Afr. Butterfl.* **3** : 286.

There are two subspecies in Southern Africa, both of which occur in South Africa.

Spialia agylla agylla (Trimen)

Pyrgus agylla Trimen, 1889. *S. Afr. Butterfl.* **3** : 286. Type locality: Griqualand West, between Modder River and Riet River. Holotype male in Natural History Museum, London.

IDENTIFICATION

Adult. Male. Upperside: ground colour blackish-brown with large white spotting. Forewing with central cell spot closer to discocellular spot than to basal spot; basal spots in areas R_1 and R_2 well developed. Hindwing with irregular median band. Underside: hindwing with median band very irregular, along vein CuA_2 pointing basad and reaching series of basal spots; fringes conspicuously chequered black and white. Female. Similar to male but slightly larger with rounder wings.

Forewing lengths: male 9,2-10,5 mm; female 10,5-11,8 mm.

DISTRIBUTION

South Africa, from the Western, Eastern and Northern Cape, North-West Province, Gauteng, Free State, Mpumalanga, and Lesotho and Botswana.

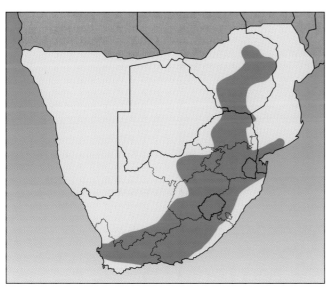

Distribution map of *Spialia asterodia*

Spialia agylla agylla male upperside

Spialia agylla bamptoni Vári

Spialia agylla bamptoni Vári, 1976. *Ann. Transv. Mus.* **30** : 123-124. Type locality: Hondeklipbaai, Namaqualand. Holotype male in the Transvaal Museum, Pretoria.

IDENTIFICATION

Adult. Male. Upperside: and underside with spots larger and more whitish than in nominate subspecies. Hindwing underside ground colour also more whitish in the subbasal and submarginal areas. It is also slightly smaller than subspecies *agylla*. Female. Similar to male, but with rounder wings.

Forewing lengths: male 9-10 mm; female 10,5-11 mm.

Early stages. Egg: pale greenish-blue with white ribbing. Larva: first instar pale greenish-white; final instar greyish-brown with a black head. It attains a length of approximately 18 mm. Pupa: 9-12 mm; greyish-brown in colour.

DISTRIBUTION

South Africa, from Namaqualand in the Western and Northern Cape Provinces.

HABITAT AND ECOLOGY

Nominate *S. agylla* inhabits the grassveld of Southern Africa. It may be encountered on mountains, their slopes, in valleys or on the grassy plains. The subspecies *bamptoni*, however, is found in Namaqualand at sea level in the sandveld. It is frequently observed feeding at flowers. It has the same rapid flight as other species of the genus, with frequent rests on the ground.

The males do not show hilltopping behaviour and establish their territories among the food plants frequented by the females. They settle on the ground or stones, flying up and chasing off any intruders that might encroach their territory.

The females can usually be encountered near their food plants in search of suitable positions to lay their eggs. They lay their eggs singly among young buds on the food plant. The eggs take some 11 days to hatch. The young larva at first shelters in a partly open, young leaf, and feeds on the inner surface. The larva later constructs a shelter by partially binding leaves together with silk. The final larval shelter is usually near the ground and the larva finally pupates in here.

This species is on the wing from August to April.

LARVAL FOOD PLANTS

An unidentified species of *Hermannia* (Sterculiaceae) and *Pavonia burchellii* (Malvaceae).

CONSERVATION

Spialia agylla is fairly widespread and is under no threat.

Spialia agylla agylla male underside

Spialia agylla bamptoni male upperside

Spialia agylla bamptoni male underside

Spialia agylla bamptoni pupa (Photo: H. Wykeham)

Spialia agylla bamptoni final instar larva (Photo: H. Wykeham)

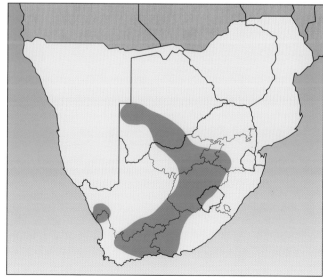

Distribution map of *Spialia agylla*

101

Spialia colotes (Druce)

BUSHVELD SANDMAN

Pyrgus colotes Druce, 1875. *Proc. zool Soc. Lond.* **1875**: 416.

There are three subspecies of which only one occurs in Southern Africa. The nominate subspecies comes from Angola. The subspecies *semiconfluens* De Jong, 1978, comes from Aden, Ethiopia and Somalia and southwards into Kenya.

Spialia colotes transvaaliae male upperside

Spialia colotes transvaaliae (Trimen)

Pyrgus transvaaliae Trimen, 1889. *S. Afr. Butterfl.* **3**: 286. Type locality: Transvaal. Holotype male in Natural History Museum, London.

IDENTIFICATION

Adult. Male. Upperside: ground colour blackish-brown with medium-sized white spotting. Forewing with central cell spot not closer to discocellular spot than to basal spot; no spots in areas R_1 and R_2; inner median spots in CuA_2 fused into a single spot that is often the largest spot on the forewing. Hindwing with submarginal spots M_1 and M_2 not in line with other submarginal spots, being placed more basad; median band of white spots extended across most of the wing. Underside: with lighter markings similar to upperside. Hindwing with median band of well separated spots. Costal fold present. Female. Similar to male but larger with slightly rounder wings.

Forewing lengths: male 9,6-11,9 mm; female 12,8-13,6 mm.

Early stages. Unrecorded.

Spialia colotes transvaaliae male underside

HABITAT AND ECOLOGY

This species is an inhabitant of dry bushveld, woodlands and savannah. It flies near the ground, and is often encountered resting on low shrubs in the shade of trees, or feeding at flowers, especially along roads.

The males do not exhibit hilltopping behaviour and select territories in more low-lying places at the foot of mountains or hills or about the bush in flat country. They usually establish their territories near thorn trees, perching often on low shrubs in the shade of trees or on the ground. From their perches they dart out and chase off intruders.

The females frequent the same places as the males where they fly at random in search of suitable food plants.

The species is on the wing from December to May, being most numerous from February to April.

LARVAL FOOD PLANTS

Hibiscus fuscus (Malvaceae).

DISTRIBUTION

South Africa, from the North-West Province, Mpumalanga and Northern Province and Swaziland to Botswana, Namibia, Zimbabwe, Moçambique, Tanzania, Kenya and Uganda.

CONSERVATION

S. colotes transvaaliae is a widespread species and is under no threat.

Spialia confusa (Higgins)

CONFUSING SANDMAN

Hesperia transvaaliae var. *confusa* Higgins, 1925. *Trans. R. ent. Soc. Lond.* **1925**: 90.

There are two subspecies of which only the nominate occurs in Southern Africa. The subspecies *obscura* occurs in Kenya and Tanzania.

Spialia confusa confusa (Higgins)

Hesperia transvaaliae var. *confusa* Higgins, 1925. *Trans. R. ent. Soc. Lond.* **1925**: 90. Type locality: S.W. shore of Lake Nyasa, between Ft. Johnston and Monkey Bay, Malawi. Holotype female in Natural History Museum, London.

IDENTIFICATION

Adult. Male. Readily distinguished from all *Spialia* species, other than *colotes*, by the basad shift of the submarginal spots M_1 and M_2 of the hindwing. Upperside: blackish-brown with medium-sized white spotting. Forewing with central cell spot not closer to discocellular spot than to basal spot; no spots in areas R_1 and R_2. Differs from *S. colotes* in having the median spots of hindwing fused into a short continuous band. Underside: hindwing with continuous unbroken central band extended right across the wing. Female. Similar to male, but with a more rounded wing shape.

Forewing length: male 9-11 mm; female 11-12 mm.

Early stages. Unrecorded.

Distribution map of *Spialia colotes*

Spialia confusa confusa male underside

103

HABITAT AND ECOLOGY

S. confusa is very local and confined to thick coastal bush and forest from sea-level to 500 m. Pennington (1994) recorded a male on the top of a koppie in Swaziland and other records from neighbouring territories record it on the slopes of hills. Most South African records, however, record it on the flat areas between False Bay and the Makhathini Flats. It has a very fast low buzzing flight, settling frequently. The small size and swift flight render this species difficult to follow when it flies in the shade amongst the bushes. At times it can be observed feeding at flowers.

The males do not appear to show hilltop-ping behaviour in their normal habitats. They are to be found flying around sandy patches between the thick bush, or on paths or roads. They settle frequently on grass, small bushes or on the ground. The males select territories a couple of metres across, usually at a conspicuous spot such as a large sandy patch or where the road or path enters the thick bush. Here they buzz about during the warmer hours of the day, either basking in the sun or investigating intruders. The various territories in an area are usually situated far apart, often on different paths or separated by large patches of thick bush. Favourite territories are used continuously over a number of years by successive generations.

The females frequent the same places as the male where they fly at random in search of suitable food plants.

This species is on the wing throughout the year.

LARVAL FOOD PLANTS

The food plant in South Africa is not known but in East Africa it has been recorded breeding on *Melhania* sp. (Sterculiaceae) and *Triumfetta* sp. (Tiliaceae).

DISTRIBUTION

South Africa, from northern KwaZulu-Natal and records from above Waterval Onder and Barberton in Mpumalanga and from Messina in the Northern Province; it also occurs in Swaziland, Moçambique, Zimbabwe and northwards into Zambia, Malawi and Tanzania.

CONSERVATION

The few remaining patches of bush in South Africa which are inhabited by this species have fairly robust populations. The destruction of much of the thick bush in northern KwaZulu-Natal for farming, and the ongoing chopping of bush for firewood is always an imminent danger. These scattered patches of suitable bush may be only a few hectares in extent so that even small farming activi-

Spialia confusa confusa male upperside

ties can lead to some of these localities being destroyed. *S. confusa* has apparently not been recorded in any of the northern KwaZulu-Natal reserves. It could possibly be found in the False Bay Reserve and steps should be taken to ascertain whether this is so. Failing the finding of this species in this or any other reserve the conservation bodies in KwaZulu-Natal should be contacted and shown existing colonies with the objective that some habitat conservation measures be adopted.

S. confusa is considered by S.F. & G.A. Henning in the *South African Red Data Book – Butterflies* (1989) to be rare. Although a rare marginal species in South Africa it is widely distributed when considering Africa as a whole. Taking this into consideration *S. confusa* is not threatened as a species.

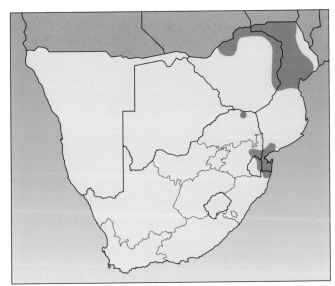

Distribution map of *Spialia confusa*

Spialia mafa (Trimen)

MAFA SANDMAN

Pyrgus mafa Trimen, 1870. *Trans. ent. Soc. Lond.* **1870**: 386.

There are two subspecies in Africa of which only the nominate is found in Southern Africa. The subspecies *higginsi* Evans (1937: 62) occurs in the central and northern part of Africa from Malawi, Tanzania, Zaire right through to southern Arabia.

Spialia mafa mafa male underside

Spialia mafa mafa (Trimen)

Pyrgus mafa Trimen, 1870. *Trans. ent. Soc. Lond.* **1870**: 386. Type locality: Maseru, Basutoland (Lesotho). Holotype male in Natural History Museum, London.

IDENTIFICATION

Adult. Male. Upperside: blackish-brown with small pale spots. Forewing with basal spot below cell absent. Hindwing with a small-ish central patch. Underside: hindwing with a spot between median and submarginal spots in area 3A; inner spot in area Sc+R_1 usually narrow and irregular, submarginal spot in 3A double, the upper part out of line; median spot in 3A usually not joined to median spot in CuA_1. Female. Similar to male, but with a stouter abdomen.

Forewing lengths: male 9,9-11,7 mm; female 10,2-12,5 mm.

Early stages. Egg: pale green with white ribbing; diameter 0,65 mm, height 0,6 mm; with 16 longitudinal ribs and 18 to 20 cross ribs. Larva: first instar greyish-green and white with a black head; second instar white; third and fourth instars basically green with some white scaling; fifth (final) instar greyish-green with white marking, a brown and white prothoracic shield and a brown hairy head. The larva attains a length of some 21 mm. Pupa: 12 mm long; greyish-green in colour, covered with a white chalky powder (Clark, 1978: 238).

HABITAT AND ECOLOGY

S. mafa is a localised species scattered over most of Southern Africa. It appears to prefer the open savannah, largely avoiding low-lying areas, being found mainly in hilly or mountainous regions. On the Western Cape coast it is usually found in coastal dune country, flying near the ground in short grass. The species is frequently attracted to flowers.

The males do not appear to show hilltopping behaviour, usually establishing their territories on the slopes or flats wherever the food plants are to be found. They select a small area as their territory, usually perching on a low plant, stone or the ground. From here they dart off and chase away any intruders.

The females frequent the same localities as the males, flitting near the ground in search of food plants. Eggs are laid singly on young buds. The eggs hatch after some 8 days. On emergence the young larva crawls into a half-open young leaf and feeds on the inner surface. Later it constructs a shelter by binding leaves together. At first the larva feeds on the surface of the leaf but may crawl out to feed on adjoining leaves. As it grows, it has to construct larger shelters and the last one is close to the ground. The larval stage lasts 51-68 days. Moulting and pupation takes place in these shelters. The pupal stage lasts 18-25 days. The larvae are parasitised by flies (Diptera) belonging to the family Tachinidae (Clark, 1978: 238).

This species is on the wing practically all the year in the warmest localities, but elsewhere from September to April.

LARVAL FOOD PLANTS

Hermannia depressa (Sterculiaceae); *Hibiscus aethiopicus and Pavonia* sp. (Malvaceae).

DISTRIBUTION

Throughout South Africa, Lesotho, Swaziland, Moçambique, Zimbabwe, Botswana, Namibia and into Zambia, Malawi and southern Zaire.

CONSERVATION

S. mafa is a local but widespread species and is under no threat.

Spialia mafa mafa final instar larva (After G.C. Clark 1978)

Spialia mafa mafa pupa (After G.C. Clark 1978)

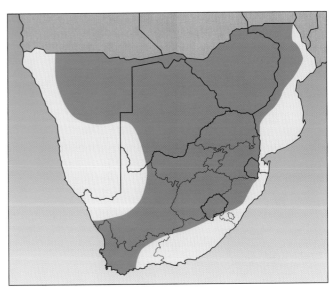

Spialia mafa mafa male upperside

Distribution map of *Spialia mafa*

Spialia paula (Higgins)

MITE SANDMAN

Hesperia paula Higgins, 1925. *Trans. R. ent. Soc. Lond.* **1925**: 77. Type locality: Bulawayo, Zimbabwe. Holotype male in Natural History Museum, London.

IDENTIFICATION

Adult. Male. Upperside: brownish-black with small white spots. Hindwing spots M_1 and M_2 in line with other submarginal spots. Underside: variegated ochre and brown with white spots and patches. Hindwing with median spots 3A to M_1, basal cell spot and basal spot in 3A shining white, median spots 3A and CuA_1 entirely fused, no spot between median and submarginal spots in area 3A; median spot in Rs absent. Female. Similar to the male, but with a stouter abdomen. The small size and shiny white patch on the hindwing underside readily distinguish *S. paula*.

Forewing lengths: male 10-12 mm; female 11-13 mm.

Early stages. Unrecorded.

HABITAT AND ECOLOGY

S. paula is an inhabitant of bushveld or savannah. Usually occurring on slopes of hills where it flies about at speed. Its small size renders it difficult to observe as it flies rapidly about in the grass. It is often observed feeding at flowers.

The males show hilltopping behaviour when the weather is hot and sunny and a slight wind is blowing. They are seldom found on the actual peak of a hill, ridge or koppie. They usually select any spot along the highest parts of the hills some distance from places where other larger butterflies are hilltopping. When two or more males are on the same hill each one has its own territory to which he constantly returns, often chasing intruders away. The territory usually consists of a small patch of gravel.

The females fly at random but often appear in the territories of males where they may rest on the ground for short in-

Spialia paula male underside

Spialia paula male upperside

107

tervals or feed at flowers. Most of the time however they search for suitable food plants on which to lay their eggs.

This species is on the wing from August to April, the best months for observation being from August to October.

LARVAL FOOD PLANTS

Unrecorded.

DISTRIBUTION

South Africa, from the Northern Cape, North-West Province, Free State and the Northern Province; then into eastern Botswana and Zimbabwe.

CONSERVATION

This rare little species is more plentiful in Zimbabwe than in South Africa, but is still a scarce insect. Most of the recorded localities are far from industrial or urban development, although agricultural and mining activities are possible threats. At this time however, there appears to be no danger. The species is also fairly widely distributed. It was included in the *South African Red Data Book – Butterflies* (1989) as indeterminate.

Spialia secessus (Trimen)

WOLKBERG SANDMAN

Pyrgus secessus Trimen, 1891. *Proc. zool. Soc. Lond.* **1891**: 102. Type locality: Damaraland (Omrora), Namibia. Holotype male in the South African Museum, Cape Town.

IDENTIFICATION

Adult. Rather similar to *S. depauperata*. Male. Upperside: ground colour blackish-brown; forewing with basal spot present in cell, lower spot in outer median row of CuA_2 absent. Hindwing with median spots incomplete, only CuA_1 and M_1 and M_2 present and of the sub-marginal spots only CuA_1 and M_3 well developed. Underside: with hindwing median band brown, straight and of even width through-out, with the outer margins finely denticulate; this denticulation is accentuated by darkening of the ground colour along the outer margin of the band. Female. Similar to male but larger with rounder wings.

The wet-season form *trimeni* Aurivillius (1925, in Seitz *Macrolep. of World* **13**: 564. Type locality: Rhodesia [Zimbabwe]) differs from the nominate dry form in having the hindwing underside median band white or cream-coloured.

Forewing lengths: male 12,8-13,6 mm; female 13,2-14 mm.

Early stages. Unrecorded.

HABITAT AND ECOLOGY

S. secessus is mainly an inhabitant of grassy montane regions. It is a local species, being a lover of the grassy slopes where it can be observed skipping or zig-zagging slowly near the ground and resting every few metres. It is readily attracted to flowers and during Sep-

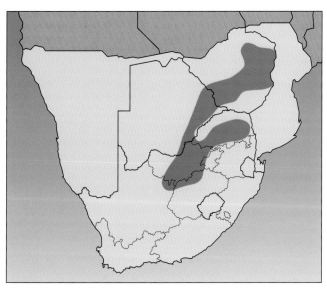

Distribution map of *Spialia paula*

Spialia secessus female underside

tember on the farm Helpmekaar near Munnik, Northern Province, the variety of veld flowers along the railway line attracts large numbers of *S. secessus* at times (Swanepoel, 1953).

The males show hilltopping behaviour, ascending usually to grassy peaks on hot sunny days, mainly between 11:00 and 14:00. They can be observed skipping around the dry grass in their territories, resting every few metres on the ground, usually with their wings half opened to the sun. From their perch on the ground they dart off to chase passing butterflies. The males occupy their territories for quite a few hours at a time.

The females frequent the same places as the males where they fly in search of suitable food plants.

The species is on the wing from July to March in South Africa, throughout the year further north.

LARVAL FOOD PLANTS

Unrecorded.

DISTRIBUTION

South Africa, from KwaZulu-Natal and Mpumalanga and Northern Province, Swaziland, northwards into Zimbabwe, possibly also adjacent areas of northern Namibia and Botswana, Angola, Zambia, southern Zaire and western Tanzania.

CONSERVATION

S. secessus is a widely distributed species and is under no threat.

Spialia secessus female upperside

Spialia secessus form *trimeni* male underside

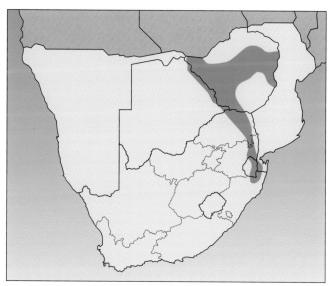

Distribution map of *Spialia secessus*

Spialia secessus form *trimeni* male upperside

109

Spialia dromus (Plötz)

FOREST SANDMAN

Pyrgus dromus Plötz, 1884. *Mitt. nat. Ver. Greifsw.* **45**: 6. Type locality: Congo. Type(s) lost.

IDENTIFICATION

Adult. Male. Upperside: blackish-brown with white spotting. Forewing basal spot clearly defined; central cell spot midway between basal cell spot and discocellular spot; inner median spots in CuA_2 present, forming a bar from vein CuA_2 to 1A+2A. Hindwing with a kidney-shaped white central patch and well developed submarginal spots. Underside: hindwing yellowish-ochreous with a complete but irregular white median band from vein 1A+2A to costa, sharply bent basad in area CuA_1; an incomplete white band and dark spots nearer the base and a submarginal row of white dots. Female. Similar to male but larger with rounder wings.

Forewing lengths: male 11-14 mm; female 14,2-15,6 mm.

Early stages. Egg: whitish-green, changing to dirty white; diameter 0,8 mm, height 0,7 mm; with 20 longitudinal ribs which break up towards the crown and only some seven very disjointed pieces of which reach the micropyle; cross-bracing about 20 distinct ribs. Larva: first instar greenish-white with a black head; second instar green, while the third and fourth are greenish-white; the fifth (final) instar is olive-green with a black prothoracic shield and black hairy head. The larva attains a length of 20 mm; Pupa: 12,5 mm long; greenish white, speckled with black (Clark, 1978: 232).

HABITAT AND ECOLOGY

S. dromus is an inhabitant of woodland, forest margins and open clearings in forest. It is occasionally found in grassveld areas of Gauteng and in the drier thorn country of Mpumalanga and Northern Province and KwaZulu-Natal. However its true habitat is forest along the KwaZulu-Natal coast and along the eastern slopes of the Wolkberg in the Northern Province. It can normally be observed skipping or zig-zagging slowly near the ground and resting every few metres. It is readily attracted to flowers and it often frequents muddy places along streams.

The males occasionally show hilltopping behaviour. However, they usually establish their territories on the slopes and flats near the food plants. They skip slowly around their territories, resting at intervals on the ground with their wings half-opened in the sun or perching on low shrubs. From their perches they dart out and chase off passing butterflies.

Spialia dromus male underside

The females frequent the same spots as the males but fly at random searching for suitable food plants on which to lay eggs. They lay their eggs singly among young shoots. The eggs take some 7 days to hatch. The young larva hides in the fold of a young half-opened leaf and feeds on the inner surface. Later it binds leaves together to form a shelter in which it lives. It feeds on the surface of the leaf or crawls out to feed on adjacent leaves where it generally eats the edges. Moulting and pupation take place within the shelter. By the time the larva is ready for pupation, after some 44 days, this shelter is generally situated near the ground. The pupal stage lasts some 18 days. The larvae are attacked by parasitic flies (Diptera). The fly maggot emerges from the side of the larva or pupa and pupates within the shelter or among debris on the ground below the plant (Clark, 1978: 232).

This species is on the wing throughout the year.

LARVAL FOOD PLANTS

Triumfetta tomentosa and *T. rhomboidea* (Tiliaceae); *Melhania* sp., and *Waltheria* sp. (Sterculiaceae).

DISTRIBUTION

South Africa, from the Eastern Cape, KwaZulu-Natal, North-West Province, Gauteng, Mpumalanga and Northern Province to Swaziland, Zimbabwe, Moçambique and northwards across tropical Africa to Ethiopia and Senegal.

CONSERVATION

S. dromus is a widespread species and is under no threat.

Spialia dromus final instar larva (After G.C. Clark 1978)

Spialia dromus pupa (After G.C. Clark 1978)

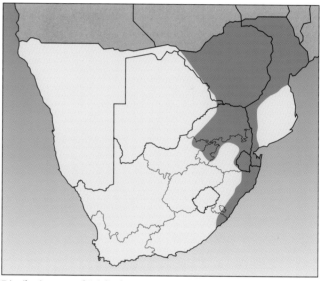

Distribution map of *Spialia dromus*

Spialia dromus male upperside

Spialia diomus (Hopffer)

COMMON SANDMAN

Pyrgus diomus Hopffer, 1855. *Mber. dt. Akad. Wiss. Berl.* **1855**: 643.

There are two subspecies in Africa of which only one, *ferax*, occurs in South Africa. The nominate subspecies occurs in Zambia, northern Moçambique, northwards and westwards through Tanzania to West Africa, Ethiopia and Yemen.

Spialia diomus ferax male underside

Spialia diomus ferax (Wallengren)

Syrichtus ferax Wallengren, 1863. *Wien. ent. Mschr.* **7**: 137. Type locality: Kuisip (Kuiseb) River, Namibia. Holotype male in the Naturhistoriska Riksmuseet, Stockholm.

IDENTIFICATION

Adult. Male. Upperside: blackish-brown with white spots. Forewing with basal spot present in cell; outer median spots in CuA_2 are both present, forming a bar extending from vein 1A+2A to vein CuA_2; upper inner median spot absent and lower one usually smaller than one of the outer median spots. Underside: hindwing with straight median band entire, not broken in area R_5; submarginal spots conjoined into a continuous line merged to the white marginal area. Female. Similar to the male but larger with rounder wings.

Forewing lengths: male 13,2-14,8 mm; female 13,5-15,4 mm.

Early stages. Egg: pale bluish-green; diameter 0,75 mm, height 0,7 mm; with some 16 longitudinal ribs, cross-braced by about 18 very fine ribs. Larva: first to fourth instars greyish-green with a black head; fifth (final) instar greyish-green with an orange-brown prothoracic shield surrounded posteriorly by black and white; head black with long hairs. The larva attains a length of 22 mm. Pupa: 13,5 mm long; pale brown with a white powdery substance all over the surface giving it a white appearance (Clark, 1978: 234).

Spialia diomus ferax male upperside

HABITAT AND ECOLOGY

S. diomus ferax is an inhabitant of wood-land, savannah and open montane habitats, in fact almost anywhere in South Africa. It is perhaps scarcer in the Karoo, and finds the grass and bushveld more to its liking. Its flight is rather rapid and close to the ground. It is readily attracted to flowers and may frequently be seen on them.

The males show hilltopping behaviour on hot sunny days. They usually arrive on the peaks by 11:00, sometimes earlier, depending on the heat. Here they select a territory, usually settling on the ground with their wings half-opened to the sun. From here they dart off every now and again to chase off intruding butterflies. They have even been observed chasing a *Papilio demodocus* which is nearly twenty times their own size. Usually they return to their particular spot but occasionally choose another place nearby. They normally skip or zig-zag slowly near the ground and rest every few metres. When chasing intruders out of their territories their speed is considerably faster. They are often lost from sight when circling about chasing after intruders. They usually fly off the koppies about 15:00. Occasionally they establish territories on the slopes or the flats where they may be observed flying about the spot for hours.

The females frequent the same areas as the males, flying slowly near the ground and settling every few metres in search of suitable food plants. Eggs are laid singly, concealed between young shoots or on a leaf. The eggs hatch after some 10 days. The young larvae at first feed on the surface of a partially opened young leaf. They form shelters by drawing the leaf-edges together with silk. Later, leaves are spun together, and feeding may occur on the edges of adjacent leaves. The whole larval stage is spent within the protection of these shelters. The larval stage lasts some 57 days. Pupation also takes place in the shelters. The pupal stage usually lasts some 15 to 33 days. In cold areas hibernation occurs during the pupal stage (Clark, 1978: 234).

This subspecies is on the wing throughout the year, in the colder parts from August to April.

LARVAL FOOD PLANTS

Hermannia diffusa, H. incana, H. comosa and *H. cuneifolia, Waltheria* sp. (Sterculiaceae); *Hibiscus aethiopicus, P. burchellii* and *Sida* sp. (Malvaceae).

Spialia diomus ferax final instar larva

Spialia diomus ferax pupa (After G.C. Clark 1978)

DISTRIBUTION

Throughout South Africa, Lesotho, Swaziland, Namibia, Botswana, Zimbabwe, Moçambique and venturing into Zambia.

CONSERVATION

S. diomus ferax is common and widespread and is under no threat.

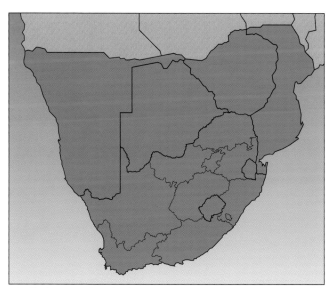

Distribution map of *Spialia diomus*

113

Spialia spio (Linnaeus)

MOUNTAIN SANDMAN

Papilio plebeius urbicola spio Linnaeus, 1767. *Mus. Lud. Ulr. Reg.*: 338. Type locality: Cape of Good Hope. Types lost.

IDENTIFICATION

Adult. Male. Upperside: blackish-brown with large white spots. Forewing with 2 basal white spots. Hindwing with large median patch but with median spot in Rs absent; submarginal spots M_1 and M_2 are usually fused to form a large conspicuous patch. Underside: hindwing light ochreous-brown with a white spot between median and submarginal lines in area 3A, inner spot in area Sc+R_1, usually large and rounded, submarginal spot 3A usually single, median spot 3A joined to median spot CuA_1. Female. Similar to male but larger with rounder wings.

Forewing lengths: male 10,8-14 mm; female 13,5-14,6 mm.

Early stages. Egg: pale green, with delicate white ribbing; diameter 0,75 mm, height 0,7 mm; with some 18 irregular longitudinal ribs and some 16 to 20 fine cross-ribs. Larva: all instars more or less greenish-grey in colour, with short hair and a black hairy head; final instar with a black and white prothoracic shield. The larva attains a length of some 21 mm. Pupa: 12 mm long; greenish-grey in colour, covered with a white chalky powder (Clark, 1978: 236).

HABITAT AND ECOLOGY

S. spio is an inhabitant of open areas, woodland, forest margins and clearings in forest. Its flight is rather rapid and close to the ground. It is readily attracted to flowers and to muddy places along streams.

The males show hilltopping behaviour, ascending to the peaks on hot sunny days mainly between 11:00 and 15:00. Here they select a territory, usually settling on low plants, stones or even on the ground with their wings half-opened. From here they dart off every now and again to chase off intruding butterflies. They usually return to the same spots on the ground. They also regularly establish territories on the lower slopes of hills and valleys near where the food plants grow.

The females frequent the same places as the males, flying slowly near the ground and settling every few metres in search of suitable food plants. They lay their eggs singly among young shoots. The eggs take some 7 days to hatch. The young larvae feed at first on the surface of a half-opened, young leaf, but later draw leaves together to form a shelter. They continue to feed on the surface of the leaf but may crawl out to feed on adjacent leaves. The larval stage lasts some 90 to 110 days. Pupation generally takes place within the final shelter, generally near the ground. The pupal stage lasts some 18 days. The larva is parasitised by species of Diptera, one of which has been identified as *Thecocarcelia latifrons* (Tachinidae) (Clark, 1978: 236).

This species is on the wing throughout the year, becoming scarcer during the winter months in the colder areas.

Spialia spio female upperside

Spialia spio female underside

Spialia spio final instar larva

Spialia spio pupa (Photo: A.J.M. Claassens)

LARVAL FOOD PLANTS

Hermannia incana, H. diffusa, H. cuneifolia, H. coccocarpa, H. comosa (Sterculiaceae); *Pavonia burchellii, P. columella, Hibiscus pusillus, H. aethiopicus, Lavatera arborea, Sida* sp. (Malvaceae); *Triumfetta* sp. (Tiliaceae).

DISTRIBUTION

Throughout most of South Africa; also Lesotho, Swaziland, Namibia, Botswana, Zimbabwe, Moçambique and throughout the rest of the Afrotropical Region.

CONSERVATION

S. spio is a widespread species and is under no threat.

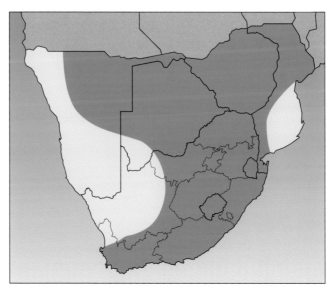

Distribution map of *Spialia spio*

Genus *Gomalia* Moore

Gomalia Moore, 1879. *Proc. zool. Soc. Lond.* **1879**: 114. Type species: *Gomalia albofasciata* Moore, 1879, by monotypy.

Similar to *Spialia,* differing only in the irregular hindwing outer margin and the different facies. The male has a faint costal fold on the forewing above. The sexes are alike.

Egg with sinuate, highly fluted, ribs. Larva pale with a dark head. Head with short setae, becoming longer dorsally. Pupa greyish white, blunt anteriorly.

There is only one species in Southern Africa.

Gomalia elma (Trimen)

GREEN-MARBLED SANDMAN

Pyrgus elma Trimen, 1862. *Trans. ent. Soc. Lond.* (3)**1**: 288.

Two subspecies are recognised, the second being oriental.

Gomalia elma elma (Trimen)

Pyrgus elma Trimen, 1862. *Trans. ent. Soc. Lond.* (3)**1**: 288. Type locality: Plettenberg Bay, South Africa. Type in Natural History Museum, London.

Gomalia elma female in sleeping position (Photo: R. Paré)

Gomalia elma final instar larva (After G.C. Clark 1978)

Gomalia elma pupa (After G.C. Clark 1978)

IDENTIFICATION

Adult. Male. Upperside: mottled dull greenish-brown; forewing with small central and subapical hyaline dots; hindwing with a white median bar. Underside: paler. Female. Similar to the male, but with rounder wings.

Forewing lengths: male 12,6-14,5 mm; female 14,2-17,2 mm.

Early stages. Egg: pale yellow-brown when laid, changing to pale brown; diameter 1,0 mm, height 0,7 mm; deeply fluted by wavy ribs, about 18 in number, but only 7 or 8 of which reach the micropyle. Larva: greenish-white with black prothoracic shield and a hairy black head. It attains a length of 22,5 mm. Pupa: 9 to 9,5 mm long; greyish-white in colour and covered with a white powdery substance (Clark, 1978: 240).

HABITAT AND ECOLOGY

G. elma inhabits bush, woodland, forests, riverine evergreens and forest glades from near sea-level to 2 200 metres. It is often found in wet places, and males are attracted to mud. It flies low and fast, frequently settling on low shrubs. It is readily attracted to flowers and mud where it settles with wings held open. When at rest during the night it assumes a peculiar moth-like posture with its wings held downwards and the abdomen curled over the thorax (R. Paré, pers. comm.).

The males seldom show hilltopping behaviour, generally preferring lower ground, establishing territories in open spots, paths, clearings, or the more open parts of the woods. Here they patrol about, zig-zagging slowly, or perching on low shrubs and chasing off all intruders. They seldom perch for long in any one spot but dart from one to another in the territory.

The females frequent the same places as the males, flying at random in search of suitable food plants on which to lay. They lay their eggs singly on the surface of a leaf. The eggs take from 12 to 14 days to hatch. On hatching, the larvae draw the sides of a young leaf together to form a shelter, and feed on the inner surface of the leaf. Later they join two leaves together. The entire larval and pupal periods are passed in shelters, the final one being low down, near or on the ground. The larval stage lasts some 32 days, while the pupal period takes from 13-18 days. They are parasitised in the early stages by braconids and in the later stages by Diptera (Clark, 1978: 240).

This species is on the wing throughout the year in the warmer areas and from August to April in the cooler ones.

Gomalia elma female upperside

LARVAL FOOD PLANTS

Abutilon guineense and *A. intermedium* in East Africa and in South Africa *A. grandiflorum*, *A. someratianum* and *A. grantii* (Malvaceae).

DISTRIBUTION

Throughout most of South Africa, also in Lesotho, Swaziland, Namibia, Botswana, Zimbabwe, Moçambique and on to tropical Africa and Arabia.

CONSERVATION

G. elma is an uncommon but widespread species and is under no threat.

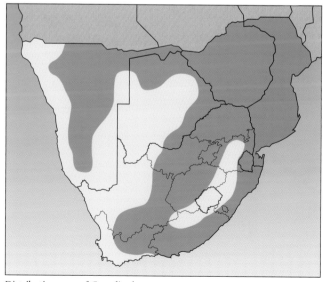

Distribution map of *Gomalia elma*

117

Genus *Alenia* Evans

Alenia Evans, 1935. *Trans. R. ent. Soc. Lond.* **83**: 409. Type species: *Pyrgus sandaster* Trimen, 1868, by original designation.

A small species closely related to *Spialia*, differing from it in having the club of the antennae flattened to a thin oval disc with the tip bent over. Venation as in *Spialia* but end of forewing cell is convex instead of straight; and on the hindwing vein 1A+2A is very short and the vein M_2 is slightly decurved at its origin. The outer margin of the forewing is indented slightly below vein M_3; of hindwing slightly concave between ends of veins Rs and M_2 and indented below CuA_1.

Egg, elongated dome with flattened top. Larva, body rounded, head with short feathery setae. Pupa speckled greyish-brown, anteriorly conical. Food plants Acanthaceae.

There are two species in Southern Africa, both of which occur in South Africa.

KEY TO THE SPECIES OF *ALENIA*

1. LHW with strong white irroration .... *A. namaqua*

   LHW brown and the median fascia is without white irroration
   .... *A. sandaster*

Alenia sandaster male upperside

Alenia sandaster (Trimen)

KAROO DANCER

Pyrgus sandaster Trimen, 1868. *Trans. ent. Soc. Lond.* **1868**: 92. Type locality: Murraysburg, Cape Province. Holotype female in Natural History Museum, London.

IDENTIFICATION

Adult. Male. Upperside: ground colour brown, finely studded with white on forewing. Underside: hindwing with white irroration, and two irregular silvery bands, median fascia brown without distinct irroration. Female. Similar to male, but with a stouter abdomen.

Forewing lengths: male 11-12,8 mm; female 12,5-13,5 mm.

Early stages. Egg: yellow when laid, changing to pale green, then dull gold; diameter 0,6 mm; height 0,5 mm; with 12 or 13 longitudinal ribs, reduced to 7 at micropyle, and about 16 staggered cross-ribs. Larva: first instar yellowish-white with a black head; second instar becomes more greyish; third to fifth instar greyish-brown with a white dorso-lateral stripe down each side, a white-speckled black prothoracic shield, and a black head clothed with feathery yellowish setae. It attains a length of some 16,5 mm. Pupa: 11 mm long; yellowish white, speckled with black giving it a greyish appearance (Clark, 1978: 242).

HABITAT AND ECOLOGY

A. sandaster is an inhabitant of dry bush-country Karoo (Karoid vegetation). It prefers dry stony places where either of its food plants may grow. It feeds readily on small flowers, including those of mesembryanthemums, if these are present. When settled on the ground or low rocks it is well camouflaged, making it very difficult to observe. It usually flies low, resting every few metres on the ground with its wings half-opened.

The males do not show hilltopping behaviour, but establish their territories in the vicinity of the larval food plants or along the sandy bottoms of gullies. Here they perch on a low plant, stone, or on the ground. Occasionally they fly quite rapidly in a skipping fashion from one plant to another.

Alenia sandaster final instar larva (After G.C. Clark 1978)

Alenia sandaster pupa (After G.C. Clark 1978)

The females frequent the same places as the male, and can often be observed hovering about the food plants, settling on them or flying rapidly in a skipping fashion from one plant to another. Eggs are laid singly on a bud of the food plant. The eggs hatch after 8 to 12 days. The young larva eats its way into a young flower bud. When this is hollowed out it enters another bud. If the plant withers the larva remains dormant (diapause) until the plant revives. The duration of the instars can thus be very erratic. The larval stages last some 50-60 days. The final instar is generally completed amongst the seeds. An escape hole is eaten through the seed pod and, if necessary, through a leaf as well. The hole is covered with silk until needed, or may be blocked by the head of the larva. There is slight colour variation in the larvae. The pupal stage lasts some 15-37 days or longer. A chalcid wasp was recorded parasitising a third instar larva (Clark, 1978: 242).

This species is on the wing from August to January.

LARVAL FOOD PLANTS

Blepharis capensis and *Barleria* sp. (Acanthaceae).

DISTRIBUTION

South Africa, mainly in the Eastern Cape Province from Grahamstown in the east, through parts of the Karoo in the Western and Northern Cape, and is replaced in Namaqualand by the closely allied *A. namaqua*.

CONSERVATION

A. sandaster is fairly widespread and is under no threat.

Alenia namaqua Vári

NAMAQUA DANCER

Alenia namaqua Vári, 1974. *Ann. Transv. Mus.* **29**: 13. Type locality: Springbok, Northern Cape. Holotype male in the Transvaal Museum, Pretoria.

IDENTIFICATION

Adult. Male. Upperside: brown, finely spotted with white on the forewing. Underside: hindwing brown and differs from *A. sandaster* in having strong white irroration, and two irregular silvery bands. Female. Similar to male but larger.

Forewing lengths: male 10,5-12,5 mm; female 13-14 mm.

Early stages. Unrecorded.

HABITAT AND ECOLOGY

This colonial species is found in subdesert habitat in Namaqualand and the Richtersveld, wherever its larval food plants occur. It is often observed feeding at flowers, especially mesembryanthemums. It flies relatively slowly near the ground and rests every few metres.

The males do not show hilltopping behaviour and are usually found in the vicinity of the food plants, or along the sandy bottoms of gullies. Usually they establish their territories in open stony spots where they flit about the low plants, and settle on the ground with half-opened wings.

The females frequent the same localities as the males, often hovering around their food plants, settling on them or flying quite rapidly in a skipping fashion from one plant to another.

They are on the wing from September to late November.

Distribution map of *Alenia sandaster*

Alenia namaqua male underside

Alenia namaqua male upperside

LARVAL FOOD PLANTS

Unrecorded.

DISTRIBUTION

South Africa, Namaqualand in the Western Cape and northwards into the southern part of Namibia.

CONSERVATION

A. namaqua is fairly widespread and is under no threat.

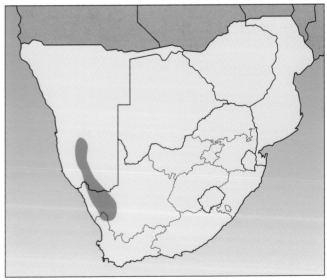

Distribution map of *Alenia namaqua*

SUBFAMILY HESPERIINAE

Small to medium-sized skippers. At rest the adults hold their wings erect, but when feeding or settled in sunshine, they may depress their hindwings. The forewing of the male is without a costal fold, but often bears a sex-brand.

The eggs are relatively large and hemispherical, with a smooth surface. The larvae are usually pale green in colour, with inconspicuous hairs. The pupae are usually pale green or brown, sometimes covered with a white waxy powder.

The subfamily is made up of 17 genera and 51 species in Southern Africa, namely *Metisella* Hemming (1934: 99); *Tsitana* Evans (1937:75); *Astictopterus* C. & R. Felder (1860: 401); *Kedestes* Watson (1893: 96); *Acleros* Mabille (1887: 347); *Andronymus* Holland (1896: 80); *Moltena* Evans (1937: 139); *Zophopetes* Mabille (1904: 183); *Artitropa* Holland (1896: 92); *Parnara* Moore (1881: 166); *Borbo* Evans (1949: 46); *Pelopidas* Walker (1870: 56); *Platylesches* Holland (1896: 72); *Zenonia* Evans (1935: 405); *Parosmodes* Holland (1896: 45); *Gegenes* Hübner (1819: 107); *Fresna* Evans (1937: 164).

KEY TO THE GENERA OF HESPERIINAE

1. Hindwing cubitus and M_3 collinear 2

   Not so 7

2. Hindwing costa as long as dorsum of forewing, antennae short, not hooked at apex 3

   Hindwing costa shorter, antennal club often obtuse or hooked 5

3. Hindwing cell longer than half wing; antennal club blunt, arcuate .... *Metisella*

   Hindwing cell not longer than half wing; antennal club not blunt, arcuate 4

4. Antennal club flattened and hollowed, blunt .... *Tsitana*

   Antennal club normal, bent about middle to short, obtuse, pointed apiculus .... *Astictopterus*

5. UFW colour blackish, with or without white hyaline spots; abdomen white-tipped .... *Acleros*

   UFW brown, less often blackish, with orange, yellow or ochreous markings, rarely whitish; or orange with blackish markings 6

6. Antennal club straight, blunt not hooked (but bent in *K. callicles*) .... *Kedestes*

   Antennal club hooked, pointed apiculus .... *Parosmodes*

7. Hindwing with a large hyaline spot in cell .... *Andronymus*

   Not so 8

8. Thorax shaggy below, coxae and tibiae densely fringed; hindwing vein M_2 well developed 9

   Thorax and legs not so; hindwing with M_2 poorly developed or absent 11

9. Palpi erect, third segment very short and stout; antennae without white scales .... *Artitropa*

   Palpi porrect; antennae with some white scales 10

10. Middle tibiae spined; UFW without hyaline spots .... *Moltena*

    Middle tibiae without spines; UFW with hyaline spots in discal cell and area CuA_1 and M_3 .... *Zophopetes*

11. Palpi porrect, third segment of palpi long and thin 12

    Palpi erect, third segment of palpi not long and thin 13

12. Palpi third segment moderate, not equal to half of second segment; head and palpi white spotted; forewing with cell spots and spot in area CuA_1 not in line; underside of wings *Acraea*-like .... *Fresna*

    Palpi third segment long and thin, second segment flattened; forewing with cell spots and the spot in area CuA_1 in line; underside of wings not *Acraea*-like .... *Platylesches*

13. Conspicuous orange markings .... *Zenonia*

    Dark fuscous, with whitish, less commonly ochreous spots 14

14. Male UFW with an oblique sex brand replacing the discal spot in CuA_2 .... *Pelopidas*

    Male with a simple spot in CuA_2 of UFW, lacking brand 15

15. Antennae very short, 0,33 costa, apiculus absent or minute .... *Gegenes*

    Antennae longer, apiculus distinct 16

16. Forewing with CuA_2 rising nearer base than end of cell .... *Parnara*

    Forewing with CuA_2 rising nearer end of cell than wing base ... *Borbo*

Genus *Metisella* Hemming

Metisella Hemming, 1934. *Stylops* **3**: 99. Type species: *Papilio metis* Linnaeus, 1764, by original designation.

Smallish broad-winged, narrow-bodied brown skippers, usually marked with orange or yellow spots. Forewing cell short, nearly straight; vein R_1 more or less united with vein Sc; vein M_3 arising midway between veins M_3 and M_1; vein CuA_2 arising from midway between wing base and vein CuA_1. Hindwing costa very long, longer than forewing dorsum; cell longer than halfway; vein CuA_2 arising well before vein Rs; vein 1A+2A short. Antennae short, not hooked at apex. Apical segment of palpi short and almost hidden, but straightly porrect.

Eggs domed without ribs. Larva very elongate, green with longitudinal stripes; head held flat, green with tiny setae. Pupae elongated and tapering at both ends.

Food plants Poaceae.

There are six species in Southern Africa.

KEY TO THE SPECIES OF *METISELLA*

1. LHW blackish with two distinctly prominent white longitudinal streaks, one in the discal cell and one in 3A 2

   LHW without a white longitudinal streak on a dark ground colour 3

2. Underside with small triangular yellow marginal spots; LHW with inner margin white .... *M. meninx*

   Underside without light marginal spots; LHW with inner margin not white .... *M. syrinx*

3. LHW with a white ground-colour and distinctly prominent black veins. LFW with whitish-yellow marginal spots .... *M. willemi*

   LHW with a blackish-brown or greyish-yellow ground colour and similar veins. LFW without marginal spots 4

4. Upperside of wings blackish-brown with three small yellowish subapical dots in R_4 to M_1 of the forewing .... *M. aegipan*

   Both wings with distinctly defined, bright yellow or orange spots 5

5. LHW dark brown and with only one small yellow dot near the base of the costal margin or with some dull reddish-yellow spots, corresponding to those above .... *M. metis*

   LHW greyish-yellow or pale brownish-yellow with dull yellow spots. Upperside spots small and ochreous yellow .... *M. malgacha*

Metisella aegipan (Trimen)

MOUNTAIN SYLPH

Cyclopides aegipan Trimen, 1868. *Trans. ent. Soc. Lond.* **1868**: 94.

There are two subspecies found in Southern Africa, the nominate from the Republic of South Africa, the other, *inyanga* Evans, 1955, from Zimbabwe.

Metisella aegipan aegipan (Trimen)

Cyclopides aegipan Trimen, 1868. *Trans. ent. Soc. Lond.* **1868**: 94. Type locality: Amatola Mountains, Eastern Cape Province. Holotype male in Natural History Museum, London.

IDENTIFICATION

Adult. Male. Upperside: ground colour blackish-brown with three small yellowish-orange subapical spots on the forewing. Underside: forewing brown becoming lighter orange along costa, apex and down outer margin; with three yellowish-orange subapical spots. Hindwing ground colour orange-brown, becoming darker along inner margin. Female. Similar to male but ground colour paler and forewing yellowish-orange subapical spots larger and better developed.

Forewing lengths: male 13,5-16,5 mm; female 13,5-17 mm.

Early stages. Unrecorded.

HABITAT AND ECOLOGY

M. aegipan is an inhabitant of marshes and damp patches on hills and mountains. In Mpumalanga, Northern Province and in KwaZulu-Natal it is found on the eastern slopes of mountains. It is a slow-flying species. It is usually observed flying up and down marshy gullies, frequently settling on grass, damp spots and often feeds on flowers.

The males are territorial, usually occupying certain marshy spots on the slopes. Here they patrol up and down, flying or skipping in zig-zag fashion among the grass, on which they perch at times.

The females can be encountered anywhere around the marshy areas, apparently searching for suitable plants on which to lay.

The species is on the wing from the beginning of December and flies until February.

Metisella aegipan aegipan male upperside

Metisella aegipan aegipan male underside

LARVAL FOOD PLANTS

Unrecorded.

DISTRIBUTION

South Africa, from the Eastern Cape, on the Drakensberg in Kwa-Zulu-Natal, Mpumalanga and Northern Province and Lesotho.

CONSERVATION

M. aegipan is widespread and is an inhabitant of generally inaccessible mountainous areas and is under no threat.

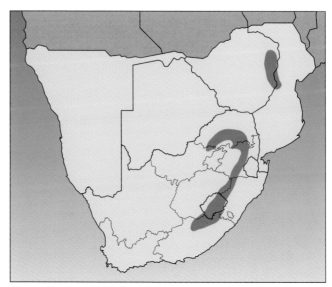

Distribution map of *Metisella aegipan*

Metisella malgacha (Boisduval)

GRASSVELD SYLPH

Steropes malgacha Boisduval, 1833. *Faune ent. de Madag.*: 67.

There are two subspecies in Southern Africa, both of which occur in South Africa.

Metisella malgacha malgacha (Boisduval)

Steropes malgacha Boisduval, 1833. *Faune ent. de Madag.*: 67. Type locality: Madagascar (*Patria falsa*). Holotype male in the Natural History Museum, London.

IDENTIFICATION

Adult. Male. Upperside: dark brown-fuscous, forewing irrorated with ochreous scales, especially in basal area. Forewing with two ochreous-yellow spots at upper end of cell; small discal spots in R_3-R_5, M_3, CuA_1 and a faint spot in CuA_2; postdiscal area with a complete series of ochreous-yellow streaks. Hindwing with a series of ochreous yellow postdiscal spots and two larger discal spots. Underside: forewing brown with brownish-yellow scaling along costa and outer margin; spots as on upperside. Hindwing greyish or pale brownish yellow with dull yellow spots. Female. Similar to male but upperside postdiscal markings absent and other ochreous-yellow spots larger and better developed.

Forewing lengths: male 12-14 mm; female 13-15 mm.

Metisella malgacha malgacha male underside

DISTRIBUTION

South Africa, from the Cape Peninsula in the Western Cape, along the southern edge of the Karoo and up through the Eastern Cape to the Free State, North-West Province, the KwaZulu-Natal Midlands and some portions of Gauteng and Mpumalanga. Evans (1937) records specimens from Moçambique.

Metisella malgacha malgacha male upperside

Metisella malgacha orina Vári

Metisella malgacha orina Vári, 1976. *Ann. Transv. Mus.* **30**: 122. Type locality: Mokhotlong, Lesotho. Holotype male in the Transvaal Museum, Pretoria.

IDENTIFICATION

Adult. Upperside: similar to the nominate subspecies but with the ochreous-yellow spots smaller. Underside: forewing as in *malgacha* but hindwings coarsely irrorated with ochreous-yellow, marginal spots more distinct than in nominate subspecies.

Forewing lengths: male 12-13 mm; female 13-14 mm.

Early stages. Egg: light blue; diameter 0,8 mm, height 0,6 mm; with numerous very small, round indentations on the surface. Larva: first to third instars white with a black head; fourth instar light green with longitudinal dark green stripes running the length of body, head white with brown markings; fifth (final) instar green with light and dark green longitudinal stripes and green head. It attains a length of some 21 mm. Pupa: 17 mm long; green becoming whitish at the extremities with darker and lighter longitudinal lines (Clark, 1978: 244).

DISTRIBUTION

South Africa on the Drakensberg in KwaZulu-Natal and Lesotho.

HABITAT AND ECOLOGY

M. malgacha occupies a variety of habitats: it flies about gardens and the flats of the Cape Peninsula, the grasslands of the Northern Cape, eastern Free State, North-West Province and Gauteng, to vleis at 1 500 metres in KwaZulu-Natal and the slopes of the highest part of the Drakensberg in Lesotho at 3000 metres. It is a slow-flying species and always keeps near to the ground. It frequently settles on grass, usually with closed wings, but occasionally with its wings open, sunning itself. The species is also fond of visiting flowers on which it feeds readily.

The males establish territories in the vicinity of the larval food plants. Here they rest on the ground, on shrubs or grass, occasionally skipping about before coming to rest again.

The females fly at random searching for suitable food plants on which to oviposit. They lay their eggs singly on a blade of grass. The egg takes from 10 to 14 days to hatch. The young larva eats the egg shell, after which it crawls to the end of a blade of grass and constructs a tube by drawing its edges together with silk. It lives within this tube and feeds on the tip of the blade, extending the tube backward as necessary. The larva may also feed from the lower end of the tube downwards so that the tube remains attached to the blade by a thin strip of leaf tissue only. The larval stage lasts for about five weeks. Pupation occurs within the tube. The pupa is secured by cremastral hooks and a girdle. The pupal stage lasts about 12 days (Clark, 1978: 244).

This species is on the wing from August to June in many parts, with an occasional July record.

LARVAL FOOD PLANTS

Ehrharta erecta (Poaceae).

CONSERVATION

M. malgacha is a widespread and fairly common species and is under no threat.

Metisella malgacha malgacha pupal shell and freshly emerged female upperside (Photo: A.J.M. Claassens)

Metisella malgacha malgacha final instar larva (Photo: A.J.M. Claassens)

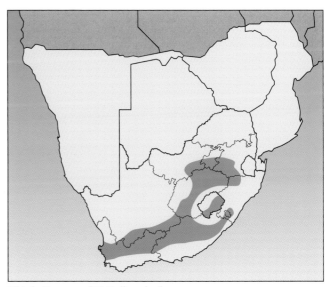

Distribution map of *Metisella malgacha*

Metisella metis (Linnaeus)

GOLD SPOTTED SYLPH

Papilio plebeius urbicola metis Linnaeus, 1764. *Mus. Lud. Ulr. Reg.*: 325.

There are two subspecies in Southern Africa, both of which occur in South Africa.

Metisella metis metis (Linnaeus)

Papilio plebeius urbicola metis Linnaeus, 1764. *Mus. Lud. Ulr. Reg.*: 325. Type locality: Cape of Good Hope.

IDENTIFICATION

Adult. Male. Upperside: dark brown and adorned with golden-orange spots on both wings. Underside: dark brown with no spots on the hindwing, but with golden spots on the forewing as on upperside. Female. Similar to male but underside is lighter chocolate brown with orange spots on the forewing and with pale yellow-brown spots also occurring on the hindwing.

Forewing lengths: male 13,5-14,5 mm; female 15-15,5 mm.

DISTRIBUTION

South Africa, from the Cape Peninsula, eastward to the Swellendam area in the Western Cape.

Metisella metis paris Evans

Metisella metis paris Evans, 1937. *Cat. Afr. Hesper.*: 71. Type locality: KwaZulu-Natal. Holotype male in Natural History Museum, London.

IDENTIFICATION

Adult. Markings in both sexes reduced, particularly the forewing cell spot in male, which is no larger than any other spot, while in *M. m. metis* it is very much larger.

Forewing lengths: male 12,5-16,5 mm; female 15-16 mm.

Early stages. Egg: pure white when laid, later developing irregular red blotches; hemispherical, diameter 0,75 mm, height 0,5 mm; with some 120 longitudinal ribs composed of small moles, which diminish in number towards the micropyle. Larva: first instar pale greenish-white with a black head; second to fourth instars yellow or pale greenish-white with darker green longitudinal stripes and black to brown head; fifth (final) instar pale green or yellowish with three dark green longitudinal stripes and a whitish head with a blackish-brown lateral line. It attains a length of 31 to 35 mm. Pupa: 14-18 mm long; green with longitudinal white stripes (Clark, 1978: 246).

DISTRIBUTION

South Africa, from the Swellendam area in the Western Cape eastward through the Eastern Cape, KwaZulu-Natal, Mpumalanga and Northern Province, Swaziland, Zimbabwe and Moçambique.

Metisella metis metis male upperside (Photo: A.J.M. Claassens)

Metisella metis paris male underside

Metisella metis paris male upperside

Metisella metis paris female in flight showing upperside

HABITAT AND ECOLOGY

M. metis is an inhabitant of woodland and forested areas. It is often seen near the edges of forests, in borders of mixed vegetation including various mixed grasses such as are found near cultivated lands and in lush vegetation along roads, lanes or paths. The nominate race inhabits more open areas while *paris* is largely a forest insect, although specimens are sometimes encountered in unusual places such as grassy mountain peaks. It is possible this habitat difference indicates that two species are involved. It has an active, somewhat fluttering flight and often rests on the ground, low shrubs or taller plants. It is also fond of flowers.

The males do not exhibit hilltopping behaviour and can usually be observed in open places in the bush where they establish their territories. They perch on the ground or on the surrounding shrubs or other plants. Occasionally they fly off around the clearing or along the road for quite a distance before returning to their perch.

The females fly about the same places as the males in search of suitable food plants. They lay their eggs singly on a blade of grass. The larva emerges after 8 to 9 days. The discarded shell is generally eaten, leaving only the base. The larva, on hatching, crawls to the tip of the blade of grass and forms a tube by drawing and binding the edges together. It feeds at intervals on the tip. As the blade is eaten the edges are drawn together lower down, and when it is nearly all eaten the larva moves to another one. The whole larval stage is spent in a grass tube where pupation also takes place. When the larva becomes too big for a tube, it may lie along the midrib of a blade before constructing another one. The larval stage lasts about 34 days and the pupal about 14 days. The larvae are attacked in the later instars by *Apanteles* and other parasites. *Meteorus testaceus* (Hymenoptera) has been identified in the fourth instar. Tachinids also attack larvae but the resulting maggot generally emerges from the side of the pupa and pupates amongst debris. Two species identified are *Nemorilla (Jesuimgia) cruciata* and *Thecocarcelia incedens* (Diptera: Tachinidae) (Clark, 1978: 246).

This species is on the wing throughout the year in the warmer areas.

LARVAL FOOD PLANTS

Stenotaphrum glabrum, S. dimidiatum, Panicum deustum, Ehrharta erecta, Stipa dregeana, Setaria megaphylla (Poaceae).

CONSERVATION

M. metis is a widespread species and is under no threat.

Metisella metis paris female underside

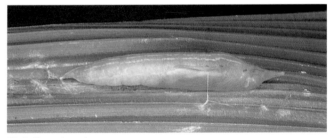

Metisella metis paris final instar larva

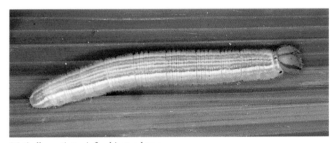

Metisella metis paris pupa

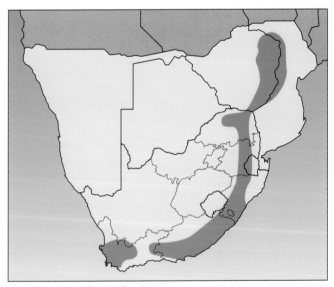

Distribution map of *Metisella metis*

Metisella willemi (Wallengren)

NETTED SYLPH

Heteropterus willemi Wallengren, 1857. *K. svenska VetenskAkad. Handl.* (N.F.) **2**(4): 47. Type locality: Kaffraria.

IDENTIFICATION

Adult. Male. Upperside: ground colour dark brown; forewing with a submarginal row of pale yellow spots and an irregular row of rectangularly shaped postdiscal spots; hindwing without spots. Underside: forewing dark brown with yellow submarginal streaks at apex. Hindwing white to pale yellow with brown veins and crosslines giving a netted appearance. Female. Similar to male, but paler with more rounded wings.

Forewing lengths: male 14,5-15,5 mm; female 14-15,5 mm.

Early stages. Unrecorded.

HABITAT AND ECOLOGY

M. willemi is an inhabitant of grassy areas in deciduous woodland and bushveld and is usually encountered along rivers at the foot of hills, koppies and mountains. It is also found on their slopes and sometimes on their summits, if they are not too high. This species may also be encountered among clumps of trees on the flats. Occasionally specimens venture into gardens or select the shade of a solitary tree. It prefers flying among the long grass in the shade of trees. Usually it flies slowly, skipping or zig-zagging about near the ground. It is often observed feeding at flowers. Males have been recorded sucking moisture in wet places.

Metisella willemi male underside

Metisella willemi male upperside

The males do not appear to exhibit hilltopping behaviour but are usually found close to the larval food plants. They establish their territories in the shade of trees where they may be observed perching on the stems or blades of grass for long periods. Occasionally they venture into the sunlight, flying quite rapidly but quickly returning to their territory in the shade. The males chase off any intruders from adjacent territories.

The females fly at random in the area where their food plants occur.

This species is on the wing from December to May.

LARVAL FOOD PLANTS

Various grasses including *Setaria* sp. (Poaceae).

DISTRIBUTION

South Africa, in the North-West Province, Gauteng, Northern Province and Mpumalanga, northwards into Botswana, Zimbabwe and Moçambique. It is in fact common in savannah country right through to East Africa and eastern Zaire.

CONSERVATION

M. willemi is a widespread and relatively common species and is under no threat.

Metisella meninx (Trimen)

MARSH SYLPH

Cyclopides meninx Trimen, 1873. *Trans. ent. Soc. Lond.* **1873**: 121. Type locality: Transvaal. Holotype male in Natural History Museum, London.

IDENTIFICATION

Adult. Male. Upperside: velvety black with a coppery reflection. Underside: hindwing with white and yellow radiating stripes. Female. Similar to male but has a yellow costal spot on the forewing upperside.

Forewing lengths: male 12,5-13 mm; female 13-14 mm.

Early stages. Unrecorded.

HABITAT AND ECOLOGY

M. meninx is an inhabitant of marshy areas in the eastern highveld where it usually occurs in some numbers flying slowly in the grass. It may fly around for some time skipping and darting around the thick clumps of marsh grass which characterise its habitat. *M. meninx* is on the wing as early as 08:00 and flies as late as 17:00 – sometimes earlier and also later – depending on the weather. It can often be seen feeding at flowers or settled on blades of grass.

The males establish their territories around the clumps of marsh grass. Here they may be observed perching on a blade of grass or patrolling slowly around their area. The territories are evenly dispersed around its habitat.

The females are found in the same places as the males where they fly at random in search of suitable food plants on which to lay.

This species is on the wing from December to March.

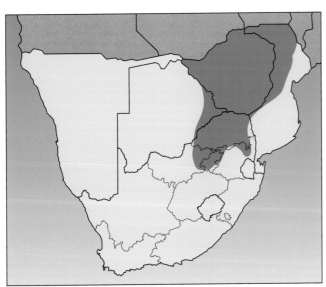

Distribution map of *Metisella willemi*

Metisella meninx male underside

LARVAL FOOD PLANTS

Unidentified marsh grass (Poaceae).

DISTRIBUTION

South Africa, from northern KwaZulu-Natal, the northern Free State, North-West Province, Gauteng, Mpumalanga. Also apparently recorded from Angola (Evans, 1937) but this record is likely to be of another species.

CONSERVATION

M. meninx is a marsh species, which requires thick clumps of marsh grass and an unpolluted environment. A marsh habitat is one of the most easily disrupted habitats and the apparent plight of this species brings this sharply into focus. In recent times many of these marshy localities occupied by *M. meninx* have been destroyed. Although not yet endangered, this species should be closely monitored so that preventive measures can be taken timeously if required. This species appears in the *South African Red Data Book – Butterflies* (1989) as one that will probably require further investigation in the future. It has not yet been ascertained whether *M. meninx* occurs in any of the nature reserves in Mpumalanga or KwaZulu-Natal.

Metisella meninx male upperside

Metisella meninx female

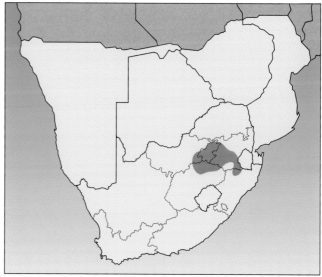

Distribution map of *Metisella meninx*

131

Metisella syrinx (Trimen)

BAMBOO SYLPH

Cyclopides syrinx Trimen, 1868. *Trans. ent. Soc. Lond.* **1868**: 93. Type locality: Gaika's Kop, Amatola Mountains, Eastern Cape Province. Holotype male in Natural History Museum, London.

IDENTIFICATION

Adult. Male. Upperside: dark greenish-brown with pale yellow spots. Underside: hindwing yellowish-brown with one very broad and one thinner radiating creamy-yellow stripe. Female. Similar to male, but larger with more rounded wings and abdomen.

Forewing lengths: male 15-16 mm; female 15-17,5 mm.

Early stages. Unrecorded.

HABITAT AND ECOLOGY

M. syrinx is entirely associated with Mountain Bamboo on which the larvae feed. This plant grows only at high elevations on certain mountains. It flits around the stands of bamboo which grow among the rocks on the peaks. When found, *M. syrinx* may sometimes be seen in their hundreds.

The males establish their territories in the stands of bamboo where they perch on the stems or fly slowly around.

The females fly in the same places as the males and search for suitable plants on which to lay their eggs.

This species is on the wing in January and February.

LARVAL FOOD PLANTS

Thamnocalamus tessellatus (Mountain Bamboo) (Poaceae).

DISTRIBUTION

Endemic to South Africa, being found in the Eastern Cape and adjacent Lesotho and the KwaZulu-Natal Highlands.

CONSERVATION

M. syrinx is a rare species although there are no known threats. The inaccessibility of its habitat precludes the possibility of any threats at this time. It is recorded as a rare species by S.F. & G.A. Henning in the *South African Red Data Book – Butterflies* (1989). Also on the Protected Wild Animal list of the Cape Province 1976 (Ordinance 19 of 1974, amendment of schedule 2 in 1976). In addition it is found in the Mzimkulu Wilderness in the southern KwaZulu-Natal Drakensberg.

Summit of Gaika's Kop habitat of *Metisella syrinx* with its food plant *Thamnocalamus tessellatus* in the foreground

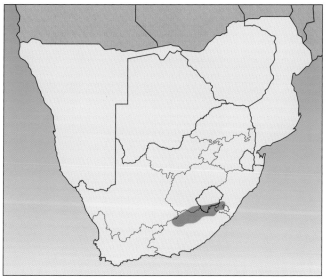

Distribution map of *Metisella syrinx*

Metisella syrinx male underside

Metisella syrinx male upperside on its food plant *Thamnocalamus tessellatus*

Genus *Tsitana* Evans

Tsitana Evans, 1937. *Cat. Afr. Hesper.*: 75. Type species: *Cyclopides tsita* Trimen, 1870, by original designation.

Small to medium-sized dull brown skippers resembling *Metisella* but having vein R_1 separate from Sc. Antennae are as long as costa; club flattened and hollowed, ending in a broad, turned-over point. Forewing with vein M_2 arising rather closer to vein M_3 than to vein M_1. Hindwing cell about half as long as the wing; vein 2A rather long. Abdomen equal in length to dorsum.

Egg domed. Larvae elongate and cylindrical; anal segment quadrate; head dark in earlier instars. Pupae elongate and cylindrical, white darkening at both ends; head, erect bilobate, truncate. Food plants Poaceae.

There are four species in Southern Africa, all of which occur in the Republic of South Africa.

KEY TO THE SPECIES OF *TSITANA*

1. LHW with no sharply defined white streak along vein M_2, sometimes with ill-defined grey radial streaks, sometimes the entire area between these streaks grey-scaled .... *T. tsita*

    LHW with sharply defined white streak along vein M_2 2

2. LHW with a sharply defined narrow white streak from the base through the cell and along vein M_2 to outer margin. FW length not more than 15 mm .... *T. uitenhaga*

    LHW with a narrow white streak along vein M_2 from base through cell but NOT reaching outer margin. FW length 16,5 mm or more 3

3. LHW with ground colour ochreous-brown; generally smaller .... *T. dicksoni*

    LHW fawn to dark brown; generally larger .... *T. tulbagha*

Tsitana tsita (Trimen)

DISMAL SYLPH

Cyclopides tsita Trimen, 1870. *Trans. ent. Soc. Lond* **1870**: 386. Type locality: KwaZulu-Natal. Holotype male in Natural History Museum, London.

IDENTIFICATION

Adult. Male. Upperside: dark dull brown without any spots. Underside: forewing dark brown becoming paler distally; hindwing usually pale brown with pale veins, sometimes with ill-defined grey radial streaks, sometimes the entire area between these streaks grey-scaled. Cilia grey, preceded by narrow whitish line. Female. Similar to male, but paler with a stouter abdomen.

Forewing lengths: male 15-18,5 mm; female 15,8-17,5 mm.

Early stages. Unrecorded.

Tsitana tsita male underside

HABITAT AND ECOLOGY

T. tsita is an inhabitant of grassy hillsides from sea level to 2 600 metres. Although it ranges over a wide area it is quite local in its habits. In many places where grass grows abundantly the species is entirely absent, although in a spot half a kilometre or so from there, numbers may be observed. Areas also exist where one locality is separated from the other by many kilometres. It is a slow flier, skipping and zig-zagging at the same time in any direction. It is often observed at flowers, and frequently rests on the stems of grass, or on the ground.

The males occasionally show hilltopping behaviour, although they normally establish their territories in the vicinity of the larval food plants. Here they perch on the grass or on the ground, or fly slowly around the area.

The females are found in the same places as the males, flying at random in search of suitable food plants.

This species is on the wing from December to March, with January appearing to be the best time.

LARVAL FOOD PLANTS

Stipa dregeana (Poaceae).

DISTRIBUTION

South Africa, from the Eastern Cape Province, northwards through KwaZulu-Natal Midlands, Lesotho, northern Free State, North-West Province, Gauteng, Northern Province and Mpumalanga, Zimbabwe and Moçambique.

CONSERVATION

T. tsita is a widely distributed species and is under no threat.

Tsitana tsita male upperside

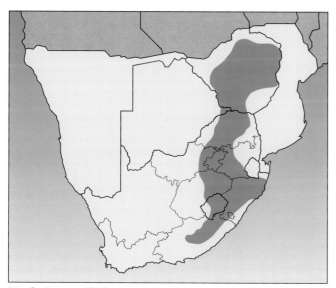

Distribution map of *Tsitana tsita*

Tsitana uitenhaga Evans

UITENHAGE SYLPH

Tsitana uitenhaga Evans, 1937. *Cat. Afr. Hesper.*: 75. Type locality: Uitenhage, Eastern Cape. Holotype male in Natural History Museum, London.

IDENTIFICATION

Adult. Male. Upperside: dark, dull brown, without any spots. Underside: hindwing dark ochreous-brown, veins not pale; a sharply defined narrow white streak from base through cell and along vein M_2 to the outer margin and traces of a streak along vein 3A. Cilia brown without the anteciliary white line. Female. Similar to male but paler with more rounded wings.

Forewing lengths: male 14,5-16,5 mm; female 15-17 mm.

Early stages. Egg: white at first, changing to very pale salmon; diameter 1,1 mm, height 0,8 mm; with some 48 longitudinal ribs, cross-braced by 20 faint staggered ribs, which break up into a netting pattern towards the micropyle. Larva: first and second instars greenish-white with a black head; third and fourth instars more greenish with a brown and black head; fifth and sixth (final) instars green with a dark brown and white head. The larva attains a length of some 28 mm. There is occasionally an additional seventh instar. Pupa: 15 mm long; greenish-white in colour with a dark brown head and dark patches anteriorly on the thorax, dorsally along the abdomen and posteriorly (Clark, 1978: 248).

HABITAT AND ECOLOGY

T. uitenhaga occurs in hot, dry scrubby areas including dry riverbeds, where it may fly in the shade. It is a very local species, frequenting certain spots, of limited extent only, where it skips in a leisurely fashion about the plants near the ground. It is occasionally observed feeding at flowers.

The males establish their territories in the vicinity of the larval food plants. Here the males perch on the stems of grasses or on the ground, occasionally flying slowly around before settling again.

The females frequent the same places as the males, flying at random in search of suitable food plants. They lay their eggs singly on a blade of grass. The eggs take some 20 days to hatch. The larva draws the edges of a blade of grass together to form a tube, in which it lives, crawling out at intervals to feed on the end of a blade. The larval stage lasts about 135 days. Moulting and pupation take place within the tube. The pupal stage lasts 15 to 20 days (Clark, 1978: 248).

This species is on the wing from late September to about the middle of December, with occasional records up to March.

Tsitana uitenhaga male underside

LARVAL FOOD PLANTS

Stipa dregeana (Poaceae).

DISTRIBUTION

South Africa, from Bedford, Grahamstown and Port Elizabeth in the Eastern Cape westwards to Seven Weeks Poort and Heidelberg in the Western Cape.

CONSERVATION

T. uitenhaga is an uncommon and local species but is apparently under no immediate threat.

Tsitana uitenhaga final instar larva (After G.C. Clark 1978)

Tsitana uitenhaga pupa (After G.C. Clark 1978)

Tsitana tulbagha Evans

TULBAGH SYLPH

Tsitana tulbagha Evans, 1937. *Cat. Afr. Hesper.*: 76.

There are two subspecies in Southern Africa, both of which occur in South Africa.

Tsitana tulbagha tulbagha Evans

Tsitana tulbagha Evans, 1937. *Cat. Afr. Hesper.*: 76. Type locality: Piketberg, South Africa. Holotype male is in the Natural History Museum, London.

IDENTIFICATION

Adult. Male. Forewing squarer than in *T. uitenhaga* which it generally resembles. Upperside: dark, dull brown without any markings. Underside: forewing dark brown with apex and costa much paler brown. Hindwing pale fawn brown, with only the central white streak present from the base along vein M_2, not quite reaching the outer margin; the streak along 3A only indicated by some grey scaling. Female. Similar to male, but larger and paler.

Forewing lengths: male 16-18 mm; female 19-20,5 mm.

Early stages. Unrecorded.

DISTRIBUTION

South Africa, from the Western Cape Province in the Tulbagh District, Vanrhynsdorp and at Piketberg.

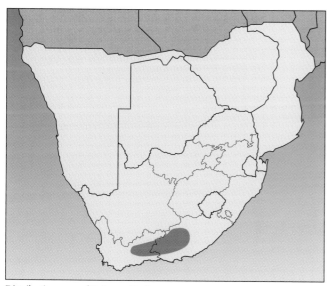

Distribution map of *Tsitana uitenhaga*

Tsitana tulbagha tulbagha female underside

Tsitana tulbagha kaplani Dickson

Tsitana tulbagha kaplani Dickson, 1976. *Entomologist's Rec. J. Var.* **88**: 312. Type locality: Seven Weeks Poort, Western Cape Province. Holotype male in Natural History Museum, London.

IDENTIFICATION

Adult. Generally larger than nominate subspecies. Male. Upperside: generally darker brown in colour than nominate *tulbagha*. Underside: hindwing differs from nominate in being a darker brown colour; the white streak is less well developed owing to its outline being obscured by heavier adjoining white suffusion. Female. Similar to male, but larger and paler.

Forewing lengths: male 14,5-19 mm; female 18,5-20 mm.

Early stages. Unrecorded.

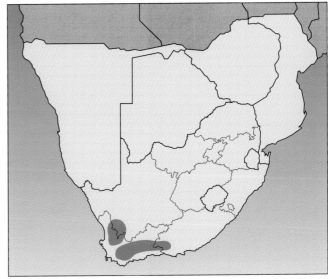

Distribution map of *Tsitana tulbagha*

DISTRIBUTION

South Africa, being confined to the Karoo region of the Western and Eastern Cape Provinces from the Hex River Valley, Karbonaatjies Kraal, hills near Brandvlei, Roodeberg, Montagu, Swellendam to the Swartberg and Uitenhage.

HABITAT AND ECOLOGY

T. tulbagha is an inhabitant of rocky, grassy slopes. It has a moderately fast, sustained, rather regular flight up to a metre above the ground. When strong winds prevail they show very little inclination for flying and rest on the ground or on rocks. They are rarely observed feeding at flowers.

The males do not exhibit hill-topping behaviour but establish their territories among the large clumps of coarse tussock grass which is the larval food plant. Here they patrol up and down, perching here and there on the ground or rocks.

The females frequent the same area as the males, flying in search of suitable food plants on which to lay their eggs. They lay their eggs singly on the blades of the grass. The larvae form shelters by turning over the edges of the blades and binding them together with strands of silk to form tubes. Pupation also occurs in these tubes.

This species is on the wing from September to December.

LARVAL FOOD PLANTS

A coarse tussock grass, *Merxmuellera* sp. (Poaceae).

CONSERVATION

T. tulbagha is fairly widely distributed and is under no threat.

Piketberg, Western Cape, typical habitat of *Tsitana tulbagha*

Tsitana dicksoni Evans

DICKSON'S SYLPH

Tsitana dicksoni Evans, 1955. *Ann. Mag. nat. Hist.* (12)**8**: 882. Type locality: Franschhoek Pass, Western Cape. Holotype male in Natural History Museum, London.

IDENTIFICATION

Adult. Male. Upperside: dark brown without markings. Underside: hindwing ochreous-brown with the central white streak present from the base along vein M_2 not quite reaching outer margin; the streak along 3A less well developed. Female. Similar to male but has paler, rounder wings and a stouter abdomen.

Forewing lengths: male 17-18 mm; female 19-20 mm.

Early stages. Unrecorded.

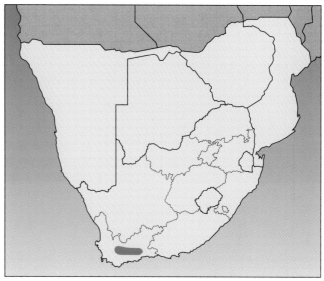

Distribution map of *Tsitana dicksoni*

HABITAT AND ECOLOGY

T. dicksoni is an inhabitant of partly grassy slopes. Its flight is quite fast, skipping around bushy shrubs that grow in its habitat. It rests frequently on the ground or on rocks and is rarely seen at flowers.

The males establish their territories in the vicinity of the larval food plants, often selecting a shrub as a central point. They then circle around the shrub, settling occasionally on the ground or rocks.

The females frequent the same places as the male, flying at random in search of suitable food plants on which to lay. The eggs are laid singly on the leaves of this plant.

This species is on the wing in November and December.

CONSERVATION

T. dicksoni is an inhabitant of high grassy or shrub-covered slopes which are fairly inaccessible, so that the possibility of deliberate habitat destruction is remote. It is considered, however, that the all too frequent mountain fires do constitute a real hazard to the survival of this localised species where it may still occur. This species has been placed on the protected wild animal list of the Cape Province in 1976 (Ordinance 19 of 1974, amendment of Schedule 2 in 1976). It is also recorded as a rare species by S.F. & G.A. Henning in the *South Africa Red Data Book – Butterflies* (1989).

LARVAL FOOD PLANTS

A species of grass, probably *Pseudopentameris macrantha* (Poaceae).

DISTRIBUTION

South Africa, endemic to the Western Cape, above Du Toit's Kloof, the Franschhoek Pass and the Klein Drakenstein Mountains. Also recorded on the Garcia and Robinson Passes.

Tsitana dicksoni male underside

Genus *Astictopterus* C. & R. Felder

Astictopterus C. & R. Felder, 1860. *Wien. ent. Mschr.* **4**: 401. Type species: *Astictopterus jama* C. & R. Felder, fixed by Butler (1870: 95).

Smallish broad-winged, narrow-bodied skippers. Antennae half the length of costa, club gradually pointed and more obtuse than bent. Palpi porrect, or nearly so, third segment in continuation of the second. Forewing venation as in *Tsitana*. Hindwing cell equal to half the wing, end straight; vein Sc+R$_1$ arising opposite a point midway between the origin of CuA$_1$ and M$_3$.

Early stages unrecorded. Food plants Poaceae.

Two species occur in Southern Africa, one of which occurs in South Africa.

Rank grasslands on the margin of the Kubusi Forest, Eastern Cape, a typical habitat of *Astictopterus inornatus*

Astictopterus inornatus (Trimen)

Cyclopides inornatus Trimen, 1864. *Trans. ent. Soc. Lond.* (3) **2**: 179. Type locality: Bashee River, Kaffraria. Holotype male in Natural History Museum, London.

IDENTIFICATION

Adult. Male. Upperside: dull brown, forewing with a row of small whitish apical spots in a straight line, otherwise unmarked. Underside: ferruginous-brown with white spots. Female. Similar to male, but larger and paler.

Forewing lengths: male 12-14,2 mm; female 13,2-14 mm.

Early stages. Unrecorded.

HABITAT AND ECOLOGY

A. inornatus is an inhabitant of the coastal and mist-belt areas of Eastern Cape to KwaZulu-Natal. It usually flies in patches of somewhat tall broad-bladed Tamboekie grass on which its larvae feed, along streams or the edges of forests. It is a weak flier and settles frequently on the stems or blades of grass. Occasionally it ventures out into shorter grass to feed on flowers but does not go far from the Tamboekie grass.

The males establish their territories among the Tamboekie grass. Here they can be seen slowly zig-zagging about the grass in their territories, frequently perching on a stem of grass. Any intruders are rapidly chased off before they return to their original spots.

The females occur in the same places as the males where they fly at random in search of suitable places to oviposit.

This species is on the wing from September to March-April. The best month appears to be January.

LARVAL FOOD PLANTS

Imperata cylindrica (Poaceae).

DISTRIBUTION

South Africa, from the Eastern Cape to KwaZulu-Natal.

CONSERVATION

It is a local species with a specialised habitat but it is fairly widely distributed and is under no immediate threat.

Asticfopterus inornatus male underside

Asticfopterus inornatus female upperside

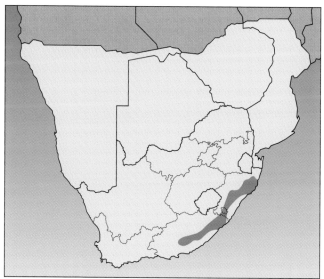

Distribution map of *Asticfopterus inornatus*

141

Genus *Kedestes* Watson

Kedestes Watson, 1893. *Proc. zool. Soc. Lond.* **1893**: 96. Type species: *Hesperia lepenula* Wallengren, 1857, by original designation.

Small to medium-sized skippers with narrowish forewings and white or orange-spotted, brown uppersides. Antennae equal to half the costa: club straight and blunt or with a very short obtuse apiculus. Apical segment of palpi horizontally porrect. Forewing vein CuA_2 arising from midway between wing base and end of the cell; vein M_2 bent down at origin. Hindwing with lower end of cell slightly bent up; vein M_2 well marked and slightly bent down at its origin; vein Rs arising about opposite vein M_2; vein 1A+2A long. Abdomen longer than dorsum.

Egg domed. Larva elongate green with flattened anal segment; head ornate. Pupa elongate cylindrical, anteriorly rounded, dark brown. Food plants Poaceae.

There are fifteen species in Southern Africa, ten of which occur in South Africa.

Kedestes mohozutza (Wallengren)

FULVOUS RANGER

Hesperia mohozutza Wallengren, 1857. *K. svenska Vetensk-Akad. Handl.* (N.F.) **2**(4): 50. Type locality: Kaffraria. Holotype female apparently lost.

IDENTIFICATION

Adult. Male. Upperside: blackish-brown, forewing with three subapical white spots, a row of submarginal yellow streaks; two conjoined cell spots, a large spot in area CuA_1 and a smaller one on each side of it. Hindwing without spots. Underside: forewing brown except orange costally and apically; cream spots as above; outer margin bordered by a black line. Hindwing ground colour orange; area $Sc+R_1$ creamy-yellow with 3 black spots; a single creamy-yellow band down postdiscal area bordered on both sides by a series of black spots; a continuous black marginal line and reduced basal spotting. Female. Similar to male but hindwing upperside with yellow streaks.

Forewing lengths: male 13-15 mm; female 16-20 mm.

Early stages. Unrecorded.

KEY TO THE SPECIES OF *KEDESTES*

1. UHW at least with one yellow spot in centre; LHW without white longitudinal streaks or white veins 2

   UHW unicoloured blackish or at the most with one white discal spot; LHW with light veins or light stripes from the outer margin almost to the base 7

2. Upperside of both wings without reddish-yellow submarginal spots between veins, but sometimes with veins coloured at the margin 3

   At least UFW with a distinct row of red, reddish-yellow or whitish submarginal spots; on the underside these spots are combined into a submarginal band; LHW pale yellow, variegated with black dots and orange spots and streaks 5

3. LHW unicoloured, light yellow without markings .... *K. lepenula*

   LHW with dots or spots 4

4. Upperside with orange spots; LHW with several black dots, but without white spots .... *K. macomo*

   Upperside with discal spots yellowish; LHW with a complete row of light yellow discal spots encircled with black and a similar spot at apex of discal cell .... *K. callicles*

5. UFW without discal spots in M2 and M3; LHW with 3 black spots in area $Sc+R_1$ .... *K. mohozutza*

   UFW with discal spots in M_2 and M_3. LHW with 4 black dots or transverse streaks in area $Sc+R_1$ 6

6. LHW with basal spot in area Rs well basad of other basal spots, the 2nd spot being more in line; inner submarginal series of black spots W-shaped; one indistinct pale band; LFW with a pale bar at end of cell, followed by a broad, distinct, pale area to subapical and submarginal spots .... *K. nerva*

   LHW with basal spot in area Rs in line with other basal spots or nearly so; inner submarginal series of black spots NOT W-shaped; two distinct pale bands .... *K. chaca*

7. Cilia white with black spots at ends of veins; UHW with a light spot at end of discal cell; LHW with two light longitudinal stripes, one in 3A and one in the discal cell and area M_1; forewing with a discal spot in area M_1 .... *K. barberae*

   Cilia spotless, grey or whitish; UHW without markings; forewing without discal spot in area M_1 8

8. LHW with a white longitudinal stripe filling up the anterior half of the discal cell and whole area M_1; a similar, though narrower stripe extends from the centre of area 3A to the margin .... *K. wallengrenii*

   LHW without these two white longitudinal streaks 9

9. Forewing white markings well developed .... *K. niveostriga*

   Forewing white marking reduced or absent .... *K. lenis*

Kedestes mohozutza male underside

HABITAT AND ECOLOGY

K. mohozutza is an inhabitant of grassy slopes, montane grasslands and forest margins. It appears to favour short grass. It seems to frequent marshy spots more often than others, especially in the mountains where water oozes from the ground among the grass. Its flight is quite rapid but it often settles. This species is often observed feeding at flowers, especially *Scabiosa* species.

The males do not exhibit hilltopping behaviour, instead they establish their territories along the slopes. Here they perch on a blade of grass, occasionally flying off to investigate an intruder before settling again.

The females frequent the same places as the males where they fly at random, apparently in search of suitable food plants.

This species is on the wing from November to March.

LARVAL FOOD PLANTS

Unrecorded.

DISTRIBUTION

South Africa, from the Eastern Cape, northwards along the grassy hills of KwaZulu-Natal Drakensberg, into Mpumalanga and Gauteng highveld. Eastern highlands of Zimbabwe and adjacent Moçambique, Zambia, Malawi, Zaire, Tanzania, Kenya and Uganda.

CONSERVATION

K. mohozutza is a widespread species and is under no threat.

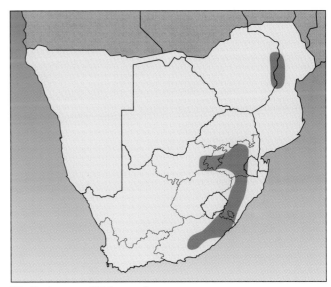

Distribution map of *Kedestes mohozutza*

Kedestes mohozutza male upperside

143

Kedestes chaca (Trimen)

CHAKA'S RANGER

Pyrgus chaca Trimen, 1873. *Trans. ent. Soc. Lond.* **1873**: 118.
Type locality: Grahamstown, South Africa. Holotype male in
Natural History Museum, London.

IDENTIFICATION

Adult. Male. Upperside: forewing dark brown with pale yellow
spots, a row of submarginal orange streaks and a streak of yellow
scales along dorsum. Hindwing dark brown with paler streaks
basally and a discal patch of yellow-orange hairs, usually distinct
with a weak series of submarginal orange streaks. Underside:
forewing dark brown, except orange costally, apically and down submarginal area; pale yellow spots as above. Hindwing orange except
for two distinct creamy bands (subbasal and postdiscal) which are
bordered on both sides by a complete series of black spots, and a
series of marginal black streaks not forming a continuous line. Female. Similar to male but wings paler and hindwing upperside
with discal orange patch and submarginal series of orange streaks
distinct; orange submarginal streaks of forewing also better developed.

Kedestes chaca female underside

Forewing lengths: male 17-18 mm; female 19-21 mm.

Early stages. Unrecorded.

Kedestes chaca female upperside

HABITAT AND ECOLOGY

K. chaca, an inhabitant of grassy slopes on mountains where it frequents long grass in damp areas. They may often be found on the grassy slopes and spurs of the Drakensberg in KwaZulu-Natal.

They fly rapidly, keeping close to the ground, but do not fly far before resettling on blades of grass or flowers. They often visit flowers, especially those of *Basananthe sandersoni* (Passifloraceae), a very common low plant in our veld.

The males exhibit hilltopping behaviour and establish their territories on the summits of grassy hills and mountains. Here they can be observed resting on the ground or grass stalks or vigorously chasing an intruder around the peak.

The females are usually found on the slopes where they fly at random, presumably in search of food plants. Occasionally they can be found near the summit in search of males with which to mate.

This species is on the wing from October to April, the best months for observation being December and January.

LARVAL FOOD PLANTS

Unrecorded.

DISTRIBUTION

South Africa, from the Eastern Cape as far south as Grahamstown, northwards into KwaZulu-Natal, along the mountains to as far north as Dargle.

CONSERVATION

A rather local species but has a fairly wide distribution and is under no immediate threat.

Kedestes nerva (Fabricius)

SCARCE RANGER

Hesperia nerva Fabricius, 1793. *Syst. Ent.* **3** (1): 340. Type locality: "Indiis". The type was probably collected in KwaZulu-Natal.

IDENTIFICATION

Adult. Male. Upperside: blackish-brown; forewing with three subapical white spots and two postdiscal spots in areas M_2 and M_3; submarginal area with a row of yellow streaks; two conjoined cell spots, a large spot in area CuA_1 and a smaller one on each side of it. Hindwing with a yellow discal patch of four postdiscal spots. Underside: forewing brown, except orange costally and apically with cream spots. Hindwing orange with a creamy-yellow bar at end of cell, followed by a broad, distinct pale area to apical and submarginal black spots; four black spots in area $Sc+R_1$ and on both sides of the pale bands, inner submarginal row being arranged in a W-shaped pattern. Female. Similar to male but hindwing upperside with discal orange patch larger and submarginal series of orange streaks distinct; range of submarginal streaks of forewing also better developed.

Forewing lengths: male 13-15 mm; female 16-17,5 mm.

Early stages. Unrecorded.

HABITAT AND ECOLOGY

K. nerva is an inhabitant of dry bush, woodland and grassveld areas. It usually flies near the ground among grass, settling occasionally on grass stems or the ground. It skips about quite rapidly

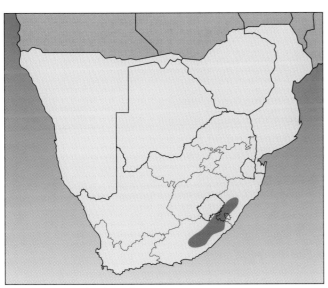

Distribution map of *Kedestes chaca*

Kedestes nerva male upperside

in circles but for short distances only. It is often encountered feeding at white *Scabiosa columbana* flowers along the banks of dry streams or dongas.

The males exhibit hilltopping behaviour although they also establish territories lower down the slopes. The males usually perch on grass stems or on the ground. They occasionally fly off circling around their territories before settling again. If another male is encountered he will be chased for quite a distance before they return to their respective territories.

The females are usually observed flying at random in search of suitable places on which to lay.

This species is double brooded, appearing in October and November and again from February to April.

Kedestes nerva male underside

LARVAL FOOD PLANTS

Unrecorded.

DISTRIBUTION

South Africa, from the north-eastern districts of KwaZulu-Natal and into the North-West Province, Gauteng, Northern Province and Mpumalanga.

CONSERVATION

K. nerva is a local and uncommon species, however it is fairly widespread and is under no immediate threat.

Kedestes nerva female underside

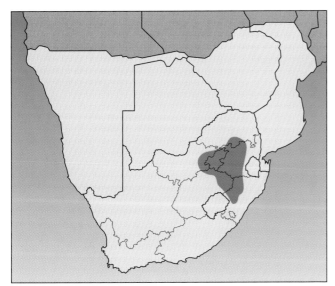

Distribution map of *Kedestes nerva*

Kedestes nerva female upperside

Kedestes barberae (Trimen)

BARBER'S RANGER

Thymelicus barberae Trimen, 1873. *Trans. ent. Soc. Lond.* **1873**: 120.

There are three subspecies in Southern Africa, all of which occur in South Africa.

Kedestes barberae barberae (Trimen)

Thymelicus barberae Trimen, 1873. *Trans. ent. Soc. Lond.* **1873**: 120. Type locality: Cape Colony. Holotype female in Natural History Museum, London.

IDENTIFICATION

Adult. Male. Antennal club thick. Upperside: blackish-brown; forewing with 3 subapical white spots in line and one in M_1 more distad, one postdiscal spot in M_2, one large spot at end of cell and median spots in M_3 and CuA_2; hindwing unmarked. Underside: brown; forewing with a white triangular patch from apex down outer margin, white spots as above; hindwing with very characteristic arrow-shaped, shiny white streaks. Female. Similar to male but larger with rounder wings.

Forewing lengths: male 14-16 mm; female 16,5-18 mm.

DISTRIBUTION

South Africa, from the Eastern Cape, KwaZulu-Natal, Free State, Gauteng, Northern Province and Mpumalanga, into Lesotho and Zimbabwe.

Kedestes barberae bunta Evans

Kedestes barberae bunta Evans, 1955, *Ann. Mag. nat. Hist.* (12) **8**: 883. Type locality: Steenberg Railway Station, Western Cape.

IDENTIFICATION

Adult. Similar to nominate subspecies but is a smaller darker race with a distinctive rich brown hindwing underside.

Forewing lengths: male 13,5-15 mm; female 14,5-15,5 mm.

DISTRIBUTION

South Africa, confined to the Cape Peninsula flats in the Western Cape.

Kedestes barberae barberae male underside

Kedestes barberae barberae final instar larva (After G.C. Clark 1978)

Kedestes barberae barberae pupa (After G.C. Clark 1978)

147

Kedestes barberae bonsa Evans

Kedestes barberae bonsa Evans, 1955. *Ann. Mag. nat. Hist.* (12) **8**: 883. Type locality: Steynsburg, Eastern Cape.

IDENTIFICATION

Adult. Differs from the other subspecies by the fact that the white markings on the underside of the hindwing form two separate lines.

Forewing lengths: male 12,5-14,5 mm; female 14-15 mm.

Early stages. Egg: milk-white, changing to pale yellow and then salmon and finally brown as development proceeds; diameter 1,3 mm, height 0,8 mm; with some 60 faint and ill-defined longitudinal ribs from the base to about a third of the way up the side, with minute indentations between them. Larva: first to third instars yellowish with a black head; fourth and fifth instars green with a pale brown head with darker brown markings. It attains a length of some 33 mm. Pupa: 16,5 mm long; brownish-grey in colour (Clark, 1978: 250).

DISTRIBUTION

South Africa, from the Eastern Cape to the southern Free State.

HABITAT AND ECOLOGY

K. barberae is an inhabitant of open grassland and has been recorded on the grassy slopes of mountains at an elevation of 2 000 to 2 800 metres in the Drakensberg. It is often found along the grassy banks of streams or vleis where it flies rapidly about, frequently settling on the blades of long grass. The subspecies *bunta*, however, is recorded at sea level at Strandfontein a few miles east of Muizenberg, Cape Peninsula, where it flies about some broad-bladed marsh grass among the sand dunes. The species zig-zags or skips rapidly low above the ground. It is particularly fond of flowers and is often encountered feeding on them.

The males occasionally exhibit hilltopping behaviour but usually establish their territories in the vicinity of the food plants. Here they perch on the ground, grass or low shrubs, occasionally circling about before settling again.

The females are found in the vicinity of the food plants where they search for suitable places on which to oviposit. They lay their eggs singly on the grass. They take some 15 days to hatch. The larvae draw the edges of the grass together to form tubes in which they live. They feed on the upper end of the blade. The larval stage lasts some 73 days. Pupation takes place within the grass tube. The pupal stage lasts 23 to 29 days (Clark, 1978: 250).

The species is on the wing during October and November and again in March. The subspecies *bunta* flies during September.

LARVAL FOOD PLANTS

Imperata cylindrica (Poaceae).

CONSERVATION

K. barberae is a fairly widespread species and is under no immediate threat. The local habitats of the subspecies could be threatened, particularly that of the subspecies *bunta* in the Cape Peninsula.

Kedestes barberae bonsa female upperside

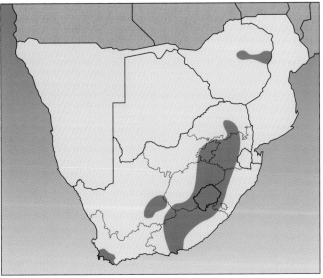

Distribution map of *Kedestes barberae*

Kedestes niveostriga (Trimen)

DARK RANGER

Pamphila niveostriga Trimen, 1864. *Trans. ent. Soc. Lond.* (3)
2: 179. Type locality: Bashee River, Kaffraria. Holotype male
in Natural History Museum, London.

IDENTIFICATION

Adult. Larger than *K. lenis,* the whitish spots on the forewing also
more prominent. Male. Upperside: dark brown; forewing with 2
small subapical spots, one postdiscal spot in M_2, one spot at end of
cell, large discal spot in M_3 and a smaller one in CuA_2; cilia plain
brown; hindwing unmarked. Underside: forewing dark brown
basally and along inner margin and ochreous-brown discally with
same white marking as above but no spot in CuA_2; hindwing ochreous-brown with lighter veins. Female. Similar to male but larger with
rounder wings.

Forewing lengths: male 15-17 mm; female 16-17,5 mm.

Early stages. Egg: pure white; diameter 1,2-1,25 mm, height 0,75-
0,95 mm; with some 50 longitudinal ribs reaching halfway up the
sides and cross-braced by staggered ribs which resolve into a hexagonal pattern. Larva: first instar greenish-white with long black
setae on posterior segment and a black head; second and third instars green with blackish-brown head; fourth and fifth instars green
with a brown head. It attains a length of some 32 mm. Pupa: 19 mm
long; greyish-brown in colour (Clark, 1978: 252).

Kedestes niveostriga male underside

Kedestes niveostriga male upperside

HABITAT AND ECOLOGY

K. niveostriga is an inhabitant of long Tamboekie grass fringing streams in the moister areas of the country, often in the vicinity of rainforests. The grass in these areas often reaches a height of 3 metres. *K. niveostriga* flies from 1 to 2 metres above the ground where short grass grows. It is a vigorous flier, often darting about at high speed, but sometimes it skips slowly in zig-zags or circles around. It usually rests on the grass stems. They are often attracted to flowers.

The males do not exhibit hilltopping behaviour but establish their territories in the long grass around the breeding areas. Here they perch on the long grass, often circling slowly about their territory before settling again.

The females are less active than the males but fly in the same area in search of suitable food plants on which to oviposit. Eggs are laid singly on a blade of the grass. The eggs take from 9-14 days to hatch. The larva on emergence eats the egg shell. The larvae draw and bind together the edges of a blade of grass to form the tubes in which they live. They crawl out at intervals to feed on the end of the blade. The larval stage lasts some 73 days. Pupation takes place within the tube. The pupal stage lasts about 26 days (Clark, 1978: 252).

This species is on the wing from August to April.

LARVAL FOOD PLANTS

Imperata cylindrica (Poaceae).

DISTRIBUTION

South Africa, the Eastern Cape from the Bashee River to the Tugela River in KwaZulu-Natal and into adjacent Lesotho.

CONSERVATION

K. niveostriga is a local species with a specialised habitat of long grass and rushes in the neighbourhood of water. Where it occurs it can be very common and Swanepoel (1953) observed more than fifty specimens over an area the size of a tennis court. The species is fairly widespread and is under no immediate threat but an eye must be kept on their habitat to ensure that it is not cleared for "development" since they are found in prime positions near water.

Kedestes niveostriga final instar larva (After G.C. Clark 1978)

Kedestes niveostriga pupa (After G.C. Clark 1978)

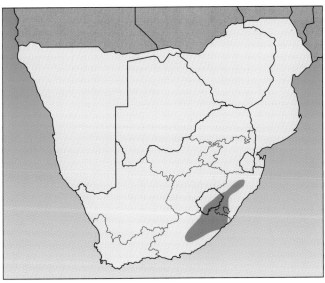

Distribution map of *Kedestes niveostriga*

Kedestes lenis Riley

UNIQUE RANGER

Kedestes lenis Riley, 1932. *Ann. Mag. nat. Hist.* (10) **10**: 150.

There are two subspecies, both endemic to South Africa.

Kedestes lenis lenis Riley

Kedestes lenis Riley, 1932. *Ann. Mag. nat. Hist.* (10) **10**: 150. Type locality: Cape of Good Hope. Holotype male in Natural History Museum, London.

IDENTIFICATION

Adult. Smaller than *K. niveostriga* with fainter, much reduced, white markings. Palpi ochre-coloured beneath. Male. Upperside: dark brown with faint spots in M_2 and M_3 of forewing, otherwise unmarked. Underside: forewing reddish-brown becoming darker along inner margin with only faint white median marks in M_2 and M_3; hindwing reddish-brown with paler veins becoming white along inner margin. Female. Similar to male but larger with rounder wings.

Forewing lengths: male 14-15 mm; female 16-16,5 mm.

DISTRIBUTION

South Africa, at Strandfontein east of Muizenberg along the False Bay coast in the Western Cape.

Kedestes lenis alba male underside (Paratype)

Kedestes lenis alba ssp. n.

DIAGNOSIS

Smaller than nominate subspecies, lower surface of palpi white, ground colour of underside more ochre-brown, cilia greyish-white not ochre-tinged.

DESCRIPTION

Adult. Male. Upperside: ground colour dark brown. Forewing with spots in areas M_2 and M_3. Hindwing unmarked. Cilia greyish-white. Underside: forewing ground colour ochre-brown becoming darker along inner margin and only faint white median marks in areas M_2 and M_3. Hindwing ochre-brown with paler veins and a broad silvery-white inner marginal line. Female. As in male except that the wing-shape is rounder and with an additional spot in area R_5 of forewing.

Genitalia. Male. Valve longer than nominate, with dorsal and distal lobes more pronounced.

Forewing lengths: male 12,5-14,5 mm; female 14-15,5 mm.

Early stages. Unrecorded.

MATERIAL EXAMINED

Holotype male. South Africa, Golden Gate Highlands National Park, Free State, 16.xii.1993, S.F. Henning. Paratypes: 4 males, 2 females same data as holotype; 1 female same data but G.A. Henning; 1 female same data but 2.i.1989, G.A. Henning; 3 males, 3 females same data but 2.i.1993, G.A. Henning; 10 males same data but 21.xi.1993, S.E. Woodhall; 3 females same data but 16.xii.1993, S.E. Woodhall. Holotype in the Transvaal Museum, Pretoria. Paratypes in the collections of W.H., S.F. & G.A. Henning and S.E. Woodhall.

Kedestes lenis alba male upperside (Paratype)

Kedestes lenis alba female upperside (Paratype)

Kedestes lenis alba female underside (Paratype)

HABITAT AND ECOLOGY

K. lenis is an inhabitant of grassy areas, especially along streams and marshy places. It prefers shorter grass on which it constantly rests. The nominate subspecies has been recorded at sea level on the Cape Flats while *alba* has been found in parts of the KwaZulu-Natal Drakensberg at altitudes above 1 800 metres. The species skips about fairly rapidly, settling frequently to rest. It is rarely observed feeding at flowers.

The males do not appear to exhibit hilltopping behaviour and they establish their territories near the food plants where they perch on the short grass. They occasionally fly around their territories before settling again. If another male is encountered it is rapidly chased from the area.

The females occur in the same areas as the male, where they fly about in search of suitable food plants on which to lay.

They are on the wing from October and November to about March.

LARVAL FOOD PLANTS

Imperata cylindrica (Poaceae).

DISTRIBUTION

South Africa from the Golden Gate Highlands National Park in the Free State Province, the KwaZulu-Natal Drakensberg at about 1 800 metres and the northerly mountains of the Eastern Cape.

CONSERVATION

Widely distributed in inaccessible habitats. Recorded from the Golden Gate Highlands National Park and Drakensberg reserves.

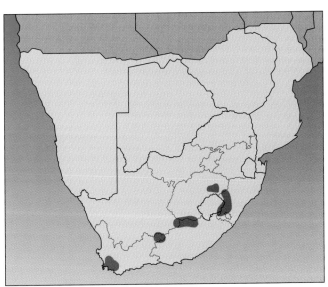

Distribution map of *Kedestes lenis*

Kedestes wallengrenii (Trimen)

WALLENGREN'S RANGER

Thymelicus wallengrenii Trimen, 1883. *Trans. ent. Soc. Lond.* **1883**: 361.

There are two subspecies of which only the nominate occurs in South Africa. The subspecies *fenestratus* Butler, 1893, comes from Tanzania and Malawi

Kedestes wallengrenii wallengrenii (Trimen)

Thymelicus wallengrenii Trimen, 1883. *Trans. ent. Soc. Lond.* **1883**: 361. Type locality: Zululand. Holotype male in Natural History Museum, London.

IDENTIFICATION

Adult. Male. Upperside: dark brown; forewing with three small subapical spots, one postdiscal spot in M_2, double spot at end of cell, large discal spot in M_3 and a smaller one in CuA_2; hindwing unmarked. Underside: forewing reddish-brown becoming darker along inner margin and paler distally with white spotting as on upperside; hindwing reddish-brown with grey-white longitudinal stripes. Female. Similar to the male but larger with rounder wings.

Forewing lengths: male 13-15 mm; female 14,5-17 mm.

Early stages. Unrecorded.

HABITAT AND ECOLOGY

K. wallengrenii is an inhabitant of grassland and woodland. It appears to favour shorter grass although it also occurs near rivers where the grass is long. It is a fast flier, and often disappears from view when disturbed. *K. wallengrenii* is readily attracted to flowers. When not feeding it flies about the grass, resting on the leaves or on the ground.

The males do not appear to exhibit hilltopping behaviour but establish their territories on the slopes or flats where the food plants are growing. They can be found perching on grass, leaves or on the ground. At times they circle about, skipping up and down near the ground in their territories before alighting again.

The females frequent the same spots as the males, apparently searching for suitable food plants on which to lay.

This species is on the wing from August to April.

LARVAL FOOD PLANTS

Unrecorded.

DISTRIBUTION

South Africa, from the grassy hills of KwaZulu-Natal, ranging westwards along the grassy highveld of Gauteng and northwards along the Drakensberg of Mpumalanga and Northern Province, Zimbabwe and Moçambique.

CONSERVATION

K. wallengrenii is a scarce and local species, however it is fairly widespread and is under no threat at present.

Kedestes wallengrenii wallengrenii male underside

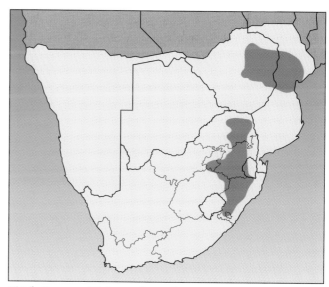

Distribution map of *Kedestes wallengrenii*

Kedestes lepenula (Wallengren)

CHEQUERED RANGER

Hesperia lepenula Wallengren, 1857. *K. svenska VetenskAkad. Handl.* (N.F.) **2** (4): 50. Type locality: Kaffraria.

IDENTIFICATION

Adult. Male. Upperside: dark brown; forewing with 4 orange sub-apical spots, orange postdiscal spots in M_3, CuA_1 and CuA_2 fused into a band, basally orange up to median area and below costa; hindwing with an orange spot in cell and a broad orange postdiscal band from veins Rs to 3A. Underside: ochre-yellow without markings. Female. Similar to male but larger with rounder wings.

Forewing lengths: male 13-14 mm; female 14,5-16 mm.

Early stages. Unrecorded.

HABITAT AND ECOLOGY

K. lepenula is an inhabitant of grasslands and bushveld. It is a fast flier, whirling about so rapidly at times that one quickly loses sight of it. The species is occasionally observed feeding at flowers.

The males exhibit hilltopping behaviour, establishing territories along the tops of koppies or ridges at midday. Here they perch on stones, grass stems, leaves of low plants, rocks or the ground. They occasionally dart off to chase an intruder or simply to circle around before settling again.

The females fly at random through the veld in search of suitable food plants on which to lay. They occasionally ascend to the tops of koppies and ridges in search of males.

This species is on the wing from September to April.

LARVAL FOOD PLANTS

Imperata cylindrica (Poaceae).

DISTRIBUTION

South Africa, Eastern and Northern Cape, Free State, North-West and Northern Provinces, into Botswana and Namibia.

CONSERVATION

It is a widespread species and is under no threat.

Kedestes lepenula female underside

Kedestes lepenula female upperside

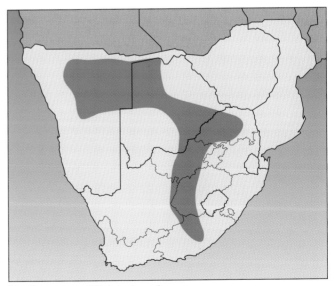
Distribution map of *Kedestes lepenula*

Kedestes macomo (Trimen)

MACOMO RANGER

Cyclopides macomo Trimen, 1862. *Trans. ent. Soc. Lond.* (3) 1: 405. Type locality: King William's Town, Eastern Cape Province.

IDENTIFICATION

Adult. Male. Upperside: dark brown; forewing with 3 yellow-orange subapical spots, 3 yellow-orange squarish postdiscal spots in M_3, CuA_1, CuA_2 and a large yellow-orange patch at upper end of cell; hindwing with a small cell spot and 3 postdiscal spots in Rs, M_1 and M_2. Underside: yellow-orange except for third of forewing nearer the inner margin which is dark brown; the hindwing is spotted with black and, although the forewing bears one or two spots it tends to be streaked with brown, especially in the outer half of the wing; there is a narrow brown-black border to the outer margins of both wings. Female. Similar to male but larger with rounder wings.

Forewing lengths: male 13,5-15,5 mm; female 16-17 mm.

Early stages. Egg: pale milky-white; diameter 1,2 mm, height 0,75 mm; with some 48 faint longitudinal ribs which reach only half-way up the side, and with extremely fine staggered cross-bracing; this all breaks up into a rough hexagonal pattern over the top of the egg. Larva: first instar white with a black head; second to fourth instars green with a black to dark brown head; fifth instar larva pale greenish-white with a black and green patterned head. Pupa: 18 mm, brown in colour (Clark, 1978: 254).

Kedestes macomo male underside

HABITAT AND ECOLOGY

K. macomo is an inhabitant of bushveld area where it is usually observed flitting about the long grass in the shade of trees. Its flight is low and fairly rapid. It often settles on the ground, low plants or grass. Occasionally it can be observed feeding at flowers or drinking at muddy spots.

The males do not exhibit hilltopping behaviour, instead they establish territories in the long grass in the shade of trees. Here the males perch on the ground, low plants or grass, occasionally circling rapidly around their territories before settling again. If another male, or even another species, encroaches on its territory it is rapidly chased out of the area. The males occupy their territories for hours and are particularly active on hot, sunny days.

Kedestes macomo female underside

155

Kedestes macomo final instar larva

The females are much scarcer and fly at random through the area in search of food plants. Eggs are laid singly on blades of grass. The eggs take about 9 days to hatch. The larvae join the edges of grass leaves together with silk to form tubes in which they can shelter. They crawl out of these tubes at intervals to feed on the end of a grass blade. The larval stage lasts some 50 days. Pupation takes place within the tube. The pupal stage lasts some 26 days (Clark, 1978: 254).

The species is on the wing from October until May, and occasionally during winter. The best time appears to be around March and April.

Kedestes macomo pupa (After G.C. Clark, 1978)

LARVAL FOOD PLANTS

Imperata cylindrica (Cotton-wool grass) (Poaceae).

DISTRIBUTION

South Africa, from the Eastern Cape, through KwaZulu-Natal northwards into Gauteng, Northern Province and Mpumalanga, Swaziland, Zimbabwe and Moçambique.

CONSERVATION

K. macomo is a widespread species and is under no threat.

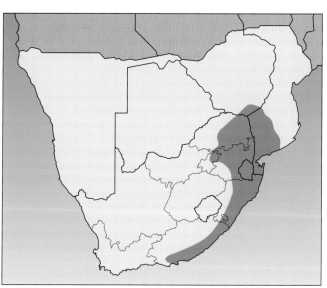

Distribution map of *Kedestes macomo*

Kedestes callicles (Hewitson)

PALE RANGER

Cyclopides callicles Hewitson, 1867-1868. *Descriptions of one hundred new species of Hesperiidae*: 42. Type locality: Damara-land. Holotype female in Natural History Museum, London.

IDENTIFICATION

Adult. Male. Upperside: dark brown with several squarish or rectangular yellow spots; forewing with a row of pale yellow spots near apex to middle of vein 1A+2A, the spot in CuA_1 largest, two cell spots and three subapical spots; hindwing with highly irregularly-placed spots. Underside: yellow-gold except for half of forewing nearest to inner margin which is dark brown; yellow spots of upperside are in same positions but are distinctly dark-edged; veins outlined in black as they approach outer margins, which themselves have a narrow black border. Female. Similar to male, but larger with more rounded wings.

Forewing lengths: male 13-14 mm; female 15-16 mm.

Early stages. Unrecorded.

HABITAT AND ECOLOGY

K. callicles is an inhabitant of dense bushveld country at altitudes from 600 to 1 500 metres. Where the thornbush is particularly dense it will usually be found on the edges but keeping to the shade of the trees. *K. callicles* seldom ventures into the bright sunlight. Its flight is fairly rapid but it settles frequently on the ground. It is occasionally observed feeding at flowers.

The males seldom show hill-topping behaviour, keeping to the flats where they establish territories in the shade of the thorn trees. Here they perch on the plants or grass in the shade, occasionally circling around the area before returning to their original perch site. Any intruding male is quickly chased off.

The female frequents the same places as the male where she flies in search of suitable food plants which are probably grasses.

The species is on the wing from about the beginning of November until April.

LARVAL FOOD PLANTS

Unrecorded.

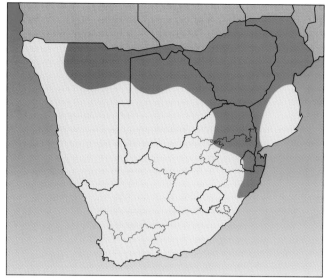

Distribution map of *Kedestes callicles*

DISTRIBUTION

South Africa, from the bushveld of northern KwaZulu-Natal, Gauteng, Northern Province and Mpumalanga, Swaziland, Botswana, Namibia, Zimbabwe, Moçambique, East Africa and Somalia, west to Nigeria.

CONSERVATION

K. callicles is a widespread species and is under no threat.

Kedestes callicles male underside

Genus *Parosmodes* Holland

Parosmodes Holland, 1896. *Proc. zool. Soc. Lond.* **1896**: 45.
Type species: *Pamphila morantii* Trimen, 1873, by original designation.

Small skippers with orange markings. Apiculus of antennal club sharply pointed and bent down almost in a right angle. Forewing origin of vein CuA_2 equidistant between wing base and end of cell; vein M_2 decurved; origin of vein CuA_1 equidistant between veins M_3 and CuA_2. Hindwing outer margin uniformly convex; lower end of cell slightly bent up; origins of veins CuA_2 and Rs opposite. Male forewing underside with a black hair-pencil at the posterior margin (Evans, 1937: 114).

Eggs flattened domes with moderately sculptured ribs. Larvae long but fairly broad, narrowing at both ends; final instar larval head-shield large, ornately marked; first segment with prothoracic shield dorsally. Pupae short and squat, pilose, anteriorly bluntly rounded.

Food plants Combretaceae, Euphorbiaceae and Myrtaceae.

There is only one species in Southern Africa.

Parosmodes morantii morantii male underside

Parosmodes morantii (Trimen)

MORANT'S ORANGE

Pamphila morantii Trimen, 1873. *Trans. ent. Soc. Lond.* **1873**: 122.

There are two subspecies, of which only the nominate occurs in Southern Africa. The subspecies *axis* Evans (1937: 114) is found in Tropical Africa.

Parosmodes morantii morantii (Trimen)

Pamphila morantii Trimen, 1873. *Trans. ent. Soc. Lond.* **1873**: 122. Type locality: KwaZulu-Natal. Holotype female in Coll. Morant.

IDENTIFICATION

Adult. Male. Upperside: ground colour brown, forewing with costa basally ochreous, orange spot in cell and an orange discal band which may be broken in areas M_1-M_2; hindwing with orange discal and basal patch, fringe orange. Underside: brownish-orange with irregularly placed black dots on the hindwing. Female. Similar to male but larger and rounder wings with less extensive orange markings.

Forewing lengths: male 13,5-14,5 mm; female 15,5-16,5 mm.

Early stages. Egg: pale yellow at first, changing to bright salmon, then to salmon-tinted grey; diameter 1,4 mm, height 0,8 mm; with 14 to 17 longitudinal ribs joining up to a collar round the micropyle, there are some 52 faint cross-ribs, better seen on the longitudinal rib. Larva: first instar reddish-brown becoming ochreous dorsally, with a blackish-brown head; second and third instar greyish-brown with one dark dorsal longitudinal band and a dark brown head; fourth instar ochre-brown with a darker brown dorsal stripe and a yellow and brown head; fifth and sixth (final) instar ochre with pale to whitish spots and a darker dorsal stripe, head ochre and brown. It attains a length of 24 mm. Pupa: 13-15 mm; colour varies from pale salmon to pale dull yellow with a dark brown head (Clark, 1978: 256).

HABITAT AND ECOLOGY

P. morantii is an inhabitant of woodland and savannah, flying about the grass on the flats and along the slopes of hills. It flies on the edge of bush in the late afternoon as well as earlier in the day on occasion. It is rarely seen at flowers.

The males often exhibit hilltopping behaviour, generally perching on trees about 2 metres above the ground. They usually ascend to the hilltops at midday. They sometimes settle on low plants, or stems of grass, but more usually selects bushes about 1-2 metres high. Intruders are quickly chased off.

The females fly in search of suitable food plants on which to lay. They lay their eggs singly on the surface of a leaf. The eggs hatch after about 8 days. The larvae conceal themselves in shelters which they make by turning over and binding together portions of leaves of the food plants. When in an advanced state a shelter may be formed by a larva from a single relatively large leaf which is completely turned over, from the upperside. In other cases two or more smaller leaves may be bound together. Parts of the leaf or leaves forming the shelter are apparently, from their appearance in the field, eaten by the larva from inside the shelter. The larval stage lasts some 68 days. Pupation occurs in a shelter of silk-bound leaves and the pupa is secured to the internal webbing by its cremastral hooks. The adult emerges after 20-25 days (Clark, 1978: 256).

This species is double-brooded, being on the wing from July to September and, later, between December and May, but with specimens also emerging between the main periods.

Parosmodes morantii morantii male upperside

Parosmodes morantii morantii final instar larva brown form

Parosmodes morantii morantii final instar larva green form (Photo: R. Paré)

159

LARVAL FOOD PLANTS

Terminalia sp., *Quisqualis* sp., *Combretum molle* (Combretaceae); *Bridelia micrantha* (Euphorbiaceae); *Syzygium cordatum* (Myrtaceae).

DISTRIBUTION

South Africa, from KwaZulu-Natal, Gauteng, Northern Province and Mpumalanga, Botswana, Zimbabwe, Moçambique to East Africa (Kenya and Tanzania) and west to Malawi, Zambia, Zaire and Angola.

CONSERVATION

P. morantii is a widespread species and is under no threat.

Parosmodes morantii morantii pupa (Photo: R. Paré)

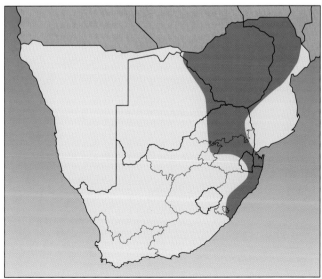

Distribution map of *Parosmodes morantii*

Genus *Acleros* Mabille

Acleros Mabille, 1887. *Hist. Phys. Natur. et Polit. Madag.* 18: 347. Type species: *Cyclopides leucopyga* Mabille, 1877, by monotypy.

Small dark-brown skippers with white cilia on hindwing and the abdomen white at or before the apex. Antennae rather less than half the length of the costa; club hooked to a short apiculus beyond middle, white before apiculus. Palpi with long, thin apical segment. Forewing vein CuA_2 arising midway between wing base and end of cell; vein M_2 straight. Hindwing cell end straight, vein M_2 well marked and arising nearer to vein M_1; vein CuA_2 arising well before vein Rs (Evans, 1937: 116). The males have UFW uni-coloured black, whereas the females have 2 or 3 white or whitish discal spots. LHW shows a peculiar, interwoven marking consisting of striae and indistinct scaled spots on a lighter ground.

Eggs domed with parallel sides, finely sculptured. Larvae long but fairly broad, narrowing at both ends, with leaf-like markings dorsally; final instar larval headshield large, ornately marked. Pupae short and blunt anteriorly, with green leaf-like markings.

Food plants Anacardiaceae and Malpighiaceae.

There are two species in Southern Africa. *A. ploetzi* (Mabille) is found in Zimbabwe and Moçambique, while *A. mackenii* (Trimen) is also found in South Africa.

Acleros mackenii (Trimen)

MACKEN'S DART

P*amphila mackenii* Trimen, 1868. *Trans. ent. Soc. Lond.* **1868**: 95. Type locality: Durban, KwaZulu-Natal. Holotype male in Natural History Museum, London.

IDENTIFICATION

Adult. Form *mackenii,* the dry-season form. Male. Upperside: blackish-brown; forewing unmarked or with small dull ochreous spots in areas CuA_1 and CuA_2; hindwing dark brown with a white fringe. Underside: forewing apex ferruginous; hindwing with basal half ferruginous-brown but outwardly broadly lilacine, faint traces of a ring spot at end of cell. Female. Similar to male but with spots in areas CuA_1 and CuA_2 larger and nearly white. Underside: forewing apex variegated lilacine and ochreous; hindwing with basal half ochreous.

Form *denia* Evans (1937. *Cat. Afr. Hesper.*: 118) is the wet-season form. Male. Generally like *mackenii* but upperside hindwing with white outer marginal area wider and the female has a dot in area M_3 of the forewing and faint traces of apical spots. Underside: much darker due in part to the reduction of the lilacine scaling and sparse dark ochreous-green scaling at the apex of the forewing and in the middle of the hindwing, where the outer area appears uniformly dark and the ring spot at end of cell is prominent.

Forewing lengths: male 13-15,5 mm; female 14-15,5 mm.

Early stages. Egg: brownish-red, then pale brown with a touch of purple or red but darkening with age; diameter 0,95 mm, height 0,65 mm; with 19 to 24 longitudinal ribs braced by some 27 very fine staggered ribs, which break up into an extremely fine hexagonal pattern near the top of the egg. Larva: first instar greenish-white with a black head; second instar olive-green with a dark brown head; third instar pale whitish-green with a blackish head; fourth instar colour variable olive or pale green with darker green oblique dorso-lateral stripes and longitudinal dorsal line. It attains a length of some 18 mm. Pupa: 13 mm; irregularly shaped and olive green resembling a crumpled leaf and is difficult to detect (Clark, 1978: 258).

HABITAT AND ECOLOGY

A. mackenii is an inhabitant of swampy spots in forest, thick bush or undergrowth near forest streams. Both sexes are often observed along the forest edge, in clearings and roads, flying about in the sunshine. It is a very common insect in the coastal bush and rainforest of the eastern side of the country. It is a frequent visitor to flowers but is not often seen feeding. It has also been observed feeding at bird droppings. Flying in the shade it is readily recognised by the white tip of its abdomen. It is a relatively slow flier and is not very active.

The males establish territories along the edges of the forest, where they can be observed skipping about in the shade of the trees from one plant to another, sometimes slowly, sometimes rapidly. They are often also observed perching on broad green leaves. When disturbed they seldom fly far away, and usually return to their original territory.

The females frequent the same places as the males where they fly at random in search of food plants. Eggs are laid singly on the underside of a leaf of the food plant. The eggs take from 9-11 days to hatch. The larvae construct a shelter by joining a leaf or leaves together. Young first and second instar larvae partly bite away and turn down a portion of a leaf, attaching it to the underside of the same leaf. They crawl out at intervals to feed on the edge of a nearby leaf. The larval stage lasts some 37 days. Moulting and pupation take place within the shelter. The pupa is secured to a silken pad by its cremastral hooks within the leaf shelter. The pupal stage lasts 21 to 22 days (Clark, 1978: 258).

The species is on the wing throughout the year.

Acleros mackenii form *denia* male underside

LARVAL FOOD PLANTS

Rhus coriarius (Anacardiaceae); *Acridocarpus smeathmanni* (Malpighiaceae).

DISTRIBUTION

South Africa, from Port St. Johns in the Eastern Cape, to KwaZulu-Natal, Mpumalanga and Northern Province, Swaziland, Zimbabwe and Moçambique, to equatorial Africa.

CONSERVATION

A. mackenii is a fairly widespread species and is under no immediate threat.

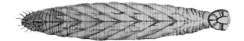

Acleros mackenii final instar larva (After G.C. Clark, 1978)

Acleros mackenii pupa (After G.C. Clark, 1978)

Distribution map of *Acleros mackenii*

Genus *Andronymus* Holland

Andronymus Holland, 1896. *Proc. zool. Soc. Lond.* **1896**: 80. Type-species: *Pamphila philander* Hopffer, 1855, by original designation.

Medium to large skippers with narrow forewings and white hyaline spots. Margin of forewing at M_3 the most prominent, behind it somewhat emarginated. Forewing with cell long, equal to dorsum; vein CuA_2 arises midway between wing base and end of cell; vein M_2 decurved at origin. Hindwing with lower end of cell bent up; outer margin excavate before anal angle; in female origins of vein Rs and CuA_2 opposite and vein M_2 arising nearer to vein M_1. Male hindwing above, with a tuft of black hairs from before middle of area $Sc+R_1$ entering a fold running below the costal vein from origin of vein Rs to the basal part of vein M_1. Antennae short, less than half costa; club stout, bent beyond middle abruptly to a fine, upturned, apiculus. Sexes usually alike (Evans, 1949: 129).

Eggs domed. Larvae elongate with ornately coloured head. Pupae brown, elongated posteriorly but rounded anteriorly.

Food plants Fabaceae, Sapindaceae.

There are two species in Southern Africa.

KEY TO THE SPECIES OF *ANDRONYMUS*

1. LHW with a strong dark marginal band .... *A. caesar philander*

   LHW lacks strong dark marginal band .... *A. neander*

Andronymus neander (Plötz)

NOMAD DART

Apaustus neander Plötz, 1884. *Stettin. ent. Ztg.* **45**: 154.

There are two subspecies of which only the nominate occurs in Southern Africa. The subspecies *thomasi* Riley (1925) occurs on the islands of Sao Tomé and Principé.

Andronymus neander neander (Plötz)

Apaustus neander Plötz, 1884. *Stettin. ent. Ztg.* **45**: 154.
Type locality: Loango.

IDENTIFICATION

Adult. Male. Forewing greatly elongated. Upperside: ground colour; forewing cell with lower pale spot lying immediately above spot in area CuA_1 and with apical pale spot; hindwing with median band which usually reaches vein 1A+2A. Underside: hindwing generally dark violet-grey without pale discal area, but having a small central hyaline area. Female. Similar to male, but with more rounded wings and spots of a more cream colour.

Forewing lengths: male 18-22 mm; female 20-23 mm.

Early stages. Unrecorded.

Andronymus neander neander male underside

HABITAT AND ECOLOGY

A. neander is an inhabitant of woodland, forest margins and riverine vegetation from sea level to 2 350 metres. Its presence in South Africa is probably due to migratory ability. Its flight is fairly swift and from 1 to 2 metres above the ground. It is seldom seen at rest. It appears to be particularly fond of flowers and has been recorded feeding on the flowers of aquatic plants and those of trees at considerable heights. This species shows strong migratory tendencies. In January 1958, the Cooksons observed a vast east-to-west migration near Mutare, Zimbabwe, lasting for two weeks.

The males establish their territories near their food plants. Here they patrol the area.

The females frequent the same places as the males and fly at random in search of suitable food plants on which to lay.

The species is on the wing throughout the year in the warmer parts and from September to April in the cooler areas.

LARVAL FOOD PLANTS

Brachystegia boehmii (Caesalpinioideae).

DISTRIBUTION

South Africa, from KwaZulu-Natal and Gauteng, Northern Province and Mpumalanga where it is considered a sparse migrant, northwards into Zimbabwe, northern Namibia and Moçambique and throughout the rest of the Afrotropical Region.

CONSERVATION

A. neander is a widespread species throughout Africa, although it is mainly a rare migrant in South Africa. It is therefore under no threat. It has been recorded in a note in the *South African Red Data Book – Butterflies* by S.F. & G.A. Henning (1989).

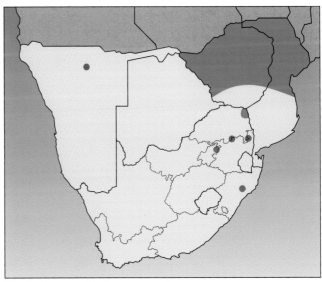

Distribution map of *Andronymus neander*

Andronymus caesar (Fabricius)

WHITE DART

Hesperia urbicola caesar Fabricius, 1793. *Syst. Ent.* 3(1): 340.

There are two subspecies, only one of which occurs in Southern Africa. The nominate race occurs in West Africa from Sierra Leone to Ghana.

Andronymus caesar philander (Hopffer)

Pamphila philander Hopffer, 1855. *Mber. dt. Akad. Wiss. Berlin.* **1855**: 643. Type locality: Moçambique. Syntype female in Zoological Museum, Berlin.

IDENTIFICATION

Adult. A long-winged species. Male. Upperside: ground colour dark brown; forewing with several hyaline spots across middle, cell with upper and apical pale spots immediately above spot in area CuA_1 and without apical pale spot; area CuA_2 with pale spot; hind-

wing cream to white with prominent translucent area. Underside: hindwing with pale discal area joined to pale fringe near anal angle, brown marginal band and a brown blotch above anal angle. Female. Similar to male but larger with broader wings and a stouter abdomen.

Forewing lengths: male 16-20 mm (mean 17,6 mm); female 16-20 mm (mean 18 mm).

Early stages. Egg: creamy-white with some reddish-brown shading. Larva: final instar creamy-white in colour with an orange head with big black spots on it. Pupa: 18-20 mm long and thin, tapering posteriorly, and is pale brown in colour (S.F. Henning & G.A. Henning, 1989: 158).

HABITAT AND ECOLOGY

A. caesar philander is an inhabitant of savannah or adjacent riverine bush and forest paths and roads (but is not a forest species) from near sea level to 1 500 metres. Often observed in undergrowth, rarely emerging into the open. Very fond of flowers on herbs and short bushes. Flight is relatively slow but when disturbed, greater speeds can be attained. It frequently settles with wings erect on low vegetation or on flowers. In Malawi it is found in deciduous woodland and is common on flowers in gardens. It has been recorded in migrations north of Southern Africa.

The males do not appear to show hilltopping behaviour and are usually observed perching on low vegetation near the food plants, from whence they dart out to investigate any intruders.

The females can be seen flying about the undergrowth in search of suitable food plants on which to lay. The egg is laid singly on very fresh young shoots of the food plant which are a bronze colour. The larva curls up the leaf of the food plant and creates a silken tunnel. The edge of the leaf is curled in the earlier instars while in later instars the entire leaf is curled up. The larva pupates in the curled up leaf and is attached by its cremaster and a silken girdle around the base of the thorax (S.F. Henning & G.A. Henning, 1989: 158).

This species is on the wing throughout most of the year.

Andronymus caesar philander male underside

LARVAL FOOD PLANTS

Phialodiscus zambesiacus, Deinbollia sp., *Blighia unijugata* (Sapindaceae); *Macrolobium coeruleum, Julbernardia globiflora, Pericopsis angolensis* (Caesalpinioideae).

DISTRIBUTION

South Africa, from the furthest north-eastern corner of the Kruger National Park, Northern Province and one record from Blyderivierspoort in Mpumalanga. It is common and widespread in Zimbabwe and Moçambique and northwards to east and central Africa to Sudan.

CONSERVATION

A. caesar philander is a widespread species in Southern Africa and is under no threat. It has been classified as indeterminate by S.F. & G.A. Henning (1989:158) in the *South African Red Data Book – Butterflies.*

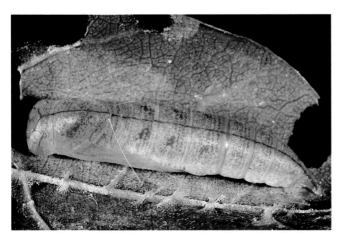

Andronymus caesar philander pupa (Photo: R. Paré)

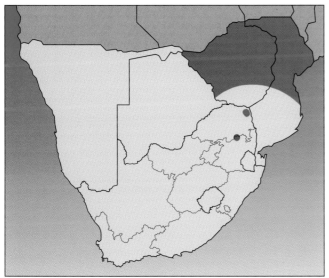

Distribution map of *Andronymus caesar*

Genus *Moltena* Evans

Moltena Evans, 1937. *Cat. Afr. Hesper.*: 139. Type species: *Proteides fiara* Butler, 1870, by original designation.

A large reddish-brown species resembling *Zophopetes* but differs in the closeness of the antennae at their base and in the absence of hyaline markings on the forewing. Antennae about half costa, more or less white, closer together than usual at base; hooked well beyond middle to a short apiculus. Forewing with vein CuA_2 equidistant between wing base and vein M_3; vein M_2 decurved at its origin. Hindwing vein M_2 faintly decurved; vein Rs arising before vein CuA_1 and vein 1A+2A. Spurs on mid-tibiae vestigial and lower, very short. Haustellum normal (Evans, 1937:139).

Eggs domed, finely sculptured. Final instar larvae greenish, broad posteriorly. Final instar larval headshield white rimmed with black; small prothoracic plate on first segment. Pupae brown, not elongate, anteriorly rounded.

Food plants Strelitziaceae.

There is one species in Southern Africa.

Moltena fiara (Butler)

BANANA-TREE NIGHTFIGHTER

Proteides fiara Butler, 1870. *Trans. ent. Soc. Lond.* **1870**: 503. Type locality: Kaffraria. Type female in Natural History Museum, London.

IDENTIFICATION

Adult. Male. Upperside: dull ochreous-brown, hindwing dark with a median space of light reddish-ochre. Underside: pale dull brownish-grey without markings. Female. Similar to male but much larger and paler with more rounded wings.

Forewing lengths: male 25-26,5 mm; female 27-29,5 mm.

Early stages. Egg: yellowish-green; diameter 2,0 mm, height 1,8 mm; with some 39-40 longitudinal ribs, a third of which stop part of the way up the side, the remainder joining in pairs to form a single very short rib just short of the micropyle. Larva: first instar red with a black head; second instar brown with a black head; third instar dark green with dark pinkish lateral spots around spiracles, head black with 2 large ochre dorso-lateral patches; fourth instar paler green dorsally with white lines, becoming ochre-yellow anteriorly, posteriorly and laterally, spiracles pinkish-red, head black with two creamy-white patches; fifth instar similar to fourth but with a dark dorsal line and laterally creamy-white, head white with a narrow black marginal and dorso-medial line and a brown lower 'face'. It

165

attains a length of some 60-65 mm. Pupa: 31-32 mm; dark brown in colour and covered with a white chalky powder (Murray, 1932: 585; Clark, 1978: 260).

HABITAT AND ECOLOGY

M. fiara is an inhabitant of the eastern coastal forests wherever its larval food plant, the common 'wild banana' (*Strelitzia nicolai*) is found. This species is usually on the wing at dusk and is not seen during the day unless it is dull or overcast. The adults are usually observed feeding at flowers at sunset. The most striking feature is the white antennae which are the only parts clearly visible as they dash about the gathering darkness at dusk. They rest through the day inside a rolled-up leaf of the food plant.

The males establish territories in the vicinity of the food plants and can be seen or even heard chasing the intruders out of their territories. The males make a distinct clapping sound with their wings while in flight.

The females frequent the same places as the males where they fly at random in search of suitable food plants on which to lay. Eggs are laid singly on the upper surfaces of food plant leaves. The eggs take about 7 days to hatch. On emergence the larva turns the edge of the leaf over and lives in the fold, crawling out at night to feed. When too big for this shelter it crawls to another spot, or a fresh leaf, and makes a larger one. The larval stage lasts some 65-80 days. Pupation takes place within a folded leaf secured with a silken girdle. The pupal stage lasts 30-86 days. The parasitic fly *Thecocarcelia incedens* (Tachinidae) has been recorded emerging from the pupa (Murray, 1932: 585; Clark, 1978: 260).

This species is on the wing throughout most of the year, the best times for observation being from August to October and January to April.

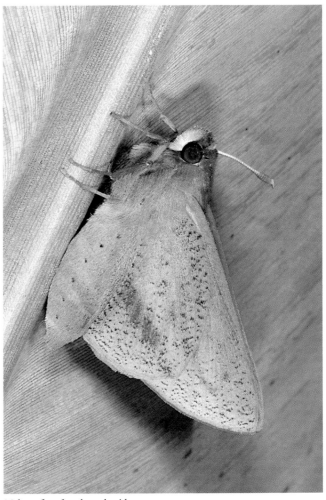

Moltena fiara female underside

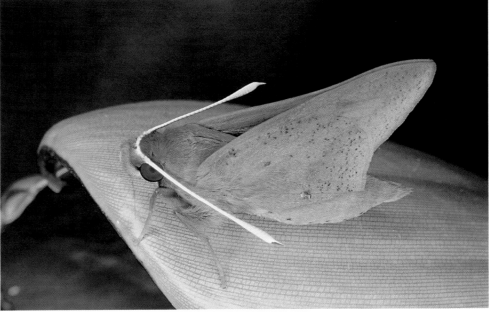

Moltena fiara male showing vivid white antennae used as visual cues in its crepuscular trysts

Moltena fiara female upperside

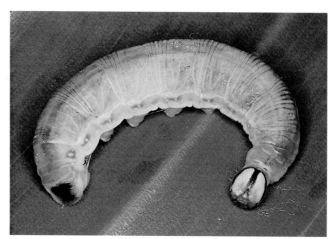

Moltena fiara final instar larva

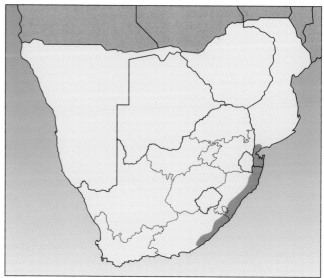

Moltena fiara pupa

LARVAL FOOD PLANTS

Strelitzia nicolai (Strelitziaceae).

DISTRIBUTION

South Africa, from the Eastern Cape, KwaZulu-Natal and into Moçambique as far north as Maputo.

CONSERVATION

M. fiara is a fairly widespread species and is under no immediate threat.

Distribution map of *Moltena fiara*

Genus *Zophopetes* Mabille

Zophopetes Mabille, 1904. *Genera Insect.* **17**: 183. Type species: *Pamphila dysmephila* Trimen, 1868, by selection Lindsey, 1925, *Ann. ent. Soc. Amer.* **18**: 100.

Large brown skippers with antennae rather longer than half costa, white on apical third only. Palpi porrect. Very stout bodies with thorax shaggy below, coxae and tibiae densely fringed. Forewing vein CuA_2 equidistant between wing base and origin of vein R_1; vein M_2 decurved. Hindwing with vein M_2 decurved and well developed; Rs arising before vein CuA_2; lower end of cell bent up (Evans, 1937: 142). They fly at dusk around *Phoenix* palms and other Arecaceae on which their larvae feed.

Eggs domed, finely ribbed. Larvae elongate, green with markings dorsally; final instar larval headshield white with fine black lateral and central stripes. Pupae brown, fairly short and squat, anteriorly blunt.

Food plants Arecaceae.

Only one species is found in Southern Africa.

Zophopetes dysmephila male underside

Zophopetes dysmephila (Trimen)

PALM-TREE NIGHTFIGHTER

Pamphila dysmephila Trimen, 1868. *Trans. ent. Soc. Lond.* **1868**: 96. Type locality: Kaffraria. Type female in Natural History Museum, London.

IDENTIFICATION

Adult. A large skipper with antennal club white. Male. Forewing with apex sharply pointed. Upperside: ground colour cinnamon-brown with a distinct purple sheen on outer half of forewing; forewing with outer margin and apex white with three white hyaline spots centrally of which one is in cell; hindwing unmarked. Underside: hindwing brown with a slight purplish sheen, and many irregularly placed black dots. Female. Similar to male but wings rounder and hindwing underside with a silver-white stripe from base to apex.

Forewing lengths: male 18,5-23 mm; female 21-23 mm.

Early stages. Egg: whitish-brown to pale brown, with a pinkish crown; diameter 1,5 mm, height 1,00 mm; with 28-30 longitudinal ribs. Larva: first instar pale creamy-white with a black head; second and third instars pale green with a brown head; fourth instar green with dark dorsal stripe and a brown head; fifth instar green with a dark dorsal line margined with white and a brown head with creamy lateral patches; sixth instar similar to fifth but head with dark markings in middle reduced to two thin lines. It attains a length of 46 mm. Pupa: 27 mm long; dark brown in colour (Clark, 1978: 262).

HABITAT AND ECOLOGY

Z. dysmephila is an inhabitant of savannah, riversides and forests, where its food plants, palm trees, grow. It flies at dusk, after sundown, and is occasionally attracted to bright lights. Consequently, comparatively few are seen on the wing except on warm wet days or very late in the afternoon. Often only the white antennae can be observed in the gloom. During daylight hours, specimens rest with folded wings inside leaves at the base of their food plant.

The males are territorial and perch on the tips of the palm leaves and will vigorously chase off any other males invading their territories. They are often seen in rapid flight, chasing each other around the crowns of the palm trees. When chasing off an intruder they make a distinct clapping or humming sound with their wings.

The females are found in the same places as the males and fly at random, searching for suitable oviposition sites. They lay their eggs singly or in clusters on the upper surface of a leaf of the food plant. The eggs take from 16 to 25 days to hatch. The young larva crawls to the end of a blade and joins the edges together to form a shelter, and feeds on the tip, leaving it characteristically straight-edged at a 45 degree angle. In this way it eventually eats the shelter itself, but it then draws together the edges of the blade behind it, and the blade thus becomes progressively shorter. Moulting occurs in the shelter. After consuming the original blade, the larva moves to another one. In the final instar, two blades may be joined

Zophopetes dysmephila female underside

together. The larval stage lasts some 63 days. Pupation takes place within the shelter, and the larva generally lines this finally with silk and exudes a white powdery substance before pupating. The pupal stage lasts 33 to 55 days. The early stages are parasitised by chalcids, species of *Pimpla* (Hymenoptera) and several species of Tachinidae (Diptera) (Clark, 1978: 262).

This species is on the wing for most of the year, being most common from December to May.

LARVAL FOOD PLANTS

Phoenix reclinata, P. dactylifera, P. canariensis, Cocos sp., *Borassus* sp., *Raphia* sp., *Chrysalidocarpus lutescens* (Arecaceae).

DISTRIBUTION

South Africa, from the Eastern Cape, KwaZulu-Natal and extending into Mpumalanga and Northern Province, northern Botswana, northern Namibia, Zimbabwe, Moçambique to East Africa. In the 1980's it was introduced into the Western Cape on palms brought in from elsewhere in South Africa.

CONSERVATION

Z. dysmephila is a widespread species and is under no immediate threat.

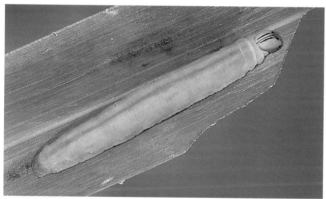

Zophopetes dysmephila final instar larva

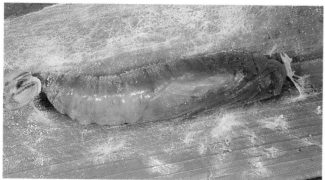

Zophopetes dysmephila pupa

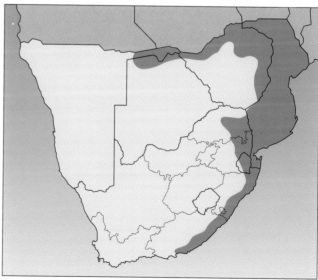

Distribution map of *Zophopetes dysmephila*

Genus *Artitropa* Holland

Artitropa Holland, 1896. *Proc. zool. Soc. Lond.* **1896**: 92. Type species: *Pamphila erinnys* Trimen, by original designation.

Large skippers with the tip of antennal club moderately long, shorter than the double transverse diameter of club. Palpi erect, apical segment very short, stout. Discal cell of forewing long, at least as long as two thirds of the costal margin; apex of forewing extended. Upperside: brown with small yellowish translucent or hyaline spots in middle of forewing and an orange band across middle of hindwing. Hindwing with anal angle conspicuously orange. Hindwing underside with a white band decorated with black dots and blotches. Generally flies at dusk, favouring forested areas and often visiting flowers.

Eggs domed. Larvae cylindrical, broad posteriorly; final instar larval headshield yellow with black spots. Pupae yellowish; bluntly rounded anteriorly, somewhat elongated posteriorly; proboscis sheath very long, extending beyond end of abdomen.

Food plants Dracaenaceae.

There are two species in Southern Africa, only one of which occurs in South Africa.

Artitropa erinnys erinnys male underside

Artitropa erinnys (Trimen)

BUSH NIGHTFIGHTER

Pamphila erinnys Trimen, 1862. *Trans. ent. Soc. Lond.* (3) **1**: 290.

This species is restricted to the eastern Afrotropical Region. There are five subspecies, two of which occur in Southern Africa. The nominate race occurs in South Africa and the subspecies *nyasae* Riley occurs in Zimbabwe.

Artitropa erinnys erinnys (Trimen)

Pamphila erinnys Trimen, 1862. *Trans. ent. Soc. Lond.* (3) **1**: 290. Type locality: Port Natal. Type male in Natural History Museum, London.

IDENTIFICATION

Adult. Male. Upperside: ground colour dark brown; forewing with ochreous and yellow-ochreous translucent or hyaline spots. Hindwing with an orange outer margin and discal band. Underside: paler with a greenish-bronzy surface glow. Female. Similar to male but forewings are blunter; hindwing with yellow-ochreous discal band broader and less curved.

Forewing lengths: male 24,5-26,5 mm; female 27,5-29,5 mm.

Early stages. Egg: greyish-white, changing to light salmon-brown; diameter 2 mm; height 1,2 mm; with some 50 longitudinal ribs, composed of small moles, and reaching three-quarters of the way up the side, then breaking into a hexagonal pattern. Larva: first instar light green with black head; second to fourth instars pale bluish-green with a yellowish-green head; fifth (final) instar is pale bluish-green with a yellow posterior end and yellow head with six black spots. It attains a length of approximately 60 mm. Pupa: 31 mm in length; bluish-green in colour, changing to light brown, with a black line down the centre of the thorax and black spots about the head (Murray, 1932: 585; Clark, 1978: 264).

HABITAT AND ECOLOGY

A. erinnys is an inhabitant of rainforest, often favouring forest stream areas. It flies about at sunset, as a rule, but on warm and cloudy days will visit flowers much earlier in the afternoon. During the day it usually rests on rocks among moss and ferns, or on the trunks of trees.

The males establish territories in the vicinity of the food plants, where they may be found perching on the tree trunks.

The females fly at random through the forest in search of suitable food plants on which to lay. Eggs are laid singly or in small batches on both sides of a leaf of the food plant in the late afternoon. On emergence the young larva eats a small portion of the leaf at the

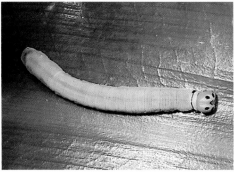

Artitropa erinnys erinnys final instar larva

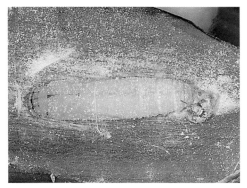

Artitropa erinnys erinnys male upperside

Artitropa erinnys erinnys pupa

edge, then turns this flap completely over itself, joining the edges together with a silken thread. To moult it sometimes closes up the end of the leaf tunnel. The larva spends its whole time within the folds of the leaf, only emerging at night to seek a new leaf on which to feed. The frass is shot out as from a pea-shooter, often falling a metre or so away. The larval stage lasts some 100 days. To pupate the larva spins a very strong hammock of silken bands across the underside of a leaf, with an additional band across the centre of the body. The pupal stage lasts 23-26 days (Murray, 1932: 585; Clark, 1978: 264).

This species is on the wing throughout the year, the best months for observation being August to May.

LARVAL FOOD PLANTS

Dracaena hookeriana, D. afromontana, D. angustifolia, D. fragrans, D. steudneri (Dracaenaceae).

DISTRIBUTION

South Africa, from East London in the Eastern Cape to KwaZulu-Natal, the Northern Province and Mpumalanga, eastern Zimbabwe, Swaziland and Moçambique.

CONSERVATION

A. erinnys is a fairly widely spread species and is under no threat.

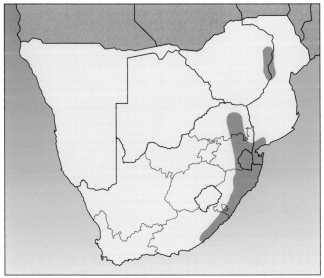

Distribution map of *Artitropa erinnys*

171

Genus *Fresna* Evans

Fresna Evans, 1937. *Cat. Afr. Hesper.*: 164. Type species: *Hesperia netopha* Hewitson, 1878, by original designation.

Medium-sized skippers with a brown upperside with white spots and an *Acraea*-like underside. Antenna short, about half the length of the costa. Above head and palpi white-spotted, and palpi below white or yellow, black-striped at side. Forewing vein CuA_2 equidistant between wing base and end of cell; vein M_3 arising midway between veins M_1 and CuA_1; vein M_2 decurved. Hindwing with lower end of cell bent up and vein M_1 absent; vein $Sc+R_1$ arising opposite CuA_1; outer margin excavate between veins 1A+2A and CuA_1; vein 3A longer than vein CuA_1. Male hindwing upperside with a recumbent hair-tuft from base cell over the swollen bases of veins CuA_1 and M_3; the centre of vein 1A+2A also swollen and a thin hair tuft alongside.

Eggs rose pink in colour. Larvae cylindrical, early instars bright scarlet with black heads, while later instars are whitish with brown heads.

The larval food plants are Caesalpinioideae.

There is only one species in Southern Africa.

Fresna nyassae (Hewitson)

VARIEGATED ACRAEA HOPPER

Hesperia nyassae Hewitson, 1878. *Ann. Mag. nat. Hist.* (5) **1**: 345. Type locality: Solwezi. Type male in Natural History Museum, London.

IDENTIFICATION

Adult. Male. Upperside: ground colour brown, with a cluster of white spots in middle of forewing and two or three on hindwing. Underside: hindwing pinkish-red or violet with a group of black dots in the basal half, in and around the cell. Veins on underside usually emphasised with black on hindwing and apex of forewing. Female. Similar to male but with more rounded wings.

Forewing lengths: male 16-18 mm; female 18,5-19,5 mm.

Early stages. Egg: rose pink in colour. Larva: first instar bright scarlet with a black head, while later instars are whitish in colour with a brown head. Final instar is smooth and white with a discrete black dorsal, longitudinal stripe on each segment except the first two and last; head reddish-brown with symmetrical orange markings.

Fresna nyassae female underside (Photo: R. Paré)

HABITAT AND ECOLOGY

F. nyassae is an inhabitant of grassland and savannah. It is occasionally observed feeding at flowers.

The male establishes a territory around trees where it perches high up in the afternoon sun. While settled it looks rather like a small *Acraea*.

The females fly at random through the bush in search of suitable food plants on which to lay. They lay their eggs singly on new growth.

They are on the wing throughout the year, but are more common in the spring and summer months.

LARVAL FOOD PLANTS

Julbernardia globiflora (Caesalpinioideae).

DISTRIBUTION

South Africa, from northern KwaZulu-Natal, Moçambique, Zimbabwe, northwards into Angola, Malawi, Tanzania, Kenya and into Central and West Africa.

CONSERVATION

A rare species in South Africa, having been recorded only twice in the northern areas of KwaZulu-Natal. It is, however, quite widespread elsewhere and is under no threat.

Fresna nyassae pupa (Photo: R. Paré)

Fresna nyassae final instar larva (Photo: R. Paré)

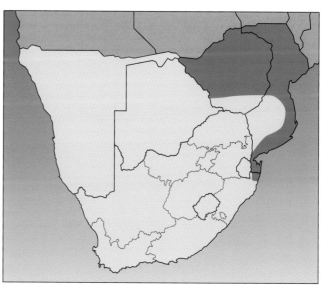

Distribution map of *Fresna nyassae*

Genus *Platylesches* Holland

Platylesches Holland, 1896. *Proc. zool. Soc. Lond.* **1896**: 72. Type species: *Parnara picanini* Holland, 1894, by original designation.

Small to medium-sized, strongly built skippers with stout bodies and broad wings, with short antennae. Palpi porrect, the apical segment long and thin, projecting from the scaling of second segment. Vein M_2 of the forewing rises much nearer to M_3 than M_1. Upperside of both wings blackish or brownish-black with uniform pattern of spots. Upperside of forewing with a row of white or yellowish hyaline spots at end of cell, joining a row of subapical dots and thus roughly forming a U or Y. Hindwing upperside with a few whitish or yellow dots in a short bar across the middle. The hindwing underside, however, shows the different patterns of the species. There may be a nebulous coloured zone, with or without white spots; or grey speckling; or with a broad yellow or white band.

Egg unrecorded. Larvae stout, green to reddish-brown, head ornately marked with crescentic white markings on black or red. Pupae cream, unattached, in thin white cocoon within curled and stitched leaf shelter.

All species recorded appear to use *Parinari* (Chrysobalanaceae) as their food plants. Records of Poaceae are apparently incorrect.

There are eleven species in Southern Africa, seven of which occur in South Africa.

KEY TO THE SPECIES OF *PLATYLESCHES*

1. LHW with a pale band .... *P. picanini*

   LHW without a pale band 2

2. UFW usually with a single subapical spot in male, possibly two in female .... *P. tina*

   UFW with two or three subapical spots 3

3. Abdomen white-tipped; forewing usually with spot in M_1
   .... *P. galesa*

   Abdomen lacking white tip; forewing usually lacks spot in M_1 4

4. LHW with apical half outer margin conspicuously overlaid with pale scales 5

   LHW lacking pale apical scales 6

5. LHW evenly striated .... *P. ayresii*

   LHW with purple or violet scaling; faint spots, veins not dark
   .... *P. robustus*

6. LFW without pale apical scaling .... *P. moritili*

   LFW with apical half of outer margin conspicuously overlaid with pale scales .... *P. neba*

Platylesches galesa (Hewitson)

WHITE-TAIL HOPPER

Pamphila galesa Hewitson, 1877. *Ann. Mag. nat. Hist.* (4) **19**: 79. Type locality: West Africa. Type male in Natural History Museum, London.

IDENTIFICATION

Adult. Male. Forewing normally with 2 or 3 subapical dots and usually with a spot in area M_1. Hindwing with conspicuous white cilia. Abdomen with a distinctive white tip. Female. Similar to male but lacks the white tip of the abdomen.

Forewing lengths: male 15,5-17,5 mm; female 17-18 mm.

Early stages. Egg: unrecorded. Larva: third instar, head black, body light-green with black markings. Attained a length of 11 mm. Fourth instar very similar to that of *P. picanini*; body pale green with fine darker-green mottling so that it appears solid green from any distance greater than 30 cm; head brown with eight creamy-white spots in a radial pattern, outlined in darker brown. Spots larger than those of *picanini*. Attains a length of 18 mm. Fifth (final) instar still similar to *picanini*; salmon-pink with a brown head; head with eight creamy-white patches in a radial pattern, outlined with darker brown. Attains a length of 25 mm; girth before pupation 7 mm and length reduced to 20 mm. Pupa. Length 18 mm, off-white with adult features outlined with yellow-brown.

HABITAT AND ECOLOGY

P. galesa is an inhabitant of dense rainforest from which it ventures into more open bush. It is most often observed as it darts about the edges of forest and along forest paths. It is a relatively fast-flying

Platylesches galesa male underside

species and settles frequently. In flight the male is rendered quite conspicuous by the white tip of its abdomen and the edges of the hindwings. It is often attracted to flowers, near the ground or in trees.

The males establish their territories along the edge of the canopy of the forest in clearings, along streams or roads. Here they often perch on prominent branches or twigs some 2 to 3 metres above the ground. At times several males can be seen in a clearing, each on its own perch. Sometimes they even dart about near the ground or perch on stones, grass stems or leaves of shrubs, frequently returning to the same perch. Any male intruding into their territories is quickly chased off.

The females occupy the same areas as the males where they fly at random in search of suitable food plants on which to lay. The shelter for the larva is constructed from an entire leaf folded over and held tightly closed with very fine silk threads. Duration of fourth instar 10 days and final instar 12 days. Pupation is in a loose cocoon in the larval shelter. The adult emerges after about 21 days.

The species is on the wing throughout the year, but appears to be most plentiful from April to June.

LARVAL FOOD PLANTS

Parinari curatellifolia (Chrysobalanaceae).

DISTRIBUTION

South Africa, in the Northern Province and Mpumalanga. Eastern Zimbabwe and Moçambique, northwards over most of Africa south of the Sahara.

CONSERVATION

P. galesa is fairly wide-spread and is under no threat.

Platylesches galesa female underside

Platylesches galesa male upperside

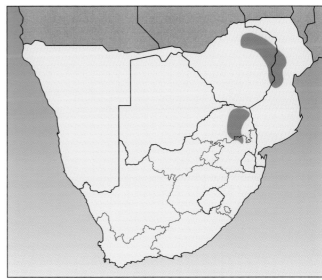

Distribution map of *Platylesches galesa*

175

Platylesches ayresii (Trimen)

PEPPERED HOPPER

Pamphila ayresii Trimen, 1889. *S. Afr. Butterfl.* **3**: 321. Type locality: Lydenburg, Mpumalanga. Type female in South African Museum.

IDENTIFICATION

Adult. Male. Forewing with 3 subapical spots. Underside: with apex of forewing with some white scales; hindwing greyish, evenly and heavily striated with darker lines, otherwise unmarked. Female. Similar to male, but paler with rounder wings.

Forewing lengths: male 13-15,5 mm; female 17-18 mm.

Early stages. Unrecorded.

HABITAT AND ECOLOGY

P. ayresii is an inhabitant of grassland and bushveld. It may be encountered skipping along the slopes of hills, or on the flats. Its flight is extremely fast but of short duration. It settles on the ground after flying only a short distance. It can also be observed feeding at flowers and occasionally visits damp spots or fresh cow-dung in the road.

The males exhibit marked hilltopping behaviour and along the Witwatersrand there is scarcely a koppie or ridge on which they cannot be found during hot, sunny days. The males usually arrive on the peaks about midday, sometimes much earlier, depending on the heat of the day. They nearly always perch on rocks, small stones or the ground and occasionally on stems of grass or low plants. They usually occupy these territories for many hours. They will vigorously chase any intruders out of their territories.

The females fly at random through the bush in search of suitable food plants on which to lay. They usually ascend the hills only to mate.

This species is on the wing from July to April with September and January appearing to be the best months for observation.

LARVAL FOOD PLANTS

Parinari capensis (Chrysobalanaceae) (M.C. Williams, pers. comm.).

DISTRIBUTION

South Africa, from northern KwaZulu-Natal, Gauteng, the Northern Province and Mpumalanga, North-West Province, Swaziland, Moçambique and Botswana.

CONSERVATION

P. ayresii is a fairly widespread species and is under no threat.

Platylesches ayresii female underside

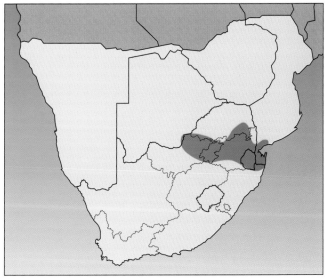

Distribution map of *Platylesches ayresii*

Platylesches neba (Hewitson)

FLOWER-GIRL HOPPER

Hesperia neba Hewitson, 1877. *Ann. Mag. nat. Hist.* (4) **19**: 84. Type locality: KwaZulu-Natal. Type male in Natural History Museum, London.

IDENTIFICATION

Adult. Male. Upperside: forewing with 3 subapical spots. Underside: forewing with apical half of outer margin strewn with purple-white scales; hindwing chocolate-brown, outer half overlaid with purple-white scales, leaving the veins dark, no discal spots. Female. Similar to male, but with rounder wings.

Forewing lengths: male 14-16 mm; female 14,5-16,5 mm.

Early stages. Egg: unrecorded. Larva: first instar was 5 mm long when found and grew to 7 mm; body yellowish leaf-green; head black. Second instar pale leaf green with faint paler yellow-green mottling, head black, grew to 10 mm long. The third instar larva was similar to the second in colouring and grew to 15 mm long. Fourth instar with a leaf green body and more clearly discernable pale yellow-green mottling, which makes the entire larva appear pale green; head pale tan with creamy-white spots on front, outlined with brown; it grew to 23 mm long. Fifth instar larva identical to fourth in all respects except size; it grew to 31 mm then shrank to 25 mm whilst its girth grew from 3 mm to 6 mm before pupation. Pupa. Length 22 mm, similar to that of *P. moritili* but with more pronounced dark lines along the wing cases and a blackish-brown head and thorax.

HABITAT AND ECOLOGY

P. neba is an inhabitant of coastal bush and forests. In thick bush it can usually be found along the edges. It is often observed feeding at flowers or muddy places.

The male does not exhibit hilltopping behaviour, instead taking possession of a certain tree near the larval food plants. From the lower branches of this tree it darts out at nearly everything that approaches its perch. At times, however, it may also select a low plant or grass stem among the trees as a perch site. In thick bush it usually establishes its territory along the edges.

The females fly apparently randomly through the bush in search of suitable food plants on which to lay. The young larvae live in the folded-over edges of young leaves of *Parinari capensis*, spinning a silken shelter by attaching the leaf edge to the midrib with fine silken threads. In the first instar the second instar head capsule becomes visible under the skin two days before the moult. The second instar lasted 14 days. In the third instar the shelter changed to two young leaves held together by short silk threads in a similar manner to that of *P. tina*. The duration of the third instar was 12 days. The fourth instar is similar to *P. moritili* but with the ground colour much paler; it took 15 days. In the fifth instar the shelter consists of three fresh but not young leaves and is 70 - 80 mm long. It is held together with fine, short silk threads. It took 12 days before the prepupal stage which lasted a further 5 days. The larva spun a loose cocoon in its shelter and pupated. The pupa hatched into a female after 25 days.

This species is on the wing throughout the year.

Platylesches neba female underside

Platylesches neba male underside

Platylesches neba male upperside

Platylesches neba second instar larva

LARVAL FOOD PLANTS

Parinari capensis (Chrysobalanaceae).

DISTRIBUTION

South Africa, from northern KwaZulu-Natal, Gauteng, Northern Province and Mpumalanga, Swaziland, the eastern border of Zimbabwe and northern Namibia.

CONSERVATION

P. neba is fairly widely spread and is under no immediate threat.

Platylesches neba fifth instar larva

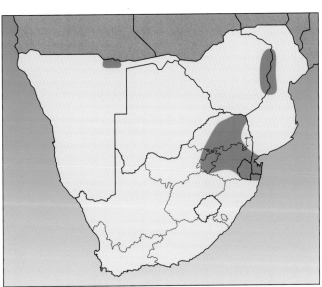

Distribution map of *Platylesches neba*

Platylesches neba pupa

Platylesches robustus Neave

ROBUST HOPPER

Platylesches robustus Neave, 1910. *Proc. zool. Soc. Lond.* **1910**: 83.

There are two subspecies but only the nominate occurs in Southern Africa. The other subspecies comes from the Cameroon.

Platylesches robustus robustus Neave

Platylesches robustus Neave, 1910. *Proc. zool. Soc. Lond.* **1910**: 83. Type locality: Chambezi Valley. Type male in Natural History Museum, London.

IDENTIFICATION

Adult. Largest of the genus. Male. Upperside: forewing with 3 subapical spots. Underside: forewing with apical half of outer margin overlaid with pale scaling; hindwing with pale bluish-purple or violet scaling, with faint spots, veins not dark. Female. Similar to male but with rounder wings.

Forewing lengths: male 15-19 mm; female 17-19,5 mm.

Early stages. Unrecorded.

HABITAT AND ECOLOGY

P. robustus is an inhabitant of bushveld, riverine vegetation and woodland. It appears to favour areas with tamboekie grass. At times it can be seen on low shrubs and it also rests on the ground or roads. In the morning it usually feeds on the flowers of trees. Sometimes it can be found drinking at muddy places. It is fairly local and not seen as often as some of its congeners.

The males show hilltopping behaviour, often ascending the peaks quite early in the morning and may continue until very late in the afternoon. Here they perch on rocks, low trees and bushes, darting out to chase off any intruders from their territories. Occasionally the males establish territories about tamboekie grass, where they perch on the thick stems.

The female tends to fly at random through the bush, presumably in search of suitable food plants on which to lay.

The species appears to be on the wing throughout the year, the best time for observation being from March to April. It is rarely seen in December and January.

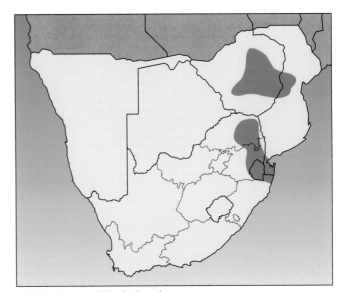

Distribution map of *Platylesches robustus*

LARVAL FOOD PLANTS

Unrecorded.

DISTRIBUTION

South Africa, from the bushveld of northern KwaZulu-Natal, Mpumalanga and Northern Province, Swaziland, Moçambique, Zimbabwe, northwards to Zambia, Tanzania, Malawi, Zaire and Rwanda.

CONSERVATION

P. robustus is fairly widely spread and is under no threat.

Platylesches robustus robustus male underside

Platylesches moritili (Wallengren)

HONEY HOPPER

Hesperia moritili Wallengren, 1857. *K. svenska. VetenskAkad. Handl.* (N.F.) **2** (4): 49. Type locality: Kaffraria.

IDENTIFICATION

Adult. Male. Upperside: forewing normally with 3 subapical spots and a prominent spot in CuA_2; hindwing with short prominent cream-coloured discal band. Underside: forewing without pale apical scaling; hindwing dark brown with diffuse greyish-violet shading in basal and discal areas. Female. Similar to male, but slightly larger with more rounded wings.

Forewing lengths: male 14,5-15,5 mm; female 15,5-16,5 mm.

Early stages. Egg: unrecorded. Larva: third instar leaf green in colour, head black with six white tear-drop-shaped dots in a radial pattern; fourth and fifth instar leaf green, head brown, marked with creamy-white outlined by darker brown. The larva attains a length of 38 mm. Pupa: 17,5-20 mm long; creamy white with adult features outlined in pale brown (Woodhall, 1994:128).

HABITAT AND ECOLOGY

P. moritili is an inhabitant of bushveld, woodland and riverine forests, where it can be found almost anywhere. Occasionally it penetrates the grassveld. It is a fast and irregular flier and rests on the ground, stems of grass, low shrubs and high leaves of trees. It feeds at flowers near the ground or in trees. It can also be observed sucking at mud.

The males do not show hilltopping behaviour, but select a territory about a low tree or shrub among other tall trees. Where thick bush occurs they are found on low bushes along the edges. They are sometimes also observed in the interior of the bush where sunlight falls on a low tree and along paths that lead through the bush. They occupy these territories for hours, perching on a prominent plant or even on the ground, and vigorously chasing intruders. They are often observed pursuing other butterflies up and down the edges of forest. They repeatedly return to the same perch.

The females fly at random through the bush in search of suitable food plants on which to lay. The eggs are laid singly on a leaf of the food plant. The larva folds over the edge of a leaf which is held closed by struts of white silk 3 mm long, so that the larva is visible inside. The larva pupates inside the final larval shelter and is enclosed within in thin silken cocoons. The pupal stage lasts some 14 days (Woodhall, 1994:128).

This species is on the wing throughout the year, but is scarcer during winter. September to April may be the best time for seeing it.

Platylesches moritili male underside

LARVAL FOOD PLANTS

Parinari curatellifolia (Chrysobalanaceae).

DISTRIBUTION

South Africa, from KwaZulu-Natal and Gauteng, Mpumalanga and Northern Province, to Swaziland, Moçambique and Zimbabwe, northwards to most of Africa south of the Sahara.

CONSERVATION

Although not very common, *P. moritili* is widely distributed throughout the bushveld of the northern and eastern regions and is under no threat in South Africa.

Platylesches moritili early instar larva

Platylesches moritili final instar larva

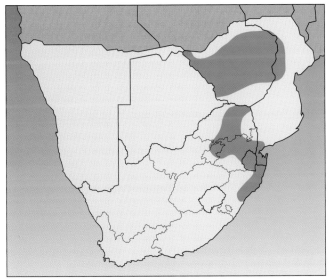

Distribution map of *Platylesches moritili*

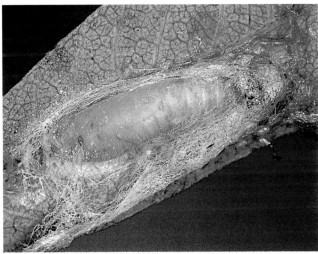

Platylesches moritili pupa

Platylesches tina Evans

SMALL HOPPER

Platylesches tina Evans, 1937. *Cat. Afr. Hesper.*: 170. Type locality: Mlanje, Malawi. Holotype male in Natural History Museum, London.

IDENTIFICATION

Adult. This is the smallest species of the genus. Male. The forewings are elongated and the hindwings are proportionally smaller. Upperside: dark brown with a median row of white spots on forewing, usually with a single subapical spot. Underside: forewing with apical half of outer margin broadly paler, no pale scaling in area CuA_2; hindwing violet-brown with faint traces of pale discal spots in areas M_2-CuA_1. Female. Similar to male but often has two subapical spots on forewing.

Forewing lengths: male 12-13 mm; female 13-14 mm.

Early stages. Egg: unrecorded. Larva: final instar leaf green, head brown marked with cream patches outlined with darker brown in a radial pattern. It attains a length of about 10 mm. Pupa: 10 mm; dull cream in colour outlined with dark brown (Woodhall, 1994:129).

HABITAT AND ECOLOGY

P. tina is an inhabitant of well-wooded bushveld areas and nearby riverine bush. Individuals are often found along rocky riverbeds which run through evergreen forest, where they gather to drink water from wet sand or fresh bird droppings on the rocks. They can also be observed flying busily around low trees on the upper slopes of wooded hills. They have been seen to feed at a considerable height on the flowers of trees .

The males do not appear to exhibit hilltopping behaviour but appear to favour the upper slopes or clearings in the bush. They often select a leaf on a bush in a clearing as a perch site. From here they dart off to chase away intruders, often to be pursued in turn as they invade a neighbour's territory.

The females fly at random through the bush in search of suitable food plants on which to lay. The larval shelter is formed from whole small leaves being folded in two along the midrib and then secured closely together with short silk strands along the edges. Pupation takes place inside the final larval shelter, the pupa being enclosed within a thin silken cocoon. The pupal stage lasts 87-91 days (Woodhall, 1994:129).

This species is on the wing throughout the year.

Platylesches tina female underside

LARVAL FOOD PLANTS

Parinari curatellifolia (Chrysobalanaceae).

DISTRIBUTION

South Africa, a marginal species found in the far north-eastern parts of the Northern Province with the occasional record from Mpumalanga, northwards to the Caprivi strip, Zimbabwe and into East Africa as far north as Uganda and Kenya.

CONSERVATION

P. tina appears to be very rare throughout its range. The only known breeding site in South Africa is the area around Sibasa in the Northern Province, which is probably worthy of protection. This species is classified as rare by S.F. & G.A. Henning (1989: 159) in the *South African Red Data Book - Butterflies*.

Platylesches tina final instar larva

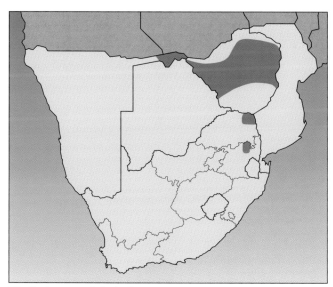

Distribution map of *Platylesches tina*

Platylesches picanini (Holland)

BANDED HOPPER

Parnara picanini Holland, 1894. *Ent. News* **5**: 91. Type locality: Liberia. Type male in Holland Collection.

IDENTIFICATION

Adult. Male. Upperside: forewing with a single subapical spot. Underside: hindwing dark brown with a wide white or yellow band, interrupted by the ground colour in area 3A. Female. Similar to male, but with slightly more elongated wings with more rounded angles.

Forewing lengths: male 14-17,5 mm; female 17-18 mm.

Early stages. Egg: unrecorded. Larva: fourth instar leaf green, head brown with eight white teardrop-shaped dots in a radial pattern; fifth instar bright salmon pink, dark brown head marked with a radial pattern of cream-white patches. The larva attains a length of some 35 mm. Pupa: 15 mm long; dull creamy-white in colour, with adult features outlined in dark brown (Woodhall, 1994:128).

HABITAT AND ECOLOGY

P. picanini is an inhabitant of forests and riverine vegetation. It appears to fly about the canopy, some 6-7 metres above the ground. Occasionally, however, it has been observed to descend to feed on flowers at the edge of the bush in late afternoon or early morning. Males are occasionally attracted to fresh bird droppings.

The males establish their territories about the branches of tall trees some 6 metres above the ground. Here they perch on a prominent twig or leaves and dart out to chase off any intruding males. The males are usually most active from 10:00 to about 14:00 when the weather is warm and sunny.

Platylesches picanini male underside

The females frequent the same places as the males but fly at random in search of suitable food plants. The larva makes an incision in a leaf of the food plant, leaving a small portion 'uncut'. It then pulls the cut-out portion over the adjoining surface of the leaf and secures it with many fine, short brown silk threads, to form a shelter. Inside the shelter, the larva spins a bed of strong struts of white silk on which it rests. Pupation takes place within the final larval shelter within a thin silken cocoon. The pupal stage lasts some 12 days (Woodhall, 1994:128).

This species appears to be on the wing from June to August and again from January to May.

LARVAL FOOD PLANTS

Parinari curatellifolia (Chrysobalanaceae).

DISTRIBUTION

South Africa, from Mpumalanga and Northern Province, Zimbabwe and Moçambique, northwards to most of Africa south of the Sahara.

CONSERVATION

P. picanini is a fairly widely distributed species and is under no threat.

Platylesches picanini early instar larva

Platylesches picanini final instar larva

Platylesches picanini pupa

Platylesches picanini form *goetzei* male underside

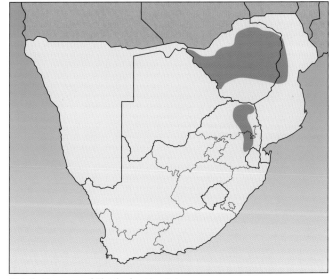

Distribution map of *Platylesches picanini*

Genus *Zenonia* Evans

Zenonia Evans, 1935. *Trans. R. ent. Soc. Lond.* **68**: 405. Type species: *Pamphila zeno* Trimen, 1864, by original designation.

Smallish skippers with conspicuous orange markings. Antenna with apiculus very sharp but little longer than the club is thick. Palpi erect. Forewing with vein CuA_1 almost arising from the posterior angle of the discal cell and far from vein CuA_2 which arises from the centre of the cell. Hindwing with a broad lobe at anal angle; vein M_2 poorly developed or absent.

Larval food plants belong to the Poaceae.

There is only one species in Southern Africa.

Zenonia zeno (Trimen)

ORANGE-SPOTTED SKIPPER

Pamphila zeno Trimen, 1864. *Trans. ent. Soc. Lond.* (3) **2**: 179. Type locality: Bashee River, Kaffraria. Type male in Natural History Museum, London.

IDENTIFICATION

Adult. Male. Upperside: dark brown with irregular orange bands and spots; on forewing two such bands extend from base and nearly meet beyond end of cell with a few subapical spots; hindwing with an orange medial patch and a curved postdiscal band on outer half of wing. Underside: hindwing orange with vague brownish bands. Female. Similar to male but paler with more rounded wings.

Forewing lengths: male 16-18,5 mm; female 17-19 mm.

Early stages. unrecorded.

HABITAT AND ECOLOGY

Z. zeno is an inhabitant of dense bush or rainforest in the moister eastern areas of South Africa. Here it is usually encountered along forest edges, paths, streams and, in some habitats, on quite open ground. It has a rapid flight, settling on low shrubs or grass stems, on the ground or on stones. It sits with forewings slightly and hindwings fully open. It is often observed feeding at flowers.

The males establish their territories along the edges of the bush. Here they can be observed flying rapidly up and down and perching frequently on the ground or low plants. Any intruding males are rapidly chased out of their territories.

The females frequent the same areas as the males but fly at random in search of suitable food plants on which to lay their eggs.

This species is on the wing throughout the year.

Zenonia zeno male upperside

LARVAL FOOD PLANTS

Cultivated maize and sorghum and wild grasses (Poaceae).

DISTRIBUTION

South Africa, from the Eastern Cape, KwaZulu-Natal, Northern Province and Mpumalanga, Swaziland, Moçambique, Zimbabwe and northwards into East and West Africa.

CONSERVATION

Z. zeno is a widespread species and is therefore under no threat.

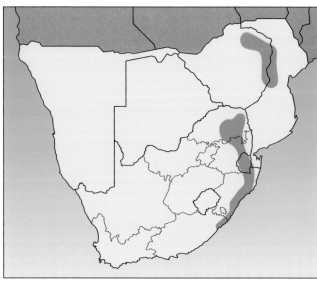

Distribution map of *Zenonia zeno*

Genus *Pelopidas* Walker

Pelopidas Walker, 1870. *Entomologist* **5**: 56. Type species: *Pelopidas midea* Walker, 1870, by monotypy.

Medium-sized skippers with antenna shorter than half costa; club stout, apiculus equal to width of club. Mostly dull brown species with a few small hyaline spots on forewing. Males usually carry a linear sex-brand on the forewing, and there is sometimes a cell spot on hindwing underside.

Eggs, flattened dome. Larvae green, cylindrical, broad posteriorly; final instar larval headshield rimmed with dark coloration. Pupae long and narrow, anteriorly with long pointed process.

The larvae feed on grasses (Poaceae), and some are a pest of rice and sorghum in some parts of the world.

There are only two species in Southern Africa.

KEY TO THE SPECIES OF *PELOPIDAS*

1. Male sex brand black; LHW brown with grey scaling, discal spots from 3A to Sc+R_1 .... *P. mathias*

   Male sex brand whitish; LHW greenish ochreous, discal spots only from CuA_1 to Rs .... *P. thrax*

Pelopidas mathias male underside

Pelopidas mathias (Fabricius)

BLACK-BANDED SWIFT

Hesperia mathias Fabricius, 1798. *Suppl. Syst. Ent.*: 433. Type locality: India.

IDENTIFICATION

Adult. Male. Upperside: dark brown with greenish-yellow hairs; forewing with a more or less semi-circular group of hyaline spots, which include three minute subapical dots; sex brand black, divided by a very fine white line. Underside: hindwing greyish-brown with a curved row of normally 7 postdiscal spots in areas 3A to Sc+R_1 and also a more basal dot in discal cell. Female. Similar to male but lacks the sex-brand on the forewing upperside.

Forewing lengths: male 17-18 mm; female 18-19 mm.

Early stages. Egg: pale greenish-white; diameter 1,2 mm; height 0,75 mm; with longitudinal and, staggered, cross-braces but these are very faint, being more apparent at the base. Larva: first and second instars green with a black head; third instar green with lighter and dark longitudinal stripes and a dark brown head; fourth instar as in third instar but head green and black; fifth instar larva pale green with a single dark dorsal stripe, flanked by a pair of whitish dorso-lateral ones, head green with a lateral white-bordered black stripe down each side. The larva attains a length of 38 mm. Pupa: 28-29 mm long; green with white and darker green lateral stripes along abdomen (Clark, 1978: 765).

HABITAT AND ECOLOGY

P. mathias is an inhabitant of grassy woodlands and forest. It is usually observed flying rapidly about open wooded areas or along the edges of forests. Very swift on the wing, it often settles on flowers to feed. It frequents at damp spots and is often observed basking in the sun.

The males show hilltopping behaviour and on warm sunny days may arrive as early as 07:00. However, they often also establish territories on the outskirts of a forest or along paths where they select a prominent perch from which they chase all intruders.

The females fly at random through the bush in search of suitable food plants on which to lay. Eggs are laid singly on the grass. The egg takes some ten days to hatch and the discarded shell is eaten by the newly emerged larva. The entire larval stage is spent in a tube constructed by the larva by joining together the edges of a blade of grass. It crawls out at intervals to feed on the end of the blade. Successive tubes are constructed as the larva grows. When too big to occupy a tube, the larva lies along the midrib of a blade, the mark-

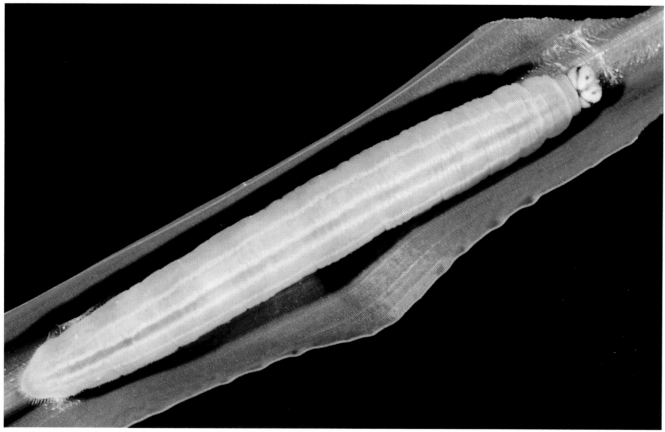

Pelopidas mathias final instar larva (Photo: R. Paré)

ing of the dorsum rendering it inconspicuous. The larval stage lasts some 37 days. Pupation occurs on a blade of grass. The pupa is secured to a silken mat spun on a blade of grass, by means of its cremastral hooks and a silken girdle. The pupal stage lasts some 26 days.

The species is on the wing throughout the year, being scarcer in winter.

Pelopidas mathias pupa (After G.C. Clark, 1978)

LARVAL FOOD PLANTS

Ehrharta erecta, Panicum sp., *Andropogon* sp., *Zea* sp. (Poaceae).

DISTRIBUTION

South Africa, from the Eastern Cape, KwaZulu-Natal, North-West Province, Gauteng, Mpumalanga and Northern Province, into Botswana, Namibia, Zimbabwe, Swaziland, Moçambique, northwards over the whole of Africa south of the Sahara and the Oriental Region.

CONSERVATION

P. mathias is common and widespread and is under no threat.

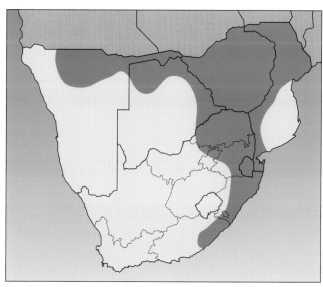

Distribution map of *Pelopidas mathias*

Pelopidas thrax (Hübner)

WHITE-BANDED SWIFT

Gegenes thrax Hübner, 1821. *Samml. exot. Schmetterl.* **2**: pl. 150.

There are two subspecies, only one of which occurs in Southern Africa. The nominate subspecies does not occur in Africa but comes from the Oriental Region.

Pelopidas thrax inconspicua male upperside

Pelopidas thrax inconspicua (Bertolini)

Hesperia inconspicua Bertolini, 1850. *Atti. Accad. Sci. Ist. Bologna. Mem.* **2**: 179. Type locality: Moçambique.

IDENTIFICATION

Adult. Male. Upperside: distinguished by their prominent white, linear sex-brand on forewing. There are also always two hyaline spots in forewing cell. Underside: hindwing greenish-ochreous with 5 white discal spots only from areas CuA_1 to Rs which are rarely as well-developed as in *P. mathias*. Female. Similar to male but lacks sex-brand on forewing upperside.

Forewing lengths: male 19,5-21,5 mm; female 23-24 mm.

Early stages. Egg: yellow at first, changing to salmon; diameter 1,5 mm, height 0,9 mm; with some 60 faint longitudinal ribs reaching two-thirds up the side and cross-braced by some 13 staggered braces, which resolve into a hexagonal pattern up to the micropyle. Larva: can have 5 or 6 instars; first to third instars pale olive-green with a black head; fourth and fifth instars greenish-olive with a darker dorsal longitudinal stripe and a black head; sixth (final) instar pale olive green with a darker dorsal longitudinal stripe and white head margined with black and a black Y down disc. The larva attains a length of some 45 mm. Pupa: 29 mm long; pale olive green with a pointed blackish head (Clark, 1978: 268).

HABITAT AND ECOLOGY

P. thrax is an inhabitant of woodland and forest margins. It is encountered only occasionally in grass-, thorn- or bushveld. It is more often found in dense rainforests. It flies everywhere except perhaps on the highest peaks of the Drakensberg or the dry bossieveld of the Karoo. It has a swift flight and frequently visits and settles on flowers in the veld and in gardens. It is also attracted to muddy places.

The males exhibit hilltopping behaviour, ascending to the peaks as early as 07:00 on warm sunny days. They often also select territories along the outskirts of forest or along paths where they perch on a leaf or twig from whence they actively chase off all intruders.

The females fly at random in search of suitable food plants on which to lay. They lay their eggs singly on the food plant. The larva emerges after about eight days and eats the discarded shell. The larva then constructs a grass tube by binding the edges of the grass together with silk, and crawls out at intervals to feed on the end of the grass. Successive tubes are constructed as the larva grows and, finally, when it is too big for a tube, it lies along a blade of grass. The larval stage lasts some 117 days. The pupa is secured to a silken mat spun by the larva on a blade of grass, by its cremastral hooks and a silken girdle. It is occasionally found in a tube made of blades of grass by the larva. The pupal stage lasts some 12 days (Clark, 1978: 268).

This species is on the wing throughout the year, but is commoner in summer.

LARVAL FOOD PLANTS

Imperata cylindrica; reared on *Ehrharta erecta* and other grasses (Poaceae).

DISTRIBUTION

South Africa, from the Western and Eastern Cape, KwaZulu-Natal, Free State, North-West Province, Gauteng, Northern Province and Mpumalanga, into Botswana, Namibia, Zimbabwe, Swaziland, Moçambique and the whole of Africa south of the Sahara.

CONSERVATION

P. thrax is a common and widespread species and is under no threat.

Pelopidas thrax inconspicua final instar larva (After G.C. Clark, 1978)

Pelopidas thrax inconspicua pupa (After G.C. Clark, 1978)

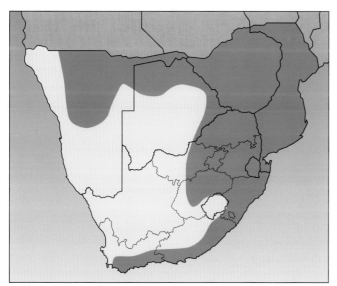

Distribution map of *Pelopidas thrax*

Genus *Borbo* Evans

Borbo Evans, 1949. *Cat. Hesp. Europe, Asia, Australia*: 44.
Type species: *Hesperia borbonica* Boisduval, 1833, by original designation.

Small to medium-sized skippers with antennae rather longer than in *Parnara*, with a longer apiculus. The male is without a sex-brand. Mostly dull brown species with whitish or yellowish hyaline spots, especially on forewing. Hindwing underside never has spot in cell, whereas it is sometimes present in *Pelopidas*.

Eggs domed, laterally finely ribbed. Larvae cylindrical broad posteriorly; final instar larval headshield white with dark margins. Pupae green, narrow and elongated, acute at both ends.

Food plants Poaceae. Some of the species are pests of rice and sugar cane.

There are 11 species in Southern Africa, 9 of which occur in South Africa.

KEY TO THE SPECIES OF *BORBO*

1. Antennae half as long as costa, club gradual, long 2

    Antennae shorter than half costa, club stout 4

2. Underside bright red-brown, LFW with inner margin broadly black
    .... *B. ferruginea*

    Underside brown or blackish-brown 3

3. Male upperside immaculate; LFW with dark subapical band; LHW
    with dark discal area; female with discal and subapical spots on
    forewing; underside with marginal area paler, suffused whitish dis-
    cal spots from 2A-Rs on a pale discal patch .... *B. lugens*

    Both male and female with white spots on forewing; LHW usually
    with spots in M$_1$, CuA$_1$, CuA$_2$, often on a grey discal patch
    .... *B. fatuellus*

4. Forewing with two cell spots; LHW with irregular spots in CuA$_1$-M$_1$,
    faintly showing through above .... *B. fallax*

    Forewing at most one spot in upper cell 5

5. Palpi more or less ochreous below 6

    Palpi grey below 8

6. LHW with at most spots in areas CuA$_1$, M$_3$ and Rs .... *B. borbonica*

    LHW with very variable, spots in M$_2$ and M$_3$ present, sometimes
    complete series from Rs to CuA$_2$ 7

7. UFW in male lacks a spot in CuA$_2$; orange-brown with ochreous
    spots; LHW in female with a straight row of discal spots in M$_2$ to
    CuA$_2$, a spot in M$_1$; UFW spots ochreous .... *B. micans*

    UFW with a spot in CuA$_2$ and with costa conspicuously ochreous;
    LHW with spots irregular .... *B. detecta*

8. LHW with prominent spots in CuA$_1$, M$_3$ and Rs; male with promi-
    nent spot in CuA$_2$ of forewing .... *B. gemella*

    LHW with variable spots, white or dark, in 3A to Sc+R$_1$, also in cell;
    male UFW with spot in CuA$_2$ .... *B. holtzii*

Borbo lugens (Hopffer)

LESSER-HORNED SWIFT

P*amphila lugens* Hopffer, 1855. *Mber. dt. Akad. Wiss. Berl.*
1855: 643. Type locality: Moçambique.

IDENTIFICATION

Adult. Wings more rounded than usual in the genus. Male. Uniformly dark brown without markings on both upper and undersides. Female. Forewing with small hyaline spots and ground colour
a paler brown than in male.

Forewing lengths: male 14-16,5 mm; female 17-18 mm.

Early stages. Egg: white, with a very pale pink patch developing, in
time, over the top; diameter 0,95 mm, height 0,7 mm; with some
40 faint ribs, more apparent at the base, these ribs break up into a
faint hexagonal or pentagonal pattern, up to the small micropyle.
Larva: first to fourth instars pale green with a black head; fifth instar greenish-white, becoming yellowish anteriorly and posteriorly with darker green dorsal and dorso-lateral longitudinal lines, head
white with a black margin and Y down front of disc. It attains a
length of 33 mm. Pupa: 26 mm long; green with two white dorso-
lateral lines on abdomen (Clark, 1978: 270).

HABITAT AND ECOLOGY

B. lugens is an inhabitant of forests, riverine thickets and forest edges.
Its favoured habitat is grassy clearings in fairly dense woodland. It
is usually observed settling on vegetation and flowers of low bushes.

The males establish their territories about the edges of the forest. They perch on grass, low shrubs or the leaves of the creepers surrounding the trees, at times in dense shade dotted with sunbeams.
After chasing off an intruder they quickly return to the same perch.

The females frequent the same places as the males but fly at
random in search of suitable food plants on which to oviposit.
Eggs are laid singly on the food plant. The larva constructs a tube
by spinning together the edges of a blade of grass. It crawls out at
intervals to feed on the end of the blade. The larval stage lasts
some 40 days. Pupation takes place in the grass tube and is secured
to a silken mat by its cremastral hooks. The pupal stage lasts from
15-17 days (Clark, 1978: 270).

This species is on the wing throughout the year.

Borbo lugens final instar larva (After G.C. Clark, 1978)

Borbo lugens pupa (After G.C. Clark, 1978)

Borbo lugens male underside

LARVAL FOOD PLANTS

Ehrharta erecta, S. megaphylla, Panicum deustum, Stipa sp., *Pennisetum* sp. (Poaceae).

DISTRIBUTION

South Africa, from KwaZulu-Natal, into Moçambique, Zimbabwe and extending northwards into East and Central Africa.

CONSERVATION

B. lugens is a fairly common and widespread species and is under no threat.

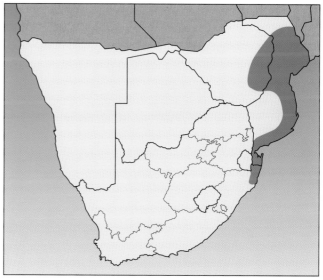

Distribution map of *Borbo lugens*

Borbo fatuellus (Hopffer)

LONG-HORNED SWIFT

Pamphila fatuellus Hopffer, 1855. *Mber. dt. Akad. Wiss. Berl.* **1855**: 643.

There are 3 subspecies of which only the nominate occurs in Southern Africa. The subspecies *thomea* Evans (1937) comes from Sao Tomé and *dolens* Mabille (1897) comes from the Comoro Islands.

Borbo fatuellus fatuellus (Hopffer)

Pamphila fatuellus Hopffer, 1855. *Mber. dt. Akad. Wiss. Berl.* **1855**: 643. Type locality: Moçambique.

IDENTIFICATION

Adult. Male. Upperside: dark brown with only small hyaline spots on forewing. There are no hyaline spots in cell or on hindwings. Underside: hindwing with ground colour uniformly dark brown, usually with spots in areas CuA_1, M_3 and Rs. Female. Similar to male but has larger hyaline spots and may have small hyaline spots in cell and/or on the hindwings.

The dry-season form *cinerea* (Holland) (1896, *Proc. zool. Soc. Lond.* **1896**: 66) differs from the nominate wet-season form in having the central part of the hindwing underside overlaid with grey scales.

Forewing lengths: male 15,5-20 mm; female 18,5-20,5 mm.

Early stages. Egg: whitish to pale watery green; diameter 1,0 mm, height 0,6 mm; with 40 to 50 faint longitudinal ribs braced by some 36 very faint cross-ribs which break up into a hexagonal pattern at the top of the egg. Larva: first instar white with a black head; second and third instars green with a black head; fourth instar green with darker longitudinal stripes and a blackish head; fifth (final) instar pale green with darker longitudinal stripes and a black and white head. It attains a length of 33-39 mm. Pupa: 26-32 mm; green with a pair of white dorsal longitudinal stripes on abdomen (Clark, 1978: 276).

HABITAT AND ECOLOGY

B. fatuellus occupies most habitats, particularly woodland, forest margins and light forest. It settles low on grass or shrubs along the edge of bush. At times it feeds at flowers or damp patches.

The males establish their territories along the edge of forest, forest paths or water courses. At times they can be seen in their hundreds perching on the stems of grass. Every now and then one will fly up and intrude on a neighbour's territory, leading to it being actively chased. At times five to ten specimens can be involved and can be seen whirling about over the grass or shrubs, ascending occa-

Borbo fatuellus fatuellus male underside

Borbo fatuellus fatuellus final instar larva

sionally to the tops of the highest trees or branches. They all eventually return to their respective perches on the grass in their own territories. At times a male can be encountered perching on the leaves of a tree, but not too high above the ground.

The females frequent the same area but fly at random in search of suitable plants on which to lay their eggs. Eggs are laid singly on a blade of grass. The entire larval stage is spent within a grass tube constructed by the larva, but the exterior end of the blade is eaten at intervals. Larger tubes are formed as the larva grows and, finally it may lie along the midrib of a blade of grass, after spinning a silken web over the portion of the blade used for this purpose. The larval stage lasts some 36 days. The pupa is secured to a silken pad, spun on a blade of grass, by its cremastral hooks and a silken girdle, or the larva may remain in the grass tube and pupate in it. The pupal stage lasts some 18-32 days (Clark, 1978:276).

This species is on the wing throughout the year, but June to August and the mid-summer months are the best times to find it.

Borbo fatuellus fatuellus pupa (After G.C. Clark, 1978)

LARVAL FOOD PLANTS

Setaria megaphylla, Ehrharta erecta (Poaceae).

DISTRIBUTION

South Africa, from the Eastern Cape, KwaZulu-Natal, Mpumalanga and Northern Province, into Botswana, northern Namibia, Zimbabwe, Swaziland, Moçambique, to all of Africa south of the Sahara.

CONSERVATION

B. fatuellus is a widespread species and is under no threat.

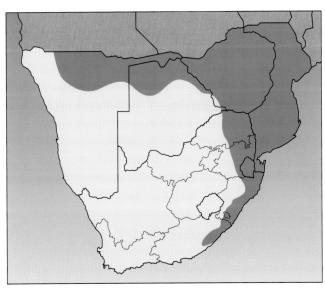

Distribution map of *Borbo fatuellus*

Borbo fallax (Gaede)

FALSE SWIFT

Parnara fallax Gaede, 1916. *Int. ent. Z.* **9**: 126. Type locality: Cameroon.

IDENTIFICATION

Adult. Male. Upperside: forewing with spot in area CuA_2 present or absent, but always well marked on underside; forewing also with two well-marked hyaline spots in cell. Underside: hindwing brown overlaid with greenish-grey scales and the white spots are small: there is usually a spot in area Rs as well as the irregular series in areas M_1-CuA_1, but sometimes only the spots in spaces M_1 and M_2 are present. Female. Similar to male but with more rounded wings.

Forewing lengths: male 17-20 mm; female 19-20,5 mm.

Early stages. Egg: white, later developing pale pink maculae; diameter 1,05 mm, height 0,65 mm; with some 60 faint longitudinal ribs. Larva: first instar pale greenish-white with a black head; second instar pale greenish white with darker green longitudinal stripes and a blackish head; third to fifth (final) instar greenish-white with darker longitudinal stripes and greenish head. The larva attains a length of 40,5 mm. Pupa: 30 mm long; green, becoming paler at the extremities and with white longitudinal stripes (Clark, 1978: 272).

HABITAT AND ECOLOGY

B. fallax is an inhabitant of coastal bush and extends inland into bushveld, savannah and woodland. It even penetrates open grassland in places. It has a swift flight. Here and there the species feeds at flowers or at damp places.

The males show hilltopping behaviour and on warm sunny days may arrive there as early as 07:00. However they as often establish territories on the outskirts of a forest or along paths. They usually select a perch site on the ground, a stone or grass stem, from where they dart off to chase intruders out of their territory.

The females fly at random in search of suitable food plants on which to oviposit. Eggs are laid singly on a blade of grass. The eggs take some 11 days to hatch. The larva constructs tubes of grass by drawing the edges together and binding them with silk. When the larva grows too long for a tube, it lies along the midrib of a blade of grass. The larval stage lasts about 50 days. The pupa is attached to a blade of grass by its cremastral hooks which are entangled in the silk which the larva has spun on the surface of the leaf, and there is also a supporting silken girdle. Although not verified, it is presumed that pupation may take place at times in a grass tube formed by the larva, if the blades have been large enough to allow the larva to use a tube in the final part of the last larval stage. The pupal stage lasts some 11 days (Clark, 1978: 272).

This species is on the wing throughout the year, being scarcer during winter.

LARVAL FOOD PLANTS

Ehrharta erecta, Saccharum sp. and other grasses (Poaceae).

DISTRIBUTION

South Africa, from KwaZulu-Natal, Northern Province and Mpumalanga, North-West Province, Gauteng, Swaziland, Moçambique, Zimbabwe, Botswana, northern Namibia, northwards over most of Africa south of the Sahara.

Borbo fallax final instar larva (After G.C. Clark, 1978)

Borbo fallax pupa (After G.C. Clark, 1978)

Borbo fallax male

CONSERVATION

B. fallax is a widespread species and is under no threat.

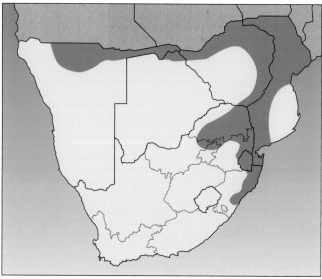

Distribution map of *Borbo fallax*

RUSTY SWIFT

Pamphila detecta Trimen, 1893. *Trans. R. ent. Soc. Lond.* **1893**: 141. Type locality: KwaZulu-Natal. Type male in Natural History Museum, London.

IDENTIFICATION

Adult. Male. Upperside: pale brown with yellowish hairs; hindwing with tiny white dots. Underside: hindwing and costa of forewing conspicuously ochreous; hindwing with irregularly placed discal spots. Female. Similar to male but hindwing upperside more distinctly spotted.

Forewing lengths: male 16-17 mm; female 17-18 mm.

Early stages. Unrecorded.

Borbo detecta male showing upperside

HABITAT AND ECOLOGY

B. detecta is an inhabitant of bushveld and woodlands from sea level to 2 000 m. It is a swift flying species, keeping low to the ground in relatively open areas. It settles frequently on bare ground or rocks. It is rarely observed at flowers.

The males exhibit strong hilltopping behaviour. Here they establish their territories, perching on rocks about the peaks and vigorously chasing off intruders.

The females fly at random in search of suitable food plants on which to oviposit.

The species is probably on the wing throughout the year, being scarcer during the winter months.

LARVAL FOOD PLANTS

Ehrharta erecta and similar grasses (Poaceae).

DISTRIBUTION

South Africa, from KwaZulu-Natal, Louws Creek in Mpumalanga, into Swaziland, Moçambique, Zimbabwe, northwards over much of Africa south of the Sahara and Sao Tomé.

CONSERVATION

B. detecta is a fairly widespread species but is by no means common and must be considered scarce in South Africa. It is, however, under no threat.

Borbo micans (Holland)

MARSH SWIFT

Parnara micans Holland, 1896. *Proc. zool. Soc. Lond.* **1896**: 63. Type locality: Ogowe.

IDENTIFICATION

Adult. Male. Upperside: ochreous-brown suffused with a bright golden colour which obscures the ochreous spots; hindwing with yellow hyaline discal spots. Underside: indistinct as above. Female. Upperside: quite distinctly spotted, hyaline spots of forewing large with a non-hyaline discal spot near inner margin. Underside: hindwing with a straight row of discal yellowish spots.

Forewing lengths: male 15-17 mm; female 17-19 mm.

Early stages. Unrecorded.

HABITAT AND ECOLOGY

B. micans is an inhabitant of marshes, swamps and marshy areas along rivers. Here it flies low and relatively slowly over the grass, often settling on conspicuous blades. It is a local species but may be common where it occurs, though some of its colonies are restricted to a few dozen square metres.

The males establish their territories in the marshy areas where they perch on low clumps of grass. From here they dart out and chase off intruders. Two males will buzz around each other at quite a speed, before parting and returning to their respective territories.

The females fly at random throughout the swampy area, presumably searching for suitable food plants on which to lay.

This species appears to be on the wing throughout the year, although it appears to be more plentiful in autumn and winter.

Distribution map of *Borbo detecta*

Borbo micans male underside

LARVAL FOOD PLANTS

Possibly swamp grasses (Poaceae).

DISTRIBUTION

South Africa, from northern KwaZulu-Natal, Moçambique, Zimbabwe, in the Okavango Delta in Botswana and northwards over most of Africa south of the Sahara.

CONSERVATION

B. micans is a marginal species in South Africa, only one specimen being recorded from near Kosi Bay on 10 July 1929. As no established colony is known no possible threat in South Africa can be commented on. However, little research has been done in the swamp on the northern side of the entrance to Kosi Bay where the specimen was caught, so perhaps a colony still exists there. Further research is necessary. The species is, however, widespread throughout Africa and is certainly not under threat in these areas. Its status in South Africa was given as indeterminate by S.F. & G.A. Henning (1989) in the *South African Red Data Book – Butterflies*.

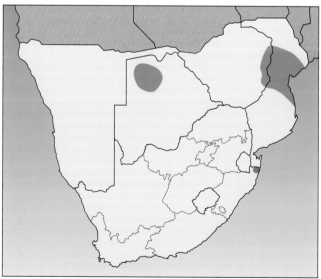

Distribution map of *Borbo micans*

197

Borbo ferruginea (Aurivillius)

FERRUGINOUS SWIFT

Parnara ferruginea Aurivillius, 1925. *Macrolep. of World.* **13**: 536.

There are two subspecies but only *dondo* occurs in Southern Africa. The nominate subspecies comes from East Africa.

Borbo ferruginea dondo Evans

Borbo ferruginea dondo Evans, 1955. *Ann. Mag. nat. Hist.* (12) **2**: 885. Type locality: Dondo, Moçambique. Holotype male in the Natural History Museum, London.

IDENTIFICATION

Adult. Male. Upperside: dark brown with only traces of hyaline spots on forewing. Underside: hindwing deep ferruginous-brown with clearly defined white spots only in areas Rs, M_3 and CuA_1. Female. Similar to male but hyaline spots on forewing better developed.

Forewing lengths: male 17-18,5 mm; female 19,5-22 mm.

Early stages. Unrecorded.

HABITAT AND ECOLOGY

B. ferruginea dondo is an inhabitant of lowland forest. It flies in thick forest, probably descending from the canopy in the early morning and late afternoon. Both sexes can often be observed feeding on flowers.

The males establish territories in sunny glades where they select a low perch and chase all intruders.

The females fly at random through the forest, presumably in search of suitable food plants on which to lay.

This species is on the wing from October to May, but is likely to occur in other months as well.

LARVAL FOOD PLANTS

Unrecorded.

DISTRIBUTION

South Africa, from northern KwaZulu-Natal, eastern Zimbabwe and Moçambique.

CONSERVATION

B. ferruginea dondo is a marginal subspecies in South Africa, being recorded at Richards Bay, Dukuduku, Cape Vidal and other local-

Borbo ferruginea dondo male underside

ities in northern KwaZulu-Natal. This subspecies probably occurs in the Tembe Elephant Reserve, Enseleni Nature Reserve and other conservation areas in KwaZulu-Natal, so is apparently quite safe from the threat of habitat destruction. Its colonies in the Dondo and Amatongas Forests are probably not so well off. Its status is given as indeterminate by S.F. & G.A. Henning (1989) in the *South African Red Data Book – Butterflies.*

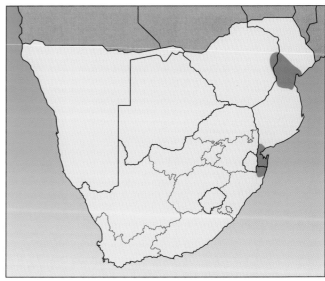

Distribution map of *Borbo ferruginea*

Borbo borbonica (Boisduval)

OLIVE-HAIRED SWIFT

Hesperia borbonica Boisduval, 1833. *Faune ent. de Madag.*: 65.

There are three subspecies of which only the nominate occurs in Southern Africa. The subspecies *morella* (Joannis, 1893) occurs in the Seychelles and Aldabra, while *zelleri* (Lederer, 1855) is recorded from Algeria, Morocco, Egypt, Gibraltar and Syria.

Borbo borbonica borbonica (Boisduval)

Hesperia borbonica Boisduval, 1833. *Faune ent. de Madag.*: 65. Type locality: Réunion (formerly Îsle de Bourbon).

IDENTIFICATION

Adult. Male. Forewing extremely elongated and pointed without a sex-brand. Upperside: dark brown; forewing with large hyaline spots, roughly in the form of a Y and there is only one spot in the cell; hindwing with a postdiscal row of four hyaline spots in areas Rs-M$_2$. Underside: with costa and apex of forewing and hindwing dusted with olivaceous-yellow scales; hindwing with three round, brown-bordered white spots in postdiscal area. Female. Similar to male but with more rounded wings.

Forewing lengths: male 18,5-20,5 mm; female 19,5-21 mm.

Early stages. Unrecorded.

Borbo borbonica borbonica male underside

HABITAT AND ECOLOGY

B. borbonica is an inhabitant of bushveld, woodlands, coastal bush and open habitats up to 2 600 metres. It tends to be migratory and its flight is low and powerful. Migration over sea was observed on Mauritius during March 1986, the specimens arriving from the direction of Madagascar at 08:00 in the morning. It is seldom encountered, but is occasionally observed feeding at flowers.

The males do not appear to show hilltopping behaviour. They have been found establishing territories anywhere in the veld among short grass, along dry river beds and swampy areas wherever the larval food plants occur. Here they can be observed patrolling around their territories, or perching on grass stems, bare ground or rocks. Males can also be found establishing territories along the margins of woodlands where they perch on top of low bushes and occasionally dart off to investigate passing insects.

The females frequent the same places as the males but fly at random in search of suitable food plants on which to lay.

This species is on the wing throughout the year, the best months for observation being April and October.

LARVAL FOOD PLANTS

Various grasses, including *Ehrharta erecta*, *Oryza* sp., *Pennisetum* sp. and *Zea* sp. (Poaceae).

DISTRIBUTION

South Africa, from the Eastern Cape, KwaZulu-Natal, odd migratory records in the Free State, Gauteng, Northern Province and Mpumalanga, Swaziland, Moçambique, Zimbabwe, Botswana, Namibia, northwards throughout the rest of Africa south of the Sahara.

CONSERVATION

B. borbonica is a widespread species and is under no threat.

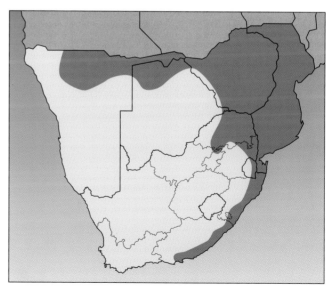

Distribution map of *Borbo borbonica*

Borbo gemella (Mabille)

TWIN SWIFT

Pamphila gemella Mabille, 1884. *C. r. Soc. ent. Belg.* **28**: 187.
Type locality: Madagascar.

IDENTIFICATION

Adult. Closely related to *B. borbonica* but has apical portion of forewing less pointed. Male. Upperside: forewing usually with one spot in cell. Underside: hindwing greyish-brown with three rather indistinct white spots in spaces Rs, M$_3$ and Rs. Female. Similar to male but larger with rounder wings.

Forewing lengths: male 16-18 mm; female 18,5-19,5 mm.

Early stages. Unrecorded.

HABITAT AND ECOLOGY

B. gemella is an inhabitant of bushveld, savannah, woodland and rainforest. Its flight is low and swift, but it frequently settles on the ground, stone or grass stem. It often is observed feeding at flowers and damp patches.

Borbo gemella male underside

The males exhibit hilltopping behaviour, often ascending to the peaks as early as 07:00 if it is warm and sunny. Here they can be found perching on the ground, stone or grass stem. In dense rainforests they select certain spots along clearings or paths, where they can be observed perching on low branches or shrubs.

The females fly at random in search of food plants on which to oviposit.

This species is on the wing throughout the year, the best months for observation being March and April.

LARVAL FOOD PLANTS

Triticum sativum, Ehrharta erecta, Saccharum sp. and *Zea* sp. (Poaceae).

DISTRIBUTION

South Africa, from Port St. Johns in the Eastern Cape, through KwaZulu-Natal, Mpumalanga and Northern Province, into Moçambique, Swaziland, Zimbabwe, Botswana, northern Namibia, northwards throughout most of Africa south of the Sahara.

CONSERVATION

B. gemella is a widespread species and is under no threat.

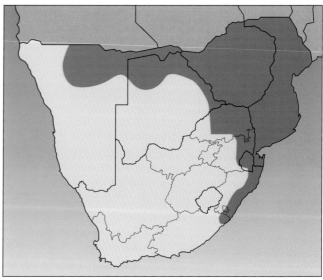

Distribution map of *Borbo gemella*

Borbo holtzii (Plötz)

VARIABLE SWIFT

Hesperia holtzii Plötz, 1883. *Stettin. ent. Ztg.* **44**: 44. Type locality: Angola.

IDENTIFICATION

Adult. Male. Upperside: forewing with upper cell spot small or absent and no spot in CuA_2. Underside: brown; hindwing and most of forewing overlaid with grey scales; hindwing with a straight row of dark spots, which can be indistinct or absent in some dry-season form specimens; in the wet-season form the spots are usually white-centred. Female. Similar to male but hyaline spotting may be larger and better developed.

Forewing length: male 17-19 mm; female 16,5-18,5 mm.

Early stages. Unrecorded.

HABITAT AND ECOLOGY

B. holtzii is an inhabitant of bushveld, savannah and open woodland. It has a swift flight. It is frequently observed feeding at flowers and muddy places.

The males occasionally show hilltopping behaviour, but usually establish their territories near to the larval food plants. They often perch along the edges of bush making rapid sorties after intruding insects.

The females fly at random in search of suitable food plants on which to oviposit.

This species is on the wing throughout the year, although the best time for observing it is from July to May.

LARVAL FOOD PLANTS

Unrecorded.

DISTRIBUTION

South Africa, from northern KwaZulu-Natal, Northern Province and Mpumalanga, into Swaziland, Moçambique, Zimbabwe and possibly eastern Botswana, northwards through most of Africa south of the Sahara.

CONSERVATION

B. holtzii is a widespread species and is under no threat.

Borbo holtzii male underside

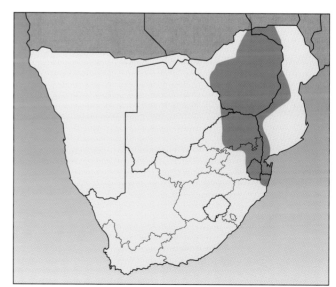

Distribution map of *Borbo holtzii*

Genus *Parnara* Moore

Parnara Moore, 1881. *Lepid. Ceylon* **1**: 166. Type species: *Eusamus guttatus* Bremer & Grey, 1852, by original designation.

Medium-sized skippers with antennae very short, just over one third length of costa; with a short strongly bent apiculus with its tip upturned. There is no sex-brand in the male. They are generally grey-brown species with whitish or yellowish hyaline spots, especially on the forewing.

Eggs slightly domed, fairly flattened. Larvae cylindrical, broad posteriorly, green; final instar larval headshield rounded, with setae, orange with broad black margins. Pupae dark brown, broadly truncate anteriorly; short and squat.

Food plants are Poaceae – larvae feed on grasses and some of the species in the Far East are pests of rice.

The genus was revised by Chiba and Eliot in 1991. There is only one species in Southern Africa.

Parnara monasi male underside

Parnara monasi female underside

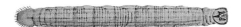

Parnara monasi final instar larva (After G.C. Clark, 1978)

Parnara monasi (Trimen)

Pamphila monasi Trimen, 1889. *S. Afr. Butterfl.* **3**: 317. Type locality: Durban. Type male in the Natural History Museum, London.

IDENTIFICATION

Adult. Male. Upperside: brown, forewing with two small subapical spots, a single upper cell spot, one small spot in mid area M_2, and two larger hyaline spots basally in areas M_3 and CuA_1 respectively; hindwing with a straight row of white discal spots in areas M_1-CuA_1. Underside: hindwing ochreous-brown with a conspicuous row of white discal spots as on upperside with outer edges often darkened. Female. Similar to male but differs in having an additional hyaline in area CuA_2 of forewing.

Forewing lengths: male 14-15,5 mm; female 15-16 mm.

Early stages. Egg: yellow, changing in time to pale blue-green and later developing red maculae; diameter 0,9 mm, height 0,5 mm; with very faint hexagonal tracery. Larva: first and second instars greenish-white with a black head; third instar green with a black head; fourth instar green with darker longitudinal stripes and a green and black head; fifth (final) instar pale olive-green with darker longitudinal stripes and a brown and black head. It attains a length of some 30 mm. Pupa: 17 mm long; greyish-black in colour with two pairs of white spots dorsally on each abdominal segment (Clark, 1978: 278).

HABITAT AND ECOLOGY

P. monasi is an inhabitant of grassy areas along riverbanks and in riverine forest, or marshy places. Its flight is rapid and irregular and it settles every few metres.

The males establish their territories in the vicinity of the food plants. Here they can be observed perching on the leaves of the grass and water plants, darting off to chase away encroaching intruders before returning to their perch.

The females frequent the same places as the males but fly at random in search of suitable food plants on which to lay. Eggs are laid singly on a blade of the grass. The eggs take some 9 days to hatch and the young larva partially eats the egg shell. The larva joins the edges of a blade of grass together to make a tube for itself. The larval stage lasts some 45 days. Pupation takes place within the grass-tube formed by the larva. The pupa is secured by its cremastral hooks and is covered in a thick white fluff. The pupal stage lasts 19 days.

This species is on the wing throughout the year, the best months for observation being January to April-May.

Parnara monasi pupa (After G.C. Clark, 1978)

LARVAL FOOD PLANTS

Saccharum sp. and various unidentified riverine grasses (Poaceae).

DISTRIBUTION

South Africa, from KwaZulu-Natal, Northern Province and Mpumalanga, into Swaziland, Moçambique, Zimbabwe, Botswana, northwards to large areas of Africa south of the Sahara.

CONSERVATION

Parnara monasi is a widely distributed species and is under no threat.

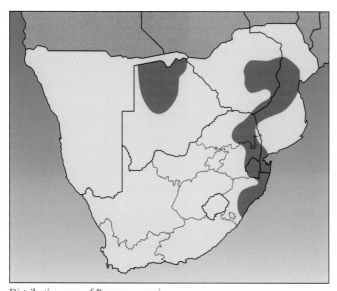

Distribution map of *Parnara monasi*

Gegenes pumilio gambica female underside

Genus *Gegenes* Hübner

Gegenes Hübner, 1819. *Verz. bek. Schmett.* (7): 107. Type species: *Papilio pumilio* Hoffmansegg, 1804, by designation by the Commission.

Small skipper with short antennae about one third length of costa; apiculus absent or minute. Palpi with apical segment hidden or coniform and shortly projecting. Wings in the male dark above without any markings. Forewing in female generally with light discal spots. Venation as in *Pelopidas*.

Eggs slightly domed, fairly flattened. Larvae elongate but somewhat rounded; final instar larval headshield whitish to green with red diagonal stripe laterally. Pupae green, elongated and acute at both ends.

Food plants Poaceae.

There are three species in Southern Africa.

KEY TO THE SPECIES OF *GEGENES*

1. LHW brown .... *G. pumilio*

   LHW ochreous 2

2. Male upperside uniformly dark brown, with basal ochreous tinge, UFW with obscure suffused ochreous subapical spots. LHW of female with ochreous discal band constricted along M_1 .... *G. niso*

   Male upperside pale ochreous, a large blackish mealy patch on forewing. Female discal band of LHW not constricted, or not so much as in *niso* .... *G. hottentota*

Gegenes pumilio (Hoffmansegg)

DARK HOTTENTOT

Papilio pumilio Hoffmansegg, 1804. *Mag. f. Insektenk. (Illiger)* **3**: 202.

There are three subspecies of which only *gambica* (Mabille, 1878) occurs on mainland Africa. The subspecies *monochroa* (Rebel, 1907) is found on Socotra, while the nominate is found in Europe and India.

Gegenes pumilio gambica (Mabille)

Pamphila gambica Mabille, 1878. *Petites Nouvelles.* **2**: 233. Type locality: Senegambia. Type in "Coll. Mabille" appears to be lost.

IDENTIFICATION

Adult. Male. Upperside: dark brown with no lighter markings. Underside: hindwing brown. Female. Differs from male in having some light (not hyaline) discal spots on forewing.

Forewing lengths: male 13-17 mm; female 15,5-17,5 mm.

Early stages. Egg: yellow to pale green and dome-shaped. Larva: final instar has body pale green with longitudinal white stripes, all but two of which end just short of head; body glabrous except at posterior end which is covered in fine white setae; head pale brown, finely setose, with symmetrical, lighter stripes edged with a dark brown; these start on either side of a central dorsal point on head and run down and outwards, before curving back in to end on either side of the mandibles. The larva attains a length of 35 mm. Pupa: 24 mm long; pale green with fine white stripes; cylindrical, tapering posteriorly with a pointed cephalic process; wing cases and proboscis poorly defined.

Gegenes pumilio gambica female upperside

Gegenes pumilio gambica male

HABITAT AND ECOLOGY

G. pumilio is usually an inhabitant of bushveld, preferring open areas, dry water courses being favourite haunts. It also occurs on the grassy slopes of mountains. It has a low rapid flight, resting here and there on the ground, stones, low shrubs or other plants. Sometimes it can be observed in numbers at muddy places or feeding on flowers in the veld or in suburban gardens.

The males occasionally exhibit hilltopping behaviour on hot sunny days. However, they more often establish their territories nearer the larval food plants. Here they can be observed perching on ground, stones or low shrubs.

The females usually frequent the same places as the males, but fly at random in search of suitable food plants on which to lay. They lay their eggs singly on a leaf of the food plant. The larva spends its entire life in a shelter constructed of its food plant and emerges only at night to feed. The shelter of the early instars consists of a single leaf folded over and attached with silk. However, in the penultimate and final instars, up to five leaves are used to construct a shelter. The larval stage lasts approximately 45 days. Pupation takes place in the final larval shelter. The pupal stage lasts about 60 days.

This species is on the wing from October to March in the colder areas, but throughout the year in warmer regions.

LARVAL FOOD PLANTS

Pennisetum clandestinum, *Ehrharta* sp. and *Cynodon* sp. (Poaceae).

DISTRIBUTION

South Africa, from the Eastern Cape, KwaZulu-Natal, Free State, North-West Province, Gauteng, Northern Province and Mpumalanga, into Botswana, Namibia, Zimbabwe, Swaziland, Moçambique, northwards over most of Africa south of the Sahara.

CONSERVATION

G. pumilio gambica is a widespread species and is under no threat.

Gegenes pumilio gambica pupa

Gegenes pumilio gambica final instar larva

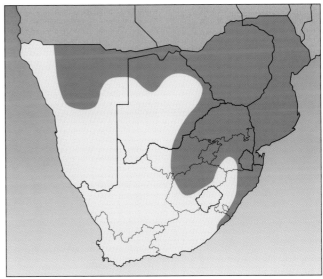

Distribution map of *Gegenes pumilio*

Gegenes niso (Linnaeus)

COMMON HOTTENTOT

Papilio niso Linnaeus, 1764. *Mus. Lud. Ulr. Reg.*: 339.

There are two subspecies of which only the nominate occurs in Southern Africa. The subspecies *brevicornis* (Plötz, 1881) occurs in West, Central and East Africa.

Gegenes niso niso (Linnaeus)

Papilio niso Linnaeus, 1764. *Mus. Lud. Ulr. Reg.*: 339. Type locality: Africa.

IDENTIFICATION

Adult. Male. Upperside: dark brown with a more or less ochreous tinge basally; forewing with small, obscure, suffused ochreous subapical spots. Lacks black androconial patch of *G. hottentota*. Underside: yellow with slight dark markings. Female. Upperside: dark brown with light yellow discal spots.

Form *ocra* Evans (1937, *Cat. Afr. Hesper.*: 190) differs from typical form in the upperside being a more yellow colour. This form is more prevalent in the more southern populations.

Forewing lengths: male 13,5-15,5 mm; female 13,5-16,5 mm.

Early stages. Egg: pale translucent yellow, when laid, changing to pale green with pinkish spots; diameter 1,0 mm, height 0,6 mm; with surface tracery of a very faint hexagonal pattern. Larva: first instar white with a black head; second instar green with faint white longitudinal lines and a black head; third and fourth instars green with white longitudinal lines and greenish-white head with pinkish-brown markings; fifth (final) instar similar to fourth but head green with a white-margined pinkish-brown lateral line. It attains a length of 30-32 mm. Pupa: 15 mm long; green in colour (Clark, 1978: 280).

HABITAT AND ECOLOGY

G. niso is an inhabitant of bushveld, savannah, woodland, entering forest where there are open patches, and occurring especially on the grassy slopes of mountains where it favours little hollows and kloofs. Its flight is swift and irregular and it is frequently observed feeding at flowers and muddy places.

The males do not show hilltopping behaviour but establish their territories near the larval food plants. Here the male often takes possession of some tall flower in an open position, and darts out at every insect which approaches his perch. He also perches on the grass, or on the ground and low shrubs.

The females are found in the same places as the males where they fly at random in search of suitable food plants on which to oviposit. Fluttering around a suitable patch of grass, they slowly investigate several blades before laying a single egg on the upper surface of a leaf. The egg takes some 16 days to hatch and the shell is eaten by the larva. The larva at first just joins the edges of a blade of grass together to form a tube, in which it lives. It crawls out at intervals to feed on the end of the blade. During the third instar it becomes too big for a tube and then lies along a midrib. It spins a mat of silk on the surface of the blade of grass on which it rests. The larval stage lasts some 51 days. The pupa is secured by cremastral hooks and a silken girdle to a silk pad spun by the larva. The pupal stage lasts 17-21 days.

This species is on the wing throughout the year, being scarcer from April to September.

Gegenes niso niso male

Gegenes niso niso female underside

Gegenes niso niso female upperside

LARVAL FOOD PLANTS

Ehrharta erecta, Pennisetum clandestinum, Themeda triandra (Poaceae).

DISTRIBUTION

South Africa, from the Western and Eastern Cape, Free State, North-West Province, KwaZulu-Natal, Gauteng, Northern Province and Mpumalanga, into Lesotho, Swaziland, Botswana, Namibia, Zimbabwe and Moçambique.

CONSERVATION

G. niso is a common and widespread species and is under no threat.

Gegenes niso niso pupa (Photo: A.J.M. Claassens)

Gegenes niso niso final instar larva (Photo: A.J.M. Claassens)

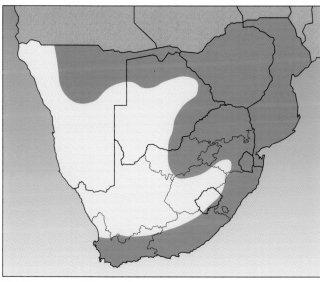

Distribution map of *Gegenes niso*

Gegenes hottentota (Latreille)

MARSH HOTTENTOT

Hesperia hottentota Latreille, 1824. *Encycl. Méth. d'Hist. Nat. (Zool.)* **9**: 777. Type locality: Cape of Good Hope (*Patria falsa*). Type male in Paris Museum.

IDENTIFICATION

Adult. Male. Upperside: a golden-ochre; forewing with a large black androconial patch in the centre. Underside: ochre with pale brown markings. Female. Upperside: brown with pale yellow markings. Underside: as in male.

Forewing lengths: male 14,5-16 mm; female 14-17 mm.

Early stages. Unrecorded.

HABITAT AND ECOLOGY

G. hottentota is an inhabitant of marshes and swamps, preferring thickly grassed areas in valleys. They fly about at speed, settling on blades of grass. They have been recorded feeding on flowers.

The males establish territories in the vicinity of the larval food plants. Here they can be observed perching on blades of grass or flowers. Occasionally they fly about their restricted areas, vigorously fending off all intruders.

The females frequent the same places as the males where they fly at random searching for suitable food plants on which to oviposit.

The species is on the wing throughout the year, but is generally more plentiful during April-May.

LARVAL FOOD PLANTS

Ehrharta erecta, Pennisetum clandestinum and *Themeda* sp. (Poaceae).

DISTRIBUTION

South Africa, from Port St. Johns in the Eastern Cape to KwaZulu-Natal, Gauteng, Northern Province and Mpumalanga, into Moçambique, Zimbabwe, Botswana, northwards to most of Africa south of the Sahara.

CONSERVATION

G. hottentota is a marginal species in South Africa. The similarity of this species to the common *G. niso* and the early confusion with the taxonomy have probably both contributed to the lack of South African records. Existing South African records include Honeydew and Pretoria in Gauteng, Nylstroom in the Northern Province and Louw's Creek, Nelspruit, Lydenburg and Makande in Mpumalanga; in KwaZulu-Natal from Margate in the south to Manguzi in Zululand. It was also recorded at Port St Johns in some numbers during 1989. The status of this species in South Africa has been given as indeterminate by S.F. & G.A. Henning (1989) in the *South African Red Data Book – Butterflies. G. hottentota* is, however, widespread throughout sub-Saharan Africa, therefore as a species it is not under threat.

Gegenes hottentota male showing upperside

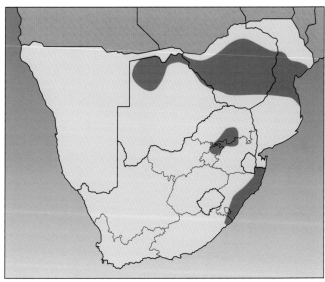

Distribution map of *Gegenes hottentota*

SUPERFAMILY PAPILIONOIDEA

These are small to large butterflies. Ocelli are absent and chaetosemata prominent. The antennae are close together at the base, slender with an abrupt club. The haustellum is naked, maxillary palpi are minute, one segmented, or absent, and the labial palpi are moderately long, more or less rough-haired with the terminal segment rather pointed. The forewing has vein M_2 arising from or above the middle of the transverse vein. The hindwing is without a frenulum and vein $Sc+R_1$ arises out of the discal cell near base thence strongly curved and diverging. Tympanal organs absent. Egg are of the upright type. First instar larvae have crochets in a circle whereas later instars have them in a mesoseries. Pupae are usually exposed and attached at the posterior end to a pad of silk, often with a central silken girdle.

The Papilionoidea differ from the Hesperioidea in having the antennae set close together at base and at least some of the peripheral veins of the wings stalked.

The Papilionoidea includes 5 families world wide, the Papilionidae, Pieridae, Nymphalidae, Riodinidae and Lycaenidae, of which only the Riodinidae do not occur in Southern Africa.

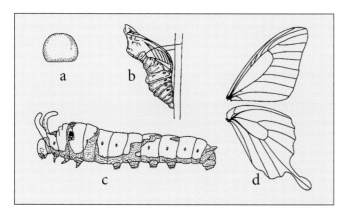

Fig 26. Family Papilionidae. a: Typical egg – side view; b: Typical final instar larva with osmeterium extruded; c: Typical pupa; d: Typical wing shape and venation

A freshly laid *Graphium morania* egg, a typical example for the Papilionidae

Left: Fertile, 'ringed' *Papilio constantinus constantinus* eggs, a typical example for the Papilionidae

KEY TO THE FAMILIES OF PAPILIONOIDEA

1. Fore tibia with epiphysis; forewing usually with transverse section of CuP near base; hindwing with one anal vein .... Papilionidae

   Fore tibia without epiphysis; forewing without transverse section of CuP; hindwing usually with two, rarely with one, anal vein 2

2. Tarsal claws bifid; foreleg in male fully developed and functional .... Pieridae

   FTarsal claws rarely bifid; foreleg in male reduced 3

3. Eyes notched or emarginate at base of antennae, or at least eye and edge of antennal socket contiguous; foreleg usually reduced but functional in male, seldom brush-like, one or both tarsal claws sometimes absent; in female not reduced, fully functional with tarsal claws .... Lycaenidae (Vols. 3 & 4)

   FEyes not notched or emarginate at base of antennae, eye and antennal socket not contiguous; foreleg abbreviated, non-functional, without tarsal claws, often brush-like in both sexes (except female Libytheinae) .... Nymphalidae (Vol. 2)

FAMILY PAPILIONIDAE

Most of the butterflies of this family are large, with forewing lengths up to 70 mm. The antennae are short, maxillary palpi are reduced to tiny projections and the labial palpi are appressed to the frons. The forelegs are fully developed with an epiphysis present. The adults are usually boldly patterned and can be distinguished from other families by the presence of six normal functional legs in both sexes, an epiphysis on the fore tibia, the simple tarsal claws, two anal veins on the hindwings and a short basal section of vein CuP on forewing. The eggs are usually smooth and almost spherical, but occasionally the surface bears a raised pattern. They are deposited singly on the food plant or sometimes on the object nearby.

The first instar larva has a series of bristle-bearing tubercles, which in the later instars may be long and fleshy, or reduced without bristles, or absent. The prothorax has an anterior dorsal slit from which can be protruded a forked, fleshy process called an osmeterium. The organ is protruded if the larva is disturbed, and it secretes a pungent gas. The pupa is fastened by the cremaster to a pad of silk and is supported by a silken girdle encircling the thorax and legs. The main larval food plants in Southern Africa belong to the families Rutaceae and Annonaceae.

The adults usually fly strongly and rapidly, and some species are thought to be migratory. They feed freely at flowers, especially during the morning. When feeding the wings are characteristically held nearly erect above the body and are constantly vibrated. Sometimes the adults congregate at damp, muddy spots on roads or in gullies to drink water. The males of some species commonly show hilltopping behaviour where they can be observed patrolling the summit.

Some phylogenetic studies have been done in recent years. Firstly Hancock (1983) in his *Classification of the Papilionidae (Lepidoptera)*, concluded that the South African representatives of the genus *Papilio* Linnaeus should be included in the genus *Princeps* Hübner. However, Miller (1987) in *Phylogenetic studies in the Papilioninae (Lepidoptera; Papilionidae)* reassessed the situation and from his analysis *Princeps* reverted back to *Papilio*. Some authors use *Princeps* as a subgenus of *Papilio*. All the African species would belong to subgenus *Princeps*.

There are 17 species of Papilionidae in Southern Africa belonging to 2 genera, 2 tribes and 1 subfamily. In South Africa there are 14 species belonging to 2 genera and two tribes.

SUBFAMILY PAPILIONINAE

Three subfamilies are recognised. The primitive Baroninae, with a single species *Baronia brevicornis* Salvin from Mexico, and the Parnassinae are not found in Southern Africa. All the species in Southern Africa belong to the Papilioninae. The distinguishing characters of this subfamily are the long and slender antennae, forewing basal spur from Cu well-developed and the male genitalia with the 9th and 10th tergites reduced.

Miller (1987) divided the Papilioninae into three tribes, Papilionini, Graphiini and Troidini. The Troidini do not occur in Southern Africa. Ackery et. al. (1995) uses Lampropterini instead of Graphiini.

KEY TO THE SOUTH AFRICAN TRIBES AND GENERA OF THE PAPILIONINAE

1. Subcostal vein of forewing free; anal fold of hindwing scarcely folded, no long silky hairs in male; tibiae and tarsi unscaled; vesica with lateral process and with opening ventrad; medial flap on labial palp; fourth instar larvae glossy, signum zipper-like, primary food plants Rutaceae .... Tribe Papilionini, Genus *Papilio*

Subcostal vein of forewing anastomosing with R$_1$, hindwing of male with prominent anal fold bearing long silky hairs; tibiae and tarsi scaled; vesica without lateral process and opening not ventrad; no medial flap on labial palp; fourth instar larvae not glossy, signum funnel-shaped, primary food plants Annonaceae .... Tribe Graphiini, Genus *Graphium*

Tribe Papilionini

THE SWALLOWTAILS

The swallowtails are a large and diverse group of butterflies which includes the largest African species *Papilio antimachus*. Despite a great diversity of coloration and pattern, a remarkable uniformity in structure has resulted in all the species of Papilionini being placed in one large genus, *Papilio*.

When feeding, the swallowtails do not settle but hover above the food source on rapidly vibrating wings with only the tips of the extended legs touching the plant or ground.

Genus *Papilio* Linnaeus

Papilio Linnaeus, 1758. *Syst. Nat.* (Ed. 10), **1**: 458. Type species: *Papilio machaon* Linnaeus, 1758, by selection by Latreille 1810.

Large swallowtails. Antennae short, about one-third length of costa of forewing or shorter, curved, smooth, gradually widened and flattened towards the rather flattened club. Forewing elongate triangular, costa arched; subcostal vein free; R$_2$ arises always separately from cell before upper angle; R$_3$ and stalk of R$_4$ and R$_5$ connate from upper angle; M$_1$ from well below upper angle; M$_2$ from lower angle, due to peculiar elongated shape of cell; M$_3$, CuA$_1$ and CuA$_2$ about equidistant from lower margin of cell. Hindwing usually elongated posteriorly, with an undulate outer margin, sometimes lobed or tailed; humeral vein connected with Sc by a bar, forming an areola; Rs from upper angle, M$_1$ from well below upper angle, M$_2$ from much nearer to M$_3$ than to M$_1$; there is no distinct lower angle because of the rounded outline of the cell below M$_1$, the points of origin of both M$_2$ and M$_3$ being nearest to the distal extremity of the cell; CuA$_1$ from nearer to M$_3$ than to CuA$_2$; anal area in male without fold, smoothly scaled (van Son, 1949: 2). Male genitalia with tegumen well-developed, uncus beak-shaped and closely united with tegumen. Female genitalia with signum elongate, finely transversely striolate area divided by a narrow median groove, without any projecting part inside the bursa.

Early stages: eggs very nearly spherical, smooth, laid singly on leaf-buds or leaves of food plants. Larvae rather short, thoracic region swollen, in early instars with numerous setiferous tubercles, but in later instars glabrous, with a typical Y-shaped glandular structure, the osmeterium, capable of being evaginated through a slit in the first thoracic segment. Pupae usually bifid anteriorly, with prominent dorsal and lateral projections, but wing-cases hardly prominent; often very cryptic; pupa attached in an upright position by the cremaster attached to silken pad spun by larva and a silken thread around the middle (van Son, 1949: 3).

There are seven species in Southern Africa, all of which occur in South Africa.

KEY TO THE SPECIES OF PAPILIO

1. Male UFW uniformly pale yellow with a broad black marginal band; female UFW black with white, yellow or reddish-orange markings, mimicking Danaidae, LHW without basal spots .... *P. dardanus*

    Upperside of wings black with white, yellow or blue discal spots and usually a series of submarginal spots of the same colour 2

2. LHW in both sexes with a sharply defined basal brown area enclosing two basal black spots above cell and narrow black stripes .... *P. echerioides*

    LHW without a sharply defined brown basal area and black basal spots 3

3. Black with green or blue markings on upperside .... *P. nireus*

    Black with yellow markings on upperside 4

4. Hindwing without a tail .... *P. demodocus*

    Hindwing with a tail 5

5. Hindwing with large ocellate markings in 3A and Sc+R$_1$ .... *P. ophidicephalus*

    Hindwing without large ocellate markings 6

6. UFW with a yellow spot in the cell; antennae with yellow tips .... *P. constantinus*

    UFW without yellow spot in cell; antennae with black tips .... *P. euphranor*

Papilio euphranor Trimen

BUSH-KITE SWALLOWTAIL

Papilio euphranor Trimen, 1868. *Trans. ent. Soc. Lond.* **1868**: 70. Type locality: Tsomo River, Kaffraria.

The only *Papilio* endemic to South Africa. It belongs to the *P. hesperus* Westwood (1843) species group, a group of five species which spans Africa. *P. euphranor* is the only Southern African representative.

IDENTIFICATION

Adult. A fairly large species with spatulate tails. Male. Upperside: black with a broad yellow diagonal stripe. Tails unmarked. Underside: similar to the upperside but with the ground colour a mottled chocolate brown. Female. Upperside: similar to the male but with a series of yellow subterminal spots on the forewing and a double row of submarginal spots on the hindwing. Underside: similar to the upperside but with the ground colour pale mottled brown.

Forewing lengths: male 41-50 mm; female 49-61 mm.

Papilio euphranor male underside

Papilio euphranor early instar larva

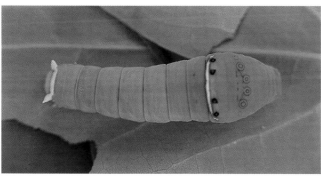

Papilio euphranor final instar larva

Early stages. Egg: pale translucent yellowish green when first laid, developing a ring of pinkish brown spots around the middle with a scattering of spots on the dorsal half; these spots form a cluster around the micropyle; diameter 1,3 mm, height 1,1 mm. Larva: resembles a bird dropping during the first three instars, thereafter becoming leaf-like. First instar black with three white transverse patches, there are processes in pairs on each segment; second and third instars are dark brown instead of black; fourth instar becomes bluish-green without white patches; fifth (final) instar lacks processes save a short, black anal pair, olive green shading to pale green at the ridge sometimes with dark sooty patches, 4th segment with a yellowish white transverse stripe. The larva attains a length of 42 mm. Pupa: 33 mm long; dark green above, light green below, leaf-like, broad across the middle and tapering at both ends (Wells, 1957: 117; S.F. & G.A. Henning, 1989: 148; Clark, 1994: 402).

HABITAT AND ECOLOGY

P. euphranor is an inhabitant of montane evergreen forest. Males have a distinctive gliding flight when patrolling their territory. Seldom do males descend from the canopy and then only to chase a female or feed on flowers when there are none in the tree tops. The females fly with a more methodical wing-beat but may glide for short distances. Although the males keep to the tree tops the females are frequently seen along the forest margins or feeding on flowers along forest paths. They are not seen on damp sand as are some of their congeners but males are commonly observed in the vicinity of waterfalls and may obtain their moisture from damp leaves in these areas. Both sexes feed on nectar from flowers. They are attracted to the colour red and have been seen investigating red cars and even road signs.

Males are aggressive with well-developed territoriality. They take up positions high in the forest canopy, in sunny openings or depressions between tall trees. They glide slowly around it during most of the warmer hours of the day. Intruders are investigated and other males are chased away. They may take a break from their constant patrolling to settle on a prominent leaf or may feed at nearby flowers. They have been seen to occupy the same territory for many days.

The females are most frequently found along forest margins, clearings or paths, where they fly at random in search of suitable food plants on which to oviposit. Eggs are laid singly on the undersides of the leaves of the food plant. The egg hatches after about 6-10 days. On emergence the larva partly eats the discarded shell. The young

Papilio euphranor female upperside

larva eats the margins of the leaf or it may eat a hole in the leaf. The osmeterium in the 3rd instar is pale yellow and becomes tinged with pale green in the final instar. The first three instars resemble bird droppings. The final two instars are leaf-like. The first instar larva stays on the underside of the leaves of the food plant. Only from the fourth instar does it remain entirely on the upperside of the leaf. The quiescent period before pupation is 3 days. The larval stage lasts some 28 days. The pupa is suspended, head upwards, under a leaf of the food plant. It is attached by the cremastral hooks to a silken pad and a silken girdle around the middle holds it upright. The pupa is leaf-like, the upper surface being darker green than the lower to blend in with the leaves of the food plant. The pupal stage lasts about 22 days (Wells, 1957: 117; S.F. & G.A. Henning, 1989: 148; Clark, 1994: 402).

This species is on the wing from August to May with peak periods being September/October and again from February to April.

LARVAL FOOD PLANTS

Cryptocarya woodii (Lauraceae).

DISTRIBUTION

South Africa, from the Eastern Cape near Stutterheim, through KwaZulu-Natal, to the Soutpansberg in the Northern Province.

CONSERVATION

P. euphranor is included by S.F. & G.A. Henning (1989) in the *South African Red Data Book – Butterflies* as indeterminate. It is under no immediate threat as many forest patches have been preserved.

Papilio dardanus Brown

MOCKER SWALLOWTAIL

Papilio dardanus Brown, 1776. *Illustr. zool.* **1776**: 52.

It is part of the *P. phorcas* Cramer (1775) species group and forms a small monophyletic assemblage of three species with *P. dardanus* and *P. phorcas* as sister species and *P. constantinus* Ward (1871) as the stem species (Vane-Wright & Smith, 1991).

The nominate race occurs in West Africa. There are twelve other subspecies. All the subspecies have a unique spotted abdomen.

This species is probably the most well-known and extensively researched butterfly mimic, with much of the original research having been undertaken by Sir Cyril Clarke and P.M. Sheppard. Only the female is mimetic and the diversity is amazing. The subspecies on Madagascar, the Comoro Islands and in northern Somalia have females that resemble the male. The subspecies in Ethiopia has a similar female as well as tailed females with mimetic coloration. The mimetic females found in each of the other subspecies generally reflect the danaid and acraeid models in their respective areas. The presence of male-like females leads to two possible theories. The first, which has been largely accepted until recently, is that the male-like females reflect the ancestral female to which populations revert in the absence of sustained reinforcement of the mimetic pattern. The lack of reinforcement could be the result of a shortage of models or a shortage of relevant predators.

The second theory (Vane-Wright, 1984 (in Vane-Wright & Ackery, 1984) & Clarke *et. al.*, 1985) is that the male-like female is a mimic of the male. The apparent advantage gained by male-like females would be due to the territorial nature of the males. The male-

Distribution map of *Papilio euphranor*

Papilio dardanus cenea male feeding in typical papilionid fashion on *Hypoestes aristata*

like female could be visually perceived as an intruder into the male's territory and would elicit an immediate defence response. On discovering his error the male's response would probably change to that of courtship. Under this hypothesis the ancestral morph should have a pattern similar to *P. constantinus*, and indeed such a female form does occur in the sister species *P. phorcas* along with the female with a male-like pattern.

Only the one subspecies *cenea* Stoll (1790) is recognised from Southern Africa although the Zimbabwean and Moçambique populations are often included in subspecies *tibullus* Kirby, 1880.

Papilio dardanus cenea Stoll

Papilio cenea Stoll, 1790. *Uitl. Kapellen.* 134. Type locality: South Africa.

TAXONOMY

This subspecies is considered to be the only one in Southern Africa. Specimens likened to the East African subspecies *tibullus* Kirby, 1880 (*Proc. R. Dublin Soc.* (2) **2**: 338) have been recorded from Zimbabwe and adjacent Moçambique. These should be considered as variations of the forms included under subspecies *cenea*. This population is apparently isolated from both *cenea* and *tibullus*.

The female forms can be divided into two groups: group A representing those forms with forewing markings confluent and group B representing those forms with forewing markings separated. The distribution of some of the female forms is indicative of an indistinct division between populations from northern KwaZulu-Natal and northwards (Northern aggregate) and those from coastal and southern KwaZulu-Natal southwards (Southern aggregate).

IDENTIFICATION

Adult. Male. A large species with a prominent lobed tail on the hindwing. Upperside: light sulphur-yellow with submarginal areas of forewing and postdiscal areas of hindwing black. Underside: yellow with black areas of the upperside light brown, hindwing with veins darkened and interneural streaks giving a cryptic, dry leaf, appearance. Female. Unlike male, it is without tails on hindwing. A very variable mimic comprising a number of distinct named forms which are described below under their individual form names. There are two categories into which the upperside pattern can be divided, firstly those with large confluent markings on the forewing and secondly those with the forewing markings separated. The undersides are similar to the uppersides but broadly brown marginally with interneural radiating streaks, like the male, giving the underside a cryptic appearance.

The female forms of group A are represented in each region as follows:

Northern aggregate

Female form *natalica* le Cerf, 1924. *Bull. Hill. Mus. Witley.* **1**: 377. All markings chrome yellow. Apparently non-mimetic in normal terms but may be an imperfect mimic of the male.

Female form near *natalica* from the Blouberg and Soutpansberg. All markings are much lighter than those of *natalica*, with supra-marginal area often infuscated with black scaling.

Female form *hippocoonides* Haase, 1891. *Bibl. Zoologica.* **8**(1): 70. All markings white. A mimic of *Amauris niavius dominicanus*.

Female form *aikeni* van Son, 1956. *Ann. Transv. Mus.* **22**(4): 503. Subapical patch white, supra-marginal area of forewing and basal area of hindwing light yellowish-orange. An apparent mimic of *Danaus chrysippus*.

Female form near *aikeni* from the Blouberg and Soutpansberg. Colour much brighter than *aikeni*, but not as brick-red as *trophonius*. It also generally has a broader subapical band.

Papilio dardanus cenea male underside

Southern aggregate

Female form *infuscata* van Son, 1956. *Ann. Transv. Mus.* **22**(4): 504. Similar to form *hippocoonides* but with all white markings reduced and some black scaling on the supra-marginal area of the UFW. A mimic of *Amauris niavius dominicanus*.

Female form *trophonius* Westwood, 1842. *Ann. Mag. nat. Hist.* **9**: 38. Similar to female form *aikeni* but with the pale yellowish-orange areas replaced by reddish-orange. An apparent mimic of *Danaus chrysippus*.

Female form *salaami* Suffert, 1904. *Dt. ent. Z. Iris.* **17**: 92. All markings reddish-orange. In the absence of form *natalica* from the southern aggregate it is possible that this very rare form may be a relict male-like mimic.

Female form *leighi* Poulton, 1911. *Proc. ent. Soc. Lond.* **1911**: 38. Forewing markings reddish-orange, supra-marginal and hindwing markings as in *cenea* of group B. Genetically apparently a combination of *salaami* and *cenea* alleles. A very rare form.

The other female forms (group B) have been recorded in both regions but do show some differences between those from the northern aggregate and those from the southern, particularly in the extent of the basal dark suffusion on the hindwing upperside which is much wider in specimens from the southern aggregate. These forms are:

Female form *cenea* Stoll, 1791. *Uitl. Kapellen*: 134. Forewing discal spot in M_1 absent, spots of forewing generally white tinged with ochreous. There is complete integration with the following form. A mimic of *Amauris echeria*.

Female form *acene* Suffert, 1904. *Dt. ent. Z. Iris.* **17**: 92. Similar to female form *cenea* but with forewing spots white. A mimic of *Amauris albimaculata*.

Female form *hypolymnides* le Cerf, 1924. *Bull. Hill. Mus. Witley* **1**: 377. Forewing discal spot in M_1 present, spots yellow. Probably an intermediate form clining towards *natalica*.

Female form *sylvicola* van Son, 1949. *Transv. Mus. Mem.* **3**: 11. Forewing discal spots white and fused into a band. Probably an intermediate form clining towards *hippocoonides*.

Female form *cephonius* Hopffer, 1866. *Stettin. ent. Ztg.* **27**: 132. As in form *sylvicola* but with forewing discal spots yellow. Probably also an intermediate form clining towards the possible male-like mimic *natalica*.

Papilio dardanus cenea female form *hippocoonides* upperside

Papilio dardanus cenea female form *trophonius* upperside

Papilio dardanus cenea female form *cephonius* upperside

Papilio dardanus cenea female form *cenea* underside

Forewing lengths: male 40-55 mm; female 42-54 mm.

Early stages. Egg: white with reddish-brown spots on the upper half forming a ring around the middle. Larva: first three instars dark brown with white markings and resembling a bird dropping; fourth instar green with similar white markings; fifth (final) instar green, with all white markings broken up into small spots or lines, the body smooth and humped at the 3rd segment. The larva attains a length of some 35-38 mm. Pupa: 33-35 mm long; leaf-like, darker green uppermost; dorso-ventrally flattened and narrowed at both ends (Clark, 1949: 14; S.F. Henning, 1984b: 30; Clark, 1994: 398).

HABITAT AND ECOLOGY

P. dardanus cenea is a coastal and montane forest species. The males fly fairly rapidly in the sunshine but can be deceptively leisurely with frequent swoops and dives to investigate flowers or passing insects. If a cloud obscures the sun they usually settle with folded wings. At night they settle on a leaf, preferably on the underside, with the wings hanging downwards. The females fly slowly and weakly in the semi-shade in the undergrowth, seldom venturing far from cover. Both sexes can be found hovering at flowers with legs extended and probosci unfurled, sucking nectar. The males seem to prefer those of higher plants or creepers. They also feed at damp sand or mud.

The males show strong territoriality and can be observed flying up and down the edges of forests, one or two metres above the ground, in search of females with which to mate. They usually patrol a circuitous path around patches of forest, following this route through most of the warmer hours of the day. When patrolling their flight speed is about 5 kph and the flight path is about a kilometre long and generally follows forest clearings. If alarmed they may soar to the treetops with surprising alacrity.

The females are usually found in the undergrowth or semi-shade where the larval food plant grows. They will hover around a food plant investigating chemical compatibility with the specially adapted spines on their legs. If found suitable they lay eggs singly on the uppersides of the leaves of the food plant. The egg takes about

9 days to hatch. The larva eats holes out of the middle of the leaves in the earlier stages, later eating from the edge. The larva rests along the mid-rib of the leaf where its cryptic coloration affords it the best protection. The larval stages last about 40 days in total. The larva pupates on the stem of the food plant or on neighbouring plants. The pupa is suspended by a silken girdle around the middle and is attached by cremastral hooks to a silken pad spun onto the stem. The pupa in shape and coloration mimics a leaf of the food plant and is generally suspended in the same plane. The duration of the pupal stage is variable from a couple of weeks to several months (Clark, 1949: 14; S.F. Henning, 1984b: 30; Clark, 1994: 398).

This species is on the wing throughout the year with peaks in December, January and April.

Papilio dardanus cenea early instar larva with osmeterium everted

Papilio dardanus cenea female form *cenea* upperside

Papilio dardanus cenea final instar larva

LARVAL FOOD PLANTS

Vepris undulata, Clausena anisata, Teclea natalensis, T. nobilis, Toddalia asiatica, Oricia bachmannii, Citrus sp. (Rutaceae); *Xymalos monospora* (Trimeniaceae).

DISTRIBUTION

South Africa, from Knysna eastward through all the montane and coastal forests of KwaZulu-Natal, Mpumalanga and Northern Province, then into Swaziland, Moçambique and eastern Zimbabwe.

CONSERVATION

P. dardanus cenea is fairly common in all the forest habitats in which it occurs. It is under no threat.

Papilio dardanus cenea pupa

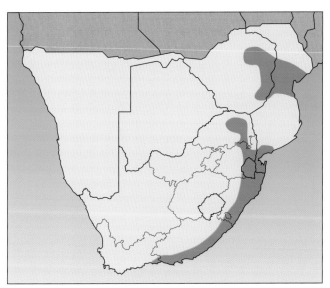

Distribution map of *Papilio dardanus*

Papilio constantinus Ward

CONSTANTINE'S SWALLOWTAIL

Papilio constantinus Ward, 1871. *Entomologist's mon. Mag.* **8**: 34.

There are three subspecies with only the nominate occurring in Southern Africa. The subspecies *monticolus* le Cerf 1924 occurs in Kenya and *mweruanus* Joicey & Talbot 1927 from south-eastern Zaire.

Papilio constantinus constantinus Ward

Papilio constantinus Ward, 1871. *Entomologist's mon. Mag.* **8**: 34. Type locality: East Africa.

IDENTIFICATION

Adult. Male. Upperside: black with a transverse yellow band; forewing with a row of submarginal yellow spots and postdiscal area with patches of black androconia scales. Underside: with markings

Papilio constantinus constantinus female underside on its food plant *Vepris lanceolata*

similar to upperside, ground colour pale brown, streaked and mottled with pale yellow and dark brown. Female. Similar to male but without androconia scales on the UFW. Underside: as in male but paler.

Forewing lengths: male 38-52 mm; female 44-53 mm.

Early stages. Egg: pale yellow; if fertile, develops a brown spot in area of micropyle and two uneven rings, the upper of which is more pronounced; approximately spherical, measuring 1,2 mm in diameter. Larva: first instar is yellow, dorsally marbled with various shades of brown; second instar has a waxy appearance with markings much the same as previously but the colour is now olive and off-white; third instar larva has thoracic segments enlarged, with a lustrous appearance and is darkly blotched olive green in colour with white markings; fourth instar similar to third but with a lightening of green and reduction in extent of white; fifth (final) instar finely mottled green with remnant white markings laterally. Larva attains a length of 33 mm. Pupa: 33 mm long; light green in colour with a pale yellow lateral stripe extending from cremaster to just short of eye; tapered at both ends and depressed dorso-ventrally particularly at the margins; head well defined and bears a bifid process (Joannou, 1992: 89).

HABITAT AND ECOLOGY

P. constantinus is an inhabitant of woodland to bushveld but it may also be found penetrating montane forest. It flies low and at random but not very rapidly, usually from one to two metres above the ground and it often pauses for visits to flowers to feed on nectar. Both sexes are fond of congregating at muddy places.

Male territoriality is not as conspicuous as in *P. dardanus*. Males establish a circuitous course through the trees which they repeatedly follow during most of the warmer hours of the day.

The females fly at random through the bush in search of suitable food plants on which to oviposit. Eggs are laid singly on either surface of the leaf. The egg hatches after some 4 days. The first instar larva on hatching consumes only a portion of the egg shell. The head is brown and tucked in below a fold of the first segment making it visible only when extended for feeding. This habit is consistently adopted by all the larval stages. The larval stage lasts some 24 days. Pupation occurs in a suitable site on the food plant, often a stem or leaf petiole inclined at 45 degrees to the vertical. The cremaster is attached to a pad and the pupa is held in a horizontal position by a girdle. The pupal stage lasts 13 days (Joannou, 1992: 89).

This species is on the wing from September to April with December to March being the best time for it.

Papilio constantinus constantinus female upperside

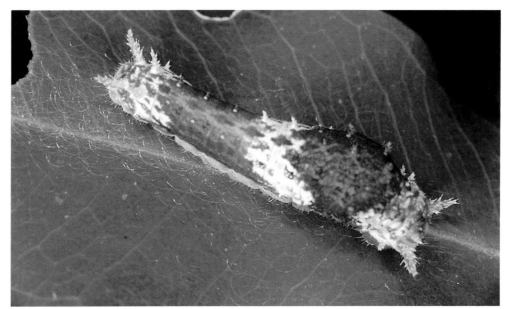

Papilio constantinus constantinus early instar larva

LARVAL FOOD PLANTS

Vepris lanceolata, V. reflexa, Clausena anisata, Teclea nobilis (Rutaceae).

DISTRIBUTION

South Africa, from northern KwaZulu-Natal northwards to the Northern Province and Mpumalanga, northern Gauteng and North-West Province, into eastern Botswana, Swaziland, Zimbabwe, Moçambique and East Africa.

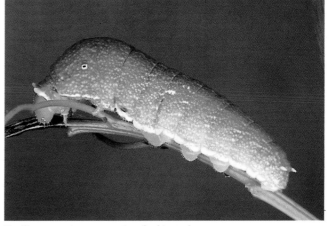

CONSERVATION

P. constantinus is a widespread species and is under no threat.

Papilio constantinus constantinus final instar larva

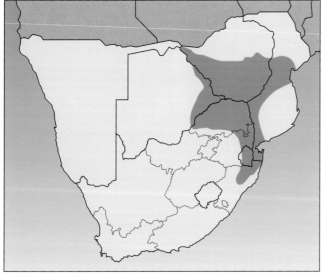

Distribution map of *Papilio constantinus*

Papilio constantinus constantinus pupa

Papilio demodocus Esper

CITRUS SWALLOWTAIL

Papilio demodocus Esper, 1798. *Ausland. Schmetterl.*: 205.

This species is a close relative of the Palaearctic *P. demoleus* Linnaeus 1758. There are two subspecies, the nominate being found on the African continent. The other subspecies is found on the island of Socotra. On Madagascar there are three species apparently evolved from successive ancient invasions of *P. demodocus* from the mainland. *P. demodocus* itself is currently also found there.

Papilio demodocus demodocus Esper

Papilio demodocus Esper, 1798. *Ausland. Schmetterl.*: 205.
Type locality: Africa.

IDENTIFICATION

Adult. Male. Upperside: black with yellow transverse band and spots; hindwing without tails. Underside: similar to upperside. Female. Similar to male but with outer margin of tornal eye-spot of hindwing orange.

Forewing lengths: male 42-55 mm; female 45-56 mm.

Early stages. Egg: white when first laid, turning to pale yellow; if fertile becoming variegated with light brown markings; spherical, smooth, with a flattened base, diameter 1,3 mm, height 1,1 mm. Larva: there are two types of pattern depending on the food plant used. The normal food plant is Rutaceae and the larvae are dark brown and white, resembling bird-droppings in the first four instars, while in the final instar they become green with a brown or black diagonal stripe and rather leaf-like; osmeterium crimson, with a short base and long, horizontal spreading branches. The larvae of all instars feeding on Apiaceae (Umbelliferae), such as fennel, are pale yellow with broken dark brown longitudinal stripes, which in the final instar are edged and spotted with light orange-red markings. This larval colouring is very rarely found in larvae feeding on Rutaceae. The larva attains a length of about 40 mm. Pupa: about 36 mm long; resembles a broken stick and may be a variable combination of grey, green, brown and black (Clark, 1949: 23; Clark, 1994: 404; S.F. Henning, 1984b: 32).

HABITAT AND ECOLOGY

P. demodocus has been recorded in most habitats from montane forest to the margins of the Namib desert and is a familiar sight in most gardens. It can be a minor pest on citrus trees. Its flight is deceptively languorous; once aroused it will fly fast and at random. The female is slower than the male and she is normally seen flying around trees and bushes searching for food plants on which to lay her eggs. Both sexes are often found feeding on flowers and at damp sand or muddy patches along stream banks.

The males show strong hilltopping behaviour and on hot sunny

Papilio demodocus demodocus male underside

days they ascend to the summits of hills, koppies or rocky knolls. Here they patrol and defend their territories against all challengers. They settle to rest only if the sun is obscured. This insect is perhaps the most conspicuous of all hilltopping species. There are very few prominences in South Africa where this large swallowtail is not seen on a warm sunny day. Some males, however, establish their territories in flat country or in gardens, where they may be observed flying in a leisurely fashion, mostly floating along and flapping their wings now and then. The male usually selects some trees or bushes as the focal point of his territory. He then circles round this point until he detects a rival, when he will dart off and spin around the rival like a miniature whirlwind in order to chase it off.

When a male finds an available female her initial reaction will be to flee at an exceptional speed, flying over, under and around trees with the male following mere centimetres behind her. If the male is able to follow she will eventually grow tired and settle on the ground or in the undergrowth whereupon the male will settle beside her and mating invariably follows.

Papilio demodocus demodocus early instar larva

Papilio demodocus demodocus final instar larva yellow form feeding on fennel

Papilio demodocus demodocus male upperside

The female laying behaviour has been seen by most gardeners as females lay eggs on Citrus trees. The female hovers around the food plant testing with outstretched legs and if satisfied will lay her eggs by curling her abdomen around the edge of a leaf or young shoot and depositing a single egg on the underside. She may lay several eggs on a single plant if it is large enough. Isolated plants seem to be preferred. If a natural food plant is available in a garden, the cultivated citrus plants will be ignored in its favour. The egg takes about 5 days to hatch. All larval instars feed on the upper surface of the leaves. The osmeterium is crimson with horizontally spreading forks, there is a strong smell of citric acid when it is everted. The larval stage lasts some 24 days. The pupa takes the general colour of the substrate on which it pupates. The pupal stage can take two weeks under favourable conditions and many months in adverse conditions (Clark, 1949: 23; Clark, 1994: 404; S.F. Henning, 1984b: 32).

This species is on the wing throughout the year but is more plentiful during the warmer months.

LARVAL FOOD PLANTS

Archangelica officinalis, Clausena anisata, Calodendrum capense, Toddalia asiatica, Vepris lanceolata, Teclea natalensis, Citrus sp., *Oricia bachmannii, Zanthoxylum capense, Z. delagoense* (Rutaceae); *Ptaeroxylon obliquum* (Ptaeroxylaceae); *Foeniculum vulgare* (fennel), *Peucedanum galbanum, P. gummiferum, Deverra burchellii* (Apiaceae); *Hippobromus pauciflorus* (Sapindaceae).

Papilio demodocus demodocus final instar larva green form

DISTRIBUTION

Throughout Southern Africa.

CONSERVATION

P. demodocus is a common, widespread species and is under no threat.

Papilio demodocus demodocus pupa

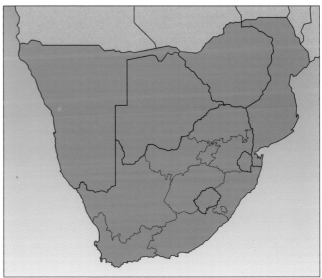

Distribution map of *Papilio demodocus*

Papilio ophidicephalus Oberthur

EMPEROR SWALLOWTAIL

Papilio ophidicephalus Oberthur, 1878. *Étud. d'Ent.* **3**: 13.

This species occurs in the eastern and southern half of Africa, and is the largest butterfly found in Southern Africa. It is part of the *P. menestheus* Drury species group which spans Africa and is the southernmost representative. The nominate subspecies was described from Tanzania and does not extend into Southern Africa. There are five subspecies in South Africa and another in Zimbabwe. The Zimbabwean subspecies is *chirinda* van Son (1939).

The subspecies differ in the extent and arrangement of markings. The nominate subspecies is large with elongated forewings and large clubbed tails on the hindwing. Male. Upperside: black with a transverse yellow band. Underside similar to upperside but basally irrorated with yellow. Female. Larger than male but with forewings not as elongated and with the ground colour more brownish. Upperside: as in the male but with the distal mark on the anal margin reddish-orange. Underside: as in male.

Papilio ophidicephalus entabeni van Son

Papilio ophidicephalus entabeni van Son, 1939. *Ann. Transv. Mus.* **19**: 60. Type locality: Entabeni Forest, Soutpansberg. Holotype male in Transvaal Museum, Pretoria.

IDENTIFICATION

Adult. Forewing discal spots smaller than in nominate subspecies and very weakly fused.

Forewing lengths: male 60-64 mm; female 65-67 mm.

DISTRIBUTION

South Africa, from the Soutpansberg and Blouberg in the Northern Province.

Papilio ophidicephalus transvaalensis van Son

Papilio ophidicephalus transvaalensis van Son, 1939. *Ann. Transv. Mus.* **19**: 61. Type locality: Woodbush, Pietersburg District. Holotype male in Transvaal Museum, Pretoria.

IDENTIFICATION

Adult. Forewing discal spots separate; discal area of hindwing strongly irrorated with yellow.

Forewing lengths: male 55-62 mm; female 61-64 mm.

DISTRIBUTION

South Africa, from north of the Olifants River in the Northern Province Drakensberg and Wolkberg.

Papilio ophidicephalus transvaalensis male upperside

Papilio ophidicephalus ayresi van Son

Papilio ophidicephalus ayresi van Son, 1939. *Ann. Transv. Mus.* **19**: 62. Type locality: Marieps Mountain, Mpumalanga. Holotype in Transvaal Museum, Pretoria.

IDENTIFICATION

Adult. Forewing discal spots very small and separate, more uniform in size and in a straighter line.

Forewing lengths: male 56-64 mm; female 59-69 mm.

DISTRIBUTION

South Africa, from south of the Olifants River in Mpumalanga Drakensberg to northern KwaZulu-Natal near Vryheid.

Papilio ophidicephalus ayresi male underside

Papilio ophidicephalus ayresi female upperside

225

Papilio ophidicephalus zuluensis van Son

Papilio ophidicephalus zuluensis van Son, 1939. *Ann. Transv. Mus.* **19**: 63. Type locality: Eshowe, Zululand. Holotype male in Transvaal Museum, Pretoria.

IDENTIFICATION

Adult. Forewing discal spots larger than *ayresi*, weakly fused in the female, those in CuA_1 and CuA_2 elongated.

Forewing lengths: male 57-62 mm; female 61-70 mm.

DISTRIBUTION

South Africa, from the Eshowe district of KwaZulu-Natal.

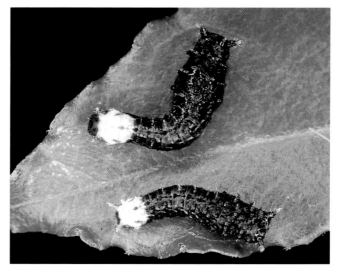

Papilio ophidicephalus ayresi early instar larvae

Papilio ophidicephalus ayresi final instar larva rufous form

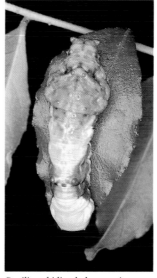

Papilio ophidicephalus ayresi final instar larva black form with osmeterium everted and thoracic segments inflated

Papilio ophidicephalus ayresi intermediate instar larva

Papilio ophidicephalus ayresi pupa

Papilio ophidicephalus phalusco Suffert

Papilio ophidicephalus ab. *phalusco* Suffert, 1904. *Dt. ent. Z. Iris.* **17**: 103. Type locality: KwaZulu-Natal

IDENTIFICATION

Adult. Forewing discal spots larger than *zuluensis*, fairly linear in arrangement, weakly fused and broader at the costa.

Forewing lengths: male 57-66 mm; female 65-74 mm.

DISTRIBUTION

South Africa, from KwaZulu-Natal south of the Tugela River, to the Eastern Cape.

Early stages. Egg: pale yellow when first laid, darkening to dull yellow; spherical, smooth, with a flattened base, diameter 1,3 mm, height 1,3 mm. Larva: first four instars dark greyish-brown with white markings, resembling a bird dropping; fifth (final) instar bluish-green with narrow, blackish-brown bands on first three segments and a large, H-shaped mark mid-dorsally; osmeterium blackish with forks spread obliquely, upcurved distally and with yellowish tips. The larva attains a length of 40-43 mm. Pupa: 34-40 mm long; fairly cylindrical, anteriorly truncate, and may be various combinations and shades of grey, brown, pink and green. It resembles a broken twig complete with processes resembling lichens (Clark, 1949: 29; Clark, 1994: 408; S.F. Henning, 1984b: 31).

HABITAT AND ECOLOGY

P. ophidicephalus is an inhabitant of montane forest. It is usually seen around kloofs in forests, especially those with a stream flowing at the bottom. It has a ponderously flapping flight, rising and falling, which may be deceptively slow and cumbersome but when aroused it can be swift and elusive. It generally keeps fairly low, seldom rising more than two or three metres above the ground. It may often be seen feeding at flowers near the ground, or drinking at damp places. In fact, they tend to congregate at damp places, sometimes five to ten or more at one spot. Like all swallowtails, their wings are kept in constant motion when feeding on nectar, but while drinking at muddy places they are at times scarcely discernible, so utterly motionless are they. They are particularly fond of the flowers of *Impatiens* sp.

Males show strong territorial behaviour and patrol in sunny places in the forest, always maintaining a height of one to three metres above the ground. They usually fly a circuitous path through forest clearings and along streams. The patrol probably passes through about a kilometre of forest. The male flies languorously at about 5 kph, with frequent diversions to investigate other butterflies and visits to flowers and damp places. They are particularly fond of patrolling forest streams. They seldom ascend to the forest canopy unless to feed on flowers. They follow their path throughout most of the warmer hours of the day.

The females are generally less conspicuous than the males, and prefer to fly in the half shade where the food plants grow. They lay their eggs singly on either the upper or lower surface of the leaf, preferably on young saplings. The egg takes about 5 days to hatch. There are five larval instars with a total duration of five weeks. The larva generally sits on the upper surface of the leaves and typically curls itself slightly, thereby enhancing its resemblance to a bird dropping. The final instar larva is green with cryptic markings to break down the outline, it generally sits along the midrib on the upperside of a leaf. The pupa resembles a broken twig or a piece of lichen-covered bark. It is attached by the cremaster to a silken pad and is held upright by a silken girdle. The pupal stage lasts from a couple a weeks to a few months (Clark, 1949: 29; Clark, 1994: 408; S.F. Henning, 1984b: 31).

The flight period is from September to March with peaks usually in October and January.

LARVAL FOOD PLANTS

Clausena anisata, Zanthoxylum capense, Z. delagoense, Calodendrum capense, Citrus spp. (Rutaceae).

CONSERVATION

P. ophidicephalus is under no threat although some subspecies are very localised. The only one which requires some research would be *zuluensis* which can be found in the Dhlinza Forest Reserve and the Nkandla Forest.

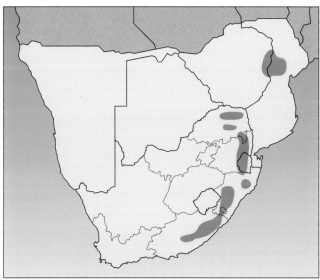

Distribution map of *Papilio ophidicephalus*

Papilio nireus Linnaeus

GREEN-BANDED SWALLOWTAIL

Papilio nireus Linnaeus, 1758. *Syst. Nat.*, (Ed. 10) **1**: 464.

This is the only Southern African representative of the large, diverse and complex *nireus* species group. There are many species in the group found throughout the Afrotropical Region. *P. nireus* is a woodland and forest species found in this habitat throughout most of Africa. The nominate race occurs in the western half of Africa. The eastern and southern subspecies is *lyaeus* Doubleday, with other races on the Comores, in Ethiopia and southern Sudan.

Papilio nireus lyaeus Doubleday

Papilio lyaeus Doubleday, 1845. *Ann. Mag. nat. Hist.* **16**: 178.
Type locality: South Africa (Durban(?), KwaZulu-Natal)

IDENTIFICATION

Adult. Male. Upperside: jet black with a greenish-blue transverse band; hindwing without tails. Underside: dark brown with submarginal series of creamy-ochreous markings on hindwing. Female. Upperside: brownish-black with a bluish-green transverse band broader than male. Underside: submarginal band of male is absent, hindwing and distal half of forewing mottled with pale silvery brown.

Papilio nireus lyaeus male upperside

Forewing lengths: male 45-57 mm; female 45-57 mm.

Early stages. Egg: pale cream when first laid, developing reddish-brown spots around the middle; spherical with a flat base, diameter 1,15 mm, height 0,95 mm; surface plain, but slightly rough, giving the appearance of fine pubescence. Larva: first instar black and brown or orange with two pairs of processes on each of the first four segments, with a single pair on each of the remaining segments; second and third instars are yellow and black; fourth instar becomes green with black, white and pink markings; fifth (final) instar green, finely irrorated with white and yellowish-white markings; osmeterium reddish-purple with horizontal fork. The larva attains a length of about 32 mm. Pupa: 26-30 mm long; leaf-shaped, broadly bifid and squared at the head; colour usually light bluish-green (Clark, 1949: 32; Clark, 1994: 406; S.F. Henning, 1984b: 32).

Papilio nireus lyaeus early instar larva on its food plant *Vepris lanceolata*

Papilio nireus lyaeus male underside

Papilio nireus lyaeus female underside

HABITAT AND ECOLOGY

P. nireus lyaeus occurs in a variety of habitats from bushveld to montane forest. The flight of this species is swift and evasive, but very persistent. It rarely flies when bad weather prevails, but may venture forth on overcast days if it is warm, and fly somewhat sluggishly. This swallowtail is readily attracted to flowers, including those in gardens. They are also fond of drinking on the mud at the edges of streams or pools, and in very hot weather they congregate in large numbers at these areas. They are also attracted to fresh animal droppings; the males usually predominate at these gatherings.

The males may often be observed patrolling in search of females. They fly around bushes and trees or along forest roads, zig-zagging and circling in some places, or flying in a fairly straight line for long distances, seemingly never to tire. They may fly one or two metres above the ground for a while, then up to three to five metres or higher. The extent of the males' territories are not readily discernible and patrols do not seem to be as rigidly adhered to as with other swallowtails. It is possible that the males patrol very long circuits which would prevent them from passing a particular reference point on a regular basis. They have been recorded sailing around high trees in forest habitats but this may be due to the presence of a flowering plant.

The females fly at random through the bush in search of suitable food plants. They hover around the food plant, investigating a number of leaves before ovipositing. They lay their eggs singly on the leaves of the food plant. The eggs take some 5 days to hatch. There are five larval instars, the final one being the most leaf-like. The colour varies according to the colour of the leaves of the food plant. The larval stage lasts about 4 weeks. The pupa resembles a leaf and is attached by the cremastral hooks to a silken pad and held upright by a silken girdle around the middle. The colour of the pupa varies according to the substrate on which the larva pupated. The pupal stage lasts two weeks under favourable conditions, but may be protracted considerably by adverse conditions (Clark, 1949: 32; Clark, 1994: 406; S.F. Henning, 1984b: 32).

It is on the wing throughout the year in warm habitats but the midsummer months are the best time for observing it.

LARVAL FOOD PLANTS

Clausena anisata, Zanthoxylum capense, Z. delagoense, Calodendrum capense, Toddalia asiatica, Vepris lanceolata, Teclea natalensis, Oricia bachmannii, Citrus spp. (Rutaceae).

DISTRIBUTION

South Africa, from the eastern areas of the Western Cape to the Eastern Cape, KwaZulu-Natal, Gauteng, Northern Province and Mpumalanga, North-West Province to Botswana, northern Namibia, Swaziland, Zimbabwe and Moçambique, northwards into East Africa. There are also odd records for the Free State.

CONSERVATION

P. nireus lyaeus is a common, widespread species and is under no threat.

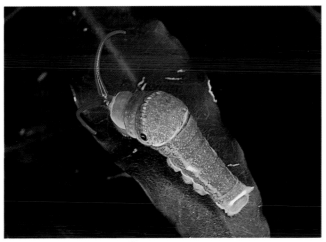

Papilio nireus lyaeus final instar larva with osmeterium everted and thoracic segments inflated

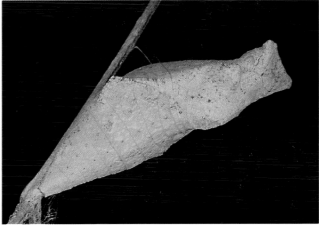

Papilio nireus lyaeus pupa

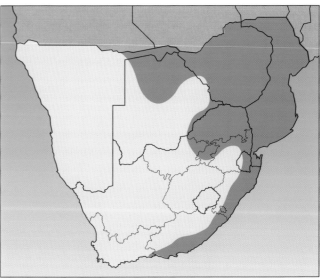

Distribution map of *Papilio nireus*

Papilio echerioides Trimen

WHITE-BANDED SWALLOWTAIL

Papilio echerioides Trimen, 1868. *Trans. ent. Soc. Lond.* **1868**: 72.

This species is part of the *P. cynorta* Fabricius (1793) species group and is the only Southern Africa representative. There are 7 species in this group. *P. echerioides* occurs down the eastern side of Africa from Ethiopia to the Eastern Cape. There are six subspecies, two of which occur in Southern Africa. The nominate comes from South Africa, while the second subspecies *chirindanus* van Son (1956) occurs in the eastern highlands of Zimbabwe and adjacent Moçambique.

The female upperside mimics the danaid genus *Amauris*. The undersides of both sexes resemble the acraeid genus *Bematistes*. This is an unusual case of double mimicry.

Papilio echerioides echerioides male underside

Papilio echerioides echerioides male upperside

Papilio echerioides echerioides Trimen

Papilio echerioides Trimen, 1868. *Trans. ent. Soc. Lond.* **1868**: 72. Type locality: Kaffraria.

IDENTIFICATION

Adult. Male. A small tailless species. Upperside: black with a diagonal creamy-white stripe; this white stripe is strongly fluorescent in ultra-violet light. Some specimens from Barberton, however, have been found to be non-fluorescent and the full implications of this fact have not as yet been ascertained. Underside: similar to upperside but with a reddish-brown ground colour, particularly on hindwing. Female. Upperside: black with white spots on forewing and an orange patch on hindwing. Some specimens, particularly from Barberton, have yellowish spots on forewings. Underside: similar to the upperside but with a pale brown ground colour.

Forewing lengths: male 38-48 mm; female 37-49 mm.

Early stages. Egg: pale yellow in colour with a few small reddish-brown spots; diameter 1,2 mm, height 1,0 mm; smooth. Larva: first instar black with first and last segments white. Second to fourth instars light brown to olive brown with white; fifth (final) instar

bright green with a brownish transverse band on 4th segment; osmeterium bright pink. The larva attains a length of about 32 mm. Pupa: 28-30 mm long; strongly arched and knobbed and mottled with green, brown, pink and white; head broadly bifid (Clark, 1949: 16; Clark, 1994: 400; S.F. Henning, 1984b: 31).

HABITAT AND ECOLOGY

P. echerioides is an inhabitant of montane forest. Both sexes fly near the ground, and their flight appears to be slower than that of most species of swallowtail in our area. Males fly fairly fast with a flitting action, while females generally flutter slowly through the undergrowth. Males frequently flit out of the undergrowth to suck on damp sand or feed on the nectar of flowers. Females can also be seen on flowers but more often than not they feed on flowers within the forest. They are seldom seen at muddy places which are the rendezvous of so many swallowtails.

The males patrol along the forest roads and in clearings where they may be observed flying up and down in great numbers. They may occasionally patrol along the edges of the wood in search of females, but they prefer the open spaces within the forest itself. They fly low and keep to a fixed course through the forest.

Females are usually observed flying low through the undergrowth in search of food plants on which to lay their eggs. They lay

Papilio echerioides echerioides female upperside

Papilio echerioides echerioides early instar larva

their eggs singly on the undersides of the leaves of the food plant. The eggs hatch after about 5 days. The first four larval instars resemble a bird dropping. The final instar larva is leaf-like. The larval stage has a duration of about 35 days. The pupa resembles a piece of partly detached lichen. The coloration is variable depending on the substrate on which it is attached and consists of mottled greys, browns and greens. The pupal stage lasts about two weeks (Clark, 1949: 16; Clark, 1994: 400; S.F. Henning, 1984b: 31).

This species is on the wing throughout the warmer months although it is more prevalent during September and October and again from February to April.

LARVAL FOOD PLANTS

Clausena anisata, Zanthoxylum capense, Z. delagoense, Vepris lanceolata, Citrus spp. (Rutaceae).

DISTRIBUTION

South Africa, from the Amatola Mountains in the Eastern Cape north through the KwaZulu-Natal forests to Swaziland and Mpumalanga and Northern Province.

CONSERVATION

The nominate subspecies is widespread through the forests of South Africa and is not threatened. The subspecies *chirindanus* from Zimbabwe is more restricted but not threatened.

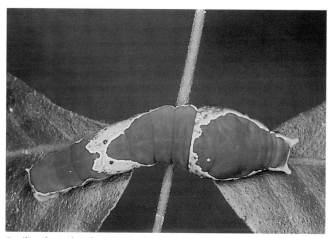

Papilio echerioides echerioides final instar larva

Papilio echerioides echerioides pupa on its food plant *Clausena anisata*

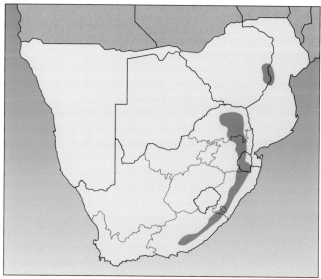

Distribution map of *Papilio echerioides*

233

Tribe Graphiini

THE SWORDTAILS

The swordtails vary superficially, but are remarkably constant in structure. A number of species of this group lack the tails on the hindwings. The sexes can be distinguished by the prominent hair-pencil in the anal fold of the male which is absent in the female. When feeding the swordtails do not settle but hover above the food source on rapidly vibrating wings with only the tips of the extended legs touching the plant or ground.

Genus *Graphium* Scopoli

Graphium Scopoli, 1777. *Introd. Hist. Nat.*: 433. Type species: *Papilio sarpedon* Linnaeus, 1758, by selection by Hemming 1933.

Medium to large butterflies which have in common the merging of veins Sc and R_1 in the forewing, which run to the costa as a single vein. Anal area of hindwing in male forming a fold enclosing long hairs and androconia. Male genitalia with tegumen reduced, band-shaped; uncus never beak-shaped, weakly sclerosed, distally more or less bifid. Female genitalia with signum funnel-like, with the broad part continuous with the wall of the bursa, the narrow part projecting into the bursa.

Early stages: eggs very nearly spherical and smooth. Larvae with setose processes bearing distally forked setae. The pupae have the head with two sharply pointed projections, thorax keeled and produced forwards into a fairly long horn; body tapering gradually and evenly to the sharp posterior end.

The main larval food plants belong to the Annonaceae.

There are ten species in Southern Africa, of which seven occur in South Africa.

KEY TO THE SPECIES OF *GRAPHIUM*

1. Hindwing without tails 2

   Hindwing with tails 4

2. UFW with inner margin brownish-black without a white discal mark .... *G. leonidas*

   UFW with a white discal mark on inner margin 3

3. UFW with large kidney-shaped spot at upper end of cell; abdomen with orange-yellow lateral bands reduced to spots on segments 2-4; two rows of white postdiscal spots at anal margin closely aligned .... *G. morania*

   UFW with large spot at end of cell in two parts, basal part being club-shaped; abdomen lateral bands complete from base to 9th segment; two rows of white postdiscal spots at anal margin not closely aligned .... *G. angolanus*

4. UHW without discal spots .... *G. colonna*

   UHW with discal spots 5

5. UFW with light transverse bars in cell straight .... *G. policenes*

   UFW with light transverse bars in cell not straight 6

6. UFW with rounded mark at end of cell, beyond 5th bar; LHW without rounded crimson spots in 1A+2A and CuA_2 .... *G. porthaon*

   UFW without rounded mark at end of cell; LHW with rounded crimson spots in 1A+2A and CuA_2 .... *G. antheus*

Subgenus *Arisbe* Hübner

Arisbe Hübner, 1823. *Verz. bek. Schmett.* (6): 89. Type species: *Papilio leonidas* Fabricius, 1793, by selection by Hemming 1967.

Male genitalia complex, ventral and central processes present; valve with dorsal process tubular and dorsal and ventral processes present.

Early stages: larva with thoracic and anal spines; pupa with lateral ridges and a dorsal thoracic projection.

Larval food plants belong to the families Annonaceae, Apocynaceae and Malpighiaceae.

Hancock (1983) placed the tailed species in the subgenus *Graphium*, however the current consensus of opinion is that all the Southern African taxa belong to the subgenus *Arisbe*.

Graphium (Arisbe) leonidas (Fabricius)

VEINED SWORDTAIL

Papilio leonidas Fabricius, 1793. *Syst. Ent.* **3**(1): 35.

This common woodland and forest species is found throughout most of Africa. It is an apparent mimic of *Tirumala petiverana* (Doubleday) although *T. petiverana* does not fly with it in South Africa. Probably also a general mimic of the genus *Amauris*. Unlike other species in the family it often chooses a perch from which to hang, with open or closed wings, and in this way enhancing its resemblance to the danaids. There are four subspecies but only the nominate occurs on mainland Africa.

Graphium (A.) leonidas leonidas (Fabricius)

Papilio leonidas Fabricius, 1793. *Syst. Ent.* **3**(1): 35. Type locality: West Africa.

IDENTIFICATION

Adult. Tailless with an elongated forewing. Male. Upperside: black with bluish-white markings. Underside: similar to upperside. Female. Similar to male.

Form *brasidas* Felder (1864. *Verh. zool.-bot. Ges. Wien.* **14**: 307) differs from the nominate in having all the light markings of the forewing smaller and often pure white; in the hindwing the post-discal spots are absent.

Form *melusina* le Cerf (1924. *Bull. Hill Mus. Witley* **1**: 397) is characterised by the reduction of all discal spots and is an extreme case of reduction of the markings of form *brasidas*.

Forewing lengths: male 41-48 mm; female 44-53 mm.

Early stages. Egg: pale yellow when first laid, becoming deeper yellow later. Larva: first instar pale yellow with light brown diagonal stripes, paired spiny processes are present along body, being longest on first three segments; second instar darker than first with processes much smaller on first three segments and absent from the

Graphium leonidas leonidas male underside

rest; third and fourth instars yellowish-green to brown with darker diagonal lines and a yellowish to brown mid-dorsal line; fifth (final) instar dull green with light brown mid-dorsal line and diagonal stripes; osmeterium indigo-blue. The larva attains a length of some 45 mm. Pupa: 33 mm long; yellowish-green with pale markings, anteriorly broad and blunt with a large dorsal projection (Clark, 1949: 44; Clark, 1994: 414).

HABITAT AND ECOLOGY

G. (A.) leonidas is an inhabitant of woodland and forest but sometimes ventures into bushveld. Its flight is fast and erratic and difficult to follow but is not as fast as some of the other swordtails. Both sexes feed on nectar from flowers and at damp sand. Unlike most swallowtails when visiting flowers, drinking at pools, or resting on a twig, this butterfly often closes its wings, so that its resemblance to a danaid is especially noticeable. It is also in the habit of roosting on the ends of twigs with the folded wings hanging downwards, exactly in the way danaids do, and there is little doubt that its behaviour has protective significance.

Males show strong hilltopping behaviour and ascend to the summits during the midday hours and patrol back and forth. They also patrol territories along forest edges. Here they may select a prominent perch about two to three metres above the ground to which they periodically return after a patrol. They vigorously chase intruders out of their territories.

Graphium leonidas leonidas male upperside

Graphium leonidas leonidas final instar larva with fore section characteristically raised

Graphium leonidas leonidas early instar larva on its food plant *Uvaria caffra*

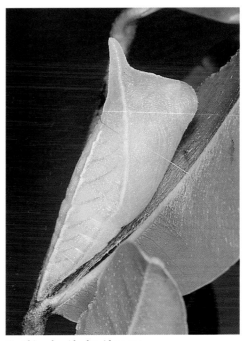

Graphium leonidas leonidas pupa

The females fly at random through the bush in search of suitable food plants on which to oviposit. When about to lay they approach the food plant with fluttering wings and extended legs. They touch the food plant with their legs and then with their antenna tips, working their way up to the young growing tips. She lays a single egg on a young shoot or leaf. The egg takes some four days to hatch. The larva rests on the midrib on the upperside of the leaf. During the earlier larval instars it eats a small hole in the leaf but in later instars it feeds along the edge. There are usually five larval instars lasting about 25 days. The pupa is attached by the cremastral hooks to a silken pad and a silken girdle around the middle holds it upright. In this species the girdle appears to be fragile and is sometimes broken, causing the pupa to hang downwards (as recorded by Trimen, 1889).

This species is on the wing during most months of the year in warm habitats but is usually more plentiful during the midsummer months.

LARVAL FOOD PLANTS

Monanthotaxis caffra, Friesodielsia obovata, Artobotrys cinerea, Uvaria caffra (Annonaceae).

DISTRIBUTION

South Africa, from around East London in the Eastern Cape, through KwaZulu-Natal to the Northern Province and Mpumalanga, Swaziland, through Moçambique and Zimbabwe, northern Botswana, northwards over most of Africa south of the Sahara.

CONSERVATION

G. (A.) leonidas is a widespread species and is under no threat.

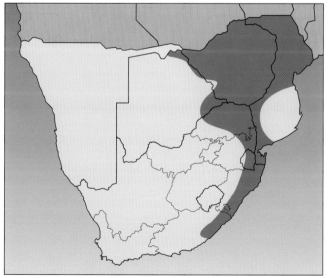

Distribution map of *Graphium leonidas*

Graphium (Arisbe) angolanus (Goeze)

ANGOLA WHITE-LADY SWORDTAIL

Papilio angolanus Goeze, 1779. *Ent. Beyträge* **3**(1): 87.

A species of open habitats found throughout most of Africa. There are three subspecies of which the nominate is found in Southern Africa.

Graphium (A.) angolanus angolanus (Goeze)

Papilio angolanus Goeze, 1779. *Ent. Beyträge* **3**(1): 87. Type locality: Angola.

IDENTIFICATION

Adult. Male. Upperside: black with large white patches and spots. Underside: similar markings to upperside but ochreous with red basally; discal area with the two rows of spots well separated, usually with an ochreous area. Female. Similar to the male.

Forewing lengths: male 34-40 mm; female 40-46 mm.

Early stages. Egg: pure white when first laid, changing to pale yellowish-brown with pink markings if fertile; roughly spherical and smooth, diameter 0,95 mm, height 0,8 mm. Larva: first instar chocolate-brown with white dorsal markings and at posterior end, three pairs of blunt, spined processes on thoracic segments, dorsal area between processes darkened; second instar with dorsal markings taking on a chess-board appearance; third and fourth instars with dorsal markings in the shape of transverse bands, and with yellow longitudinal lines; fifth (final) instar largely green with pale yellow markings and thoracic processes reduced to small spines; osmeterium green. The larva attains a length of about 30 mm. Pupa: 26-29 mm long; green to pale brown with fine yellow striations and lines; fairly cylindrical, tapering posteriorly, and there is a large forward projecting process dorsally on thorax (Coleridge, 1916: 91; S.F. Henning, 1984b: 33; Clark, 1994: 410).

HABITAT AND ECOLOGY

G. (A.) angolanus is an inhabitant of bushveld and woodland. In flight it resembles a Pierid more than a swordtail. It generally flies low and fast, dodging at random through the trees in the woodland habitats that it favours. Although not usually recorded in the mass Pierid migrations, specimens have been found far from their normal habitats. They are often found sucking moisture at damp sand or feeding on the nectar of flowers.

The males occasionally show hilltopping behaviour and fly to the top of hills where they establish territories along the summit ridges. However, they usually establish their territories on the flats where they patrol back and forth. They appear to weave a circuitous route through the woodland trees, possibly a kilometre or two in circumference. They patrol at a fairly rapid pace, probably more than 10 kph. Any intruding male is rapidly chased off.

The females fly at random through the bush in search of suitable food plants on which to lay. When they are ready to lay, they flutter into the depths of the food plant and lay on the foliage and young shoots deep within the plant. The eggs are laid singly on the upper surface of the leaves. The young larvae eat their way out of the egg near the top and devour the entire egg shell. The young larva eats the surface of the leaf, leaving small holes and later instars eat the entire leaf. The larval stage lasts about 2 weeks. The larva sits on leaves along the side of the food plant, sometimes on a prominent branch but it may also be found in a secluded spot on the tree. The pupa is green and leaf-like. It is held upright by a silken girdle and is attached by the cremaster. The pupal stage normally lasts about 12 days in season but up to two years in unfavourable conditions (Coleridge, 1916: 91; S.F. Henning, 1984b: 33; Clark, 1994: 410).

This species is on the wing throughout the warmer months of the year. It can be found in great numbers if conditions are favourable.

Graphium angolanus angolanus male upperside

Graphium angolanus angolanus male underside

LARVAL FOOD PLANTS

Annona senegalensis (Annonaceae); *Sphedamnocarpus pruriens* (Malpighiaceae).

DISTRIBUTION

South Africa, from the Tugela River in KwaZulu-Natal to Mpumalanga and Northern Province, Swaziland, Moçambique, Zimbabwe, northern Botswana to northern Namibia, northwards into Angola, Zambia, Malawi, Tanzania and eastern Kenya.

CONSERVATION

G. (A.) angolanus is a common, widespread species and is under no threat.

Graphium angolanus angolanus pupa

Graphium angolanus angolanus early instar larva

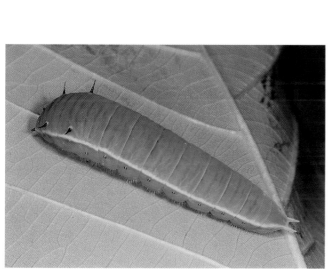

Graphium angolanus angolanus final instar larva

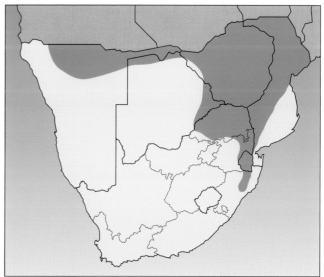

Distribution map of *Graphium angolanus*

Graphium (Arisbe) morania (Angas)

SMALL WHITE-LADY SWORDTAIL

Papilio morania Angas, 1849. *Kafirs Illustr.*: pl. 30, fig. 1. Type locality: Natal.

This species has a much more restricted range than *G. angolanus*. It occurs only in Southern Africa and is replaced to the north by *G. schaffgotschi* (Niepelt) and *G. taboranus* Oberthur.

IDENTIFICATION

Adult. Male. Upperside: similar to *G. (A.) angolanus* but smaller with the forewing mid-costal patch undivided. Underside: similar to *G. (A.) angolanus* but with the two rows of discal spots close together. Female. Similar to male.

Forewing lengths: male 32-37 mm; female 35-40 mm.

Early stages. Egg: pale greenish-yellow; spherical with a flattened base, diameter 1,0 mm, height 0,95 mm; with a faint irregular hexagonal reticulation. Larva: first to fourth instars largely yellow with dark brown transverse bands and three pairs of blunt spined processes dorso-laterally on thoracic segments: fifth (final) instar green with two parallel darker transverse lines or rows of dots across the middle, and a third similar row at anterior edge of each abdominal segment, the three pairs of laterally projecting processes on thorax reduced to spines. The larva attains a length of about 30 mm. Pupa: 25 mm long; green with yellow striations and suture lines; fairly cylindrical, tapering posteriorly, with a large dorsal projection on the thorax (Clark, 1949: 38; Clark, 1994: 412).

HABITAT AND ECOLOGY

G. (A.) morania is a bushveld and woodland species. In flight, like *G. angolanus*, it resembles a pierid more than a swordtail. It generally flies low and fast, dodging swiftly and at random through the trees. They are often found, sometimes in great numbers, sucking moisture alongside the numerous pierids. They have also been recorded feeding on flowers.

The males show hilltopping behaviour, often being observed patrolling around hilltops or along ridges. However, they also establish their territories on the slopes or flats, possibly near the larval food plants. Here they appear to weave a circuitous route through the trees, possibly a kilometre or more in circumference. They patrol it fairly rapidly, probably at more than 10 kph.

The females fly at random through the bush in search of suitable food plants on which to lay. They lay their eggs singly on young leaves. The eggs hatch after about 4 days. The larva sits on the

Graphium morania male underside

upper surface of the leaves of the food plant. There are 5 larval instars lasting about 15 days. The pupa is attached by the cremaster to a silken pad and is suspended by a girdle around the middle. The pupal stage is 12 to 15 days in optimum conditions but may be up to 2 years or more under unfavourable conditions (Clark, 1949: 38; Clark, 1994: 412).

This species is on the wing throughout the warmer months from September to May.

LARVAL FOOD PLANTS

Hexalobus monopetalus, Uvaria caffra, Artobotrys monteiroae, A. brachypetalus, Annona senegalensis (Annonaceae).

DISTRIBUTION

South Africa, from the Umzimkulu River in KwaZulu-Natal, northwards through lowveld areas of Zululand, Swaziland, Mpumalanga to the Northern Province; into Moçambique, Zimbabwe and Botswana.

CONSERVATION

G. (A.) morania has a wide distribution in Southern Africa and is under no threat.

Graphium morania male upperside

Graphium morania pupa

Graphium morania early instar larva

Graphium morania final instar larva on its food plant *Hexalobus monopetalus*

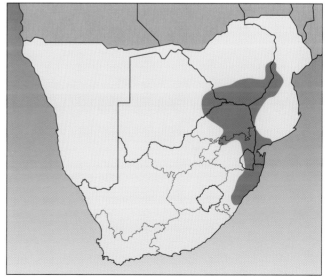

Distribution map of *Graphium morania*

241

LARGE STRIPED SWORDTAIL

Papilio antheus Cramer, 1779. *Uitl. Kapellen.* **3**: 71. Type locality: Africa.

This and the following three species comprise the typical Southern African swordtails, green and black species with long, elegant, pointed tails on the hindwings.

IDENTIFICATION

Adult. Male. Upperside: black with bright green to bluish-green markings, lines in cell of forewing broad and wavy; hindwing with long, thin, pointed tails. Underside: ochreous brown with paler markings as on upperside; in cell of hindwing there is a distinctive, rounded, red and black patch. Female. Similar to male but paler.

Forewing lengths: male 39-43 mm; female 44-52 mm.

Early stages. Egg: pale green; almost spherical in shape, flattened below, diameter 1,0 mm, height 0,95 mm. Larva: first instar dark brownish-grey with dorso-lateral processes on thoracic segments; second to fourth instars chocolate-brown with only some specimens showing faint black-edged transverse stripes; collar and last segment yellow; fifth (final) instar velvety-brown dorsally, collar yellow with a black spine on each side; body with traces of bands in some larvae; head light brown. Some KwaZulu-Natal specimens have been recorded with a green coloration in the last two instars. The larva attains a length of 35 mm. Pupa: 23 mm long; green or brown with fine cream lines; anteriorly blunt and there is a short square dorsal projection on thorax; it is cylindrical and not flattened as in *G. (A.) policenes* (Clark, 1949: 44; Clark, 1994: 416).

HABITAT AND ECOLOGY

G. (A.) antheus is an inhabitant of bushveld and coastal bush. It is sometimes found near or within forests. Its flight is fast and direct with the tails streaming out behind. It is an inquisitive insect and will investigate anything interesting in its path. Both sexes feed on the nectar of flowers, often tubular flowers and the colours red and yellow seem to be preferred. They also feed on damp sand, fluttering on their outstretched legs, while probing for moisture. Favoured places are cattle troughs or river banks where animals have come to drink and left their urine, which entices the swordtails.

The males patrol along the edges of bush but do not appear to be as aggressively territorial as some of the other species. They

Graphium antheus male upperside

have also been observed patrolling rocky hill slopes. They fly a metre above the ground at times, but normally from two to three metres, or higher.

The females fly at random through the bush in search of suitable food plants on which to lay. They lay their eggs singly on the tips of young shoots. The eggs take about four days to hatch. The larva eats small holes in the leaves in its earlier instars, later feeding from the edge of the leaves. The larva rests along the mid-rib of the leaf. The larval stage passes through five instars and lasts about two weeks. The final instar larva, when it is about to pupate, turns green. The pupa is leaf-like and is attached by the cremaster to a silken pad and held upright by a silken girdle around the middle. The pupal stage can take from a week, under ideal conditions, to several months or more in adverse conditions and depending on the individual (Clark, 1949: 44; Clark, 1994: 416). Some specimens bred on the Witwatersrand emerged only the second season after pupation.

This species is on the wing throughout the summer months.

LARVAL FOOD PLANTS

Hexalobus monopetalus, Uvaria caffra, Artobotrys monteiroae, A. brachypetalus, Cleistochlamys kirkii, Annona reticulata, A. senegalensis (Annonaceae).

DISTRIBUTION

South Africa, from the Eastern Cape, through KwaZulu-Natal to Mpumalanga and Northern Province, northern Gauteng and North-West Province, into Swaziland, Moçambique, Zimbabwe, Botswana and northern Namibia, northwards throughout most of Africa south of the Sahara.

CONSERVATION

G. (A.) antheus is a common, widespread species and is under no threat.

Graphium antheus early instar larva

Graphium antheus male underside

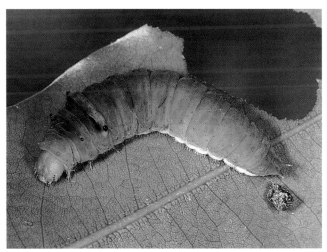

Graphium antheus final instar larva green form

243

Graphium antheus final instar larva purple form

Graphium antheus pupa

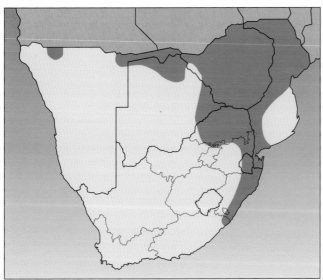

Distribution map of *Graphium antheus*

Graphium (Arisbe) policenes (Cramer)

SMALL STRIPED SWORDTAIL

Papilio policenes Cramer, 1775. *Uitl. Kapellen* **1**: 61, pl. 37: A, B.

Some authors show *G. policenes* without any subspecies. We consider the western Afrotropical population to be the nominate and the eastern Afrotropical population to be *laurentia* (le Cerf).

Graphium (A.) policenes laurentia (le Cerf)

Papilio policenes laurentia le Cerf, 1924. *Bull. Hill. Mus. Witley* **1**: 398. Type locality: Durban, KwaZulu-Natal.

IDENTIFICATION

Adult. Male. Upperside: black with bright green markings; lines in cell of forewing are broad and straight. Underside: dusky brown with paler markings as on upperside; hindwing with a transverse red stripe across wing from middle of inner margin to costa. Female. Similar to the male but paler.

Graphium policenes laurentia male underside

Forewing lengths: male 36-44 mm; female 42-44 mm.

Early stages. Egg: pale greenish-yellow; almost spherical, flattened below, diameter 1,0 mm. Larva: first instar dark brownish-grey with dorso-lateral appendages on the thoracic segments; second to fourth instar ferruginous-yellow with black edged transverse stripes, alternately yellow and white; fifth (final) instar ferruginous-yellow with stripes narrower and pale blue in colour. The larva attains a length of 32 mm. Pupa: 24 mm long; green with fine cream lines; somewhat flattened with broad wing-cases; thorax with a large, forward projecting dorsal projection (Clark, 1949: 46; Clark, 1994: 418).

HABITAT AND ECOLOGY

G. (A.) policenes is an inhabitant of coastal forest. The flight is fast and erratic, often punctuated by swift investigations of passing insects or likely food sources. If disturbed it can fly even faster. Numbers can be found sucking at damp sand or feeding on the nectar of flowers while hovering on rapidly vibrating wings.

Males patrol along the edges of suitable bush, usually covering a distance of a kilometre or more. They normally fly from two to three metres above the ground and will chase away any intruders from their territories.

Graphium policenes laurentia early instar larva

Graphium policenes laurentia male upperside on its food plant *Uvaria caffra*

Graphium policenes laurentia final instar larva yellow form

Graphium policenes laurentia final instar larva green form

Graphium policenes laurentia pupa

Females fly almost as swiftly as the males. They will interrupt their flight path to investigate possible food plants, quickly determining with legs and antennae whether or not they are suitable, and will hurriedly lay an egg on a projecting leaf before flying swiftly onwards. The eggs are laid singly on young shoots of the food plant and take some four days to hatch. The larva sits on the mid-rib. There are five larval instars which last about 12 days. In the pre-pupal stage the larva turns green. The pupa is leaf-like and is attached by the cremaster to a silken pad and held upright by the silken girdle around the middle. The pupal stage is variable, taking one week under optimum conditions to several months or more under adverse conditions (Clark, 1949: 46; Clark, 1994: 418).

This species is usually on the wing from September to April.

LARVAL FOOD PLANTS

Uvaria caffra, Artobotrys monteiroae (Annonaceae).

DISTRIBUTION

South Africa, from the northern portions of the Eastern Cape through the KwaZulu-Natal coastal regions to Moçambique and the eastern border of Zimbabwe, northwards into East Africa.

CONSERVATION

G. (A.) policenes is fairly plentiful in the coastal forests of South Africa and is under no threat.

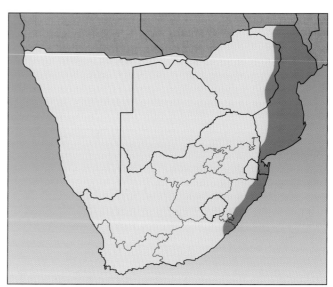

Distribution map of *Graphium policenes*

Graphium (Arisbe) porthaon (Hewitson)

DARK SWORDTAIL

Papilio porthaon Hewitson, 1865. *Exot. Butterfl.* **3**: pl. 7, figs. 21,22.

An inhabitant of woodland and forest from the eastern side of the Afrotropical region. There are three subspecies, the nominate coming from Southern Africa. The other subspecies *tanganyikae* Kielland (1978) comes from western Tanzania and the third *makiei* Collins & Larsen (1991) from Kenya.

Graphium (A.) porthaon porthaon (Hewitson)

Papilio porthaon Hewitson, 1865. *Exot. Butterfl.* **3**: pl. 7, figs. 21, 22. Type locality: Lower Zambezi.

IDENTIFICATION

Adult. Male. Upperside: black with pale creamy-green markings; lines traversing cell very narrow and wavy. Underside: brown with paler markings as on upperside; hindwing with reddish transverse line arising from inner margin, short, usually restricted to cell. Female. Similar to the male but paler.

Forewing lengths: male 39-43 mm; female 42-46 mm.

Early stages. Egg: whitish-yellow when first laid, darkening to yellow-green; almost spherical with a flattened base, diameter 0,8 mm. Larva: first instar blackish-purple, lightening to mauve-grey as it grows, fading to whitish ventrally; head black, tail bifid; first and second segments become paler as larva grows; thoracic segments with paired dorso-lateral spiny processes. It grows from 3 mm to 6 mm in six days. Second instar grey-white with fine transverse dark grey lines close together dorsally (four per segment) which make it appear mauve-grey from a distance; head brown-yellow and first and last segments orange-yellow; thoracic segments each with a pair of dorso-lateral spined processes; tail bifid with a setose process on each half. It grows from 6 mm to 10 mm in four days. Third instar resembles second but has a yellow head. It grows from 10 mm to 17 mm in seven days. Fourth instar pale green ventrally, dorsum finely striped transversely from front with stripes of black, then yellow, black again, then white-blue, black again, yellow again and finally black once more, on each segment; thoracic segments with posterior yellow stripes more pronounced; head, first segment and tail orange; bifid tail tipped with black; same setose processes as in earlier instars but smaller in relation to size of larva. It grows from 17 mm to 28 mm in five to six days. Fifth (final) instar larva has two colour morphs. Dark morph resembles fourth instar but head is brown-yellow, first segment and tail sulphur-yellow and black stripes broadened to give the larva a velvety black appearance when viewed dorsally; dorsal yellow and blue-white stripes broadened laterally

Graphium porthaon porthaon male sucking on damp sand

to give an appearance of a pale lateral band along spiracles; thoracic segments carry dorso-lateral pairs of small black spikes. Green or yellow morph with same shape and processes, and head and ventral surfaces are the same colour as dark morph; differs dorsally in being bright leaf green or yellow with only dark shadows indicating where the previous instar had black transverse stripes; just above spiracles is a pale yellow lateral stripe and a green line along them; thoracic spikes black with yellow bases. Both morphs have a pale blue-green osmeterium. Pupa: green to pale brown with yellow striations and suture lines. Dorsal thoracic projection shorter than *G. policenes* and abdominal expansion less prominent. The above description is based on specimens collected in northern KwaZulu-Natal.

The final instar larva was first briefly described by Aurivillius (1925: 26) and the pupa by Trimen (1889: 209).

HABITAT AND ECOLOGY

G. (A.) porthaon is an inhabitant of coastal and riverine bush, sometimes extending into neighbouring bushveld. The male's flight is fast and erratic, its pale colouring clearly visible. The females fly somewhat slower and not as vigorously than the male. Both sexes can be found on damp sand or feeding on flowers.

The males patrol the edges of forest and woodland, rushing back and forth along a selected stretch, investigating other butterflies or other males during the warmer hours of the day. They normally fly from two to three metres above the ground.

The females fly fast along the edges of the bush in search of suitable food plants on which to lay. When they encounter one, they slow down and go into 'oviposition mode'. The wing-beats become shallower and faster, the wings seeming to quiver, and the legs and antenna tips extended to touch the plant. Selecting a young shoot or preferably a flower or bud, the tip of the abdomen is extended under the leaf or flower bract, to lay a single egg. Several minutes are spent at the food plant, three or four more eggs being laid before the females leave to replenish their energies with nectar. The egg is hidden under a leaf or flower bract. It takes from three to four days to hatch. The young larva becomes visible through the egg shell prior to hatching. The egg shell is not eaten. The young larvae hide in the flower bracts or along the eaten edge of young shoots. Older ones rest on the upperside of a leaf along the midrib, where they are nonetheless hidden by other leaves. The pupa is leaf-like or bark-like and attached by the cremaster to a pad of silk spun on the stem of the food plant. It is held upright by a silken girdle around the middle.

This species is on the wing throughout the warmer months, with December and January being the best time for it.

Graphium porthaon porthaon male drying its wings after eclosion

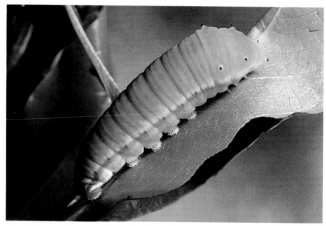

Graphium porthaon porthaon early instar larva

Graphium porthaon porthaon final instar larva green form

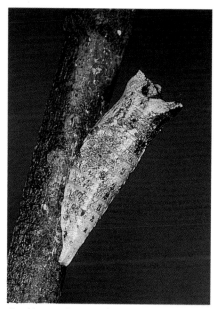

Graphium porthaon porthaon final instar larva
black form

Graphium porthaon porthaon final instar larva
yellow form

Graphium porthaon porthaon pupa

LARVAL FOOD PLANTS

Artobotrys monteiroae, Cleistochlamys kirkii, Friesodielsia obovata, Monodora junodii (Annonaceae).

DISTRIBUTION

South Africa, from KwaZulu-Natal, north of the Tugela River to northern Zululand; Mpumalanga and Northern Province, Moçambique into the lowveld of Zimbabwe, northern Botswana and north-eastern Namibia.

CONSERVATION

G. (A.) porthaon is at the limit of its range where it enters South Africa and is under no threat.

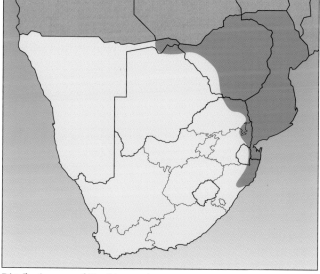

Distribution map of *Graphium porthaon*

Graphium (Arisbe) colonna (Ward)

MAMBA SWORDTAIL

Papilio colonna Ward, 1873. *Entomologist's mon. Mag.* **10**: 151. Type locality: Ribe, British East Africa.

This is an East African species which has its southernmost limits in KwaZulu-Natal.

IDENTIFICATION

Adult. Male. Upperside: black with very narrow bluish-green markings; transverse lines in the forewing cell are straight and narrow. Underside: dark brown with paler markings as on upperside; red transverse stripe on hindwing as in *G. (A.) policenes*. Female. Similar to male but slightly paler.

Forewing lengths: male 38-42 mm; female 41-46 mm.

Early stages. Egg: unrecorded. Larva: third instar mid-brown ventrally, becoming dark chocolate-brown to black dorsally on second and third segments and dorso-laterally on others; head brown; dorsum of first and fourth to thirteenth segments yellow-green to bright green in a distinctive "saddle" pattern on fourth to ninth segments; brown to black coloration spreads dorsally on tenth and eleventh segments; first to third segments and bifid tail carry well-developed pairs of brown-black dorso-lateral projections carrying whitish spiny setae. It attains a length of 10 mm. Fourth instar larva similar in appearance but setose projections smaller in proportion to body and green becoming darker and more leaf-like. It attains a length of 18 mm. Fifth (final) instar still with characteristic saddle marking but thoracic segments invaded by bright leaf green so that dorsal brown is reduced to a series of spots forming broken transverse bands, dark coloration of ninth and tenth segments is maintained albeit much lighter; and the strongly bifid tail and thoracic projections still carry relatively large (compared to other *Graphium* larvae) orange-brown setose processes, the setae now being black. The green may be invaded by yellow to give a mottled effect. Final instar attains a length of 25 mm. Pupa: pale bluish-green stippled with pale brown or yellow; dorso-ventrally flattened with wing-cases broadened and sinuate, the extremities of which bear silver metal marks. This unusual feature has not been recorded in any other member of the family. The above description is based on specimens collected in KwaZulu-Natal.

A partial description of the final instar larva and pupa were given by Trimen (1889: 211) and Monteiro (1891: 217).

HABITAT AND ECOLOGY

G. (A.) colonna is an inhabitant of coastal forest. This species flies fairly fast, low down, in forest shade or along sunlit paths. It is not always as fast as its congeners unless aroused. It is generally found not far from the forest edge and will circle around trees and bushes and often hover to investigate a likely damp patch of sand or flow-

Graphium colonna male underside

ering plant. The white-tipped tails stand out against the dark colouring of this butterfly. Both sexes can be found feeding on flowers and damp sand.

Males flutter along forest margins and do not appear to be strongly territorial. They seldom fly high, keeping usually to about one metre above the ground. They usually patrol a circular path in and about dense bush.

The saddle marking and large setose processes make the larva of this species somewhat similar to that of the well-known European notodontid *Cerula vinula*, the puss moth. It is easily distinguished from all its Southern African congeners and with its distinctive pupa hints that the taxonomy of this species may require further investigation. The pupa is attached by the cremaster to a silken pad and held upright by a silken girdle around the middle. The silken girdle is apparently weak in this species and often breaks, leaving the pupa hanging downwards. This unusual trait coupled with the unique silver metal mark make this pupa appear similar to that of some of the Nymphalids that inhabit the same forests, such as *Euphaedra neophron* (Hopffer). The pupal stage lasts about 15 days.

This species is on the wing from November to February, although specimens can often be found as late as April.

Graphium colonna early instar larva

Graphium colonna final instar larva yellow form

Graphium colonna final instar larva green form

Graphium colonna pupa

LARVAL FOOD PLANTS

Artobotrys sp., possibly *A. monteiroae* or *A. brachypetalus*. It was found breeding on *Uvaria caffra* (Annonaceae) at Makhathini Flats, northern KwaZulu-Natal.

DISTRIBUTION

South Africa, KwaZulu-Natal from Richards Bay through the coastal forests of Zululand, northwards through Moçambique to East Africa.

CONSERVATION

G. (A.) colonna has a limited distribution in South Africa. The coastal forest habitats in KwaZulu-Natal are threatened by the increasing human population. The species is found in several reserves such as Manguzi Forest, Kosi Bay, St. Lucia and Dukuduku.

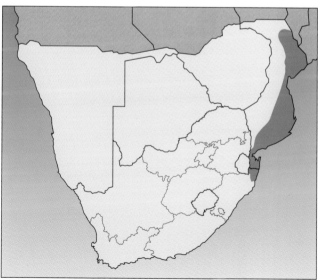

Distribution map of *Graphium colonna*

251

FAMILY PIERIDAE

Most of the butterflies in this family are of medium size, usually with white or yellow black-margined wings, and sometimes with red and yellow patterns beneath. The hindwings are never tailed. They may be distinguished from the Papilionidae, to which they appear to be most closely related, by the absence of an epiphysis on the fore tibia, by the bifid tarsal claws, by the presence of two anal veins in the hindwing, and by the absence of an osmeterium in the larva. As in the Papilionidae, they have six normal functional legs in both sexes, and the pupa is similarly attached by the cremaster and a silken girdle.

The eggs are usually narrowly, but sometimes broadly, spindle-shaped, with flattened base and vertical and horizontal ribs. They are white or yellow when laid and if white, they may change to yellow or orange later. In some species they are deposited singly, but in others are laid in batches of fifty or more. The larvae are slender and cylindrical with short, fine hairs but without fleshy spines or filaments. Their crochets are multiordinal. They are green to reddish-brown in colour, often with longitudinal lateral stripes. Some species are gregarious, usually those species which lay their eggs in batches. The pupae are fastened either horizontally or vertically to a pad of silk by the cremaster and they are supported by a central girdle. The head of the pupa is produced into a median pointed, sometimes forked, projection, and the body may be angular or spined, or the wings may be produced ventrally into a 'keel'. They are usually green, white, yellow or black.

Often the sexes are dimorphic, having different colorations and markings. In many species that fly throughout the year, the wet-season generations are different to those of the dry-season. The wet-season forms are larger and show heavier black markings, while the dry-season broods are small with the dark markings greatly reduced and usually more pinkish-brown undersides. The undersides are often cryptic or leaf-like.

Adult activity is stimulated by strong sunshine and individuals quickly settle when a cloud obscures the sun. They often congregate on moist, muddy or sandy spots where each probes for moisture with its haustellum. Flight is often rapid, but the smaller species usually fly erratically, close to the ground. Migration is a well-developed family trait and, at times, enormous numbers take part in directional flight in Southern Africa. The functions of such mass movements in butterflies still needs much research. Migratory flights may continue for several days at a time, predominantly in one direction, the butterflies resting at night on trees and bushes, often in great numbers and resuming their flight the following day.

There are 59 species of Pieridae in Southern Africa belonging to 13 genera and 2 subfamilies. In South Africa there are 46 species belonging to 13 genera and 2 subfamilies.

A freshly laid *Pontia helice helice* egg, a typical example for the Pieridae

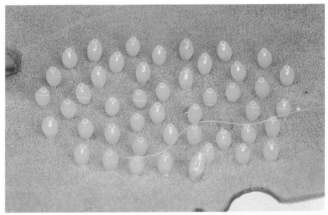

Freshly laid *Mylothris agathina* eggs, a typical example for the 'batch layers' among the Pieridae

A fertile, coloured *Colotis subfasciatus subfasciatus* egg, a typical example for the Pieridae

Colotis eris eris male feeding on *Vernonia* flower

Colotis subfasciatus subfasciatus female feeding on *Vernonia* flower

The wooded savannah of the Northern Province – a favoured habitat for Pieridae, including those depicted above

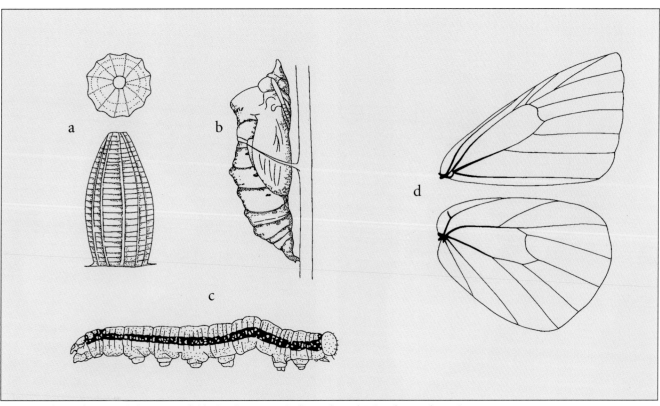

Fig. 27 Family Pieridae. a: Typical egg, top and side view; b: Pupa; c: Final instar larva; d: Wing-shape and venation

KEY TO THE SUBFAMILIES OF THE PIERIDAE

1. Humeral vein of hindwing short, curved inwards, greatly reduced or absent; patagia sclerosed; tegumen shorter than uncus; primary food plants Fabaceae .... Coliadinae

   Humeral vein of hindwing long, well developed and curved outwards; patagia weak and unsclerosed; tegumen longer than uncus; primary food plants Capparaceae and Loranthaceae .... Pierinae

KEY TO THE GENERA OF THE SOUTH AFRICAN COLIADINAE

1. Humeral vein of hindwing present .... *Catopsilia*

   Humeral vein of hindwing absent or greatly reduced 2

2. LHW with one or more pale centred spots at end of cell .... *Colias*

   LHW without pale centred spots at end of cell .... *Eurema*

SUBFAMILY COLIADINAE

Small or large pierids, with their wings frequently yellow or orange. The adults differ from those of the Pierinae in having the antennae relatively shorter; the third segment of the labial palpus is short and usually not hairy. The humeral vein (precostal spur) of the hindwing is greatly reduced or absent, the patagia is sclerosed. The uncus of the male genitalia is more strongly developed than in the Pierinae. Early stages: eggs laid singly. Larvae not gregarious. Larvae cylindrical pale green or yellow with or without stripes. Pupae are smooth with wings produced and meeting ventrally to form a prominent keel. The larvae usually feed on legumes (Caesalpiniaceae, Papilionaceae and Mimosaceae) but sometimes on Guttiferae and Euphorbiaceae. There are 3 genera in Southern Africa, namely *Colias* Fabricius (1807: 284); *Catopsilia* Hübner (1819: 98) and *Eurema* Hübner (1819: 96).

Tribe Coliadini

Genus *Colias* Fabricius

Colias Fabricius, 1807. *Mag. f. Insektenk.* (Illiger) **6**: 284. Type species: *Papilio hyale* Linnaeus, 1758, by designation by the Commission under the Plenary Powers in Opinion 146.

The 'clouded yellows' are a widespread and common genus in most parts of the world. The antennae are less than half the costa of forewing, with the club rather gradual, long and not flattened. Forewing with costa almost straight, except near base, obtusely angled at extremity of R_1, outer margin excurved between apex and middle of area CuA_1. R_1 from cell near middle; R_2 from the stalk of $R_3 + R_{4+5} + M_1$, MDC much shorter than LDC (van Son, 1949: 64).

Early stages: eggs elongate and bottle-shaped, longitudinally ribbed. Larvae elongate, cylindrical, green. Pupae with obtuse cephalic and thoracic prominences. Wing cases not prominently extended.

The larval food plants are generally legumes (Fabaceae) and some species are considered minor pests on commercial crops such as lucerne.

There is only one species found in Southern Africa.

Colias electo (Linnaeus)

AFRICAN CLOUDED YELLOW

Papilio electo Linnaeus, 1763. *Amoen. Acad.* **6**: 405.

A widespread species in Southern Africa through the highlands of the eastern Afrotropical region to Cameroon. Found also in the southern Palaearctic and northern Indo-Australian regions. Commonly known as the clouded yellow, this species is a minor pest on lucerne.

There are six Afrotropical subspecies, of which the nominate is found in Southern Africa.

Colias electo electo male underside

Colias electo electo (Linnaeus)

Papilio electo Linnaeus, 1763. *Amoen. Acad.* **6**: 405. Type locality: South Africa.

IDENTIFICATION

Adult. Male. Upperside: bright orange with black margins. Underside: greenish-yellow with a submarginal row of small spots; discal cell with a prominent white centred spot at end. Female. Upperside: similar to male but orange duller and basal area widely suffused with brownish; margin incorporates some pale spots. Underside: similar to male but darker.

Female form *aurivillius* (Keferstein, 1883. *Verh. zool.-bot. Ges. Wien* **32**: 457) is a greyish to greenish-white female form which occurs throughout the normal range.

Forewing lengths: male 19-25 mm; female 21-26 mm.

Early stages. Egg: pale yellow, changing to orange-red, then dull brown before hatching; diameter 0,4 mm, height 1,1 mm; with 21 longitudinal ribs cross-braced by 36 cross ribs. Larva: first instar pale green and darkens during subsequent instars and a white line develops low down on side; sometimes a broken black line develops in addition to the white one. It attains a length of some 30 mm. Pupa: about 23 mm long; pale green and darker anteriorly, marked with a white stripe and a short, dark stripe on each side of abdomen (Clark, 1949: 66; Clark, 1994: 352; S.F. Henning, 1984b: 35).

HABITAT AND ECOLOGY

C. electo is generally an inhabitant of grassland but is commonly found in disturbed habitats wherever herbaceous legumes grow. It can be found at most altitudes. This ubiquitous insect can be seen in most gardens and is a minor pest of lucerne fields where it can be found in abundance. The males fly fast and low but not as fast as some of the *Colotis*. The female's flight is fairly weak and fluttering. It often settles on flowers, among weeds, grass and even on the ground, usually with closed wings. Specimens are often found feeding on flowers.

Males establish their territories in the vicinity of the larval food plants. Here they fly fairly rapidly, back and forth, patrolling a selected area. Interaction between patrolling males is minimal: at most they circle each other once or twice.

The females fly more slowly than the males and the two female forms occur side by side, although the pale form is generally more scarce. They fly at random near the food plants in search of suitable places on which to oviposit. They investigate each food plant, hovering briefly before settling and swiftly laying an egg. The eggs are laid singly on the leaves of the food plant and hatch after about 6 days. The larva eats its way out of the top of the egg, and after a short rest eats the egg shell as its first meal. When it is young, the little larva lies along the midrib of the leaf, but when it grows too big for this it lies along the stalk where its green colour and the white stripe make it inconspicuous. The first instar larva feeds on the surface, while the later instars all feed on the edge of the leaf. The larva moves in a slow, jerky fashion. The pupa is attached by the cremastral hooks to a pad of silk and is held head upwards by a silken girdle about the middle. The pupa resembles a curled leaf and hangs under a leaf or on a stalk (Clark, 1949: 66; Clark, 1994: 352; S.F. Henning, 1984b: 35).

This species flies throughout the year in most areas but is more prevalent during the warmer months.

Colias electo electo male upperside

LARVAL FOOD PLANTS

Trifolium africanum (clover), *Vicia sativa* (vetches), *Medicago sativa* (lucerne), *Robinia pseudacacia* (Papilionoideae: Fabaceae).

DISTRIBUTION

Throughout Southern Africa northwards through the highlands of eastern and central Africa to south-western Arabia.

TAXONOMY

Populations with unusual coloration in both males and females have been found in the Cape Provinces. The importance of these differences has not yet been fully ascertained.

CONSERVATION

Colias electo is a common species in the Southern African region and is under no threat.

Colias electo electo female form *aurivillius* underside

Colias electo electo final instar larva on its food plant *Medicago sativa* (lucerne)

Colias electo electo pupa (After G.C. Clark 1994)

Colias electo electo female upperside

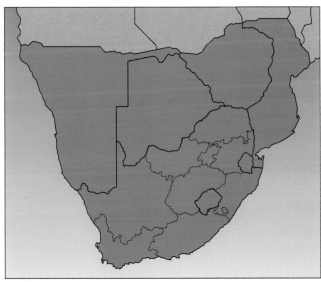

Distribution map of *Colias electo*

257

Genus *Catopsilia* Hübner

Catopsilia Hübner, 1819. *Verz. bek. Schmett.* (7): 98. Type species: *Papilio crocale* Cramer, 1775, selected by Scudder, 1871.

A genus of large, robust species often involved in migratory flights. Antennae short, a little more than one-third length of costa of forewing; club gradual, hollowed out at tip. Forewing with costa arched, outer margin straight or slightly concave below M_3, inner margin rounded basally; R_1 from about middle of cell, R_2 from just before upper angle, R_3 and R_{4+5} on a long stalk, M_1 from about middle of stalk of R_3 and R_{4+5}, M_2 from cell, MDC about half length of LDC, CuA_1 a little nearer to M_3 than CuA_2. Hindwing with costa strongly arched, especially near base, outer margin fairly evenly excurved, tornus slightly produced, anal margin broadly and angularly lobate near base; precostal spur short and curved basad, Sc and Rs arched, M_1 and M_2 separately from cell, UDC and MDC of about equal length and straight, LDC longer and incurved. Males have a fringe of long hairs on the inner margin of the forewing underside. This overlays an oblong sexual patch of specialised scales on the upperside of the hindwing costa. Abdomen short, laterally compressed, hairy at base above, smoothly scaled elsewhere (van Son, 1949: 68).

Early stages: eggs elongate, longitudinally ribbed. Larvae cylindrical with finely granulate skin. Larval headshield granulated with black. Pupae with the cephalic process moderately long and acute. Wing cases not prominently extended.

The larval food plants are generally Senna (Caesalpinioideae: Fabaceae).

There is only one species in our region.

Catopsilia florella (Fabricius)

AFRICAN MIGRANT

Papilio florella Fabricius, 1775. *Syst. Ent.*: 479. Type locality: Sierra Leone.

A common migrant throughout Africa, this well-known species extends its range into tropical Asia. It was described from Sierra Leone in West Africa. The sporadic migrations of this species have been recorded for well over one hundred years.

IDENTIFICATION

Adult. A large robust species. Male. Upperside: greenish-white. Underside: pale brownish-white with numerous small brown striations. Female. Upperside: greenish white to bright yellow. Underside: brownish white to yellowish with striations more prominent than the male. It can be distinguished by lack of male hair-pencil situated on the inner margin of the forewing. Several female forms occur.

Female form *florella* is the predominant one and is either sulphur-yellow or lemon-yellow.

Catopsilia florella male underside

Female form *hyblaea* (Boisduval, 1836. *Spéc. gén. Lépid.* **1**: 612) is whitish yellow.

Female form *pyrene* (Swainson, 1821. *Zool. Ill. Ins.* **1**: pl. 51) is greenish-white like the male.

Forewing lengths: male 28-37 mm; female 25-38 mm.

Early stages. Egg: creamy-white when first laid, changing to yellow; diameter about 0,5 mm, height 1,6 mm; with 16 longitudinal ridges and 45 cross ribs. Larva: first instar creamy-white, while subsequent instars are green and become progressively darker with each moult; fifth (final) instar may be unmarked or may have heavy black markings or even yellow. The larva attains a length of 47 mm. Pupa: 32 mm long; green to pale greenish-brown with a yellow stripe down each side (Clark, 1949: 69; Clark, 1994: 354; S.F. Henning, 1984b: 35).

Catopsilia florella female upperside

HABITAT AND ECOLOGY

C. florella is a common inhabitant of most habitats to be found in Southern Africa, from desert to tropical forest. Its flight is strong, fast and direct, being very active on warm sunny days. A frequent visitor to all sorts of flowers and at damp sand, it can be seen in hundreds at mud puddles during migrations. It is a prodigious migratory species, often flying in millions in a north-easterly direction across Botswana and the northern provinces of South Africa. These migrations usually occur from late November to January.

There is little indication of male territorial behaviour, although patrolling individuals may have a fairly long flight path, so their habits are not readily discernible. A female will investigate a potential food plant fairly briskly and if it proves suitable she will swiftly lay eggs. The eggs are laid singly on leaves or on the tips of the young shoots of the food plant. The larva eats its way out of the top of the egg and then devours the egg shell. The first instar larva sits on the mid-rib of the leaf and feeds by eating a small round hole in the leaf. The later instars feed on the edge of the leaves. When the larva is ready to moult it spins a small pad of silk between two leaves and changes its skin on it. In later instars the larva keeps to the mid-rib. The larva is cryptic green but if it feeds on the yellow flowers of the food plant it may be bright yellow. The larval stage takes about 3 weeks. The pupa is attached by the cremastral hooks and a silken

Catopsilia florella final instar larva on its food plant *Senna petersiana*

Catopsilia florella pupa

259

girdle around the middle which holds it upright. It resembles a curled leaf or a broken stem. The adult emerges after about 12 days (Clark, 1949: 69; Clark, 1994: 354; S.F. Henning, 1984b: 35).

This species is on the wing throughout the year, at least in the warmer localities.

LARVAL FOOD PLANTS

Senna abbreviata, S. didymobotryia, S. italica, S. mimosoides, S. occidentalis, S. petersiana, S. septemtrionalis, S. singueana (Caesalpinioideae: Fabaceae).

DISTRIBUTION

Throughout Southern Africa and northwards throughout the rest of Africa.

CONSERVATION

C. florella is a very common and widespread species and is under no threat.

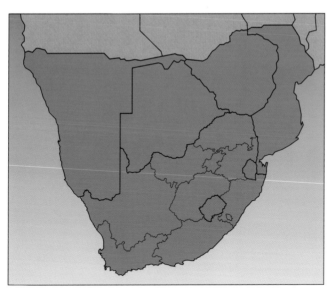

Distribution map of *Catopsilia florella*

Genus *Eurema* Hübner

Eurema Hübner, 1819. *Verz. bek. Schmett.* (6): 96. Type species: *Papilio delia* Cramer, 1780, by selection by Butler, 1870.

The small and delicate 'grass yellows' fly slowly close to the ground with a characteristic erratic flight. Antennae less than two-fifths the length of costa of forewing, with a thin shaft and gradual flattened club. Forewing with four radials: R_1 and R_2 from cell; R_3 stalked with R_{4+5}, M_1 on a short stalk with radials. Hindwing with humeral vein (precostal spur) entirely absent, Rs and M_1 from upper angle of cell, or shortly stalked. Abdomen slender and elongate (van Son, 1949: 70).

Early stages: eggs elongate, longitudinally ribbed. Larvae cylindrical, tapering slightly at both ends. Pupae slender, laterally compressed, acutely pointed at both ends. Wing cases form a prominent convex keel.

Larval food plants are generally legumes (Fabaceae) and Guttiferae.

The males of most species have patches of specialised scales beneath the forewing, near the base, and on the hindwing above. If mounted males are viewed against a strong light the position and shape of these sex brands, when present, can be seen.

There are two subgenera and five species in Southern Africa, namely *E. brigitta* (Stoll), *E. desjardinsii* (Boisduval), *E. hapale* Mabille, *E. regularis* (Butler) and *E. hecabe* (L.). Only *E. hecabe, E. brigitta* and *E. desjardinsii* occur in the Republic of South Africa.

Subgenus *Maiva* Grose-Smith & Kirby is considered synonymous with subgenus *Eurema* by some authors.

KEY TO THE SUBGENERA OF *EUREMA*

1. Male with sex patch on cubitus of forewing; both sexes with black marginal band of forewing usually strongly excised between M_3 and CuA_2 .... *Terias*

   Male without sex patch on cubitus of forewing; marginal band of forewing evenly rounded proximally or reduced to angular subapical patch .... *Maiva*

Subgenus *Terias* Swainson

Terias Swainson, 1821. *Zool. Ill. Ins.* **1**: pl. 22. Type species: *Papilio hecabe* Linnaeus, by original designation.

The male has a sex-patch above and below the base of the cubital vein on the forewing. Tegumen and uncus long.

Eurema (Terias) hecabe (Linnaeus)

COMMON GRASS YELLOW

Papilio (Danaus) hecabe Linnaeus, 1758. *Syst. Nat.* (Ed. 10)
1: 470.

Another widespread species throughout Africa in open habitats and woodland. Its range also extends into Asia where the nominate race occurs. There is one subspecies in the Afrotropical region.

Eurema (T.) hecabe solifera (Butler)

Terias solifera Butler, 1875. *Ann. Mag. nat. Hist.* (4)**15**: 396.
Type locality: Old Calabar, West Africa.

IDENTIFICATION

Adult. Male. Upperside: yellow with black margins, inner edge of which is scalloped and hindwing margin is rounded. Underside: yellow with small brown flecks; forewing with an elliptical patch of specialised grey sex scales near base. Female. Similar to male but usually has a paler ground colour and no sex patch.

Various climatic forms exist which differ in extent of dark markings on upper and under surfaces. Wet-season forms have broader dark markings than dry-season forms.

The dry-season form has been named *bisinuata* (Butler, 1876. *Ann. Mag. nat. Hist.* (4)**18**: 485) and differs on upperside in having a more narrowed marginal band on forewing and in the absence of a continuous hindwing marginal band.

Forewing lengths: male 20-25 mm; female 17-25 mm.

Early stages. Egg: whitish; diameter 0,45 mm, height 1,7 mm; with about 50 longitudinal ribs and 55-60 cross ribs; ribs are fine. Larva: first instar on hatching from the egg is white; second instar pale green above and yellowish beneath; there is a dark green to reddish dorsal stripe edged with yellow; third instar is pale green with a yellowish-white lateral line; fourth instar is darker green with a pale green lateral line; fifth (final) instar green with a dark green to reddish dorsal stripe edged with yellow and a pale yellowish lateral line. It attains a length of 24,5 mm. Pupa: 17,5 mm long; pale watery green at first which deepens to a dull green with brownish markings; wing cases produced strongly to form a prominent keel (Clark & Dickson, 1965: 253; S.F. Henning, 1984b: 36).

HABITAT AND ECOLOGY

E. (T.) hecabe is an inhabitant of open habitats and woodland with incursions into bushveld and forests. Its flight is fairly slow and hopping between the grass and bushes of the favoured habitat. It appears to be faster than *E. (T.) brigitta* and flies higher above the ground. It feeds on flowers and damp sand where it can be found in considerable numbers. Not normally found in migrations, records indicate that they may be induced to join in under certain circumstances.

The males appear to establish their territories around the foot of hills, along rivers and the edges of forest. They patrol all day, mainly in gullies and flats, in search of females.

The females fly at random in search of suitable food plants on which to lay. The eggs are laid singly between rows of small leaflets which at times tend to fold over them and conceal them. The eggs hatch after about 5 days. The first instar larva eats its way out of the egg near the top. It rests on the stalk of the leaves and feeds in minute grooves on the surface of the leaves. Thereafter the leaves are eaten along the edge and in the final instar the entire leaflet is consumed.

Eurema hecabe solifera form *bisinuata* male underside

The larvae spin a silken mat on a stalk when they are ready to pupate. They then secure themselves with their anal-claspers and hang down in a loop to pupate. The larval stages take about a month. The pupa is secured by the cremastral hooks to a silken pad and a silken girdle around the middle holds it upright. The pupal stage takes 12-14 days (Clark & Dickson, 1965: 253; S.F. Henning, 1984b: 36).

This species is on the wing throughout the year, differing slightly in its winter brood.

LARVAL FOOD PLANTS

Hypericum aethiopicum ssp. *sonderi* (Clusiaceae); *Senna mimosoides* (Caesalpinioideae: Fabaceae).

DISTRIBUTION

South Africa, from the Eastern Cape, Lesotho, through KwaZulu-Natal to Northern Province and Mpumalanga, into Botswana, Namibia, Zimbabwe, Swaziland and Moçambique, northwards throughout the rest of the Afrotropical region.

CONSERVATION

E. (T.) hecabe is a common widespread species and is under no threat.

Eurema hecabe solifera form *bisinuata* male upperside

Eurema hecabe solifera final instar larva on its food plant *Senna mimosoides*

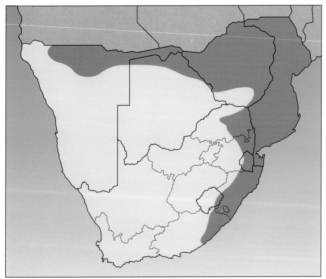

Distribution map of *Eurema hecabe*

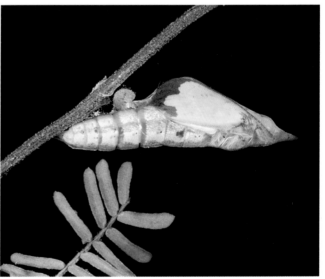

Eurema hecabe solifera pupa shortly before eclosion

Subgenus *Maiva* Grose-Smith & Kirby

Maiva Grose-Smith & Kirby, 1893. *Rhop. Exot.* **24**:96. Type species: *Maiva sulphurea* (= *brigitta*) by monotypy.

The male does not have a sex-patch at the base of the cubital vein on the forewing. Tegumen and uncus very short.

KEY TO THE SPECIES OF THE SUBGENUS *MAIVA*

1. Hindwing with outer margin evenly rounded .... *E. brigitta*

   Hindwing with outer margin distinctly angled .... *E. desjardinsii*

Eurema (Maiva) brigitta (Stoll)

BROAD-BORDERED GRASS YELLOW

Papilio brigitta Stoll, 1780. *Uitl. Kapellen.* **4**: 82, pl. 331.

The African mainland hosts the nominate subspecies while a second subspecies is found on the Indian Ocean islands.

Eurema (M.) brigitta brigitta (Stoll)

Papilio brigitta Stoll, 1780. *Uitl. Kapellen.* **4**: 82, pl. 331. Type locality: Guinea.

IDENTIFICATION

Adult. Male. Upperside: yellow with a broad black margin with inner edge evenly rounded; hindwing margin evenly rounded. Underside: pinkish-buff to yellow with numerous small striations. Female. Similar to the male but duller. The dry-season form is the nominate which has narrower borders and a pinkish-buff underside.

The wet-season form is called *zoe* (Hopffer, 1855. *Mber. dt. Akad. Wiss. Berl.* **1855**: 640) and has a very broad black border and a yellow underside.

Forewing lengths: male 18-22 mm; female 19-24 mm.

Early stages. Egg: pure white; diameter 0,35 mm, height 1,0 mm. Larva: first instar yellow on hatching, changing to green after first feed; fifth (final) instar green with a broad red dorsal stripe, changing later to yellow, lateral line is white edged with purple below, body covered with slightly clubbed hairs on white tubercles. It attains a length of some 20 mm. Pupa: 16,5 mm long; pale green with a pointed head and wing cases extended into a keel (Clark, 1949: 77; Clark, 1994: 356).

Eurema brigitta brigitta form *zoe* male upperside

HABITAT AND ECOLOGY

E. (M.) brigitta is found throughout most habitats of South Africa except the south-western parts of the Western Cape and the Karoo. Its flight is slow and low, seldom higher than a metre above the ground. It tends to go round or under bushes but not over them. If aroused it may fly faster with a more hopping flight. It has been seen to rest under small bushes hanging by one leg only. In this position the slightest breeze makes it flutter and this may deceive potential predators into mistaking it for a dry leaf. Feeding avidly on flowers and damp sand it may also be found sucking the moisture from fresh animal droppings.

Males can be observed in a particular sunny glade for some considerable time but little territoriality has been observed bar the odd circling by two specimens.

The females fly at random in search of suitable food plants on which to lay. They lay their eggs singly on the leaves of the food plant and hatching occurs after 4-5 days. There are five larval instars which last about 20 days in total. The pupa is attached by the cremastral hooks and silken girdle around the middle. The pupal stage lasts about 9 days (Clark, 1949: 77; Clark, 1994: 356).

It flies throughout the year but is usually more plentiful during the warmer months.

LARVAL FOOD PLANTS

Hypericum aethiopicum ssp. *sonderi* (Clusiaceae); *Senna mimosoides* (Caesalpinioideae: Fabaceae).

DISTRIBUTION

Throughout most of South Africa except the dry Karoo regions and the south-western parts of Western Cape, where only the occasional specimen has been recorded. It is found throughout the savannah areas of Southern Africa and northwards in similar habitats through the rest of the Afrotropical region.

CONSERVATION

E. (M.) brigitta is widespread and common and is under no threat.

Eurema brigitta brigitta form *zoe*, undersides of mating pair (female below)

Eurema brigitta brigitta form *zoe* female showing upperside

Eurema brigitta brigitta final instar larva on its food plant *Senna mimosoides*

Eurema brigitta brigitta pupa

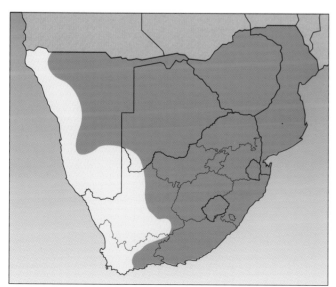

Distribution map of *Eurema brigitta*

Eurema (Maiva) desjardinsii (Boisduval)

ANGLED GRASS YELLOW

Xanthidia desjardinsii Boisduval, 1833. *Faun. ent. de Madag.*: 22.

The species was reviewed by Berger (1980). There are only two subspecies. The nominate subspecies occurs on Madagascar and the Comores. The mainland race is referable to *marshalli*.

E. (M.) desjardinsii marshalli (Butler)

Terias marshalli Butler, 1897. *Proc. zool. Soc. Lond.* **1897**: 851. Type locality: Malvern, KwaZulu-Natal.

IDENTIFICATION

Adult. Male. Upperside: yellow with a black border, inner edge of which is evenly rounded; hindwing margin strongly angled which easily identifies this species. Underside: yellow with brown flecks. Female. Similar to male.

There are a number of climatic forms which are determined by extent of dark markings. Wet-season forms have broader markings than dry-season forms. The extreme wet-season form has been named *pseudoregularis* Berger (1981, *Les Papillons du Zaire*: 83).

Forewing lengths: male 20-23 mm; female 20-24 mm.

Early stages. Egg: very pale translucent blue when first laid, changing to dull yellow; diameter 0,4 mm, height 1,25 mm; with about 40 longitudinal ribs of which a third reach micropyle; cross-braced by very fine ribs. Larva: first instar white in colour with white setae becoming pale green after feeding; second instar is watery green with a divided dorsal stripe; third instar larva pale green with green dorsal and lateral stripes; fourth instar darker green with darker stripes; fifth (final) instar bluish green with darker dorsal and lateral stripes; white lateral ridge-stripe very noticeable owing to ventral parts being bluish. It attains a length of about 23 mm. Pupa: 19 mm long; pale green (Clark & Dickson, 1965: 254).

HABITAT AND ECOLOGY

E. (M.) desjardinsii is an inhabitant of forests and coastal bush. This is a slow-flying species which keeps close to the ground. While being a forest and coastal bush inhabitant it prefers to fly in the sunny glades and avoids the shady areas. The species feeds on flowers or damp sand.

Males occupy a territory in a particular glade for days but interaction with other males appears to be minimal.

The females fly at random, searching for suitable food plants on which to lay. The eggs are laid singly, concealed among the small leaves of the food plant. The eggs hatch after 5-13 days. The larva emerges from the top of the egg. It rests on the midrib of a leaflet

Eurema desjardinsii marshalli underside showing characteristic angled hindwing

Eurema desjardinsii marshalli form *pseudoregularis* male upperside

Eurema desjardinsii marshalli final instar larva (After G.C. Clark 1965)

Eurema desjardinsii marshalli pupa (After G.C. Clark 1965)

and its presence appears to cause the leaves to fold over it. Small troughs are eaten in the leaves. Later the larva eats the edge of the leaves and by the final instar it will eat the entire leaflet. The final instar, when it is ready to pupate, spins a pad on a stalk. It attaches its anal claspers to the pad and hangs curled forward to pupate. The larval stage takes about 5 weeks. The pupa resembles a bud of the food plant. The pupal stage lasts 20 days (Clark & Dickson, 1965: 254).

It flies throughout the year in suitable habitats but is more prevalent during the warmer months.

LARVAL FOOD PLANTS

Hypericum aethiopicum ssp. *sonderi* (Clusiaceae); *Senna mimosoides* (Caesalpinioideae: Fabaceae).

DISTRIBUTION

South Africa, from the eastern regions of the Western Cape, the Eastern Cape, through KwaZulu-Natal to Mpumalanga and Northern Province, Swaziland and northwards into Moçambique and Zimbabwe and most of the Afrotropical region.

CONSERVATION

E. (M.) desjardinsii marshalli is a widespread subspecies and is under no threat.

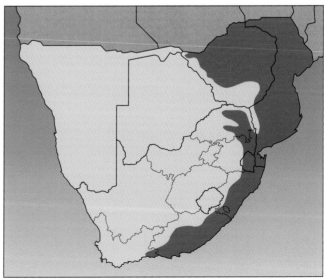

Distribution map of *Eurema desjardinsii*

SUBFAMILY PIERINAE

Small to medium-sized butterflies with white or yellow black-margined wings. The antennae with a distinct, usually widened and flattened club. Palpi with the third joint usually longer than in the Coliadinae. The tarsi with paronychia and pulvilli present. Hindwing with precostal spur well-developed and bent outwards.

Early stages: eggs laid singly or in batches; usually elongate with longitudinal ribs. The larvae may be gregarious or solitary; cylindrical, tapering posteriorly, minutely pubescent and green to brown in colour, usually marked. The pupae are laterally compressed, usually with prominent wing cases and a single cephalic projection. There are often lateral abdominal processes.

The larvae feed on several plant families including Cruciferae, Loranthaceae, Santalaceae, and Capparaceae.

There are two tribes. The Euchloini are mainly Holarctic with only one Afrotropical genus *Pinacopteryx*. All the other Southern African genera belong to the tribe Pierini. There are 10 genera in Southern Africa, namely *Appias* Hübner (1819: 91), *Belenois* Hübner (1819: 92), *Colotis* Hübner (1819: 97), *Dixeia* Talbot (1932: 36), *Eronia* Hübner (1823: 130), *Leptosia* Hübner (1818: 13), *Mylothris* Hübner (1819: 90), *Nepheronia* Butler (1870: 38), *Pinacopteryx* Wallengren (1837: 7) and *Pontia* Fabricius (1807: 283)

KEY TO THE TRIBES OF SUBFAMILY PIERINAE

1. Valve with well-developed harpe which is free at distal end
.... Euchloini

Valve without harpe, or if similar structure present then it is not free at distal end .... Pierini

---

Tribe Euchloini

Genus *Pinacopteryx* Wallengren

Pinacopteryx Wallengren, 1857. *K. svenska VetenskAkad. Handl.* (N.F.) **2**(4): 7. Type species: *Pieris eriphia* Godart, 1819, by selection by Scudder, 1875.

Medium-sized species with white to creamy-yellow wings and black stripes. Forewing with outer margin oblique, apex rounded; Sc very strong, ending at costa before middle; R_1 and R_2 arising separately from cell at about two-thirds from base; R_3 and R_{4+5} on a long stalk, M_1 from stalk of R_3-R_{4+5} at less than one-third of latter from upper angle; M_2 from cell a little below upper angle; MDC very short and oblique, LDC about six times length of MDC and strongly incurved; M_3 from lower angle; cell is about half length of wing; CuA_1 from cell nearer to M_3 than to CuA_2. Hindwing with costa arched; precostal spur very oblique, Rs, M_1 and M_2 separately from cell, MDC about one-third of LDC, the latter slightly angled inwards above middle; M_3 from lower angle of cell, CuA_1 from cell nearer to M_3 than CuA_2; cell shorter than half length of wing. The antennae are less than half the length of costa, with a rather abrupt and flattened club. The male genitalia of this genus is characterised by the presence of a distinct harpe on the inner side of the valve (van Son, 1949: 60).

Early stages: egg broadly cylindrical, spindle-shaped with longitudinal ribs. Eggs laid in small batches. Larva cylindrical, brownish with large prominent protuberances on the second and eleventh segments. Pupae brownish, slender and acute at either end. Wing cases not prominent.

Larval food plants are Capparaceae.

There is only one species of this genus in the Afrotropical region, which also occurs in Southern Africa.

Pinacopteryx eriphia (Godart)

ZEBRA WHITE

Pieris eriphia Godart, 1819. *Encycl. Méth d'Hist. Nat. (Zool.)* **9**: 157.

This widespread and common species has been split into five subspecies throughout the Afrotropical region. The nominate subspecies occurs in Southern Africa.

Pinacopteryx eriphia eriphia (Godart)

Pieris eriphia Godart, 1819. *Encycl. Méth d'Hist. Nat. (Zool.)* **9**: 157. Type locality: [Senegal?].

IDENTIFICATION

Adult. Male. Upperside: creamy-yellow with black transverse patches. Underside: ochre-brown with paler markings as on upperside. Female. Similar to male but ground colour more yellow, and dark markings are brownish.

The dry-season form *nyassae* (Lanz, 1896. *Dt. ent. Z. Iris.* **9**: 123) differs from nominate by reduction of dark markings and a pinkish-brown forewing apex and LHW.

Forewing lengths: male 25-32 mm; female 23-31 mm.

Early stages. Egg: bright yellow developing reddish-brown bands if fertile; elongate with 23 longitudinal ridges. Larva: first instar creamy-white with a lateral pinkish line and a blackish head; second instar pale green with sepia brown lines and a blackish head with small dorsal yellowish-green tubercles; third instar as in second but head pale brown with darker patches; fourth instar pale pinkish-brown, becoming darker later, with a pale dorsal line; fifth (final) instar mottled grey-pink and brown with yellowish protuberances which are largest on the second and eleventh segments. Pupa: narrow and elongate, sharply pointed at each end; greyish-brown darkening to chocolate brown (Clark, 1940: 44; Clark, 1949: 62; Clark, 1994: 350).

Pinacopteryx eriphia eriphia male underside

Pinacopteryx eriphia eriphia final instar larva

Pinacopteryx eriphia eriphia male upperside

Pinacopteryx eriphia eriphia pupa among the leaves of its food plant *Boscia albitrunca*

HABITAT AND ECOLOGY

P. eriphia is an inhabitant of bushveld and savannah. Its flight may be fairly rapid but it is just as often seen fluttering at a low level through the bush. The species feeds on flowers or may be found sucking at damp sand.

Males establish territories near the larval food plants. They may be seen to frequent a particular area for some time, flying back and forth. However, little evidence of defence of their territories has been noted.

Females fly at random through the bush in search of suitable food plants on which to lay. They circle suitable food plants, preferably low bushes, and lay small clusters on the extremities. The eggs are laid on the uppersides of the leaves and take about 8 days to hatch. The larva is stick-like. The first four instars last about 5 days each and the final instar about a week. The pupa resembles a broken twig. The pupal stage lasts about 17 days (Clark, 1940: 44; Clark, 1949: 62; Clark, 1994: 350).

This species is on the wing throughout the year in most habitats.

LARVAL FOOD PLANTS

Boscia albitrunca, B. oleoides, B. salicifolia, Maerua cafra (Capparaceae).

DISTRIBUTION

Widespread throughout Southern Africa except in the southwestern Western Cape and in high-altitude grassveld.

CONSERVATION

P. eriphia is a common and widespread species and is under no threat.

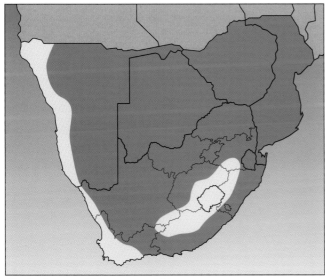

Distribution map of *Pinacopteryx eriphia*

Tribe Pierini

KEY TO THE GENERA OF THE SOUTH AFRICAN PIERINI

1. Forewing with vein M_1 on a long stalk with radials 2

    Forewing with vein M_1 arising from or near upper angle of cell 7

2. Forewing with vein M_2 arising from or very near the upper angle of cell, medial discocellular therefore is short or obsolete. If present it is outwardly oblique (i.e. outer angle formed by it with radial stalk is an obtuse angle) .... *Leptosia*

    Forewing with vein M_2 arising from well below upper angle of cell, medial discocellular well-developed and inwardly oblique (i.e. outer angle formed by it with radial stalk is acute) 3

3. Forewing with three radials (very rarely a short fourth) 4

    Forewing with four radials 5

4. Hindwing with lower discocellular not more than twice length of medial discocellular and almost straight .... *Mylothris*

    Hindwing with lower discocellular much more than twice length of medial discocellular and distinctly incurved .... *Pontia*

5. Forewing with medial discocellulars incurved, upper end at right angles to stalk of M_1 and radials. Male with corema (eversible tuft of spreading hairs) on ventral surface of abdomen between 8th and 9th segments .... *Appias*

    Forewing with medial discocellulars straight and inwardly oblique. Males without corema 6

6. Radials R_3 and R_{4+5} very short .... *Dixeia*

    Radials R_3 and R_{4+5} not very short .... *Belenois*

7. Forewing with four radials .... *Colotis*

    Forewing with five radials 8

8. Forewing with medial discocellular much less than half length of lower discocellular, both strongly incurved .... *Eronia*

    Forewing with medial discocellular half or more length of lower discocellular, lower straight .... *Nepheronia*

Genus *Eronia* Hübner

Eronia Hübner, 1823. *Samml. exot. Schmetterl.* **2**: pl. 130.
Type species: *Eronia cleodora* Hübner, 1823, by monotypy.

Antennae a little less than half the costa of forewing, with a rather gradual, but flattened and distinct club. Forewing with all five radials present: R$_1$ and R$_2$ from cell at about one-third from its base. Arising close to each other, R$_4$ and R$_5$ stalked from R$_3$; R$_3$ from upper angle, M$_1$ from very close to upper angle, MDC much less than half the length of LDC, both strongly incurved. Hindwing with UDC and MDC of about equal length and straight, LDC more than twice the length of MDC, incurved in its upper part (van Son, 1949: 81).

Early stages: eggs very elongate, attenuate towards tip, longitudinally ribbed. Laid singly. Larvae broadest at third segment, tapering gradually posteriorly. Skin finely granular with setae. Pupae with short cephalic projection and laterally compressed with very prominent wing cases.

Larval food plants are Capparaceae.

This genus is confined to the Afrotropical region and is represented by two species, both of which occur in Southern Africa.

KEY TO THE SPECIES OF *ERONIA*

1. Yellow without black borders on upperside; males with large reddish-orange apical patch on forewing .... *E. leda*

    White or pale yellow with black margins on upperside; male without orange apical patch .... *E. cleodora*

Eronia cleodora Hübner

VINE-LEAF VAGRANT

Eronia cleodora Hübner, 1823. *Samml. exot. Schmetterl.* **2**: pl. 130.

An inhabitant of the eastern Afrotropical region from the Eastern Cape to Kenya. It has been separated into two subspecies. The nominate comes from Southern Africa while the subspecies *dilatata* Butler occurs in East Africa.

Eronia cleodora cleodora Hübner

Eronia cleodora Hübner, 1823. *Samml. exot. Schmetterl.* **2**: pl. 130. Type locality: South Africa.

IDENTIFICATION

Adult. Male. Upperside: white with a broad black border. Underside: outer margin of forewing variegated brown and yellow, hindwing chrome yellow with broad variegated-brown border. Female. Similar to male but more yellowish.

A number of seasonal forms have been named all of which intergrade. They are determined by the extent of the dark margins.

Forewing lengths: male 27-33 mm; female 27-37 mm.

Early stages. Egg: very elongate and deeply fluted; diameter 0,6 mm, height 1,5 mm; with 9 or 10 longitudinal ribs and about 24 transverse ribs. Larva: first instar pale yellow, deepening in later instars to green with a white lateral line which becomes edged with red in the final instar. The larva attains a length of about 36 mm. Pupa: green to light greenish-brown with strongly produced wing cases (keel) (Clark, 1949: 85; Clark, 1994: 358).

HABITAT AND ECOLOGY

E. cleodora is an inhabitant of woodland and coastal bush. Its flight is fast and direct, usually one to three metres high along the fringes of the bush. Both sexes feed on flowers or sometimes on damp sand.

Males establish territories near the larval food plants. They have been recorded circling a particular patch of bush during most of the warmer hours of the day. They do not appear to be aggressive.

The females fly at random in search of suitable food plants on which to lay. Eggs are laid singly on the leaves of the food plant and

Eronia cleodora cleodora female upperside on its food plant *Capparis fascicularis*

they can take from 3 to 10 days to hatch. There are five larval instars taking a total of 13 to 20 days. The wing cases of the pupa are strongly produced into a prominent keel making it leaf-like. It is attached by the cremaster to a silken pad and is held in place by a silken girdle around the middle. The pupal stage lasts for about 12 days (Clark, 1949: 85; Clark, 1994: 358).

It flies throughout the year but is more plentiful during the warmer months.

LARVAL FOOD PLANTS

Capparis tomentosa, C. fascicularis (Capparaceae) and *Salvadora* spp. (Salvadoraceae) in East Africa.

Eronia cleodora cleodora female underside

DISTRIBUTION

South Africa, from Port Elizabeth in the Eastern Cape, through KwaZulu-Natal to Mpumalanga and Northern Province. It is also found in Swaziland and Moçambique but apparently not in Zimbabwe. It has been recorded from northern Botswana and occurs in suitable conditions through eastern Africa.

CONSERVATION

E. cleodora is a widespread species and is under no threat.

Eronia cleodora cleodora final instar larva

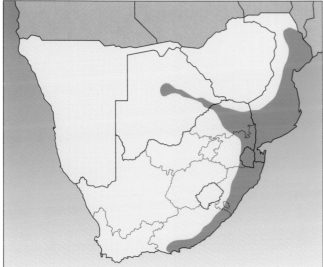

Distribution map of *Eronia cleodora*

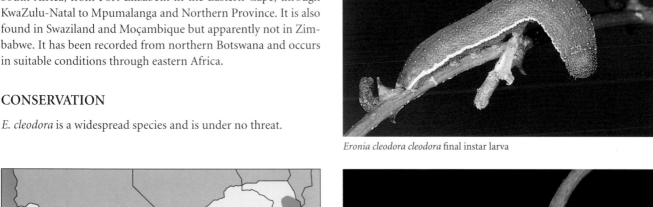

Eronia cleodora cleodora pupa

Eronia leda (Boisduval)

AUTUMN-LEAF VAGRANT

Dryas leda Boisduval, 1847. *Voy. Afr. austr.* **2**: 588. Type locality: Eastern Africa.

IDENTIFICATION

Adult. Male. Upperside: ground colour yellow, forewing with orange tip. Underside: yellow with brown flecks and striations. Female. Upperside: similar to male but forewing has less orange on tip and a subapical series of brown dots. The nominate wet-season female form has no orange on tip. Underside: similar to male but usually more heavily marked.

There are two other female forms depending on the extent of the orange in the tip. All forms intergrade.

Form *trimeni* (Oberthur, 1878. *Étud. d'Ent.,* **III**: 20) is the dry form with a well-developed orange tip.

Form *pupillata* (Strand, 1891, *Ent. Rdsch.* **28**: 137) has an intermediate amount of orange on tip.

Forewing lengths: male 27-33 mm; female 28-35 mm.

Early stages. Egg: pale lemon yellow; diameter 0,5 mm; height 1,8 mm; small, dark brown marks appear on eggshell twelve hours before it hatches. Larva: first instar ochreous at first, becoming greenish with head shiny black and grows to a length of 8 mm; second instar head and body shiny green with fine white setae and grows to a length of 11 mm; third instar head and body dull leaf-green with fine, small, yellow papillae and whitish setae. The larva attains a length of about 35 mm. Pupa: green or brownish, with brown-ringed white spot on underside of abdomen; wing cases strongly produced (keeled).

HABITAT AND ECOLOGY

E. leda is an inhabitant of bushveld and coastal bush. It is a very fast flier, usually two to three metres above the ground. This species is one of the fastest and most direct of the pierids as it wends its way between the trees. It is sometimes found flying lower or more slowly, particularly on partly cloudy days. It rarely settles but will stop to feed on flowers. It has only rarely been recorded on damp sand.

Males establish their territories near the larval food plants. Here they patrol a circuitous course through the bush in search of the elusive females.

The females fly at random through the bush in search of suitable food plants on which to oviposit. The eggs are laid singly on the leaves of the food plant, usually on the edge of a leaf. The egg stage lasts about 12 days. On hatching the larva eats the eggshell as its first meal. The duration of the first instar is about 10 days. The duration of the second instar is 8 days. No further data is available. The larva is leaf-like. The pupa is attached by the cremaster to a silken pad and a silken girdle around the middle supports the pupa.

It is on the wing throughout the year but the winter brood is smaller.

Eronia leda male

Eronia leda form *trimeni* female underside feeding on *Tecomaria capensis*

Eronia leda form *trimeni* female upperside

Eronia leda final instar larva

LARVAL FOOD PLANTS

Capparis tomentosa, C. sepiaria, Capparis spp., *Cadaba* spp. (Capparaceae). In East Africa *Salvadora* spp. (Salvadoraceae) have been recorded as host plants.

DISTRIBUTION

South Africa, from the northern areas of the Eastern Cape through KwaZulu-Natal to Mpumalanga and Northern Province, into Moçambique, Zimbabwe, northern Botswana and northern Namibia and hence through the dry regions of eastern Africa and across to Chad and Nigeria.

CONSERVATION

E. leda is a fairly common and widespread species and is under no threat.

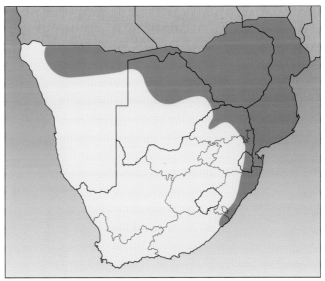

Distribution map of *Eronia leda*

273

Genus *Nepheronia* Butler

Nepheronia Butler, 1870. *Cist. Ent.* **1**:38. Type species: *Pieris idotea* Boisduval, 1836, by original designation.

A small genus containing only a few species but these are large and spectacular and females can be highly variable. Antenna shorter than half of costa of forewing, with gradual, but distinct and somewhat flattened club. Forewing with all five radial branches present: R_1 from cell at two-thirds from base, R_2 from nearer to R_1 than to upper angle of cell; R_4 and R_5 on a long stalk R_3; M_1 from, or from very near, upper angle, MDC more than half the length of LDC. Hindwing with precostal spur strong, bent outwards; LDC twice or less than twice the length of MDC (van Son, 1949: 88).

Early stages: egg elongate barrel-shaped with both ends narrowed, and numerous longitudinal ribs and transverse ridges; a third of the longitudinal ribs reach the micropylar end where they broaden. Larvae cylindrical, finely pubescent, slightly tapering from the third segment to bifid posterior end; glandular setae present which exude a drop of liquid at the tip. Pupa with wing-cases very prominent, forming an extremely high, laterally compressed keel.

Larval food plants belong to the Salvadoraceae, Rhizophoraceae and Hippocrateaceae.

There are four species of *Nepheronia* in Africa. *N. argia* (Fabricius, 1775) and *N. thalassina* (Boisduval, 1836) occur virtually throughout the region while *N. pharis* (Boisduval, 1836) is largely western Africa and *N. buquetii* (Boisduval, 1836) eastern. Only *N. buquetii* is found on Madagascar. All except *buquetii* are forest or woodland species, *buquetii* being found in bushveld and dry woodland.

Nepheronia argia (Fabricius)

LARGE VAGRANT

Pieris argia Fabricius, 1775. *Syst. Ent.*: 470.

The largest of the pierids in Africa, this variable forest species was described from West Africa. The nominate subspecies occurs from West Africa to Zaire and Angola. Subspecies *argolisia* (Stoneham, 1957) is found in Uganda and adjacent Kenya and Tanzania. Subspecies *mhondana* (Suffert, 1904) occurs down the eastern side from Kenya to Zambia, Zimbabwe and Moçambique. This subspecies requires further research. Two subspecies occur in South Africa.

IDENTIFICATION

Adult. Male. Upperside: greenish-white with a black apex. Underside: forewing apex and hindwing pale yellow with a brown subapical patch. Female. Upperside: white with narrow black borders, with or without yellow hindwings, with or without orange bases or patches. Underside: forewing apex and hindwing yellow with brown marginal markings.

Forewing lengths: male 34-40 mm; female 31-42 mm.

KEY TO THE SPECIES OF *NEPHERONIA*

1. LHW with a rounded spot at end of cell
   .... *N. buquetii*

   LHW without a rounded spot at end of cell
   2

2. LHW with a pearly lustre, white or bluish-white; there is a series of small postdiscal black spots between the veins .... *N. thalassina*

   LHW without pearly lustre, yellowish to orange-yellow; there are no postdiscal black spots between the veins .... *N. argia*

Nepheronia argia variegata form *aurora* female upperside

Nepheronia argia variegata G.A. Henning

Nepheronia argia variegata G.A. Henning, 1994. *Pennington's Butterflies of Southern Africa*: 284. Type locality: Manoutsa (Abel Erasmus Pass), Northern Province.

IDENTIFICATION

Adult. Male. Upperside: apical patch narrower than *mhondana* but broader than *varia*; inner edge not as scalloped as *varia*. Underside: hindwing much paler than *varia*. Female. Upperside: with no yellow hindwing specimens known, however many have bright orange patches on hindwing. Underside: bright yellow, apex to forewing and hindwing with brown margins, not as bright as *varia*.

Female form near *aurora* (Suffert, 1904. *Dt. ent. Z. Iris* **17**: 87) with upperside white and an orange base to forewing. Form *aurora* is a female form of *varia*, the distribution of the types is "Natal to Moçambique" thus covering all three subspecies in Southern Africa. It is therefore concluded that the type locality of *aurora* is southern KwaZulu-Natal and within the range of subspecies *varia*.

Female form near *mhondana* (Suffert, 1904. *Dt. ent. Z. Iris* **17**: 86) with upperside white without an orange base to forewing, margins are not as dark or as broad as typical *mhondana*. The type locality of *mhondana* is Mhonda, Tanzania. The entire East African population is currently accepted as subspecies *mhondana*.

Female form *variegata* G.A. Henning, (1994). Upperside: white with orange patches on hindwing, with or without an orange base to forewing.

Forewing lengths: male 34-40 mm; female 31-42 mm.

DISTRIBUTION

South Africa, from Northern Province and Mpumalanga and northern KwaZulu-Natal, Swaziland and southern Moçambique.

Nepheronia argia variegata form *aurora* female freshly emerged clinging to its empty pupal case

Nepheronia argia variegata male

Nepheronia argia variegata pupa among the leaves of its food plant *Hippocratea longipetiolata*

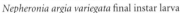

Nepheronia argia variegata final instar larva

Nepheronia argia varia (Trimen)

Eronia varia Trimen, 1864. *Trans. ent. Soc. Lond.* (3) **2**: 175. Type locality: Kaffraria (Eastern Cape Province).

IDENTIFICATION

Adult. Male. Upperside: black apex small, smaller than any other subspecies of *argia*; inner edge of apical patch strongly scalloped. Underside: forewing apex and LHW deep ochreous yellow. Female. Upperside: hindwing yellow, with or without orange forewing bases, strongly represented. Underside: bright yellow with brown markings, brighter than *variegata*.

Female form *aurora* (Suffert, 1904. *Dt. ent. Z. Iris* **17**: 87) The upperside is white with an orange base to the forewing.

Female form *varia* (Trimen, 1864) upperside of hindwing yellow and base of forewing orange.

Female form *oraria* van Son (1949, *Transv. Mus. Mem.* **3**: 91), upperside of hindwing orange and base of forewing orange-red.

Female form near *giara* (Suffert, 1904. *Dt. ent. Z. Iris* **17**: 87), upperside of hindwing light orange-yellow, and no orange at base of forewing. Typical *giara* comes from East Africa and is therefore a form of subspecies *mhondana*.

Female form *hemicrocea* van Son (1949, *Transv. Mus. Mem.* **3**: 91), upperside of hindwing orange, and no orange at base of forewing.

Forewing lengths: male 34-38 mm; female 33-40 mm.

DISTRIBUTION

South Africa, from southern KwaZulu-Natal and Eastern Cape.

Early stages. The following description is from eggs collected at the type locality of subspecies *variegata*. Egg: creamy-white when laid, developing irregular red brown bands in 24 hours if fertile; elongate, attenuated at both ends, diameter at broadest point 1,1 mm, height 2,4 mm; with 14 longitudinal ribs of which only each alternate one reaches micropyle and extends beyond it forming rounded projections, the remainder ending at a little over three quarters the way up; all 14 sections transversely marked by 48 cross ridges. Larva: first instar on hatching salmon coloured with lighter dorsal coloration posteriorly and an olive-brown head, turning green with lighter dorsal coloration extending to all segments and dark brown marks developing laterally; second instar initially maintains light dorsal coloration and dark lateral markings, but later light dorsal colour fades while lateral markings turn black and develop white moles in their centres, head green; third instar similar to second but more glabrous; fourth instar similar barring development of a thin, pale green dorsal median line and the appearance of fine brown stippling throughout; fifth (final) instar grows to 43 mm. The lateral marks lose their definition and turn a pale brown colour while the spiracles become more prominent. It attains a length of some 43 mm. Pupa: 32 mm long; pale green colour with a white 'dusting' particularly along dorsal surface, wing cases prominently keeled, measuring 16 mm from edge to edge at widest point; compressed laterally and delineated along area of hindwing margin by a thin pale yellow line; a pointed process extends forwards and downwards from head (Joannou, in G.A. Henning, 1994).

HABITAT AND ECOLOGY

N. argia is an inhabitant of riverine forest and coastal forest and adjacent woodland. The male is a fast-flying insect, usually at two to three metres above the ground. The females are much slower and fly lower, generally in the vicinity of the food plants. Specimens are often seen feeding on flowers. They have not been recorded hilltopping or feeding on damp sand.

Males patrol territories along the edge of the bush, back and forth over a distance of about half a kilometre. Clearings or dry stream beds are particularly favoured. The territory appears to be established near the food plants.

The females fly at random through the bush in search of suitable food plants on which to oviposit. When they are about to lay, they flutter about the food plant for several minutes investigating many leaves until selecting one on which to lay a single egg, generally near the bottom of the plant. After laying one egg they then swiftly depart.

The eggs are laid on the undersides of the leaves and hatch after about 6 days. The larva exits the egg by way of a small hole which it eats out in the top half of the egg and after an hour's inactivity consumes the rest of the shell. The larval stage lasts about six weeks. When it is ready to pupate it attaches itself to the silk pad, spins a girdle and prepares for pupation which does not occur for a further 2 days. The pupa is attached to a silk pad by its cremastral arrangement and held in place by a girdle. The pupal stage lasts 37 days (Joannou, in G.A. Henning, 1994).

This species is on the wing throughout the year, the winter brood is often more prolific than the summer.

LARVAL FOOD PLANTS

Hippocratea longipetiolata (Celastraceae). In East Africa it has been recorded on *Cassipourea ruwensorensis* (Rhizophoraceae) and *Ritchiea* spp. (Capparaceae).

CONSERVATION

N. argia is a local species in some regions but apparently not threatened.

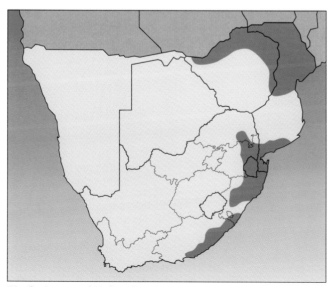

Distribution map of *Nepheronia argia*

Nepheronia buquetii (Boisduval)

BUQUET'S VAGRANT

Callidryas buquetii Boisduval, 1836. *Spéc. gén. Lépid.* **1**: 607.

Three subspecies of this largely eastern Afrotropical species are recognised, the nominate subspecies occurring from South Africa to Ethiopia.

Nepheronia buquetii buquetii (Boisduval)

Callidryas buquetii Boisduval, 1836. *Spéc. gén. Lépid.* **1**: 607. Type locality: Senegal.

IDENTIFICATION

Adult. Male. Upperside: greenish-white with a blackish-brown marginal band on forewing. Underside: greenish-white with light brown striations on the hindwing and a distinct cellular spot. Female. Similar to the male but paler.

Climatic forms are determined by the extent of the dark margins and also the striations of the LHW. Specimens from southern KwaZulu-Natal to the Eastern Cape all appear to have very narrow margins and in this way could possibly be a separate subspecies which would then be *capensis* (Hopffer, 1862. *Reise Mossamb. Ins.*: 363).

Forewing lengths: male 26-32 mm; female 26-32 mm.

Early stages. Egg: white at first, darkening to cream with bands of reddish-brown spots; diameter 0,8 mm, height 2,0 mm; with 24 longitudinal ridges. Larva: first instar very pale green with head slightly tinged with pale brown, neck shield and twelfth segment reddish-brown; second to fourth instars darker green with a pale green dorsal stripe; fifth (final) instar green with a yellow dorsal stripe. It attains a length of about 35 mm. Pupa: green with small, black-ringed, white lateral spots (Clark, 1949: 95; Clark, 1994: 360).

HABITAT AND ECOLOGY

N. buquetii is an inhabitant of bushveld, coastal bush and savannah. Its flight is fast and direct, but not as high as its congeners, normally about one or two metres above the ground. Both sexes often feed on the nectar of flowers.

Males seem to patrol a course around a particular patch of bush but have not been recorded actively defending their territory.

The females fly at random through the bush in search of suitable food plants on which to oviposit. The eggs are laid singly on the uppersides of the leaves of the food plant and take about 8 days to hatch. There are five larval instars. The first four take about 3 days each and the final instar takes about 6 days. Some larvae spend their entire life on the same twig, progressively eating the leaves from the tip downwards. The pupa is attached by the cremaster to a silken

Nepheronia buquetii buquetii male underside

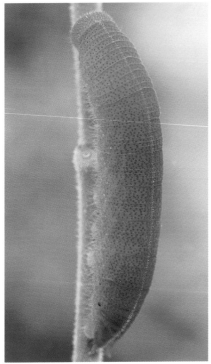

Nepheronia buquetii buquetii final instar larva
(Photo: R. Paré)

Nepheronia buquetii buquetii male showing upperside

pad and a silken girdle around the middle supports the pupa. It is well camouflaged as it is the same colour as the leaves of the food plant. The pupal stage lasts about 12 days (Clark, 1949: 95; Clark, 1994: 360).

It is on the wing throughout the year but more prevalent during the warmer months.

LARVAL FOOD PLANTS

Azima tetracantha, Salvadora persica (Salvadoraceae), also *Capparis* sp. (Capparaceae) in East Africa.

DISTRIBUTION

South Africa, from the Western and Eastern Cape, through Kwa-Zulu-Natal to Mpumalanga and Northern Province, into Swaziland, Moçambique, Zimbabwe, northern Botswana and northern Namibia, northwards to East Africa and from there across to Senegal in West Africa.

CONSERVATION

N. buquetii is a widespread species and is under no threat.

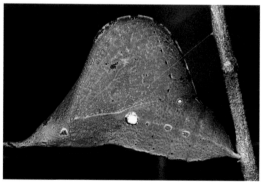

Nepheronia buquetii buquetii pupa (Photo: R. Paré)

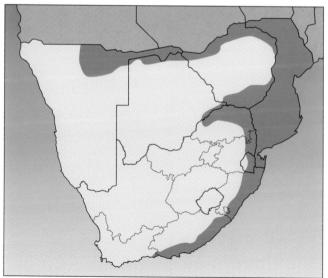

Distribution map of *Nepheronia buquetii*

╌

Nepheronia thalassina (Boisduval)

CAMBRIDGE VAGRANT

Pieris thalassina Boisduval, 1833. *Spéc. gén. Lépid.* **1**: 443.

The pastel blue of the male of this species is unmistakable as it speeds along the edge of a forest glade. There are three subspecies, the nominate being West African, *verulanus* (Ward, 1871) is from central Africa and *sinalata* from East Africa to South Africa.

Nepheronia thalassina sinalata (Suffert)

Eronia thalassina var. *sinalata* Suffert, 1904. *Dt. ent. Z. Iris* **17**: 88. Type locality: 'Dar-es-Salaam', Eastern Africa.

IDENTIFICATION

Adult. Male. Upperside: light greenish-blue with black border on forewing. Underside: pale silvery blue. Female. Upperside: light greenish-white, with or without yellow hindwings. Underside: pale silvery green with forewing basally orange and submarginal black patches.

There are three separate female forms. Form *sinalata* has the hindwing upperside pure yellow; the most plentiful form conforms to nominate *thalassina* and has the hindwing upperside greenish-white; the third form has the outer half of the hindwing upperside yellow and the inner portion greenish-white.

Forewing lengths: male 32-36 mm; female 31-37 mm.

Early stages. Egg: creamy yellow when laid, developing 3 rufous rings if fertile, one around middle and one on either side equidistant from middle to extremities, lower ring being more prominent than other two; height 2,3 mm, diameter 1,1 mm at broadest point which is midway between base and micropyle; strongly attenuated at both ends, marginally more so at the micropyle end. Larva: body salmon coloured on hatching with dark brown head, two prominent protuberances present on 12th segment which are heavily covered with setae at their extremities; setal bases of 1st segment conspicuously larger than those of rest; a brown saddle extends from dorsally on 10th segment, down to level of spiracles, then as a thin lateral line along 11th and 12th segments; dorsal area encircled by this saddle is off-white in colour; later changes colour to green heavily suffused with silver, particularly along dorsal surface, and develops brown marks laterally on 4th segment; dorsal brown on 10th segment disappears although lateral marks on 10th, 11th and 12th segments remain. The first instar grows from 3 to 6 mm in 4 days. Second instar similar to first but head changes to a grey-green colour, has an increase in number of setae and a reduction in extent of dorsal silvering. It grows to 12 mm in a further 4 days. Third instar glabrous, emerald green in colour with a further reduction in width of silver dorsal marking which is now white rather than silver; lateral markings on 4th as well as 10th, 11th and 12th segments change from dark brown to black and are centred with white; protuberances do not appear to grow in size and in relation to overall body length become less conspicuous. It grows to 20 mm in 5 days. Fourth instar loses lustrous appearance of previous stage and is finely speckled with black dots; dorsal line now reduced to a thin pale yellow stripe; protuberances are fused to form a bluntly bifid tail; black coloration of all the lateral markings is greatly reduced and replaced by white. It grows to 27 mm in 5 days. Fifth (final) instar fades in colour to a leaf green (including head) and is now more heavily speckled with brown (black in fourth instar); dorsal line remains although more faded and lateral markings show only vestiges of black outlining the white; bifid tail replaced by a squared end. It grows to 37 mm in 7 days. Pupa: 29 mm long; pale green in colour with only markings present being a thin pale yellow line delineating area of hindwing inner margin and slight black marking on 1st abdominal segment; dorsal surface highlighted by small whitish spots creating a dusting effect; from head extends a thin sharp projection; wing cases compressed laterally and strongly keeled.

HABITAT AND ECOLOGY

N. thalassina is an inhabitant of montane and coastal forest. Its flight is rapid and direct as it travels along the forest margin, often at a considerable height. It makes frequent visits to flowers. The females fly low down amongst the undergrowth and tend to settle quite often. If a specimen is disturbed it will fly directly into the undergrowth and disappear from sight. The species is very fond of flowers. Specimens can often be seen high in the canopy feeding on flowering creepers.

The males patrol a length of forest margin, usually several metres above the ground. They fly fast and investigate and pursue any females which emerge from the undergrowth.

The females fly at random in search of suitable food plants on which to oviposit. A female about to lay will flutter in and out and around the food plant in the undergrowth and will investigate several leaves before selecting one and laying a single egg. Upon completion she flies swiftly away. The egg is laid on the underside of the leaf and takes six days to hatch. The larva eats its way out at the middle of the egg and partially or totally consumes the shell. The pupa is attached to a silk pad by the cremaster and kept at an angle roughly 45° to the vertical by a silken girdle. The pupal stage lasts 24 days.

The species flies throughout the year but the best time for it is during midsummer, December and January.

Nepheronia thalassina sinalata male feeding on *Tecomaria capensis*

Nepheronia thalassina sinalata form *thalassina* female upperside

Nepheronia thalassina sinalata form *sinalata* female on its food plant *Hippocratea longipetiolata*

Nepheronia thalassina sinalata final instar larva

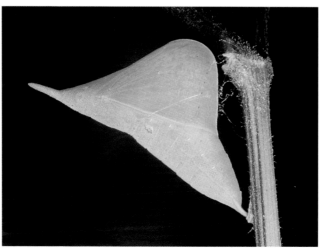

Nepheronia thalassina sinalata pupa

LARVAL FOOD PLANTS

Hippocratea africana var. *richardiana, H. longipetiolata* (Celastraceae); *Jasminum* sp. (Oleaceae).

DISTRIBUTION

South Africa, from northern KwaZulu-Natal to Mpumalanga and Northern Province, into Swaziland, Moçambique and Zimbabwe, northern Botswana and northern Namibia, northwards through East Africa to Ethiopia.

CONSERVATION

N. thalassina sinalata is not threatened at present but loss of forest habitat in South Africa is a possible threat.

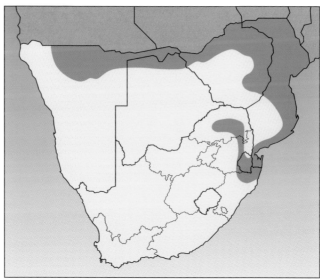

Distribution map of *Nepheronia thalassina*

Genus *Colotis* Hübner

Colotis Hübner, 1819. *Verz. bek. Schmett.* (7): 97. Type species: *Papilio amata* Fabricius, 1775, by selection by Scudder, 1875.

A large and variable genus, they are generally characteristic of the more arid areas of the Afrotropical region. There is considerable sexual and seasonal dimorphism in this genus. The dry-season forms tend to have smaller dark markings and their undersides become a more variegated pinkish or brownish shade. Antennae less than half the length of the costa, with a thin shaft and a well-marked, wide and flattened club. Forewing with four radials, R_1 and R_2 from cell, R_3 stalked with R_{4+5} for more than halfway from cell to apex; M_2 from upper angle, rarely on a very short stalk with the radials. Hindwing with precostal spur very long and strongly curved outwards; Rs from well before upper angle, M_1 from upper angle, M_2 from a little below upper angle, rarely from upper angle or on a short stalk with M_1; LDC usually much more than twice the length of MDC (van Son, 1949: 99).

Early stages: eggs laid singly in most species; elongate, attenuate towards the micropylar end, with a variable number of longitudinal ribs which are connected and braced by numerous cross ridges. Larvae elongate-cylindrical, a little attenuate posteriorly, with last abdominal segment slightly bifid; integument covered with small tubercles bearing glandular setae. Pupae laterally compressed; head conically produced; wing-cases prominent and projecting ventrally; attached by cremaster and encircled by a silken girdle (van Son, 1949: 100).

There are 19 species in Southern Africa namely *C. agoye* (Wallengren), *C. amata* (Fabricius), *C. antevippe* (Boisduval), *C. auxo* (Lucas), *C. celimene* (Lucas), *C. danae* (Fabricius), *C. doubledayi* (Hopffer), *C. eris* (Klug), *C. erone* (Angas), *C. eunoma* (Hopffer), *C. evagore* (Klug), *C. evenina* (Wallengren), *C. euippe* (Linnaeus), *C. ione* (Godart), *C. lais* (Butler), *C. pallene* (Hopffer), *C. regina* (Trimen), *C. subfasciatus* (Swainson) and *C. vesta* (Reiche). Of these 18 species occur in the Republic of South Africa as *C. eunoma* does not extend that far south.

KEY TO THE SUBGENERA OF *COLOTIS*

1. Forewing apex not very acute; aedeagus 1,5 times, or longer, length of tegumen and uncus combined, valve without apex produced and without harpe .... *Colotis*

   Forewing apex acute; aedeagus less than 1,5 times combined length of tegumen and uncus; valve with apex produced, sometimes with rudimentary harpe 2

2. Forewing M_1 stalked with radials, hindwing UDC much shorter than MDC, valve without rudimentary harpe, larva not cylindrical.. *Cuneacolotis* subgen. n.

   Forewing M_1 not stalked with radials, hindwing UDC not much shorter than MDC, valve sometimes with rudimentary harpe, larva cylindrical .... *Teracolus*

Subgenus *Colotis* Hübner

Colotis Hübner, 1819. *Verz. bek. Schmett.* (7): 97. Type species: *Papilio amata* Fabricius, 1775, by selection by Scudder, 1875.

Forewing apex not very acute; M_1 sometimes stalked with radials; aedeagus 1,5 times, or longer, length of tegumen and uncus combined; valve without apex produced and without harpe.

Egg with ten to twelve longitudinal ribs; wing-cases more prominent than in subgenera *Teracolus* or *Cuneacolotis*.

KEY TO THE SUBGENUS *COLOTIS*

(Most characters apply to both sexes but where females are distinctly dimorphic the distinguishing characteristics can be found under the relevant species in the text. (M) behind a characteristic in the key denotes for a male only.)

1. Forewing discocellular spot very large, extending across entire width of cell 2

   Forewing without large discocellular spot extending across width of cell 4

2. UHW with prominent dark discal band .... *C. vesta*

   UHW without dark band 3

3. UHW with veins darkened from base to margin .... *C. doubledayi*

   UHW with veins not darkened .... *C. amata*

4. UFW with small yellowish-white marginal spots distal to apical patch .... *C. celimene*

   UFW apical patch without small yellowish-white marginal spots 5

5. UFW apical patch violet-blue or purple (M), large species 6

   UFW apical patch not violet-blue or purple, small to medium species 8

6. Apical purple patch very broad (60 mm) (M), very large species .... *C. regina*

   Apical purple patch not very broad (50 mm) (M), not a very large species 7

7. Apical patch with small distal marginal marks .... *C. ione*

   Apical patch without distal marginal marks .... *C. erone*

8. LHW with distinctly defined discal spots .... *C. danae*

   LHW without distinctly defined discal spots 9

9. UFW apical patch orange-red 10

   UFW apical patch orange or yellowish-orange or ochreous 11

10. Forewing discocellular spot present, hindwing dark postdiscal band absent (M) .... *C. antevippe*

    Forewing discocellular spot absent, or dark postdiscal band present (M) .... *C. euippe*

11. Ground colour yellow .... *C. auxo*

    Ground colour white 12

12. Forewing apical patch large and yellowish-orange, discocellular spot absent, medium-sized species .... *C. evenina*

    Forewing apical patch orange, discocellular spot generally present, small-sized species 13

13. LFW apical area orange, LHW without irroration in cell .... *C. evagore*

    LFW apical area without orange or if orange then LHW with irroration in cell 14

14. UFW apical patch orange with purplish pink sheen .... *C. pallene*

    UFW apical patch dull ochre-orange without sheen .... *C. lais*

Colotis (Colotis) amata (Fabricius, 1775) species group

ARAB TIPS

A small group comprising three species; *amata*, *phisadia* (Godart, 1819) and *vestalis* (Butler, 1876). Only *amata* is found in Southern Africa. This group usually includes the following one but the differences are such that we feel that they should be separated. Major differences are the lack of white basal area in the male uppersides, the lack of markings on the LHW and the shape of the wings. The food plant is exclusively Salvadoraceae. *C. (C.) amata* lays eggs in batches while *C. (C.) vestalis* lays eggs singly.

Colotis (Colotis) amata (Fabricius)

TOPAZ ARAB TIP

Papilio amata Fabricius, 1775. *Syst. Ent.* : 202.

Described from India, this widespread species occurs in most of the dry areas across the Afrotropical region, Arabia and India. There are three subspecies in the Afrotropical region, the nominate from India. The Madagascan subspecies is *crowleyi* Sharpe, 1898. On the mainland subspecies *williami* G.A. & S.F. Henning, 1994, occurs in Namibia and *calais* Cramer, 1775, is found across the northern parts of the Afrotropical region and down the eastern side to South Africa.

Colotis (C.) amata calais (Cramer)

Papilio calais Cramer, 1775. *Uitl. Kapellen* **1**: 84. Type locality: "Cape of Good Hope" = *patria falsa*.

IDENTIFICATION

Adult. Male. Upperside: pinkish-buff with black marginal markings. Underside: yellow with faint markings. Female. Upperside: similar to male but ground colour is much paler distally and rosy basally. Underside: similar to male but markings more conspicuous.

The dry-season form *dynamene* (Klug, 1829. *Symb. Phys.*: pl. 6) differs from the nominate wet-season form in having less extensive black markings and an ochreous underside.

Forewing lengths: male 13-22 mm; female 17-25 mm.

Early stages. Egg: yellow. Larva: green with a darker green to cream dorsal stripe. Pupa: variable in colour from pale green to yellowish-brown with black dots (Butler, 1896. *Proc. zool. Soc. Lond.*: 245).

HABITAT AND ECOLOGY

C. (C.) amata is an inhabitant of arid bushveld. It flies fairly slowly, low down, among the thorn trees. However, it can accelerate quickly if necessary and disappear into the arid habitat it prefers. They are frequently found in good numbers on roadside flowers, particularly at the Saltpan at the north-western end of the Soutpansberg. Both sexes are frequently found on flowers.

The males establish small territories near the larval food plants. Here they fly for many hours, settling periodically on the ground to rest.

The females fly at random in search of suitable food plants on which to lay. A female about to lay will flutter around a tree of its food plant about one to two metres from the ground if it is tall enough. After investigating a number of leaves she will select a leaf on the outside of the tree and, with painstaking precision, will

Colotis amata calais male

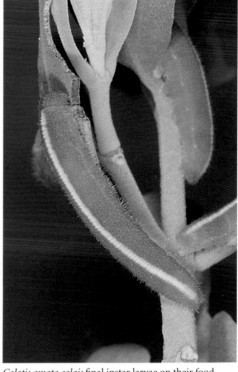

Colotis amata calais final instar larvae on their food plant *Salvadora persica*

Colotis amata calais female upperside

Colotis amata calais pupa

lay a small batch of eggs, hurrying away when the job is completed. The eggs are laid in batches of 20 to 30. The larvae are gregarious for at least half of the larval stage. The pupae are cryptically coloured and leaf-like. They are attached by the cremaster to a silken pad and have a silken girdle around the middle which holds them upright.

This species is on the wing throughout the year, being most abundant from March to May.

LARVAL FOOD PLANTS

Salvadora persica (Salvadoraceae).

DISTRIBUTION

South Africa, from northern KwaZulu-Natal to Mpumalanga and Northern Province, into Moçambique, Zimbabwe and northern Botswana, northwards into East Africa and across the northern parts of the Afrotropical region.

CONSERVATION

C. (C.) amata calais is a widespread species and is under no threat.

Distribution map of *Colotis amata*

Colotis (C.) chrysonome (Klug, 1829) species group

VEINED TIPS

This group consists of five species; *C. chrysonome*, *C. aurigineus* (Butler, 1883), *C. ungemachi* (le Cerf, 1922), *C. doubledayi* (Hopffer, 1862) and *C. vesta* (Reiche, 1849). Two of this group occur in Southern Africa. These species are usually included under the *amata* group but the differences discussed under that group indicate that they should be separate. Food plants are Capparaceae.

Colotis (Colotis) doubledayi (Hopffer)

DOUBLEDAY'S VEINED TIP

Idmias doubledayi Hopffer, 1862. *Reise Mossamb. Ins.* V: 363.

Described from West Africa the southern, more arid, subspecies just enters South Africa along the Orange River at Viool's Drift, from there it is found sporadically northwards through the western desert region of Namibia up to Kaokoland. It was thought that the Southern African representative was referable to *C. (C.) doubledayi angolanus* (Talbot) (*Teracolus aurigineus angolanus* Talbot, 1929. *Bull. Hill Mus. Witley* 3: 72. Type locality: Lobito Bay, Angola) but with the examination of true *angolanus* it is apparent that the more southern representative is a distinct subspecies.

Colotis (C.) doubledayi flavulus ssp. n.

DIAGNOSIS

Smaller than *angolanus*, wing shape not as elongate. Upperside: more ochreous than *angolanus* in both sexes and dark markings reduced. Underside: forewing orange basal area much more extensive than *angolanus*. Hindwing markings diffuse and barely discernible. In a few wet-season form specimens from Kaokoland the underside markings are discernible but not even as well defined as the dry-season form specimens of *angolanus*.

DESCRIPTION

Adult. Male. Upperside: dull yellowish-cream with a yellowish-white basal area, wider in forewing; prominently darkened veins. Forewing with a dark brown discocellular mark and a jagged postdiscal band of same colour; margin broadly dark brown on veins leaving rounded marginal spots of ground colour. Hindwing unmarked except for darkened veins which widen at outer margin, leaving semicircular marginal spots of ground colour; costal area may be broadly darkened and there may be a brownish suffusion discally. Underside: ochreous-yellow with faint markings on hindwing and darker markings on forewing. Forewing suffused with orange in cell and adjoining discal area; discocellular mark roughly crescentic, dark brown, smaller than upperside; postdiscal spots often darkened as is submarginal mark at tornus; other markings as on upperside but heavily diffused with ochreous which in some cases makes them hardly discernible. Hindwing without any dark markings; cell with a faint orange suffusion; discal area with a faint ochreous band and a faint ochreous submarginal widening of ochreous veins. Female. Upperside: similar to male but with ground colour more ochreous and largely lacking yellowish-white basal colouring, this being replaced by a greyish basal suffusion; hindwing discal suffusion darker and better developed into a series of diffuse discal 'v'-shaped marks. Underside: similar to male.

No wet-season form specimens have been recorded in the hundreds of specimens collected throughout the year at the type locality.

Forewing lengths: male 19,5-22 mm; female 19,5-23 mm.

MATERIAL EXAMINED

Holotype male. South Africa: Viool's Drift, Northern Cape Province, 29.ix.1967, K.M. Pennington. Paratypes: 11 males, 2 females, same data as holotype; 2 males same data but 14.i.1962; 10 males same data but 26.ix.1961, R. Badham; 6 males, 4 females same data but 6-10.vii.1961, van Son & Vári; 2 males, 1 female same data but 6-13.x.1971, Snyman & Jones; 6 males 2 females same data but 18-20.ix.1964, D.A. Swanepoel; 4 males same data but 2.x.1971, D.M. Kroon; 4 males same data but 1.x.1987, N.K. Owen-Johnston; 3 females 6-7.xi.1987, N.K. Owen-Johnston (bred); 2 males same data but 27.ix.1961, W. Teare; 1 male same data but 25.iv.62, W. Teare; 1 female same data but 27.vii.1961, W. Teare; 1 female same data but 16.x.1962, C.R. Barrett. Holotype male in Transvaal Museum; paratypes in Transvaal Museum, Henning Collection and Owen-Johnston Collection.

Other material examined: Namibia; Niam Hills/Keetmanshoop, Namib Desert, Blutkuppe, Kuiseb Canyon, 35 km E. of Orapembe Kaokoland, Ai Ais, Spitzkoppe.

C. (C.) doubledayi angolanus: Angola; Belas Rd. 10 km S. of Luanda and Luanda.

The holotype male is pictured in *Pennington's Butterflies of Southern Africa* 1994 as *Colotis doubledayi angolanus* (Plate 164, fig. 671 ai).

Early stages. Described from specimens collected at the type locality. Egg: pale yellow in colour; elongate, attenuate towards micropylar end, longitu-

dinally ribbed. Larva: fourth instar at first grey-green with yellowish dorsal coloration, pubescent, head grey with green shading laterally; later becoming more glabrous and developing a conspicuous white median stripe dorsally; this stripe bulges somewhat in middle of each segment with portion between bulges tinged with green; last segment with a small inconspicuous bifid process. This stage grows from at least 6 mm to 11 mm in about 4 days. Fifth (final) instar grey-green in colour, initially without dorsal stripe; as development proceeds stripe reappears and is even more pronounced than before, colour now whitish-yellow and faintly outlined with black. Shortly prior to pupation the dorsal stripe again changes colour, this time to a dark pink. Final instar lasts 5 days and attains a length of 21 mm. Pupa: straw-coloured with faint dark markings; ventral thoracic keel pronounced and wing cases laterally compressed; head well-defined and bears a short dorso-laterally depressed process approximately half the body width. When viewed laterally however this process is so short and thin that it appears as an insignificant 'beak'. It measures 10 mm from the costal margin to the area of the outer wing margin and 12 mm from tip of cephalic process to cremaster (In part by S.F. & G.A. Henning, 1989: 145, as *angolanus*).

HABITAT AND ECOLOGY

C. (C.) doubledayi flavulus is an inhabitant of arid, broken veld. It flies fairly rapidly, close to the ground, visiting small flowering shrubs. It inhabits stony valleys that run into the Orange River at Viool's Drift. It was observed there in numbers flying up and down a dry stream bed. It seldom stopped to rest or feed. It is often seen feeding on the nectar of flowers.

The males establish their territories near the larval food plants. Here they are usually seen patrolling two to three metres above the

Colotis doubledayi flavulus female underside (Paratype)

ground, up and down the dry gullies.

The females fly at random in search of suitable food plants on which to lay. Once found, they flutter among the branches of the food plant searching for a suitable leaf on which to lay. The eggs are laid singly on the leaves of the food plant. The period between the discovery of the eggs (of undetermined age) described above and pupation was 27 days. When not feeding the larvae are in the habit of resting in a trough on the leaf edge which has been eaten out, exactly the length and depth of the insect, giving the impression of an uninterrupted leaf margin. The pupa is straw-coloured, attached by its cremaster to a base of silk and held in an acutely inclined position by a girdle. The pupal stage lasts 9 days. On emerging the insect crawls to the middle of a sprig, finds adequate clearance and whilst hanging upside down, pumps the wings to maximum size within 45 seconds. For the next 30 minutes it remains hanging, intermittently swinging itself from side to side and adjusting its position whenever it makes contact with leaves.

It flies throughout the year but is more plentiful in September and October and again in April and May.

LARVAL FOOD PLANTS

Maerua schinzii (Capparaceae).

DISTRIBUTION

South Africa, at Viool's Drift, northern Namaqualand and through western Namibia.

CONSERVATION

C. (C.) doubledayi flavulus (as *angolanus*) is classified as rare in the *South African Red Data Book – Butterflies* by S.F. & G.A. Henning (1989: 144). In South Africa it is restricted to Viool's Drift. No immediate threats are apparent but it is felt by some conservationists that the area around Viool's Drift is valuable enough to warrant the proclamation of a nature reserve. Should the venture come to fruition this species will then be assured of a place in which to live where future generations may see the butterfly.

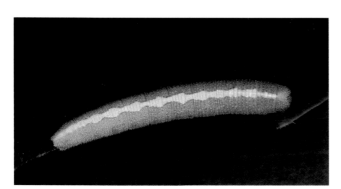

Colotis doubledayi flavulus final instar larva

Colotis doubledayi flavulus pupa detached from original pupation site

Colotis doubledayi flavulus female upperside (Paratype)

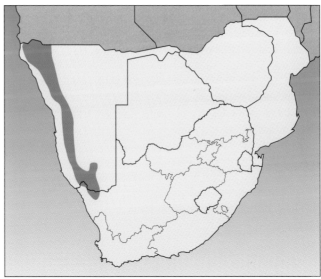

Distribution map of *Colotis doubledayi*

Colotis (Colotis) vesta (Reiche)

VEINED TIP

Idmias vesta Reiche, 1849. *Ferr. Gal. Voy. Abyss. Ent.*: 460.

Various climatic forms have been named which vary in the extent of the dark markings and underside coloration. Nine subspecies are recognised throughout Africa, with the nominate subspecies described from Ethiopia. Two subspecies occur in Southern Africa. One of these, *argillaceus* (Butler, 1877: 459), is found in South Africa while the second, *mutans* (Butler, 1877: 459), occurs in Zimbabwe, northern Botswana and Namibia.

Colotis (C.) vesta argillaceus (Butler)

Teracolus argillaceus Butler, 1877. *Ann. Mag. nat. Hist.* (4) **19**: 459. Type locality: KwaZulu-Natal.

IDENTIFICATION

Adult. Male. Upperside: ochreous-yellow with a black post-discal band joined to a broad margin by black along veins; basal area greyish-white. Underside: yellow to ochre with upperside dark markings ochreous-brown. Female. Upperside: similar to male but with greyish-white area reduced or absent. Underside: similar to male.

The wet-season form *pluvius* Talbot (1939, *Trans. R. ent. Soc. Lond.* **88**: 178) differs from the nominate dry-season form in having all dark markings prominent and ground colour of LHW sulphur yellow.

Forewing lengths: male 18-25 mm; female 20-26 mm.

Early stages. Egg: white when first laid, changing to pale yellow as development proceeds; diameter 0,45 mm; height 0,75 mm; with 16 longitudinal ribs, nine of which reach the micropyle; ribs cross braced by about 24 fine ribs. Some eggs may be blotched with pale salmon. Larva: first instar larva on hatching from the egg is about 1,5 mm long and pale yellow; second instar pale green with a light green dorsal stripe; third instar green with a yellow bordered whitish dorsal stripe; fourth instar green with a solid yellow dorsal stripe and a faint whitish green lateral line; fifth (final) instar green with dorsal stripe fragmented into alternate white and yellow blotches, lateral line white and wider forming a patch on seventh segment. It attains a length of 23 mm. Just prior to pupation the larva changes its colour to lilac. Pupa: 13,5 mm long; variable in colour from light green to light brown; wing cases extended and crossed by a diagonal creamy-white stripe; thorax with a creamy white lateral line on thorax (Clark & Dickson, 1967: 39; S.F. Henning, 1984b: 36).

HABITAT AND ECOLOGY

C. (C.) vesta argillaceus is an inhabitant of savannah, bushveld and woodland. It usually flies fairly slowly close to the ground. If disturbed it can move quite quickly. It will seldom fly above a metre from the ground unless it ascends to flowers in the trees. Specimens are frequently seen feeding at flowers.

The males establish their territories near the larval food plants. Here they may be seen circling about tall bushes, hovering and gliding in the sun about three metres above the ground. They frequently descend to rest on grass stems, or sometimes on the ground. The females fly at random in search of suitable food plants on which to lay. The eggs are laid singly on the leaves of the food plant and take about 4 days to hatch. The early larvae are pale yellow and feed on the younger leaves. The later instars feed on the edge of a leaf, occupying that part that is eaten away, with the dorsal stripe matching the missing edge. The final instar larvae are large enough to devour an entire leaf. The larval stage lasts about 18 days. The pupa is cryptically coloured. It is secured by the cremastral hooks to a silken pad and is held upright by a silken girdle around the middle. The pupal stage lasts from 6-11 days (Clark & Dickson, 1967: 39; S.F. Henning, 1984b: 36).

This species is on the wing throughout the year.

Colotis vesta argillaceus male underside feeding on *Aptenia* species

LARVAL FOOD PLANTS

Maerua angolensis (Cappa-raceae). In East Africa it has also been recorded on *Capparis* sp., *Boscia* sp., *Ritchiea* sp. (Cap-paraceae) and *Salvadora* sp. (Salvadoraceae).

DISTRIBUTION

South Africa, from KwaZulu-Natal north of Durban, to Mpumalanga, Northern and North-West Provinces and southern Moçambique and southern Zimbabwe.

CONSERVATION

C. (C.) vesta argillaceus is a common, widespread species and is under no threat.

Colotis vesta argillaceus male upperside

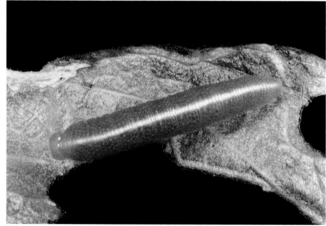

Colotis vesta argillaceus final instar larva

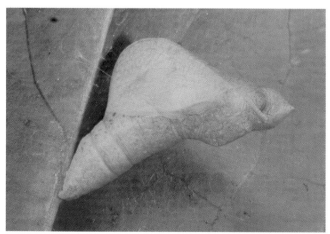

Colotis vesta argillaceus pupa

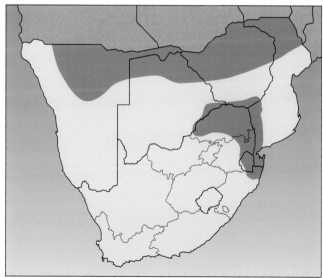

Distribution map of *Colotis vesta*

289

Colotis (C.) pleione (Klug, 1828) species group

LILAC TIPS

Although *C. celimene* (Lucas, 1852) is usually allocated its own species group we consider it to be closely related to the above group. The *pleione* group therefore consists of five species; *C. pleione, C. halimede* (Klug, 1829), *C. venosa* (Staudinger, 1885), *C. zoe* (Grandidier, 1867) and *C. celimene*. Only *C. celimene* is found in Southern Africa.

Colotis (Colotis) celimene (Lucas)

LILAC TIP

Anthocharis celimene Lucas, 1852. *Rev. Mag. Zool.* **2**: 426.

A species widespread throughout the eastern Afrotropical region. There are six subspecies with the nominate, described from Ethiopia, occurring throughout East Africa to Malawi. Two subspecies come from Southern Africa, *pholoe* (Wallengren, 1860) occurs in Namibia and Angola, while *amina* (Hewitson, 1866) is found in Zimbabwe and South Africa.

Colotis (C.) celimene amina (Hewitson)

Anthocharis amina Hewitson, 1866. *Exot. Butterfl.* **3**: pl.5. Type locality: Zambezi.

IDENTIFICATION

Adult. Male. Upperside: white with crimson-lake tip and black margins on hindwing. Underside: hindwing and apical area of forewing yellow with brown margin and brown longitudinal lines; crimson patch subapically. Female. Upperside: similar to male but crimson tip replaced with black and white. Underside: similar to male.

Forewing lengths: male 19-25 mm; female 19-24 mm.

Early stages. The early stages were recorded by F.J. Swart pers. comm. for subspecies *pholoe*. Egg: White when first laid, changing to red by the second day, 1,2 mm long by 0,4 mm in diameter. Larva: First instar light green, 2 mm on emergence. Fourth instar light green with a light cream mid-dorsal line, grew to 10 mm long. Fifth (final) instar green, broader over the abdominal segments, tapering slightly posteriorly. Similar in appearance to the larva of *C. (C.) danae annae* but without lateral oblique spots on segments seven and eight. Final length 18 mm. Pupa: Pale yellow, 18 mm long, lat-

Colotis celimene amina male feeding on *Scabiosa columbaria*

erally compressed with projecting wing-cases, pronounced dorso-thoracic elrvation, cephalic projection small. Similar in general appearance to the pupa of *C. danae annae* but with a more pronounced dorso-thoracic hump and completely pale yellow in colour.

HABITAT AND ECOLOGY

C. (C.) celimene is a local bushveld species. When not patrolling its territory the male flies like many other *Colotis*. The female is probably often overlooked due to its similarity to various *Belenois*. Specimens are often recorded feeding on nectar from flowers.

The males establish their territory on the sunny side of a large tree. They exhibit a peculiar hovering flight about three to five metres above the ground, and will hover back and forth or in circles up to three metres from the tree. They will hover in this fashion throughout the midday hours, occasionally settling on the ground or chasing intruders. The tree selected is often the food plant *Boscia albitrunca*, although *Acacias* are also used as is *Xanthocercis zambesiaca*. Males hovering around a tree can be identified from far away and even from a fast-moving vehicle.

The females fly at random through the bush in search of suitable food plants on which to oviposit.

Information on early stages recorded by F.J. Swart (pers. comm.) for subspecies *pholoe*. Eggs laid singly on green tender leaf. Egg hatched after six days. First instar larva ate the egg shell as its first meal. Fourth instar larva found on food plant, *Boscia albitrunca*, fed for about a week and was in the pupal stage for ten days. It pupated on a vertical surface, head upwards, and was supported by a silken girdle.

This species is on the wing throughout the year, with February to March probably the best time to see them.

LARVAL FOOD PLANTS

Boscia albitrunca, B. salicifolia (Capparaceae). Other subspecies have been recorded on *Capparis* sp. (Capparaceae).

DISTRIBUTION

South Africa, from the KwaZulu-Natal midlands to Mpumalanga, Northern and North-West Provinces, Swaziland, Zimbabwe, Moçambique and eastern Botswana, and northwards.

CONSERVATION

C. (C.) celimene is a rare species but fairly widespread and not threatened.

Colotis celimene amina female upperside

Colotis celimene amina female underside

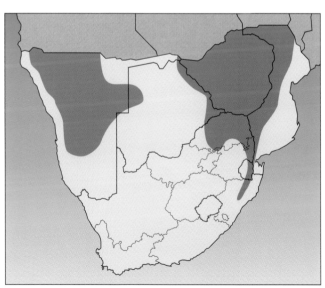

Distribution map of *Colotis celimene*

291

Colotis (C.) ione (Godart, 1819) species group

PURPLE TIPS

A species group of six species, three of which occur in Southern Africa and another extends into Moçambique. The group consists of the following species *C. (C.) ione*, *C. (C.) erone* (Angas, 1849), *C. (C.) regina* (Trimen, 1863), *C. (C.) hetaera* (Gerstaecker, 1871), *C. (C.) eunoma* (Hopffer, 1855), *C. (C.) elgonensis* (Grose-Smith, 1891). *C. (C.) ione*, *C. (C.) erone* and *C. (C.) regina* all occur in the Republic of South Africa, while *C. (C.) eunoma* comes from Moçambique.

Colotis (Colotis) erone (Angas)

COAST PURPLE TIP

Anthocharis erone Angas, 1849. *Kafirs Illustr.* pl. 30. Type locality: Durban.

Although records apparently exist outside KwaZulu-Natal it is felt that these are the result of misidentifications. No verifiable record has as yet been located from Mpumalanga and Northern Provinces, Zimbabwe or Zambia.

IDENTIFICATION

Adult. Male. Upperside: white with a purple tip usually consisting of three prominent spots, outer border of these spots black. Underside: hindwing creamy-white to pinkish-brown with postdiscal line not prominent; coloration is seasonal.

Female. Upperside: white to yellow with a black and white or orange tip. Underside: seasonal from buff to yellow; postdiscal line may be prominent. Apical spots of forewing distinctly sagittate. A number of female forms have been described:

The nominate female form *erone* is white with an orange tip and heavy upperside dark markings; LHW light yellow. This is a wet-season form.

Female form *natalensis* (Staudinger, 1888. *Samml. exot. Schmetterl.* **1**: 44) has upperside forewing apical area black and white with other dark markings heavy; underside whitish yellow or yellow. This is the predominant wet-season form.

Female form *jobina* (Butler, 1869. *Cist. Ent.* **1**: 14) is the black and white tipped dry-season form and has the upperside dark markings less heavy; underside more or less pinkish, densely marked with brown striations.

Female form *millari* (van Son, 1949, *Transv. Mus. Mem.* **3**: 117) is a rare orange-tipped dry-season form which has upperside dark markings present in apical and outer marginal area of forewing only;

Colotis erone male upperside

hindwing markings absent; underside of hindwing pinkish, densely striated with brown.

Forewing lengths: male 24-30 mm; female 24-33 mm.

Early stages. Egg: pale yellow when first laid, darkening slightly and developing pinkish brown spots if fertile; diameter 0,6 mm, height 0,9 mm; with 14-15 longitudinal ribs of which half reach the micropyle, and 25-28 cross ribs. Larva: first instar pale yellow with brown longitudinal stripes; second instar is pale green with brown mottled stripes; third instar darker green with more well-developed brown stripes; fourth instar still deeper green with stripes a faint greenish-brown colour and a broad white dorsal line; fifth (final) instar green, with a thin white lateral line. It attains a length of 31 mm. Pupa: 22 mm long; mottled green (Clark & Dickson, 1967: 31).

Colotis erone female form *jobina* upperside (Photo: I. Migdoll)

Colotis erone final instar larva (After G.C. Clark 1967)

Colotis erone pupa (After G.C. Clark 1967)

HABITAT AND ECOLOGY

C. (C.) erone is an inhabitant of coastal forest. The males fly rapidly, low down, along paths or streams through the forest. They are often found frequenting clearings. The females fly much more slowly than the males and appear to keep to the bush. Specimens are often seen feeding on flowers.

Males appear to establish territories in clearings, along forest roads or on the edges of the woods. They patrol the edge of the clearings, presumably in the vicinity of the food plants.

The females fly at random in the bush in search of suitable food plants on which to oviposit. They lay their eggs singly, generally on young shoots of the food plant. The eggs hatch within 4-7 days. The larva eats its way out of the top of the egg and consumes the egg shell as its first meal. It feeds on the surface of the leaf. In the later instar they feed on the edge of the leaf, filling out the eaten portion of the leaf with their bodies. The pupa is attached by the cremaster to a silken pad and is held upright by a silken girdle around the middle. It is leaf-like and blends in well with its surroundings (Clark & Dickson, 1967: 31).

It flies throughout the year with peaks during December and January and again during June and July.

LARVAL FOOD PLANTS

Maerua racemulosa (Capparaceae).

DISTRIBUTION

South Africa, from the Eastern Cape to KwaZulu-Natal.

CONSERVATION

C. (C.) erone has a limited distribution down the eastern coast. As an endemic species, whose habitat is slowly shrinking with the destruction and pollution of the coastal forest, special attention must be paid to this species and populations should be monitored.

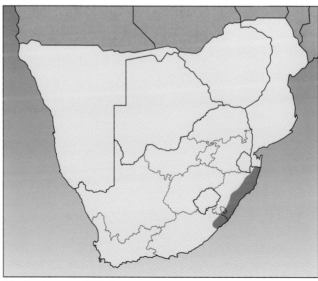

Distribution map of *Colotis erone*

Colotis (Colotis) ione (Godart)

BUSHVELD PURPLE TIP

Pieris ione Godart, 1819. *Encycl. Méth. d'Hist. Nat. (Zool.)*
9: 140. Type locality: Senegal.

This species was described from Senegal and is found through most of the savannah and woodland regions of sub-Saharan Africa. There are many regional forms and local populations but as the distribution appears to be continuous no subspecies are currently recognised.

IDENTIFICATION

Adult. Male. Upperside: white, forewing with a purple tip consisting of at least four prominent spots; outer border black dusted with grey. Underside: usually plain but may be similar to *erone*. Female. Upperside: similar to *erone* but with apical black spots square or rounded. Underside: similar to *erone* but generally not as well-marked.

The nominate female is the orange-tipped wet-season form. Wet-season forms have heavy black markings and veins blackened. Dry-season forms have reduced black markings, veins are not blackened and they are generally paler in colour.

Many female forms have been described. Some have black and white tips on the forewing upperside, others orange to reddish or pinkish brown and some specimens have purplish scales in the orange tip. The ground colour also varies from white to yellow.

Coastal specimens have a well-marked underside with a clearly defined discal dark brown line. It is presumed at this time that these are related to climatic differences.

The male wet-season form which is found in the inland areas of South Africa is form *phlegyas* (Butler, 1865. *Proc. zool. Soc. Lond.* **1865**: 431). It differs from the nominate coastal form in having on the upperside the inner black edging of purple apical area less heavy, hindwing without marginal spots; underside of hindwing with veins not blackened.

Wet-season female forms include:

Form *xanthosona* (Talbot, 1939. *Trans. ent. Soc. Lond.* **88**: 186) has the ground colour yellow with a well-developed black marginal band on hindwing upperside.

Form *hydrophobus* (Suffert, 1904. *Dt. ent. Z. Iris* **17**: 86) has an orange tip and blackened veins on LHW. It is an extreme wet-season form.

Form *woodi* (Gifford, 1965. *Butterflies of Malawi*: 29) is the normal wet-season form without an orange tip.

Form *anomalus* (Aurivillius, 1910. *Macrolep. World* **13**: 54) is the extreme wet-season form which lacks the orange tip, but has upperside black markings heavy and light sulphur-yellow LHW with darkened veins.

Form *pepita* (Gifford, 1965. *Butterflies of Malawi*: 29) lacks an orange tip and has a yellow ground colour.

The normal dry-season form has been named *jalone* (Butler, 1869. *Cist. Ent.* **1**: 14) and has an orange tip with hindwing black marginal band vestigial or absent.

Dry-season female forms include:

Form *leda* (Talbot, 1939. *Trans. ent. Soc. Lond.* **88**: 186) has a yellow ground colour and an orange tip with marginal black band of hindwing upperside vestigial or absent.

Form *xerophila* (Talbot, 1939. *Trans. ent. Soc. Lond.* **88**: 186) lacks the orange tip with upperside black markings reduced and LHW pinkish striated or freckled in brown.

Form *erubescens* (Talbot, 1942. *Proc. R. ent. Soc. Lond.* **11**: 51) has apical areas russet-brown to pinkish-brown.

Forewing lengths: male 23-33 mm; female 24-34 mm.

Early stages. Egg: white at first, becoming pale pinkish-brown with darker spots of same colour; diameter 0,45 mm, height 0,8 mm; with 14-15 longitudinal ribs of which 7-8 reach micropyle; ribs are cross-braced by about 24 fine ribs. Larva: first instar pale yellow in colour with irregular brown lateral lines; second instar greyish-green with a pale dorsal stripe; third instar is lighter greyish-green with a thin white lateral line; fourth instar green with a white dorsal line

Colotis ione form *phlegyas* male upperside

and a pale green lateral line; fifth (final) instar green with a thin pale-green dorsal stripe and a white lateral line. It attains a length of some 24 mm. Pupa: 22 mm long; greyish-white to green in colour (Clark & Dickson, 1967: 33; S.F. Henning, 1984b: 41; Migdoll, 1987: photo 185a (larva) & 185b (pupa)).

HABITAT AND ECOLOGY

C. (C.) ione is generally a bushveld species which fly in suitably dry coastal bush. The males fly fast at about a metre above the ground. They tend to remain in the open and seldom venture into thick bush. The females fly much more slowly and are often found fluttering in thick bush or around the margins of thickets. Specimens can often be seen feeding on the nectar of flowers, in particular those of a pur-ple-flowered *Vernonia* sp. which is a common roadside plant to the north of the Soutpansberg in the Northern Province.

The males patrol their territory along a circuitous course which will wend through clearings in the bush for a couple of kilometres. The male will patrol this course through most of the warmer hours of the day. Specimens can be seen on hilltops and these may be in-corporated in the patrol. Any females or other males encountered during the patrol will be investigated and the appropriate action ini-tiated.

The females fly at random through the bush in search of suitable food plants on which to oviposit. They lay their eggs singly on the

Colotis ione form *ione* female underside

Colotis ione form *ione* female upperside

295

leaves of the food plant. The first instar larva eats its way out near the top of the egg and consumes the egg shell as its first meal. The pupa is attached by the cremaster to a silken pad and held upright by the silken girdle around the middle (Clark & Dickson, 1967: 33; S.F. Henning, 1984b: 41).

This species is on the wing throughout the year although it is more prevalent during summer and autumn.

LARVAL FOOD PLANTS

Maerua rosmarinoides, M. racemulosa, M. juncea (Capparaceae). Recorded in East Africa on *Boscia* sp., *Capparis* sp., *Cadaba* sp. and *Ritchiea* sp. (Capparaceae).

Colotis ione near form *woodi* female upperside

DISTRIBUTION

South Africa, from Port St. Johns through KwaZulu-Natal to Northern Province and Mpumalanga, into Swaziland, Moçambique, Zimbabwe, Botswana and northern Namibia, and northwards throughout most of the bushveld areas south of the Sahara.

CONSERVATION

C. (C.) ione is a widespread species and is under no threat.

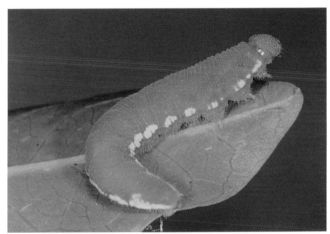

Colotis ione final instar larva

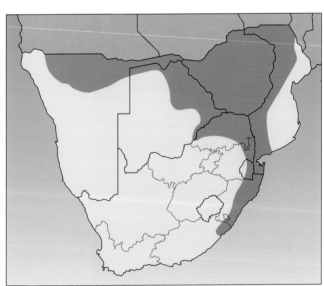

Distribution map of *Colotis ione*

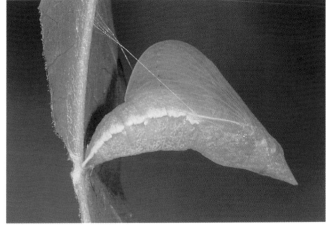

Colotis ione pupa

Colotis (Colotis) regina (Trimen)

QUEEN PURPLE TIP

Anthocharis regina Trimen, 1863. *Trans. ent. Soc. Lond.* (3)**1**: 520. Type locality: N'Gami.

This is the largest of the purple tips and is found in the bushveld regions from South Africa to eastern Kenya.

IDENTIFICATION

Adult. Male. Upperside: white with a large black-edged purple tip, with a blue to green iridescence. Underside: white or pinkish brown depending on season. Female. Upperside: white with a large purple or white tip with transverse black spots across it. Underside: similar to male but with better developed markings.

The nominate dry-season female form *regina* has a large purple tip with margin of hindwing above unmarked.

The wet-season form is *anax* (Grose-Smith, 1889. *Ann. Mag. nat. Hist.* (6) **3**: 125) and differs from the nominate form in having white spots in black apical area, usually only dusted with purple; hindwing above with marginal spots or band present.

There is a rare yellow female form named *louisa* (Suffert, 1904. *Dt. ent. Z. Iris* **17**: 128).

Forewing lengths: male 30-37 mm; female 27-37 mm.

Early stages. Egg: unrecorded. Larva: first instar pale yellow with irregular brown lateral lines; fifth (final) instar green with a thin pale green dorsal stripe and a cream lateral line. It attains a length of some 35 mm. Pupa: green in colour (Paré, pers. comm.).

HABITAT AND ECOLOGY

C. (C.) regina is an inhabitant of bushveld areas. The males' flight is fast and direct, between one and two metres above the ground. The females are much slower and tend to stay around the food plants. Both sexes can be seen feeding on the nectar of flowers.

Males patrol a circuitous course through the thorn trees in the vicinity of the food plants. They keep to this course through the midday hours, stopping only to investigate other butterflies or for brief rests on the ground. Males visit hilltops during their patrols but do not stay long.

The females fly at random in search of suitable food plants on which to oviposit.

This species is on the wing throughout the year but is more plentiful in the late summer and autumn.

Colotis regina male upperside

LARVAL FOOD PLANTS

Boscia albitrunca, B. salicifolia. Recorded in East Africa on *Boscia* sp. and *Capparis* sp. (Capparaceae).

DISTRIBUTION

South Africa, in bushveld areas from KwaZulu-Natal to Mpumalanga and Northern Province, northern Gauteng and North-West Province, Swaziland, Moçambique, Zimbabwe, northern Botswana and northern Namibia, northwards in Central and East Africa.

CONSERVATION

C. (C.) regina is a widespread species and is under no threat.

Colotis regina female upperside

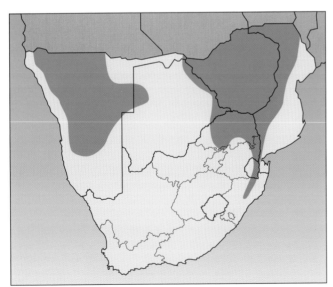

Distribution map of *Colotis regina*

Colotis regina female underside on empty pupal case (Photo: I. Migdoll)

MEDIUM-SIZED TO SMALL ORANGE AND RED TIPS

This group was divided into nine species groups by Talbot, 1939 and Peters, 1952. Our groupings differ slightly. There are five groups in Southern Africa based on wing shape, colour and structure of upperside apical area and markings. The Southern African species groups are *danae, aurora, antevippe, euippe and evagore*.

Colotis (Colotis) danae (Fabricius, 1775) species group

A small group consisting of three species; *C. (C.) danae, C. (C.) guenei* (Mabille, 1878) and *C. (C.) hildebrandti* (Staudinger, 1885). Characterised by an oval discocellular spot on the hindwing underside which is centred with red or white. Only *C. (C.) danae* is found in Southern Africa.

Colotis (Colotis) danae (Fabricius)

SCARLET TIP

Papilio danae Fabricius, 1775. *Syst. Ent.*: 476.

Described from India, this species is divided into four subspecies throughout the Afrotropical region, two of which occur in Southern Africa. The subspecies *annae* (Fabricius, 1775: 476) occurs widely in Southern Africa, while a second subspecies *walkeri* (Butler, 1884: 403) is found in western Namibia and Angola.

Colotis (C.) danae annae (Wallengren)

Thestias annae Wallengren, 1857. *K. svenska VetenskAkad. Handl.* (N.F.) **2**(4): 16. Type locality: Kaffraria.

IDENTIFICATION

Adult. Male. Upperside: white with grey basal area; forewing with large carmine-red tip; hindwing with a continuous dark marginal band. Underside: white with clearly defined dark-ringed brown

Colotis danae annae male upperside

markings. Female. Upperside: white to yellow with dark brown wing bases and black dots; forewing tip varies from yellowish-orange to orange-red. Underside: similar to male but more brightly marked.

The dry-season form is form *wallengrenii* (Butler, 1876. *Proc. zool. Soc. Lond.* **1876**: 157) and has upperside basal areas not or very slightly darkened; hindwing with separate dark marginal spots.

Forewing lengths: male 19-30 mm; female 20-30 mm.

Early stages. Egg: whitish-yellow when laid, developing red blotches later; diameter 0,6 mm, height 1,0 mm; with 11-13 longitudinal ribs and 22-24 cross ribs. Larva: first instar pale whitish-yellow with a black head; second to fourth instars light green, with yellow dorsal stripe; fifth (final) instar green, with a narrow dorsal stripe, occasionally lateral oblique light spots on segments seven and eight, head light green. It attains a length of 24-25 mm. Larva takes on a purplish hue in pre-pupal phase. Pupa: about 20 mm long; purple for about 5 days before changing to the final colour which can be bluish-green to yellowish-green or greyish-brown to pinkish-yellow (Clark, 1949: 128; Clark, 1994: 362).

HABITAT AND ECOLOGY

C. (C.) danae is an inhabitant of bushveld areas. The flight of this species can be comparatively slow compared to other *Colotis* but elusive. It can fly rapidly if disturbed or when searching for females. It will normally fly in a leisurely fashion around the thorn trees. A common visitor to roadside flowers.

Males are not strongly territorial but may well patrol slowly over a predetermined course. Individuals have been seen to occupy a particular area for some time.

The females fly at random through the bush in search of suitable food plants on which to oviposit. They lay their eggs singly on the leaves or young shoots of the food plant. The larva eats its way out of the side of the egg near the top and eats the egg shell as its first meal. The larval stage takes about 18 days. The pupa is cryptic and takes its colour from the substrate on which it pupates. It is attached by its cremaster to a silken pad and is held upright by a silken girdle around the middle. The pupal stage lasts about 9 days (Clark, 1949: 128; Clark, 1994: 362).

This species is on the wing throughout the year in most suitable habitats but appears to be in greater numbers during autumn.

Colotis danae annae female upperside

Colotis danae annae female underside

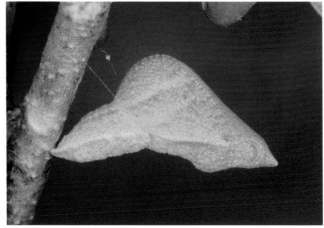

Colotis danae annae final instar larva on its food plant *Cadaba termitaria*

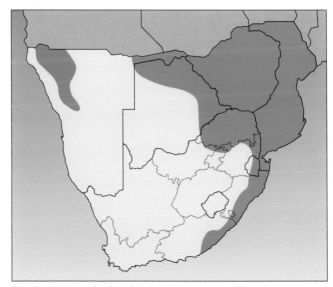

Colotis danae annae pupa

LARVAL FOOD PLANTS

Cadaba termitaria, C. natalensis, Maerua angolensis (Capparaceae).

DISTRIBUTION

South Africa, from the Eastern Cape and KwaZulu-Natal to the Northern Province and Mpumalanga, northern areas of the North-West Province, into Swaziland, Moçambique, Zimbabwe, Botswana and north-eastern Namibia.

CONSERVATION

C. (C.) danae annae is a widespread species and is under no threat.

Distribution map of *Colotis danae*

Colotis (C.) aurora (Cramer, 1780) species group

Another small species group consisting of three species; *C. (C.) aurora, C. (C.) dissociatus* (Butler, 1897) and *C. (C.) auxo* (Lucas, 1852). The apical area in the male reaches below vein CuA₁ in this group. Only *C. (C.) auxo* is from Southern Africa.

Colotis (Colotis) auxo (Lucas)

SULPHUR ORANGE TIP

Anthocharis auxo Lucas, 1852. *Rev. Mag. Zool.* **2**(4): 422.

Described from KwaZulu-Natal, this species is closely related to *C. aurora* with which it flies in East Africa. It is common and many hundreds of specimens may be seen at suitable localities. There are two subspecies, with the nominate from Southern Africa. The other subspecies *incretus* (Butler, 1881) is from Malawi and East Africa.

Colotis (C.) auxo auxo (Lucas)

Anthocharis auxo Lucas, 1852. *Rev. Mag. Zool.* **2**(4): 422. Type locality: Port Natal (Durban).

IDENTIFICATION

Adult. Medium-sized. Male. Upperside: yellow to pale greenish-yellow with orange forewing tip. Underside: pale yellow with faint brown markings. Female. Upperside: yellow to greenish-white with orange forewing tip and dark markings. Some specimens lack the orange tip and many intermediates occur. Underside: similar to male but with darker and more extensive markings.

The dry-season form *topha* (Wallengren, 1860. *Wien. ent. Mschr.* **4**: 34) has hindwing underside tinged with pinkish-brown and striated with brown.

Forewing lengths: male 19-24 mm; female 19-23 mm.

Early stages. Egg: creamy-white when laid, becoming dull yellow with pinkish-brown spots; diameter 0,6 mm, height 1,0 mm; with 13 longitudinal ribs and about 25 cross ribs. Larva: first instar yellow with a black head on emergence, later developing brown mottling; second instar pale yellowish-green; third instar green or bluish-green with two dorso-lateral yellowish stripes; fourth instar bluish-green, with a lateral longitudinal white stripe edged with pinkish below; fifth (final) instar is variable green to bluish green, with or without lateral spots or lines, head green. Pupa: variable, ranging in colour from green to cream or yellow with or without heavy black blotches (Clark, 1949:131; Clark, 1994: 364).

Colotis auxo auxo male underside

Colotis auxo auxo female showing upperside

HABITAT AND ECOLOGY

C. (C.) auxo is an inhabitant of bushveld and savannah. It can be seen flying fairly slowly and fluttering around a particular bush. It can more usually be seen flying fast and at random around the thorn trees and is often found feeding on nectar.

Males keep to a particular area, usually a clearing with food plant nearby, and remain in the vicinity during the warmer hours of the day.

The females fly at random through the bush in search of suitable food plants on which to oviposit. They lay the eggs singly on leaves or young shoots of the food plants. The egg stage takes 4 days. There are 5 larval instars lasting about 11 days. The larvae are cryptic, being a leaf-green colour, and blend in well with the leaves of the food plant. The pupa is cryptic, taking the colour of its surroundings. The pupal stage lasts about 10 days but may be longer in adverse climatic conditions. The pupa is attached by the cremaster to a silken pad and is held upright by a silken girdle around the middle (Clark, 1949: 131; Clark, 1994: 364).

This species is on the wing throughout the year but is more common during summer and autumn.

Colotis auxo auxo pupa

Colotis auxo auxo final instar larva

LARVAL FOOD PLANTS

Cadaba termitaria, C. natalensis (Capparaceae).

DISTRIBUTION

South Africa, from Eastern Cape to KwaZulu-Natal, Northern Province and Mpumalanga, to Swaziland, Moçambique, Zimbabwe and Botswana.

CONSERVATION

C. (C.) auxo is a widespread species and is under no threat.

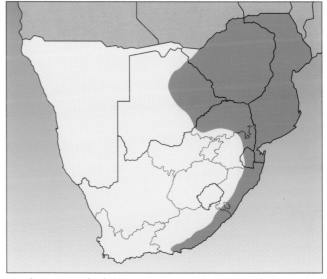

Distribution map of *Colotis auxo*

Colotis (C.) antevippe (Boisduval, 1836) species group

The inner margin of the apical area in this medium-sized group is fairly straight. There are three species: *C. (C.) antevippe, C. (C.) evenina* (Wallengren, 1857) and *C. (C.) liagore* (Klug, 1829). *C. (C.) antevippe* and *C. (C.) evenina* are found in Southern Africa.

Colotis (Colotis) antevippe (Boisduval)

RED TIP

Anthocharis antevippe Boisduval, 1836. *Spéc. gén. Lépid.* **1**: 572.

Described from Senegal, this large red tip is a common inhabitant of savannah and coastal bush. There are three subspecies, the nominate is West African, *zera* (Lucas, 1852) is East African and *gavisa* is from Southern Africa.

Colotis (C.) antevippe gavisa (Wallengren)

Anthopsyche gavisa Wallengren, 1857. *K. svenska VetenskAkad. Handl.* (N.F.) **2**(4): 13. Type locality: Kaffraria.

IDENTIFICATION

Adult. Male. Upperside: white with a large reddish-orange tip, there is usually a black bar across inner margin of forewing and a black dot at end of cell. Underside: white with dark veins or speckled finely with brown. Female. Upperside: white with a reddish orange to orange tip, base of forewing broadly black; hindwing margin usually broadly black, there is a black dot at end of cell in forewing. Underside: similar to male but with some of upperside dark markings discernible.

The dry-season form *harmonides* (Butler, 1876. *Proc. zool. Soc. Lond.* **1876**: 146) has supramarginal dark area of forewing upperside very much reduced.

Colotis antevippe gavisa female upperside (Photo: I. Migdoll)

There are other climatic form names available but all intergrade.

Forewing lengths: male 20-27 mm; female 22-27 mm.

Early stages. Egg: white when laid, developing red blotches if fertile; elongate subconical, diameter 0,5 mm, height 0,9 mm; with 12-14 longitudinal ribs braced by 30-32 cross ribs. Larva: first instar greenish-yellow with light dorsal and lateral stripes which later become heavily edged with black; later instars variable in colour, being green to brownish or yellowish-green. The larva becomes purplish-green during the pre-pupal stage. The larva attains a length of 24 mm. Pupa: lilac for about 5 days before changing to bluish to yellowish-green or greyish-brown to pinkish-yellow; laterally compressed, with a moderately high dorso-thoracic keel and strongly projecting wing cases, both rounded in lateral view (Clark, 1949: 136; Clark, 1994: 366).

HABITAT AND ECOLOGY

C. (C.) antevippe is an inhabitant of savannah, woodland and coastal bush. The male flies fast and low through the trees, frequently settling on the ground. The females fly much more slowly and keeps to the shelter of the trees. Both sexes can often be seen feeding on nectar. It occasionally visits muddy places when flowers are scarce.

The males establish their territories near the larval food plants. In dense bush this is usually along the edges of clearings or roads. Here they follow a circuitous course through the clearings during most of the warmer hours of the day. In more open habitats they may select a bush as a territory and on warm and sunny days will circle around it with hardly a rest.

The females fly at random through the bush in search of suitable food plants on which to oviposit. They lay their eggs singly on the leaves or young shoots of the food plant. The egg hatches after about 5 days. The larva is cryptic and variable in colour and markings to blend in with its environment. The final instar larva is usually green with a broad blackish-brown dorsal stripe but it may also be 'reddish-sandy above' according to Trimen. The larval instars all take about 3 days except the final instar which takes about 5 days. The pupal coloration is highly cryptic, resembling a dead leaf. It is attached by the cremaster and held upright by a silken girdle around the middle. The pupal stage lasts 11 to 15 days. (Clark, 1949: 136; Clark, 1994: 366).

The species is on the wing throughout the year in most habitats.

Colotis antevippe gavisa female underside (Photo: I. Migdoll)

LARVAL FOOD PLANTS

Boscia albitrunca, B. oleoides, Capparis sepiaria var. *citrifolia, Maerua cafra, M. juncea* (Capparaceae).

DISTRIBUTION

South Africa, from the Western Cape through the Eastern Cape, KwaZulu-Natal to Mpumalanga, Gauteng, Northern and North-West Provinces, Swaziland, Moçambique, Zimbabwe, Botswana and Namibia, northwards into Central and East Africa.

CONSERVATION

C. (C.) antevippe gavisa is a widespread species in a number of habitats and is under no threat.

Colotis antevippe gavisa male

Colotis antevippe gavisa final instar larva

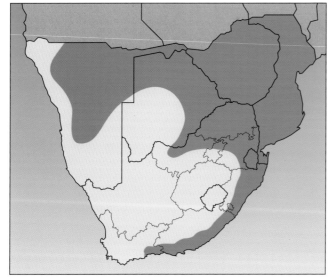

Distribution map of *Colotis antevippe*

Colotis antevippe gavisa pupa among the leaves of its food plant *Maerua juncea*

Colotis (Colotis) evenina (Wallengren)

COMMON ORANGE TIP

Anthopsyche evenina Wallengren, 1857. *K. svenska Vetensk-Akad. Handl.* (N.F.) **2**(4): 12.

This species is found throughout most of the wooded areas of Southern Africa. There are three subspecies through the eastern regions of Africa. The subspecies *casta* (Gerstaeker, 1871) is a second subspecies which just enters the Southern African region in northern Zimbabwe.

Colotis (C.) evenina evenina (Wallengren)

Anthopsyche evenina Wallengren, 1857. *K. svenska Vetensk-Akad. Handl.* (N.F.) **2**(4): 12. Type locality: Kaffraria.

IDENTIFICATION

Adult. Male. Upperside: white with a yellowish-orange tip and a diffuse grey bar along inner margin of forewing. Underside: white or pinkish buff with a characteristic transverse dark stripe from base to middle of outer margin. Female. Upperside: white with a dark grey basal patch on forewing which is characteristically scalloped distally. Underside: similar to male but with some of forewing upperside dark markings repeated.

The dry-season form *deidamioides* (Aurivillius, 1879. *Ofvers. K. VetenskAkad. Forh.* **36**(7): 45) has upperside dark markings reduced and underside of hindwing pinkish, striated with brown.

Forewing lengths: male 19-27 mm; female 19-26 mm.

Early stages. Egg: unrecorded. Larva: final instar larva cylindrical and finely setose, dark bottle green in colour dorsally and paler ventrally with a conspicuous white lateral stripe running length of body; head same colour as body without markings. The larva attains a length of 25 mm. Pupa: 18 mm long; dull green in colour flushed with a purple hue; keeled wing cases laterally compressed, bearing white spots in region of forewing cell and along outer margin; the head bears a short pointed process (Paré, pers. comm.).

HABITAT AND ECOLOGY

C. (C.) evenina is an inhabitant of savannah and woodland. The males fly low and rapidly among the trees, often settling on the ground. The females fly much more slowly than the males and keep to the undergrowth. A frequent visitor to flowers.

The males establish their territories near the larval food plants.

Colotis evenina evenina form *deidamioides* male

Colotis evenina evenina female upperside on its food plant *Boscia albitrunca*

Colotis evenina evenina female underside

Colotis evenina evenina final instar larva (Photo: R. Paré)

Colotis evenina evenina pupa (Photo: R. Paré)

Here they patrol a circuitous course around their territory, through the clearings between the trees. They follow this path during most of the warmer hours of the day. They are not aggressive towards other males but have been seen to circle each other when they meet.

The females fly at random through the bush in search of suitable food plants on which to lay. The eggs are laid singly on leaves of the food plant. The larva is cryptic in colour and blends in with its environment. The larval stage lasts approximately 25 days. The pupa is attached by the cremaster and supported by a silken girdle. The pupal stage lasts about 10 days (Paré, pers. comm.).

This species will fly throughout the year in most habitats.

LARVAL FOOD PLANTS

Boscia albitrunca, B. salicifolia, Capparis spp. (Capparaceae).

DISTRIBUTION

South Africa, from Namaqualand through the Northern Cape to the Free State, Gauteng. North-West, Northern, Mpumalanga and KwaZulu-Natal Provinces, Swaziland, Moçambique, most of Zimbabwe, Botswana and northern Namibia.

CONSERVATION

C. (C.) evenina is a common and widespread species and is under no threat.

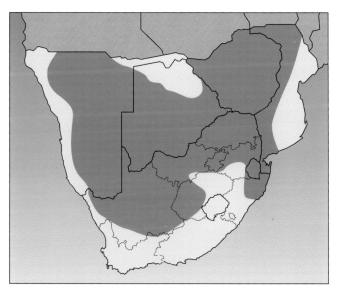

Distribution map of *Colotis evenina*

Colotis (C.) euippe (Linnaeus, 1758) species group

This small group of two medium-sized orange tips is characterised by a curved or irregular inner edge to the apical area. The only species from mainland Africa to be included in this species group is *C. (C.) euippe*. The other species is *C. (C.) evanthe* (Boisduval, 1836) from Madagascar and the Comoro Islands.

Colotis (Colotis) euippe (Linnaeus)

SMOKY ORANGE TIP

Papilio (Danaus) euippe Linnaeus, 1758. *Syst. Nat.* (Ed. 10) **1**: 469.

A common and widespread species throughout the Afrotropical region where it is divided into six subspecies. The nominate subspecies comes from West Africa. There are two Southern African subspecies, one of which, *mediata* Talbot (1939: 199), just penetrates into northern Zimbabwe, the other, *omphale* (Godart), is widespread through much of the remainder of the subregion.

Colotis (C.) euippe omphale (Godart)

Pieris omphale Godart, 1819. *Encycl. Méth. d'Hist. Nat. (Zool.)* **9**: 122. Type locality: East Africa.

IDENTIFICATION

Adult. Male. Upperside: white with a characteristically broadly bordered reddish-orange tip. Wet-season forms have a broad black cross bar centrally and across lower part of hindwing. Underside: white with faint markings and a characteristic bar, at a right angle to body, across lower hindwing. Female. Similar to male but with upperside dark markings broader. Specimens with a yellowish ground colour also occur.

The dry-season form *theogone* (Boisduval, 1836. *Spéc. gén. Lépid.* **1**: 575) has postdiscal band on hindwing upperside narrow or vestigial.

There are other climatic form names but all intergrade.

Forewing lengths: male 17-26 mm; female 13-27 mm.

Early stages. Egg: white when laid, becoming dull yellow with red blotches if fertile; diameter 0,4-0,5 mm, height 0,8-1,2 mm; with 10-15 longitudinal ribs braced by 24-30 cross ribs. Larva: first instar pale yellowish-brown, developing a greenish tint after its first meal; second to fourth instars green; fifth (final) instar green with yellow, white and black colouring around spiracles, and occasionally a faint diagonal stripe. It attains a length of 22 mm. Pupa: 17 mm long; varies in colour from green to light brown (Clark, 1949: 144; Clark, 1994: 368).

HABITAT AND ECOLOGY

C. (C.) euippe omphale is an inhabitant of savannah, woodland and coastal bush. A comparatively slow-flying species which tends to prefer to fly in the shade of the trees rather than in the open spaces so favoured by its congeners. A common visitor to flowers it may often be seen feeding on flowers along the coastal dunes of KwaZulu-Natal. It also feeds at damp places.

The males establish their territories near the larval food plants. Here they fly slowly around a selected section of bush during most of the warmer hours of the day. They usually fly near the ground and circle around the trees, low bushes or shrubs in their territory.

The females fly at random through the bush in search of suitable food plants on which to oviposit. They lay their eggs singly on the leaves or young shoots of the food plant. The first instar larva eats its way out of the side of the egg near the top, it then devours the eggshell as its first meal. The larva feeds on the surface of the leaf, often concealed in a young shoot. The first three instars take 3 days each, the fourth instar 4 days and the final instar 5 days. The pupa is attached by the cremaster and a silken girdle around the middle holds it upright. It is cryptically coloured green to light brown. The pupal stage lasts 14 days (Clark, 1949: 144; Clark, 1994: 368).

This species is on the wing throughout the year in suitable habitats.

Colotis euippe omphale female underside photographed early in the morning while still covered with dew

Colotis euippe omphale male upperside

Colotis euippe omphale female upperside

LARVAL FOOD PLANTS

Boscia oleoides, Capparis sepiaria var. *citrifolia, Maerua cafra, M. rosmarinoides, M. juncea, Cadaba aphylla* (Capparaceae).

DISTRIBUTION

Occurs throughout South Africa except the extreme south-western Western Cape and high-altitude grassveld. Also Moçambique, Zimbabwe, Botswana and Namibia.

CONSERVATION

C. (C.) euippe omphale is a common widespread species and is under no threat.

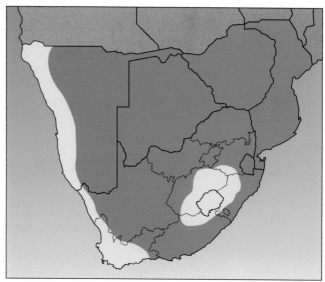

Distribution map of *Colotis euippe*

Colotis euippe omphale final instar larva just prior to pupation

Colotis euippe omphale pupa

311

| *Colotis evagore* (Klug, 1829) species group | *Colotis (Colotis) pallene* (Hopffer) |

Small orange tips. The inner edge of the apical area is strongly curved in *C. (C.) evagore*, *C. (C.) evanthides* (Holl., 1896) and *C. (C.) daira* (Klug, 1829). *C. (C.) evagore*, *C. pallene* (Hopffer, 1855) and *C. lais* (Butler) are found in Southern Africa. Other species in this group are *C. (C.) rogersi* (Dixey, 1915) and *C. (C.) ephyia* (Klug, 1829).

BUSHVELD ORANGE TIP

Anthocharis pallene Hopffer, 1855. *Mber. dt. Akad. Wiss. Berl.* **1855**: 640. Type locality: Moçambique.

This species was described from Moçambique and occurs from South Africa up to East Africa, as far as Tanzania and Uganda.

IDENTIFICATION

Adult. Male. Upperside: white with a reddish-orange tip, inner edge of orange smoothly rounded with a thin dark line; forewing with a black stripe usually along inner margin. Underside: white or with brownish irroration. Female. Upperside: white with orange tip and extensive black markings. Underside: white without orange beneath tip in wet-season form which distinguishes it from *C. (C.) evagore*, in dry-season form this difference is not so marked so it can be distinguished by complete brownish irroration of hindwing without pale area in hindwing cell which is present in *C. (C.) evagore*.

Colotis pallene male upperside

Colotis pallene male underside

The dry-season form *halyattes* (Butler, 1876. *Proc. zool. Soc. Lond.* **1876**: 145) has inner stripe of forewing in male absent; hindwing underside in both sexes fawn or pinkish, striated with brown.

There are other form names available but all intergrade.

Forewing lengths: male 16-22 mm; female 13-21 mm.

Early stages. Unrecorded.

HABITAT AND ECOLOGY

C. (C.) pallene is an inhabitant of bushveld areas. Males fly fairly weakly and keep close to the ground. They settle frequently on the ground but when disturbed may show a surprising turn of speed. The females fly even more slowly and are usually found feeding on flowers or searching for food plants. Both sexes feed avidly at flowers.

The males establish their territories near the larval food plants. Here they flutter around the selected area, usually a clearing in the bush, during most of the warmer hours of the day.

The females fly at random through the bush in search of suitable food plants on which to lay.

They are on the wing throughout the year in most localities.

LARVAL FOOD PLANTS

Capparis sp. (Capparaceae).

DISTRIBUTION

South Africa, from northern KwaZulu-Natal to the North-West Province, northern Gauteng, Mpumalanga and Northern Province, Swaziland, Moçambique, Zimbabwe, Botswana and Namibia.

CONSERVATION

C. (C.) pallene is a widespread species and is under no threat.

Colotis pallene female upperside

Colotis pallene female underside

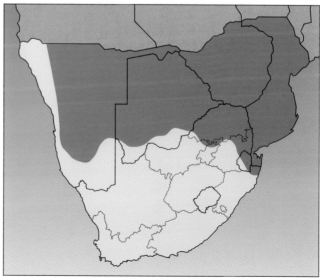

Distribution map of *Colotis pallene*

Colotis (Colotis) lais (Butler)

KALAHARI ORANGE TIP

Teracolus lais Butler, 1876. *Proc. zool. Soc. Lond.* **1876**: 145.
Type locality: Orange River.

Endemic to Southern Africa, this species was described from the
Orange River in the Northern Cape.

IDENTIFICATION

Adult. Male. Upperside: white with a characteristic burnt orange
tip without a dark stripe on inner margin of forewing. Underside:
white or pinkish-brown with a fine brown irroration. Female. Upperside: white with a burnt orange tip, dark markings similar to
other species but not as extensive. Underside: white with fine brown
stippling or pinkish-brown with brown irroration and dark discal
markings.

The dry-season form *felthami* (van Son, 1949. *Transv. Mus. Mem.*
3: 150) differs from the nominate in having reduced black markings on upperside and a pinkish colour and brown irroration of
hindwing and apical area of forewing underside.

Forewing lengths: male 17-22 mm; female 17-21 mm.

Early stages. Unrecorded.

Colotis lais male underside

Colotis lais male upperside

Colotis lais female upperside

HABITAT AND ECOLOGY

C. (C.) lais is an inhabitant of arid thornveld. Its flight is slow and close to the ground although it does show a fair turn of speed if disturbed or if chasing another butterfly. The females fly slowly about the small thorn trees and bushes of the habitat that it favours. Both sexes frequently settle on the ground. It is also frequently observed feeding on nectar.

Males appear to establish territories in clearings among the thornbushes. They patrol the area during most of the warmer hours of the day.

The females fly at random among the thornbushes in search of suitable food plants on which to oviposit.

This species is on the wing during most months of the year but is more plentiful from October to March.

LARVAL FOOD PLANTS

Unrecorded.

DISTRIBUTION

South Africa, from Kimberley in the Northern Cape to Vryburg in the North-West Province and a few records from the western areas of the Northern Province, southern Botswana and southern Namibia.

CONSERVATION

C. (C.) lais is endemic to Southern Africa and although its distribution is fairly restricted for a pierid, at this time there appears to be no need for any conservation measures.

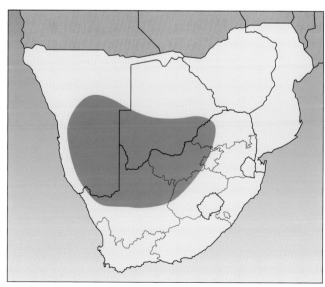

Distribution map of *Colotis lais*

315

Colotis (Colotis) evagore (Klug)

SMALL ORANGE TIP

Pontia evagore Klug, 1829. *Symb. Phys.*: pl. 8.

This species was described from Arabia, the one subspecies inhabiting most of the Afrotropical region is an extremely variable one.

Colotis (C.) evagore antigone (Boisduval)

Anthocharis antigone Boisduval, 1836. *Spéc. gén. Lépid.* **1**: 572. Type locality: Coast of Guinea.

IDENTIFICATION

Adult. Male. Upperside: white with an orange tip, inner edge of which darkened towards outer margin but from there to costa not darkened. Underside: forewing orange subapically; hindwing usually yellowish or variegated with a clear, unmarked white area in cell. Female. Upperside: extremely variable in extent of dark markings and in colour of apical patch on forewing which can vary from white, through yellow to orange and dark brown; ground colour can also vary from white to pale yellow. Underside: as in male.

As the type specimen of *antigone* is quite a unique form the normal wet-season form has been given the name *phlegetonia* (Boisduval, 1836. *Spéc. gén. Lépid* **1**: 577). The dry-season form *delphine* (Boisduval, 1836. *Spéc. gén. Lépid* **1**: 577) has upperside dark markings reduced and underside of hindwing pinkish irrorated with brown.

There are many other form names and female form names available, all of which intergrade.

Forewing lengths: male 13-21 mm; female 11-21 mm.

Early stages. Egg: white when laid, becoming brownish pink and developing red blotches if fertile; diameter 0,4-0,5 mm, height 0,6-1,0 mm; with 12-14 longitudinal ribs braced by about 30 cross ribs. Larva: first instar yellowish-brown, taking on a greenish colour after its first meal; second to fourth instars green; fifth (final) instar green with a dark dorsal stripe and a white lateral stripe edged with black below. It attains a length of about 22 mm. Pupa: 16-17 mm long; colour varies from cream and black, green to light brown (Clark, 1949: 160; Clark, 1994: 370).

HABITAT AND ECOLOGY

C. (C.) evagore antigone is an inhabitant of arid bushveld and is often found in great numbers. It regularly rests on the ground but is normally seen fluttering along close to the ground. This species has a weak flight which seldom takes the insect more than half a metre from the ground. If alarmed it will fly faster and more at random. Both sexes are often found in numbers feeding on flowers at the side of the roads.

Little territorial behaviour has been recorded. Males are sometimes seen to circle one another. The quantity of specimens usually found in any locality makes it difficult to differentiate an individual following a particular course.

Colotis evagore antigone form *phlegetonia* male

Colotis evagore antigone form *delphine* male upperside

Colotis evagore antigone form *delphine* female upperside

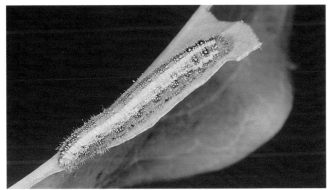

Colotis evagore antigone final instar larva

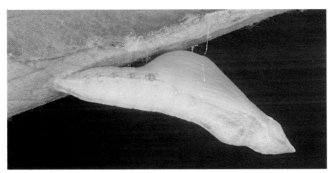

Colotis evagore antigone pupa

The females fly at random through the bush in search of suitable food plants on which to oviposit. Eggs are laid very rapidly during excursions deep within the foliage of the food plant. Although the females may spend a few minutes searching for the right spot on which to lay, the act of ovipositing is completed at great speed. The unwary observer will assume that no ovipositing took place.

The eggs are laid singly on the leaves and shoots of the food plant or even on nearby vegetation. The first instar larva eats its way out of the egg at the side near the top. It devours the discarded eggshell as its first meal. It feeds on the surface of the leaf and may be concealed in a young shoot. The first three instars take 3 days, the fourth instar 4 days and the final instar 5 days. The pupa is attached by the cremaster to a silken pad and a silken girdle around the middle holds it upright. It is cryptically coloured and ranges from cream to light brown or green (Clark, 1949: 160; Clark, 1994: 370).

This species is on the wing throughout the year but is usually most abundant in autumn.

LARVAL FOOD PLANTS

Capparis sepiaria var. *citrifolia*, *Maerua cafra*, *M. juncea*, *Cadaba aphylla* (Capparaceae).

DISTRIBUTION

South Africa, from Wilderness in the Western Cape, Eastern Cape, through KwaZulu-Natal, to Mpumalanga, northern Gauteng, Northern and North-West Provinces. It is also widespread in Moçambique, Zimbabwe, Botswana, Namibia and most of Africa south of the Sahara.

CONSERVATION

C. (C.) evagore antigone is a common and plentiful species and is under no threat.

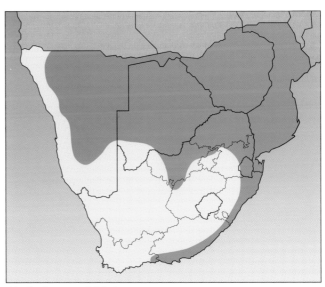

Distribution map of *Colotis evagore*

317

Subgenus *Cuneacolotis* subgen. n.

Type species: *Anthopsyche agoye* Wallengren, 1857.

DIAGNOSIS

This subgenus is situated between *Teracolus* and *Colotis*. It shares with *Teracolus* two of the three symplesiomorphic characters of that subgenus; valve of male genitalia with apex produced and apex of forewing acute. The other symplesiomorphic character in *Teracolus* is that the hindwing UDC is not much shorter than the MDC. In *Cuneacolotis* this is a synapomorphic character with the UDC being very much shorter than the MDC, a character shared with *Colotis*. Synapomorphic characters peculiar to *Cuneacolotis* are the somewhat wedge-shaped larvae, not cylindrical as in *Teracolus* and *Colotis*, and the comparatively short antennae, the antenna/wing ratio being much lower than *Colotis* or *Teracolus*, with a distinctly rounded club. A symplesiomorphic character shared with *Colotis* is that M_1 is stalked with the radials on the forewing.

DESCRIPTION

Adult. Antennae just over a third the length of the costa with a narrow shaft and a rounded spatulate club. Antenna/wing ratio 0,36 (*Colotis* 0,37-0,43, mean 0,41; *Teracolus* 0,40 - 0,41, mean 0,41). The antennal joints are very short (van Son 1949). Wings. Forewing R_1 and R_2 from cell, R_3 stalked with R_{4+5}. M_1 on a very short stalk with the radials. MDC very short compared with LDC. Hindwing precostal spur very long. Rs from well before upper angle of cell, M_1 from upper angle, M_2 from just below upper angle, MDC very short, LDC very long.

Genitalia. Male, tegumen broad and short; uncus stout and hardly down-curved; valve almost triangular, concave dorsally, convex ventrally, rounded distally with apex produced acutely into a small process; aedeagus one and a quarter times the length of tegumen and uncus combined, stout and arched with large basal prong; saccus broad and short and only slightly longer than uncus. Female, anal lobes and ostium bursae comparatively small; ductus bursae narrow and of even width; corpus bursae rounded; signum elongated, angled centrally but not narrowed, spinose except for middle and at the ends (van Son 1949).

Early stages. Egg: unrecorded. Larva: distinctly keel shaped, not cylindrical, tapering posteriorly; anal segment strongly bifid. Pupa: not as laterally compressed as in *Colotis*, wing cases not developed into a distinctive keel, frons not elongated (Larsen 1992b). Food plants are Capparaceae.

Etymology. *Cunea*, wedge shaped; *colotis*, colourful = *Colotis* Hübner; masculine.

Only the type species is represented in this subgenus at present.

Colotis (Cuneacolotis) agoye (Wallengren)

SPECKLED SULPHUR TIP

Anthopsyche agoye Wallengren, 1857. *K. svenska VetenskAkad. Handl.* (N.F.) **2**(4): 15.

This species is of special interest in that there are supposedly three subspecies, two in Southern Africa and one, *zephyrus* (Marshall, 1897), on the other side of Africa in Ethiopia and Somalia nearly 3 000 kilometres away. The two subspecies in Southern Africa have an overlap zone in Botswana where more or less intermediate transitional specimens can apparently be encountered (Larsen, 1992b: 5). This indicates that one or both of these subspecies have in recent times increased their ranges, leading to this transition zone where they are apparently interbreeding. These two populations are still well-defined in other areas. Larsen believes these subspecies to be ecologically maintained since the southern *bowkeri* appears to be more frost-tolerant than the more northern *agoye*. Some researchers are of the opinion that all three subspecies represent distinct species. Further research is required before the relationships between these three subspecies can be adequately assessed.

Colotis (C.) agoye agoye (Wallengren)

Anthopsyche agoye Wallengren, 1857. *K. svenska VetenskAkad. Handl.* (N.F.) **2**(4): 15. Type locality: Kaffraria.

IDENTIFICATION

Adult. Consistently larger than *bowkeri*. Male. Upperside: white with slightly blackened veins and an ochreous-orange apical patch which is relatively smaller than in *bowkeri*; basal area dusted with greyish-black scales. Underside: unmarked white tinged with yellowish or with a brown irroration at apex of forewing and hindwing. Female.

Colotis agoye agoye female

Upperside: white with a small orange apical patch suffused with dark brown. Underside: unmarked white, hindwing and forewing apex tinged or irrorated with brownish-yellow.

Forewing lengths: male 21-25 mm; female 20-25 mm.

Early stages. Unrecorded.

HABITAT AND ECOLOGY

C. (C.) agoye agoye inhabits bushveld areas. The males fly rapidly around the food plants, stopping only to feed on flowers or rest on the ground. The females are slower but still attain a fair turn of speed if disturbed. Both sexes are often found feeding on flowers.

Males patrol around the food plants without showing any aggressive tendencies. They patrol about the bushes near the ground on which they constantly settle.

The females fly at random through the bush in search of suitable food plants on which to oviposit.

This species is on the wing throughout the year but appears to be more abundant during summer and autumn.

LARVAL FOOD PLANTS

Boscia sp., *Cadaba* sp. (Capparaceae).

DISTRIBUTION

South Africa, from the Northern, North-West and Mpumalanga Provinces, to the Witwatersrand on rare occasions. Zimbabwe up the Sabi valley, Moçambique, westwards to northern Botswana and northern Namibia.

Colotis agoye agoye male

319

Colotis (C.) agoye bowkeri (Trimen)

Teracolus bowkeri Trimen, 1883. *Trans. ent. Soc. Lond.* **1883**: 358. Type locality: Cape Colony.

IDENTIFICATION

Adult. Consistently smaller than *agoye*. Male. Upperside: white with dark costa on hindwing; forewing apical patch tawny yellow, relatively larger than in *agoye*, with inner edge broadly and irregularly black. Underside: white with fine yellowish-brown to tawny-brown irroration on apex of forewing and hindwing. Female. Upperside: white with apical patch tawny yellow, with inner edge broadly brownish-black. Hindwing usually with a series of small subapical spots. Underside: similar to male.

Forewing lengths: male 19-22 mm; female 17-22 mm.

Early stages. Egg: unrecorded. Larva: green with slight dark irroration; there is a dorsal yellow longitudinal line and a similar lateral line on either side just below the spiracles. The dorsal line continues on head; the lateral line is variable and may be missing. Head is green with brown spot on frons. Larva is distinctly keel-shaped, tapering towards end; height at its greatest on first abdominal segment and at this point it is clearly taller than wide; anal end noticeably bifid, almost as in a Satyrid. The shape is very different from that of most *Colotis* which are cylindrical. Pupa: apple green, occasionally a very light ivory brown; not as flattened and wing cases less developed than in many small pierids, such as *C. (C.) evenina*; frons not drawn out to point, and is rather blunt, though the trace of a point can be just made out (Larsen, 1992b: 8).

HABITAT AND ECOLOGY

C. (C.) agoye bowkeri is an inhabitant of arid thornveld. Its flight is slower than *C. (C.) agoye agoye* but still fairly fast on the wing. The male flies swiftly and directly, usually near the ground, but when migrating or travelling at high speed it may fly up to 2-3 metres high. The female's flight, at times, may be fairly swift and sustained. It is often found feeding on flowers. In some years this subspecies participates in the mass migrations which fly across the north-eastern South Africa, at present they can be commonly found in the same habitat as the nominate subspecies.

Males appear to establish territories in the vicinity of the food plants. Here they patrol about the bushes, flying near the ground on which they constantly settle to rest. No aggressive behaviour has been noted.

The females fly at random through the scrub in search of suitable food plants on which to oviposit. The larvae are a lighter colour than the mature foliage of the food plant, however this together with the keel-shaped profile assists strongly in affording extremely good camouflage on the leaves of *Boscia albitrunca*. Many half-grown larvae die when single larvae of a parasitoid wasp emerges, and spins a cocoon of the *Apanteles*-type. The pupa is cryptic and is attached to a silk pad by the cremaster and held upright by a silken girdle around the middle (Larsen, 1992b: 8).

This subspecies is on the wing throughout the year but appears to be more prevalent during the warmer months.

Colotis agoye bowkeri male upperside

LARVAL FOOD PLANTS

Boscia albitrunca (Capparaceae).

DISTRIBUTION

South Africa, from the North-West Province, western Free State, Northern Cape and Namaqualand to southern Namibia and southern Botswana. During migrations this species can also be found further to the east, such as in Gauteng, Mpumalanga and the eastern Free State.

CONSERVATION

C. (C.) agoye is a reasonably widespread species and is under no threat.

Colotis agoye bowkeri female upperside

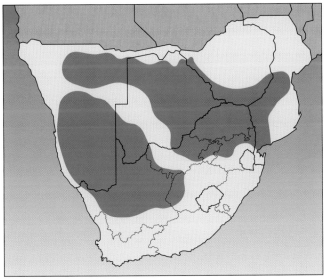

Distribution map of *Colotis agoye*

Subgenus *Teracolus* Swainson

Teracolus Swainson, 1823. *Zool. Ill. Ins.* **2**: 115. Type species: *Teracolus subfasciatus* Swainson, 1823, by monotypy.

Forewing with the apex more acute than in species of *Colotis*. M_1 never stalked with radials. Hindwing with MDC never much shorter than UDC.

Egg with 24 longitudinal ribs; pupa with wing-cases less prominent than in subgenus *Colotis.*

There are only two species in this subgenus.

KEY TO THE SUBGENUS *TERACOLUS*

1. UFW inner margin broadly darkened .... *C. eris*

   UFW inner margin not broadly darkened .... *C. subfasciatus*

Colotis (Teracolus) eris (Klug)

BANDED GOLD TIP

Pontia eris Klug, 1829. *Symb. Phys.*: pl. 6.

There are two subspecies of this fast-flying pierid. The nominate race covers most of the more arid habitats in Africa while the second, *contractus* Gabriel, 1954, is from Arabia. An arid form named *johnstoni* (Butler, 1886. *Entomologist's mon. Mag.* **23**: 29) which was described from Grahamstown in the Eastern Cape has the dark areas of the forewing smaller in both wet- and dry-season forms. This form was once thought to represent a southern subspecies but its distribution from the Eastern Cape to Botswana appears to intergrade with nominate *eris.*

Colotis (T.) eris eris (Klug)

Pontia eris Klug, 1829. *Symb. Phys.*: pl. 6. Type locality: Senegal.

IDENTIFICATION

Adult. Male. Upperside: white with inner and outer margin of forewing, and costa of hindwing, broadly black; apical area of forewing golden-ochreous with strong purplish iridescence and dark purplish-brown along the veins. Underside: white with brownish irroration on apex of forewing and hindwing; costa of hindwing thinly orange, submarginal area of forewing with large black spots. Female. Upperside: white to yellow with dark brown inner and outer margin; apex with spots of ground colour or ochreous orange to yellow; hindwing costa with dark brown patches. Underside: as in male.

The dry-season form *fatma* (Felder, 1865. *Reise Novara* **2**: 189) differs from the nominate wet-season form in the tawny or ochreous-brown underside of hindwing and apical area of forewing.

Other form names are available but all forms intergrade.

Forewing lengths: male 20-26 mm; female 20-27 mm.

Early stages. Egg: white when laid, developing red transverse bands if they are fertile; elongate barrel-shaped, diameter 0,5-0,8 mm, height 1,1-1,4 mm; with 24 to 26 longitudinal ribs braced by 40 cross ribs. Larva: first instar pale green with dorsal brick red markings and a fuscous-brown head; second instar more green, with brick-red markings broken up and whole surface sprinkled above with pale brick-red and head pale ochreous; third instar bright green with a pale dorsal line and head paler green; fourth instar less vivid green, with numerous red spots at base of setae, dorsal line narrow and inconspicuous, head pale green; fifth (final) instar much deeper green, with a broad pale cream lateral line across spiracles. It attains a length of 27 mm. Pupa: 20 mm long; moderately compressed laterally, cephalic projection short, triangular, wing-cases not very strongly projecting; bright green to dull yellow in colour and blends in remarkably well with the substrate on which it pupates (Clark, 1949: 166; S.F. Henning, 1979: 192; Clark, 1994: 372).

Colotis eris eris male upperside

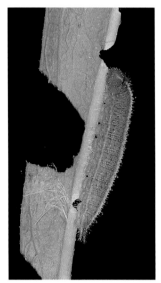

Colotis eris eris final instar larva   *Colotis eris eris* pupa

Colotis eris eris female upperside

HABITAT AND ECOLOGY

C. (T.) eris is an inhabitant of bushveld to arid thornveld. Males fly swiftly and directly, often at high speed, usually two or more metres above the ground. They swerve only to avoid obstacles in their path. Females are much slower but still fairly fast, spending most of the warmer hours of the day investigating food plants for suitable sites on which to lay their eggs. Both sexes can be found feeding on flowers.

The males establish their territories near the larval food plants and can often be observed circling rapidly around them, often quite high above the ground. Some rivers fringed with thorn trees are also favourite sites.

The females fly at random through the bush in search of suitable food plants on which to oviposit. The laying behaviour is similar in many *Colotis*. The female selects a bush and with fluttering wings will slowly manoeuvre herself through the entanglement of branches until she finds a suitable site to lay her egg. She will often lay more than one egg on a bush. The eggs are laid singly on the undersides of the leaves, usually near the young shoots. The egg hatches after 7 days. The first larval instar takes 7 days to complete, the second instar takes 6 days, third and fourth instars each take 5 days, the final instar takes 4 days. The larvae are very cryptic and are extremely difficult to detect amongst the leaves of the food plant. The pupa hatches after 17 days. It is attached by the cremastral hooks to a silken pad and is held upright by the silken girdle around the middle. It is also well camouflaged (Clark, 1949: 166; S.F. Henning, 1979: 192; Clark, 1994: 372).

This species can be found during most months of the year but appears to be particularly plentiful from September to April.

LARVAL FOOD PLANTS

Boscia oleoides, B. albitrunca (Capparaceae).

DISTRIBUTION

South Africa, from the Western Cape from as far west as Oudtshoorn, through the Eastern Cape and the Free State, KwaZulu-Natal, Northern Cape to the North-West, Gauteng, Mpumalanga and Northern Province, and into the bushveld regions of Swaziland, Moçambique, Zimbabwe, Botswana and Namibia.

CONSERVATION

C (T.) eris is a common widespread species and is under no threat.

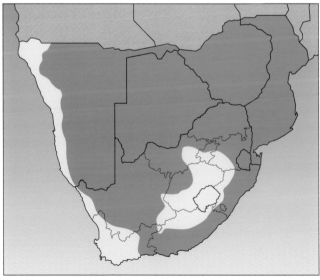

Distribution map of *Colotis eris*

Colotis (Teracolus) subfasciatus (Swainson)

LEMON TRAVELLER TIP

Teracolus subfasciatus Swainson, 1832. *Zool. Ill. Ins.* **2**: pl. 115.

There are two subspecies with the nominate from Southern Africa. The second subspecies *ducissa* (Dognin, 1891) occurs in East and Central Africa

Colotis (T.) subfasciatus subfasciatus (Swainson)

Teracolus subfasciatus Swainson, 1832. *Zool. Ill. Ins.* **2**: pl. 115. Type locality: South Africa.

IDENTIFICATION

Adult. Male. Upperside: bright yellow with black and yellow apical patch. Underside: greenish-white with darker irroration on apex of forewing and on hindwing; hindwing with a transverse, creamy white above and brown below, stripe from base to just short of the middle of the outer margin. Female. Upperside: yellow to greenish-white with broad orange tip. Underside: as in male.

Colotis subfasciatus subfasciatus form *ganymedes* male feeding on *Ehretia rigida*

Colotis subfasciatus subfasciatus form *ganymedes* male upperside

The dry-season form *ganymedes* (Trautmann, 1927. *Ent. Z., Frankf. a. M.* **41**: 301) has all dark markings of apical area of forewing much reduced, inner band only represented by separate spots; and hindwing underside light ochreous, densely striated with brown.

This species is fairly variable, particularly in the female, and males with a bluish-white ground colour have also been recorded.

Forewing lengths: male 24-30 mm; female 26-32 mm.

Early stages. Egg: pearlescent, off-white when laid, developing irregular russet rings within 48 hours if fertile; it turns dark grey-brown 24 hours before hatching; elongated, attenuated both ends, marginally so at base and pronounced at micropylar end; diameter 0,75 mm at its widest, height 1,75 mm, with 18 to 20 ribs only half of which reach micropyle, others stopping just short, and between 36 and 42 intersecting cross braces. Larva: first instar head dark brown, body initially tan but once larva has eaten, olive-green laterally and buff dorsally. Most conspicuous characteristics are well developed setal bases on 1st segment (giving impression of a collar), a forked 'tail', darker lateral markings on 11th and 12th segments and dark, prominent setal bases dorsally on 12th segment. First instar lasts 3 days and attains a length of 4 mm. Second instar head remains brown but body lighter green in colour, flecked lightly with brown and a diffuse, white dorsal median stripe spreading broadly at 1st segment; russet marking initially to be seen adjoining stripe in area of 1st & 2nd as well as 10th, 11th & 12th segments

but this later fades as it matures. Second instar grows to 7 mm and lasts 3 days. Third to fifth instars green throughout (including head) with a well-defined pale yellow dorsal stripe, duration 27 days. The larva is stout and attains a length of only 23 mm. Pupa: pale green in colour with a pale lateral line which is more pronounced along area of hindwing inner margin; wing cases shallowly keeled and maintain same depth as body (typical of subgenus *Teracolus* and unlike subgenus *Colotis* where the case is prominently keeled and flattened laterally). There is a short, pointed cephalic process.

HABITAT AND ECOLOGY

C. (T.) subfasciatus is predominantly a bushveld species. Both sexes can be found flying at exceptionally high speed which is probably only matched by *C. (T.) eris*. It too flies fairly high above the ground. Members of both sexes can be seen feeding on nectar.

The males establish their territories near the larval food plants where they can be seen flying rapidly around them. When they encounter other males they briefly circle each other before one flies off.

The females fly at random through the bush in search of suitable food plants on which to oviposit. When found they flit around the bushes of the food plant very rapidly and with equal rapidity and very little selective care, deposit eggs singly on the underside of the leaves. Several eggs were recorded being laid on grass and dead twigs in the vicinity of the food plant. Eggs are usually laid low down on the food plant on old leaves. The egg stage lasts 7 days. On hatching the 2 mm long larva partially or totally consumes the egg shell. The larval stage lasts a total of 33 days. The pupa is attached by the cremaster to a silk pad and held upright by a silk girdle. The pupal stage lasts 33 days. This species is on the wing throughout the year but is more plentiful during summer and autumn.

Colotis subfasciatus subfasciatus female

Colotis subfasciatus subfasciatus final instar larva

Colotis subfasciatus subfasciatus pupa

LARVAL FOOD PLANTS

Boscia albitrunca (Capparaceae).

DISTRIBUTION

South Africa, north of the Orange River in the Northern Cape and the Free State to the North-West, Northern and Mpumalanga Provinces. During migrations specimens may be found in the more easterly regions such as KwaZulu-Natal. It is found throughout Botswana, northern Namibia, Zimbabwe, Moçambique and northwards into central and East Africa.

CONSERVATION

C. (T.) subfasciatus is a widespread species and is under no threat.

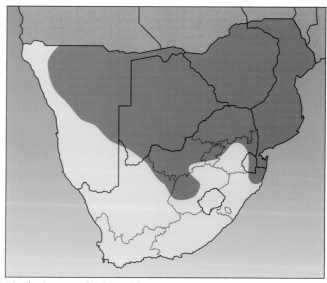

Distribution map of *Colotis subfasciatus*

Genus *Belenois* Hübner

Belenois Hübner, 1819. *Verz. bek. Schmett.* (6): 92. Type species: *Papilio calypso* Drury, 1773, by monotypy.

A large genus of very variable, predominantly African, species. Antennae long, with a rather narrow club. Forewing triangular, apex moderately acute; Sc either free (subgenus *Belenois s. str.*) or anastomosing with R$_1$ from near that vein's middle (subgenus *Anaphaeis* Hübner and *Pseudanaphaeis* Bernardi); both R$_1$ and R$_2$ arise close to each other well before upper angle; R$_3$, R$_{4+5}$ and M$_1$ stalked from upper angle, M$_1$ rising from the very long stalk of R$_3$ and R$_{4+5}$ nearer to upper angle than to origin of R$_{4+5}$; M$_3$ from lower angle; CuA$_1$ and CuA$_2$ from cell well before lower angle, CuA$_1$ arising a little nearer to M$_2$ than to CuA$_2$; 2A single from base. Hindwing with the precostal spur rather long, curved distad from near base; Rs, M$_1$ and M$_2$ arise separately from cell (van Son, 1949: 169).

Early stages: eggs elongate, tapering towards the micropyle, with about 12 longitudinal ribs (carinae) connected by numerous transverse ridges; laid either singly, or in clusters. Larvae cylindrical, slightly tapering near posterior end. Pupae with a small cylindrical cephalic projection, angular thoracic keel and with a single pair of dorso-lateral angular projections at the base of the abdomen (van Son, 1949: 169).

There are five species in Southern Africa, namely *B. thysa* (Hopffer), *B. zochalia* (Boisduval), *B. aurota* (Fabricius), *B. creona* (Cramer) and *B. gidica* (Godart).

The three subgenera *Belenois, Anaphaeis* and *Pseudanaphaeis* are available but are not all used by some authors. For example Carcasson (1981) uses only *Belenois* and *Pseudanaphaeis* while Henning, Pringle and Ball (1994) use *Belenois* and *Anaphaeis*.

This genus is famous for its mass migrations found throughout the more arid regions of Africa.

KEY TO THE SUBGENERA OF *BELENOIS*

1. Forewing with R$_2$ not anastomosed with Sc .... *Belenois*

   Forewing with R$_2$ anastomosed with Sc 2

2. Uncus longer than tegumen; aedeagus shorter than uncus; no apical spine on valve .... *Pseudanaphaeis*

   Uncus shorter than tegumen; aedeagus longer than uncus; strong apical spine on valve .... *Anaphaeis*

Subgenus *Belenois* Hübner

Belenois Hübner, 1819. *Verz. bek. Schmett.* (6): 92.

Forewing with veins Sc and R$_1$ free and not fusing with each other.

There are two species in this subgenus in Southern Africa.

KEY TO THE SPECIES OF SUBGENUS *BELENOIS*

1. UFW without black band from costa to lower angle of cell .... *B. thysa*

   UFW with black band from costa to lower angle of cell .... *B. zochalia*

Belenois (Belenois) thysa (Hopffer)

FALSE DOTTED BORDER WHITE

Pieris thysa Hopffer, 1855. *Mber. dt. Akad. Wiss. Berl.* **1855**: 639.

This species inhabits the forested areas down the eastern side of the Afrotropical region. There are three subspecies, *tricolor* (Ungemach, 1932) in Ethiopia, *meldolae* (Butler, 1872) from western Kenya and Sudan to Angola and the nominate race from eastern Kenya to South Africa. It is a possible mimic of the genus *Mylothris* which has been found to be unpalatable to birds.

Belenois (B.) thysa thysa (Hopffer)

Pieris thysa Hopffer, 1855. *Mber. dt. Akad. Wiss. Berl.* **1855**: 639. Type locality: East Africa.

IDENTIFICATION

Adult. Male. Upperside: white with black-spotted margin and small submarginal spots. Underside: white with orange base to forewing; hindwing and apex of forewing yellow; black markings similar to upperside. Female. Upperside: white to yellowish-orange, sometimes with bases broadly dusted with grey; marginal and submarginal black spots larger than on male and may be very large, forming a broad, diffuse, marginal band. Underside: similar to male but more yellowish-orange with basal orange area of forewing very broad.

The dry-season form with smaller black markings has been named form *vansoni* Pennington, 1978 (*Pennington's Butterflies of Southern Africa* (1): 170).

Forewing lengths: male 29-40 mm; female 28-38 mm.

Early stages. Egg: pale yellow when laid, becoming brownish-pink with a yellow base if fertile; diameter 0,6 mm, height 1,6 mm; with 10 longitudinal ribs, all extending to the micropyle and braced by 25-26 cross ribs. Larva: fifth (final) instar dorsal dark green, ventrally pale green, with a white lateral line below spiracles and a broad yellow dorso-lateral longitudinal stripe on each side. First instar is 1,5 mm long on emergence and grows to 4 mm, the second instar grows to 6 mm in 4 days, the third instar grows to 10 mm, the fourth instar grows to 17,5 mm and the final instar larva grows to 36,5 mm. Pupa: 26 mm long: green in colour (Migdoll 1987: photographs 196a (larva) and 196b (pupa); Clark, 1994: 374).

HABITAT AND ECOLOGY

B. (B.) thysa is an inhabitant of coastal forest. The male can be seen flying swiftly along forest edges, down paths or in sunlit glades. It often flies fairly close to the forest vegetation and infrequently alights on the forest edge. The female is more often seen within the undergrowth, only venturing out into the sunlight to move from one patch of forest to another or to feed on flowers. She settles frequently on forest vegetation or on the ground. Both sexes can be found feeding at flowers although the male does not appear to spend too long at any one flower. It may also be found sucking at damp patches of ground. Apparently this species, the female in particular, is a mimic of the genus *Mylothris* both in appearance and in the flight of the female, the genus *Mylothris* apparently being unpalatable to birds (Carpenter, 1941).

Males establish their territories along forest edges, down paths or in sunlit glades. Here they patrol along their selected stretches of forest, continually searching for females.

The females fly at random in the undergrowth in search of suitable food plants on which to oviposit. They lay their eggs singly on the edge of young shoots of the food plant. The first instar larva eats its way out of the egg near the top. It rests on the centre of the leaf

Belenois thysa thysa male upperside

Belenois thysa thysa female upperside

Belenois thysa thysa male underside

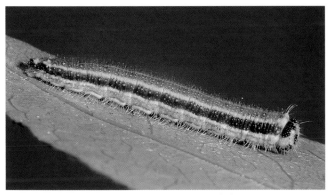

Belenois thysa thysa final instar larva (Photo: I. Migdoll)

Belenois thysa thysa pupa (Photo: I. Migdoll)

and feeds at intervals off the edge. The larva moults where it feeds and eats the discarded skin. The larval stage takes about one month with the final instar taking about 10 days. The pupa is attached by the cremaster and held upright by the silken girdle around the middle. The imago emerges after 11 to 15 days (Clark, 1994: 374).

This species is on the wing throughout the year with summer being the best time for it.

LARVAL FOOD PLANTS

Capparis sp.; *Maerua racemulosa* (Capparaceae).

DISTRIBUTION

South Africa, Eastern Cape from Port St. Johns through KwaZulu-Natal to Moçambique and the eastern border of Zimbabwe.

CONSERVATION

B. (B.) thysa is a widespread species but the forested areas are under pressure all along the eastern seaboard, so conservation measures may have to be considered in the future. At the moment it is under no threat.

NOTE: *Belenois ogygia* (Trimen) was described from two specimens collected in KwaZulu-Natal between 1866 and 1869. These two specimens were originally thought to represent a male and a female but recent information proves that they are dissimilar males. A later specimen apparently seen by Pennington has not been traced. The species was further investigated by Quickelberge (1982) with results that clearly indicate that *B. ogygia* is in all probability a hybrid of *B. thysa* and *B. zochalia. The South African Red Data Book – Butterflies* by S.F. & G.A. Henning (1989: 164) did not include it as a valid species but merely listed it as a species requiring further investigation. It was finally downgraded from a valid species in *Pennington's Butterflies of Southern Africa* **2** by G.A. Henning (1994: 294).

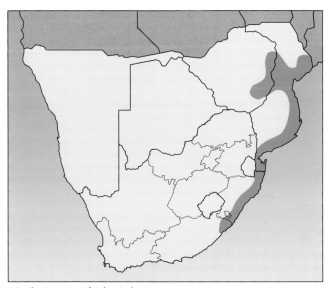

Distribution map of *Belenois thysa*

329

Belenois (Belenois) zochalia (Boisduval)

FOREST WHITE

Pieris zochalia Boisduval, 1836. *Spéc. gén. Lépid.* **1**: 506.

There are four subspecies of this woodland white. The nominate is confined to Southern Africa. Other subspecies occur in East Africa, Ethiopia and Cameroon.

Belenois (B.) zochalia zochalia (Boisduval)

Pieris zochalia Boisduval, 1836. *Spéc. gén. Lépid.* **1**: 506. Type locality: Kaffraria.

IDENTIFICATION

Adult. Male. Upperside: white; forewing with broad black and white apex, and broad black discocellular bar widening along costa. Hindwing with black spots at ends of veins. Underside: forewing white with yellow at apex and black markings as on upperside. Hindwing yellow with veins narrowly blackened. Female. Upperside: white to chrome yellow with markings similar to male, only much broader. Various combinations and shades can be found with white forewings and yellow hindwings being almost as common as pure white females. Underside: similar to male but with yellowish-orange at base of forewing.

Forewing lengths: male 25-32 mm; female 24-31 mm.

Early stages. Egg: yellowish-orange; diameter 0,5 mm, height 1 mm; with 12 longitudinal ribs braced by fine cross ribs. Larva: first instar larva yellow; second to fourth instars green; fifth (final) instar with various colour forms ranging from yellowish-green to dark green, markings vary from almost nothing to a broad yellow dorsal stripe and prominent black and yellow lateral stripes. Pupa: 20-21 mm long: cryptic, colour variable from pale to dark green (Clark, 1949: 175 ; Clark, 1994: 376).

HABITAT AND ECOLOGY

B. (B.) zochalia is an inhabitant of woodland, coastal bush and forest. The males fly rapidly and elusively along forest edges and settle frequently on the edge of the bush. The females are much slower than the males and generally keep to the undergrowth, seldom emerging unless to feed on flowers. Females also settle frequently and spend a lot of time sunning themselves in small patches of sunlight which find their way down into the undergrowth. Both sexes can be seen feeding on flowers. The species has also been recorded roosting communally at night, often with other species of pierid (Larsen, 1991).

The males establish their territories along the edges of forest or clearings. Here they patrol a fairly lengthy stretch of forest or woodland flying quite rapidly, occasionally slowing down to investigate a particular patch of vegetation in search of females. Their reaction to other males encountered in their patrolling is limited to a brief circling.

The females fly at random in the undergrowth searching for

Belenois zochalia zochalia male upperside

Belenois zochalia zochalia yellow hindwing female form upperside

Belenois zochalia zochalia female upperside

Belenois zochalia zochalia female underside

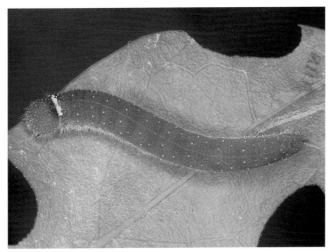

Belenois zochalia zochalia final instar larva

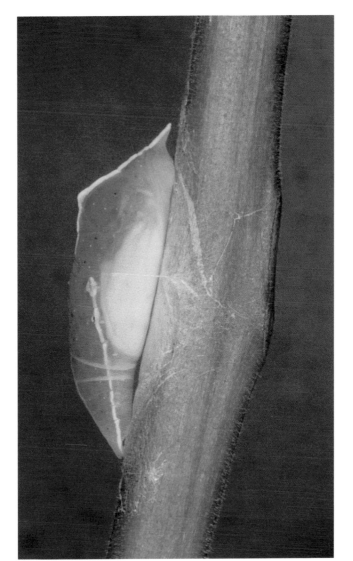

Belenois zochalia zochalia pupa

suitable food plants on which to oviposit. Eggs are laid singly and they take about eight days to hatch. There are 5 larval instars lasting a total of 30 days. The pupa is cryptic and the pupal stage lasts for about 20 days (Clark, 1949: 175 ; Clark, 1994: 376).

This species is on the wing throughout the year although in the more temperate areas the flight period may be restricted to the warmer months.

LARVAL FOOD PLANTS

Boscia oleoides, Maerua racemulosa, M. cafra, Capparis spp. (Capparaceae).

DISTRIBUTION

South Africa, from the Great Brak River in the Western Cape, Eastern Cape, to KwaZulu-Natal and to Mpumalanga, North-West, Northern and Gauteng Provinces, northwards to Swaziland, Moçambique and Zimbabwe. Also recorded from Katima Mulilo in the Caprivi, Namibia.

CONSERVATION

B. (B.) zochalia is a widespread species, being found in a variety of woodland habitats and is under no threat.

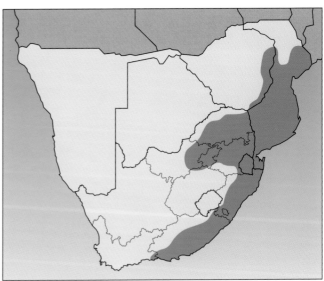

Distribution map of *Belenois zochalia*

Subgenus *Anaphaeis* Hübner

Anaphaeis Hübner 1819. *Verz. bek. Schmett* (6): 93. Type species: *Papilio creona* Cramer by selection by Scudder, 1875.

This subgenus can be distinguished at once by veins Sc and R_1 of the forewing, which unite (anastomose) and run as one vein to the costa.

There are two species in this subgenus in Southern Africa.

KEY TO SUBGENUS *ANAPHAEIS*

1. Forewing without thick blackish bar across end of cell
.... *B. creona*

   Forewing with thick blackish bar across end of cell .... *B. aurota*

Belenois (Anaphaeis) aurota (Fabricius)

BROWN-VEINED WHITE

Papilio aurota Fabricius, 1793. *Ent. Syst.* **3**: 197.

A common migrant over the entire Afrotropical region and India. Other subspecies occur in Asia.

Belenois (A.) aurota aurota (Fabricius)

Papilio aurota Fabricius, 1793. *Ent. Syst.* **3**: 197. Type locality: Coromandel (Madras coast, India).

IDENTIFICATION

Adult. Male. Upperside: white with black and white apical area; discocellular bar weak, not reaching costa. Underside: white with forewing apical area and hindwing pale yellow; hindwing veins broadly brown. Female. Upperside: white to creamy yellow, markings similar to male but brown and much broader; discocellular bar broad and fused with costa. Underside: as in male but brown markings broader.

Belenois aurota female underside

Forewing lengths: male 23-30 mm; female 24-30 mm.

Early stages. Egg: white when laid, becoming yellow later; elongate barrel-shape, diameter 0,5 mm, height 0,9 mm with 12 to 14 longitudinal ribs and 24 to 28 cross ribs. Larva: first instar pale dull yellow with dark hairs; second to fourth instars green with a broad brown (changing to black) lateral stripe; fifth (final) instar variable in colour, usually green with a broad brown to yellowish brown dorsal stripe. In pre-pupal stage larva becomes a plain translucent green. Pupa: 20 mm long; cephalic projection very slightly upturned; lateral spines at base of abdomen small, broadly triangular and usually very dark throughout; sixth segment narrow, the projections not starting from its extreme edge; a median black projection beyond wing cases; variable in colour, can be green with dull markings, white or grey with black markings, pale brown with dark-brown markings (Clark, 1949: 180; S.F. Henning, 1984b: 42; Clark, 1994: 378).

HABITAT AND ECOLOGY

Belenois (A.) aurota can be found throughout most open habitats. Its flight is fairly fast and direct although many males may be seen flying slowly around the food plants searching for females. The females can also fly fast but are often seen fluttering amongst the branches of the food plants searching for suitable sites on which to lay their eggs. Both sexes can be found feeding at flowers or on damp sand or mud.

Nearly every year, sometimes in December, but more usually in January or February or even March, millions of *B. (A.) aurota* make their way over the grasslands of the Free State, Lesotho, KwaZulu-Natal, North-West Province, Gauteng, Mpumalanga and Northern Province, always flying in a north-easterly direction. They cover vast distances, occasionally stopping to rest or to feed on flowers or to drink at muddy patches and then continue on their way. Fly-ing almost from sunrise to sunset and even crossing vast stretches of ocean, they roost at night in their hundreds on low bushes and plants. Bad weather usually brings these migrations to a halt (S.F. Henning, 1984b: 42).

The males patrol all day in search of females. They fly rapidly around the food plants but individual territories are difficult to assess due to the number of specimens on the wing. Some males can be seen slowly investigating food plants for females.

The females fly at random through the bush in search of suitable food plants on which to lay. They lay their eggs in clusters of about fifty on the leaves of the food plant. The egg stage takes about 8 days. The first instar larva emerges from the side of the egg near the top. It consumes the eggshell as its first meal. The larvae are cryptic and variable. They are gregarious in the first few instars, and cluster together when at rest and feed in close proximity to each other. They will completely defoliate a tree at times and the need for adequate supplies of food is no doubt one of the causes of migration. In the final instar the larvae feed and rest individually and pupate in isolation. The larval stage takes about 28 days. The pupa is secured by the cremaster and is held in place by a silken girdle around the middle. It is usually attached to a leaf, twig or the bark of the tree. The imago emerges after about 14 days (Clark, 1949: 180; S.F. Henning, 1984b: 42; Clark, 1994: 378).

B. (A,) aurota is on the wing throughout the year but is more plentiful during the warmer months.

Belenois aurota male feeding on the naturalised exotic *Verbena brasiliensis*

LARVAL FOOD PLANTS

Boscia albitrunca, B. oleoides, Maerua cafra, M. juncea, M. angolensis, Capparis sepiaria, C. tomentosa, C. fascicularis, Capparis sp. (Capparaceae).

DISTRIBUTION

Throughout Southern Africa.

CONSERVATION

B. (A.) aurota is a common and widespread species and is under no threat.

Belenois aurota female upperside

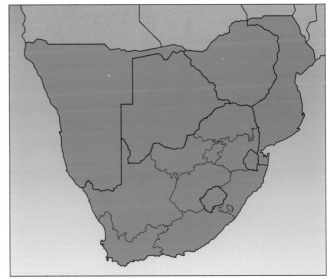

Belenois aurota final instar larva

Belenois aurota pupa

Distribution map of *Belenois aurota*

Belenois (Anaphaeis) creona (Cramer)

AFRICAN COMMON WHITE

Papilio creona Cramer, 1775. *Uitl. Kapellen* **1**: 148.

There are seven recognised subspecies spread over the Afrotropical region, the nominate from West Africa. Only one subspecies, *severina*, occurs in Southern Africa.

Belenois (A.) creona severina (Stoll)

Papilio severina Stoll, 1781. *Uitl. Kapellen* **4**: 95. Type locality: Cape of Good Hope.

IDENTIFICATION

Adult. Male. Upperside: white with black and white apical area; discocellular bar normally reduced to a dot but may become a weak bar. Underside: forewing apical area and hindwing yellow; hindwing with submarginal and marginal areas broadly dark brown to black; some veins weakly blackened, particularly near base. Female. Upperside: white to yellow with marginal and submarginal areas very broadly blackened; discocellular bar may be a dot or weak bar and may be fused with broad margin. Underside: similar to male but more orange-yellow with broader margins and an orange base to forewing.

Forewing lengths: male 21-28 mm; female 23-29 mm.

Early stages. Egg: white when laid, becoming pale yellow later; barrel-shaped diameter 0,5 mm, height 0,95 mm with 12 longitudinal ribs and about 25 cross ribs ending in slight pointed projections. (In *aurota* the top is evenly rounded). Larva: first instar yellow, later changing to green; second to fourth instars generally green in colour; fifth (final) instar very variable in colour, being green with various shades of dorsal stripe ranging from blue to yellowish-green. In the pre-pupal stage the larva turns yellow dorsally and black on the sides. Pupa: about 20 mm long; broader than in *B. aurota*, and with larger elongate-triangular lateral spines at base of abdomen; these are light coloured; sixth segment broadest (narrow in *B. aurota*), and the projections start from its extreme edge; projection beyond wing-cases is small; colour variable ranging from green to creamy white to dark brown (Clark, 1949:184; Clark, 1994: 380).

HABITAT AND ECOLOGY

B. (A.) creona is a common inhabitant of woodland and bushveld. The male does not fly as fast as the others of the genus and is more often than not seen flying in a fairly leisurely manner around its woodland habitat. The females fly more slowly than the male and can often be seen flying amongst the branches of its food plant. It can be found feeding on flowers or sucking, often in great numbers, at damp sand or mud. Larsen (1991) recorded it roosting communally at night. Also a prolific migrant at times but not as regular as *B. aurota*. It is more often recorded in migrations further to the north than in the annual South African migration.

The males establish their territories in the vicinity of the larval food plants. Here they appear to patrol a fairly extensive area around the food plants. Encounters with other males may result in circling but usually there is no other reaction.

The females fly at random about the trees in search of suitable food plants on which to lay. They lay their eggs in clusters of about fifty which take about 5 days to hatch. There are 5 larval instars lasting a total of 17 days. The larvae are gregarious in the first few instars. The pupa is held upright by a silken girdle and is attached by the cremaster to a silken pad. The duration of the pupal stage is from 2 to 4 weeks (Clark, 1949: 184; Clark, 1994: 380).

Belenois creona severina male upperside

Belenois creona severina mating pair female below

This species is on the wing throughout the year in the warmer areas but is scarce during the winter months in the more temperate areas of its range.

LARVAL FOOD PLANTS

Boscia albitrunca, B. oleoides, Maerua cafra, M. racemulosa, M. angolensis, Capparis sepiaria var. *citrifolia, C. fascicularis* var. *zeyheri, C. tomentosa, Capparis* spp. (Capparaceae).

DISTRIBUTION

South Africa, from the Western Cape extending westwards as far as Mossel Bay although some migrant records exist from further west. It extends through the Eastern Cape, KwaZulu-Natal, Northern Province, Mpumalanga, Gauteng, North-West Province, northwards into Namibia, Botswana, Zimbabwe, Swaziland and Moçambique.

CONSERVATION

B. (A.) creona severina is a common and widespread species and is under no threat.

Belenois creona severina female upperside

Belenois creona severina final-instar larvae. Note colour variations even among individuals from the same batch of eggs

Belenois creona severina pupa

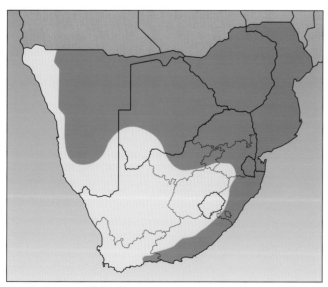

Distribution map of *Belenois creona*

Subgenus *Pseudanaphaeis* Bernardi

Pseudanaphaeis Bernardi, 1953. *Rev. franc. Ent.* **20**(1): 50. Type species: *Pieris gidica* Godart, by original designation.

The subcostal vein of the forewing is anastomosed with R_1. Genitalia differ considerably from *Belenois* in both sexes.

There is one species in Southern Africa.

Belenois (Pseudanaphaeis) gidica (Godart)

AFRICAN VEINED WHITE

Pieris gidica Godart, 1819. *Encycl. Méth. d'Hist. Nat.* (Zool.) **9**: 131.

Three subspecies are recognised through Africa with the nominate one coming from Southern Africa.

Belenois (P.) gidica gidica (Godart)

Pieris gidica Godart, 1819. *Encycl. Méth. d'Hist. Nat.* (Zool.) **9**: 131. Type locality: Cape of Good Hope.

IDENTIFICATION

Adult. Male. Upperside: white with diffuse apical patch on forewing; discocellular bar distinct but narrow. Hindwing with diffuse marginal and submarginal markings. Underside: white with pale yellow to brown hindwing and apical area of forewing; hindwing with veins narrowly dark brown which on brown specimens become paler and blend into ground colour; brown specimens with a transverse, white above dark brown below, streak from base to just short of middle of outer margin. Female. Upperside: white or yellow with broad but usually diffuse margins; discocellular bar on forewing broad to costa, on hindwing a quadrangular mark; bases may be broadly darkened with grey, even fusing with discocellulars on forewing. Underside: similar to male but more orange-yellow with base of forewing yellowish.

The normal wet-season form in Southern Africa is form *doubledayi* (Wallengren, 1857. *K. svenska VetenskAkad. Handl.* (N.F.) 2(4): 8).

Other form names are available including the white female form *westwoodi* (Wallengren, 1857. l.c.: 9).

Forewing lengths: male 28-32 mm; female 26-34 mm.

Early stages. Egg: bright red in colour; diameter 0,4 mm, height 1 mm. Larva: variable in colour; first instar pale yellow tinged with pinkish anteriorly; second to fourth instars mottled with green and with a red lateral stripe which changes later to dark green; fifth

Belenois gidica form *doubledayi* male upperside

Belenois gidica form *doubledayi* male underside

Belenois gidica male underside

(final) instar varies from a light coloured form which is largely plain green with a yellowish-green dorsal stripe to a darker reddish mottled form with less markings but with the first segment more densely white. Pupa: creamy-white to green with wing cases much larger in proportion than *B. aurota* or *B. creona*; lateral projections placed well behind middle and cephalic spine acute and directed obliquely ventrad (Clark, 1949: 189; Clark, 1994: 382).

HABITAT AND ECOLOGY

B. (P.) gidica is an inhabitant of bushveld and woodland. The male's flight is swift and direct as it dodges around the trees and bushes. It often flies up to three metres above the ground. It stops frequently to feed on flowers or to rest on the ground. The females usually fly low down and may be seen fluttering in the undergrowth. Females may settle for comparatively long periods on the ground or on sunny bushes. Both sexes can be found feeding on flowers or on damp sand or mud.

The males usually establish their territories in well-wooded areas in the vicinity of the larval food plants. Here they follow an irregular course over and among the undergrowth. They patrol this territory throughout most of the warmer hours of the day.

The females fly at random in the undergrowth in search of suitable food plants on which to oviposit. They lay their eggs singly on the leaves of the food plant and these take about 10 days to hatch. The larval stage lasts about 4 weeks and there are 5 instars. The pupa is attached by the cremaster to a silken pad and is held upright by a silken girdle around the middle. The pupal stage lasts about 25 days (Clark, 1949: 189; Clark, 1994: 382).

This species is on the wing throughout the year but is more abundant during the warmer months, with autumn being a good time for it.

LARVAL FOOD PLANTS

Capparis sepiaria var. *citrifolia, C. tomentosa* (Capparaceae).

DISTRIBUTION

South Africa, from Mossel Bay in the Western Cape, through the Eastern Cape and KwaZulu-Natal, to Mpumalanga and Northern Province, into Botswana, northern Namibia, Zimbabwe, Swaziland and Moçambique, northwards over most of Africa south of the Sahara.

CONSERVATION

B. (P.) gidica is a common widespread species and is under no threat.

Belenois gidica form *doubledayi* female upperside

Belenois gidica final instar larva

Belenois gidica pupa. Note the 'thorns' on the wing cases imitating those of the food plant – a species of *Capparis*

Genus *Pontia* Fabricius

Pontia Fabricius, 1807. *Mag. f. Insektenk* (Illiger) **6**: 283. Type species: *Papilio daplidice* L., 1758, by selection by Curtis, 1824.

A predominantly northern hemisphere genus closely related to *Pieris* Schrank (1801: 152). The antennae are long, with a rather broad and short club. Forewing with the costa straight, outer margin oblique; Sc, R_1 and R_2 free, R_3 usually fused with R_{4+5}, but occasionally the fusion is incomplete; M_1 from the stalk of R_{3+4+5}; MDC much shorter than LDC. Hindwing with precostal spur strong, curved distad in its distal portion; R_3, M_1 and M_2 separate, MDC much shorter than either UDC or LDC, the latter slightly angled (van Son, 1949: 209).

Early stages: eggs elongate, tapering towards the micropyle, with about 12 longitudinal ribs (carinae) connected by numerous transverse ridges; laid singly. Larvae cylindrical, tapering slightly near posterior end. Pupae with a small dorsally flattened cephalic projection, angular thoracic keel and with a pair of dorso-lateral angular projections at the base of the abdomen.

Food plants are species of Brassicaceae.

The genus is largely Holarctic, four species occur in Africa, but only one is found in Southern Africa.

Subgenus *Pontia* Fabricius

Pontia Fabricius, 1807. *Mag. f. Insektenk.* (Illiger) **6**: 283.

Pontia (Pontia) helice (Linnaeus)

COMMON MEADOW WHITE

Papilio helice Linnaeus, 1764. *Mus. Lud. Ulr. Reg.*: 243.

Two subspecies are recognised, the nominate from Southern Africa and *johnstoni* (Crowley, 1887) from East Africa. It occurs widely in Southern Africa but more sparingly further north, the East African subspecies being restricted to highland grassveld.

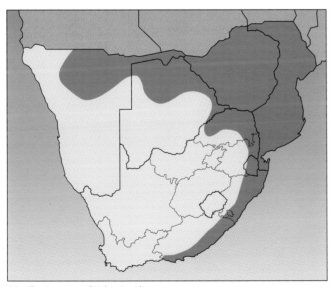

Distribution map of *Belenois gidica*

Pontia (P.) helice helice (Linnaeus)

Papilio helice Linnaeus, 1764. *Mus. Lud. Ulr. Reg.*: 243. Type locality: South Africa

IDENTIFICATION

Adult. Male. Upperside: white with black apex containing large white submarginal spots; discocellular bar broad but not confluent with costa. Underside: white with apex of forewing and veins of hindwing broadly blackish-brown with yellow edging; discocellular bar black and confluent with costa. Female. Upperside: white to yellowish-white with black apex containing large white submarginal spots; forewing with a large discocellular bar and a black postdiscal patch on inner margin; hindwing with a black postdiscal and submarginal area containing large white submarginal spots. Underside: as in male but forewing dark markings more extensive.

Forewing lengths: male 19-25 mm; female 19-27 mm.

Early stages. Egg: pale yellow when laid, becoming dull orange later; diameter 0,5 mm, height 0,9 mm; with 12 longitudinal ribs and about 30 cross ribs. Larva: first instar pale yellow with a black head; second to fourth instars yellow, with greyish-blue dorsal and lateral stripes and a bluish-grey underside, head yellow or greenish; fifth (final) instar similar but with orange subdorsal and spiracular spots on anterior part of segments, and underside greenish. It attains a length of about 28 mm. Pupa: 20 mm long; light greenish-grey with yellow longitudinal stripes and a reddish thoracic keel; cephalic projection flattened dorsally, with black edging and a fairly acute tip (Clark, 1949: 211; Clark, 1994: 390).

HABITAT AND ECOLOGY

P. (P.) helice is found throughout most open habitats. It has a slow, fluttery flight. It keeps very low to the ground as it bustles around between the herbaceous plants that it favours. It often settles on low plants or stops to feed on flowers. The species can be plentiful at times but recent migratory behaviour is scant although there are older records from both southern and eastern Africa.

The males show hilltopping behaviour on hot and sunny days. They ascend to the tops of koppies and hills and establish territories about the summits. Sometimes two to six males congregate on one hill, patrolling their particular areas. New individuals flying on to the summit are quickly chased off. At other times they establish their territories on the flats in the vicinity of the larval food plants.

The females fly at random in search of suitable food plants on which to lay. They lay their eggs singly on the young seedpods or leaves of the food plant and they take from 5 to 9 days to hatch. The discarded shell is not eaten. The larval stage lasts about 16 days. The main setae are forked at the tip and exude a liquid which may be defensive in nature. Pupation takes place on the food-plant, other neighbouring plants or any suitable object. The pupa is attached by the cremaster to a silken pad and held upright by a silken girdle. The pupal stage takes from 4 days to 2 weeks (Clark, 1949: 211; Clark, 1994: 390).

This species is on the wing throughout the year in favourable habitats.

LARVAL FOOD PLANTS

Heliophila linearis, Heliophila sp., *Lepidum capense, Lobularia maritima, Sisymbrium officinale* (Brassicaceae); *Reseda odorata* (Resedaceae).

DISTRIBUTION

Throughout South Africa, Lesotho, southern Namibia, southern Botswana, Zimbabwe, Swaziland and Moçambique.

CONSERVATION

P. (P.) helice is a common widespread species and is under no threat.

Pontia helice helice male underside feeding on *Vernonia oligocephala*

Pontia helice helice male upperside

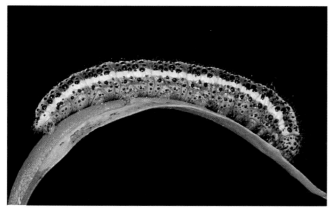

Pontia helice helice final instar larva

Pontia helice helice pupa

Pontia helice helice female upperside

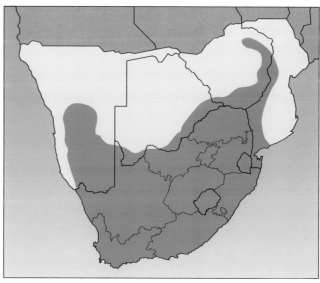

Distribution map of *Pontia helice*

343

Genus *Dixeia* Talbot

Dixeia Talbot, 1932. *Entomologist* **65**: 36. Type species: *Pieris charina* Boisduval, 1836, by original designation.

A small to moderate sized species. The antennae are long with a rather abrupt club. The wings are white or yellow, generally with dotted margins. Forewing triangular, apex subacute; R_1 and R_2 from cell, R_3 and R_{4+5} on a long stalk; MDC a little shorter than LDC. Hindwing with the precostal spur moderately long, strongly bent outwards from near base; MDC much longer than UDC; LDC shorter than UDC (van Son, 1949: 189).

Early stages: eggs elongate-conical, with about 12 longitudinal ribs (carinae) connected by 30-35 transverse ridges; laid either singly or in clusters. Larvae shortly pubescent, elongate, cylindrical, tapering to the shortly bifid posterior end. Pupae rather thick set, with a moderate cephalic projection and small, lateral processes on thorax; abdomen much widened near base, with prominent lateral processes.

Food plants species of Capparaceae.

There are ten species in the Afrotropical region, five of which occur in Southern Africa, namely *D. charina* (Boisduval), *D. doxo* (Godart), *D. leucophanes* Vári, *D. pigea* (Boisduval) and *D. spilleri* (Spiller). These all come from South Africa except *D. leucophanes* which occurs in Zimbabwe and Moçambique.

KEY TO THE GENUS *DIXEIA*

1. Ground colour yellow .... *D. spilleri*

   Ground colour white 2

2. Large species, antenna shorter than cell of forewing .... *D. pigea*

   Not large species, antenna longer than cell of forewing 3

3. Upperside veins blackened; forewing marginal band continuous; female basally dusted with grey and outer margin of forewing straight .... *D. doxo*

   Upperside veins not darkened; forewing marginal band not continuous; female not grey basally; outer margin of forewing not straight .... *D. charina*

Dixeia charina (Boisduval)

AFRICAN SMALL WHITE

Pieris charina Boisduval, 1836. *Spéc. gén. Lépid.* **1**: 525.

There are seven recognised subspecies with the nominate occurring in Southern Africa. The subspecies *simana* (Hopffer, 1855) from Moçambique was once thought to occur within the Southern African subregion but is now considered to occur from north of the subregion.

Dixeia charina charina (Boisduval)

Pieris charina Boisduval, 1836. *Spéc. gén. Lépid.* **1**: 525. Type locality: Kaffraria.

IDENTIFICATION

Adult. Male. Upperside: white, unmarked except for small black marginal dots. Underside: ground colour either white or yellowish; hindwing and apex of forewing stippled with dark grey. Female. Upperside: creamy-white with dark brown forewing margin and a series of postdiscal spots; occasionally also a spot at end of cell. Underside: similar to male but with a series of postdiscal spots on forewing.

Dixeia charina charina form *anactoriae* female (Photo: P.J. Sharland)

The dry-season form *anactoriae* (Doubleday, 1842. *Zool. Misc.*: 77) has the dark markings reduced. Underside: stippled with lighter brown and the ground colour is yellowish.

Forewing lengths: male 19-25 mm; female 19-23 mm.

Early stages. Egg: white when laid, becoming yellow later; diameter 0,4 mm, height 0,9 mm; with about 12 longitudinal ribs, half of which reach micropyle where they are produced into sharp points, and braced by about 28 cross ribs. Larva: first instar light yellowish-brown with a pinkish tinge on sides, and a blackish head; second to fourth instars light green, dorsal stripe edged with very dark green, lightening lower down the sides, and head light green with a brown crown; fifth (final) instar extremely variable in colour, light green to pinkish-brown with a dark green dorsal stripe or speckled and marked laterally with brown. It attains a length of 30 mm. Pupa: 18 mm long; head with narrow, apically rounded projection; dorsal keel angularly produced at middle; wing-cases hardly projecting; abdomen strongly widened laterally near base, with large and acute projections; colour highly variable, being light green to brown to dull yellow-green with brown markings (Clark, 1949: 192; Clark, 1994: 384).

HABITAT AND ECOLOGY

D. charina is an inhabitant of coastal forest and moist woodland. The males fly fairly swiftly around the edges of thick bush, often at random rising and falling. They are not however as fast as many of the other whites. They settle frequently along the forest edge. Females fly more slowly than the males and generally keep to the shelter of the bush, only venturing out to feed on flowers or bask briefly in the sun. Both sexes can be found feeding on flowers.

Males establish territories along forest margins. They patrol along a suitable sunny stretch of forest or woodland margin. Encounters with other males have not been observed.

The females fly at random in the bush in search of suitable food plants on which to oviposit. They lay their eggs singly on the tips of young shoots of the food plant. The egg takes about 7 days to hatch. The larva emerges from the side of the egg near the top and eats part of the egg shell as its first meal. The pupa is attached by the cremaster and is held upright by a silken girdle around the middle. It is well camouflaged on the food plant (Clark, 1949: 192; Clark, 1994: 384).

This species is on the wing throughout the year in most localities, although more plentiful during the warmer months.

Dixeia charina charina form *anactoriae* male upperside

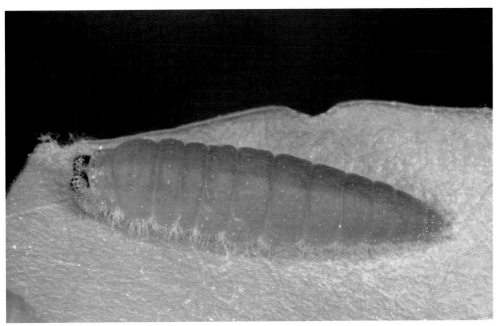

Dixeia charina charina final instar larva

LARVAL FOOD PLANTS

Capparis sepiaria var. *citrifolia* (Capparaceae).

DISTRIBUTION

South Africa, from the Western Cape at Mossel Bay to the Eastern Cape, up the KwaZulu-Natal coast to Moçambique. Isolated pockets have been recorded in Mpumalanga around Barberton.

CONSERVATION

D. charina is not threatened although some populations can be extremely local.

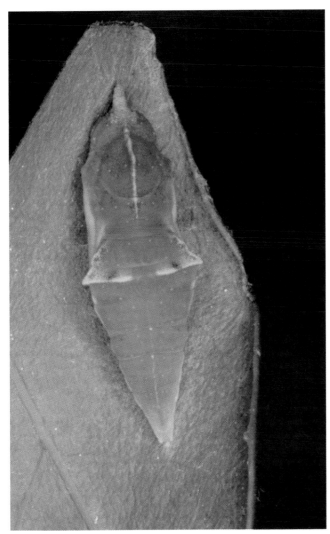

Dixeia charina charina pupa

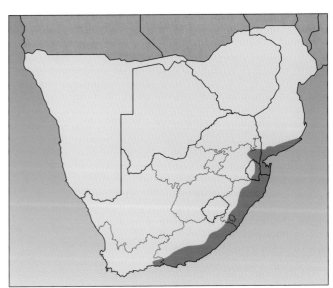

Distribution map of *Dixeia charina*

Dixeia doxo (Godart)

BLACK-VEINED SMALL WHITE

Pieris doxo Godart, 1819. *Encycl. Méth. d'Hist. Nat.* (Zool.)
9: 123.

There are five subspecies of *doxo* currently recognised, the nominate from West Africa. One subspecies, *parva*, occurs in Southern Africa. The straight outer margins and darkened veins usually identify this species. *D. leucophanes* Vári from Zimbabwe is very similar but may be identified in the male by the lack of black discocellular spots on the underside.

Dixeia doxo parva Talbot

Dixeia doxo parva Talbot, 1943. *Proc. R. ent. Soc. Lond.*
93: 112. Type locality: Southern Rhodesia (Zimbabwe)

IDENTIFICATION

Adult. Male. Upperside: white with a strong black apical patch on forewing; all veins finely blackened and there may be grey dusting at bases. Underside: white with an odd faint postdiscal spot and veins weakly blackened; fore- and hindwings with a small black discocellular spot; apex of forewing and hindwing may be finely stippled with brown in dry-season form. Female. Upperside: white with apex charcoal to dark brown and a series of black postdiscal spots, the lower one, which is situated in middle of wing, is large and distinct. Underside: white with apex of forewing and hindwing yellowish with the odd, indistinct, postdiscal spot. Dry-season form may be heavily stippled with brown on hindwing and apex of forewing.

Forewing lengths: male 21-25 mm; female 19-24 mm.

Early stages. Egg: pale cream turning red after 24 hours; height 1 mm and bottle-shaped with 10-12 longitudinal ribs. Larva: first instar on emergence 1,5 mm long, yellow-white with a faint brown dorso-lateral stripe, head black, setae black, and attains a length of 2,5 mm; fifth (final) instar green with a fawn-brown dorsal stripe, appearing as a series of diamond shapes saddling the body and joined by their points along the dorsum, head green with a black dorsal spot. It attains a length of about 25 mm. Pupa: 16 mm long; leaf-green with mottled green/brown short cephalic spike; wing-cases and dorsal ridge the same colour; there is a short blunt process on thorax at base of each wing.

Dixeia doxo parva male underside

Dixeia doxo parva male upperside

HABITAT AND ECOLOGY

D. doxo parva is an inhabitant of bushveld areas. Males fly low and fast and zig-zag through the bushveld trees. They settle frequently on low bushes or on the ground. Females fly almost as fast but may be seen slowly searching the food plants for a suitable site to lay her eggs. Specimens can be seen feeding on nectar.

The males establish their territories in the vicinity of the larval food plants. Here they fly rapidly around the food plants in their selected territory. They circle each other vigorously if they encounter a rival while patrolling. Upon encountering a female, usually on the ground beneath the food plant, courtship commences. The male approaches from behind, with rapid, shallow wingbeats. If the female's wings are still soft, she breaks off the courtship with a refusal posture (wings open, pressed to ground, abdomen raised).

If the female has hardened her wings, she flutters her wings in rapid, shallow beats. The male moves alongside her, and they touch antennae. Coupling then takes place, the male moving round until he faces away from the female. If disturbed the male flies off carrying the female inert below him. Duration of mating unrecorded.

The females usually fly at random through the bush in search of suitable food plants on which to lay. Eggs are laid in clusters on the leaves of the food plant. They hatch after about five days. The behaviour of the larval stages is unrecorded. The pupa is attached by the cremaster and a silken girdle to a twig or leaf of the food plant. In summer the pupal period is about 8 days, the adult becoming visible in the final 24 hours as the insect develops within.

This species is on the wing most of the year but is more plentiful during summer and autumn.

Dixeia doxo parva female upperside

Dixeia doxo parva final instar larva on its food plant *Cadaba termitaria*

Dixeia doxo parva female underside

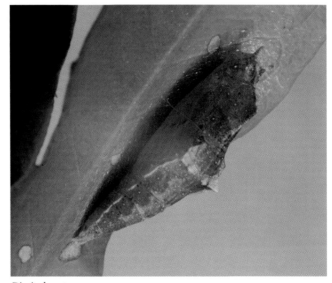

Dixeia doxo parva pupa

LARVAL FOOD PLANTS

Cadaba termitaria, Capparis sp. (Capparaceae) in East Africa.

DISTRIBUTION

South Africa, from northern KwaZulu-Natal (Zululand) to the far north-eastern areas of the Northern Province, then into Moçambique and Zimbabwe.

CONSERVATION

D. doxo parva is a fairly widespread species and is under no threat.

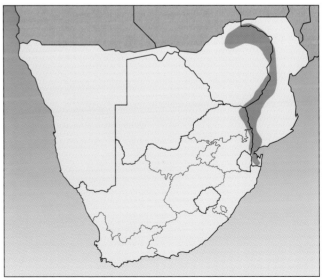

Distribution map of *Dixeia doxo*

349

Dixeia pigea (Boisduval)

ANT-HEAP SMALL WHITE

Pieris pigea Boisduval, 1836. *Spéc. gén. Lépid.* **1**: 523. Type locality: "China" = *patria falsa*.

This woodland species is larger than the others in the genus and may be distinguished from the similar *D. charina* by the presence of an ochre-yellow edging to the costa of the hindwing underside.

IDENTIFICATION

Adult. Male. Upperside: white with a narrow spotted margin. Underside: white with creamy-yellow hindwing and forewing apex; outer margin with small spots, postdiscal spots on hindwing and usually a single spot in middle of forewing. Hindwing with a distinct ochre-yellow edge to costa. Female. Upperside: white to yellowish-orange with marginal spots larger than male; postdiscal spots on forewing and hindwing; basal area can be dusted with grey or may be yellowish to reddish-orange. Underside: similar to male but with bigger spots and a yellow to reddish-orange basal patch which may be very large; ground colour varies from pale yellow to orange-yellow.

The dry-season form *alba* (Wallengren, 1857, *Rhop. Caffr.*: 10), has reduced dark markings.

Forewing lengths: male 21-30 mm; female 22-29 mm.

Early stages. Egg: pale yellow in colour; diameter 0,5 mm, height 1,2 mm; with 12 longitudinal ribs braced by about 30 cross ribs. Larva: first instar white on hatching; second to fifth instars green with a broad yellow dorsal stripe. It attains a length of 30 mm. Pupa: cephalic projection straight, directed slightly downwards; thorax with horizontally spreading small knob-like anterior projections; abdomen widened laterally near base, thence gradually narrowed to posterior end; variable in colour being green or brown (Clark, 1949: 196; Clark, 1994: 386).

HABITAT AND ECOLOGY

D. pigea is an inhabitant of forest and heavy woodland. Males fly fairly slowly compared to other members of the genus. They fly along the forest edge, frequently settling on low bushes in the sun or on flowers. The females fly slowly through the undergrowth, emerging only to sun themselves or to feed on flowers. Both sexes can be found feeding on nectar, particularly from its food plants. They can occasionally be observed sucking on damp sand.

Males patrol a territory along a particular stretch of forest where they can be seen during most of the warmer hours of the day.

Dixeia pigea male underside

Dixeia pigea female upperside

They follow an undulating path, often rising to the treetops before dropping down to search the lower bushes for females.

The females fly at random through the undergrowth in search of suitable food plants on which to oviposit. They lay their eggs in clusters on the undersides of the leaves of the food plant. The eggs take about 5 days to hatch. The larva emerges from the side of the egg near the top and eats the egg shell as its first meal. The larval stage lasts about 19 days. There are 5 larval instars. The pupa is cryptic. It is attached by the cremaster to a silken pad and is held upright by a silken girdle around the middle. The pupal stage lasts about 8 days (Clark, 1949: 196; Clark, 1994: 386).

Like most forest species they are on the wing during most months of the year but are more plentiful during the warmer months.

Dixeia pigea female underside

351

Dixeia pigea final instar larva

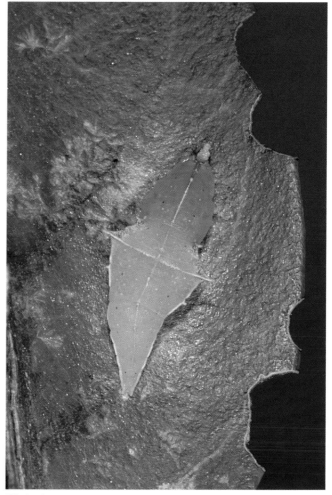

Dixeia pigea pupa

Dixeia pigea form *alba* male underside, sucking on damp sand

LARVAL FOOD PLANTS

Capparis sepiaria var. *citrifolia*, *C. tomentosa*, *Capparis* sp. (Capparaceae).

DISTRIBUTION

South Africa, from the Eastern Cape at Port St. Johns, northwards through KwaZulu-Natal to Mpumalanga and Northern Province, into Swaziland, Moçambique and Zimbabwe.

CONSERVATION

D. pigea is a fairly widespread species and is under no threat.

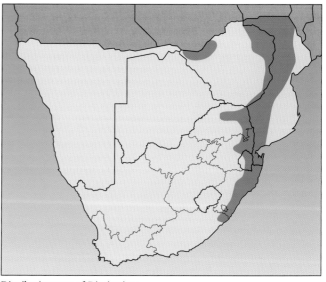

Distribution map of *Dixeia pigea*

Dixeia spilleri (Spiller)

SPILLER'S SULPHUR SMALL WHITE

Pieris spilleri Spiller, 1884. *Entomologist* **17**: 62. Type locality: KwaZulu-Natal.

This yellow species occurs up the eastern side of the Afrotropical region to as far north as Kenya.

IDENTIFICATION

Adult. Male. Upperside: bright yellow with a small black apex. Underside: yellow to brownish-yellow with small black marginal dots; hindwing may have a series of diffuse postdiscal spots. Female. Upperside: dull yellow to creamy yellow with broader brown apex than male; occasionally a reddish orange dusting at base. Underside: yellow to yellowish-white with base of forewing yellow to orange-yellow.; hindwing with a series of diffuse postdiscal spots.

Forewing lengths: male 20-24 mm; female 18-23 mm.

Early stages. Unrecorded.

HABITAT AND ECOLOGY

D. spilleri is an inhabitant of woodland and forest and sometimes the adjacent bushveld. The males fly swiftly and at random, sometimes high above the ground, but generally fairly low along the fringes of the woods or forest. The females are slower than the males. Both sexes can be found feeding on flowers.

Males patrol a territory along forest and woodland margins. Here they patrol at random and generally fairly low along the edge of the undergrowth in search of females.

The females fly at random in the undergrowth in search of suitable food plants on which to oviposit.

This species is on the wing throughout the year in some localities but is restricted in others. Along the KwaZulu-Natal coast for example it appears mainly from May to September. In some years it swarms and is found in many localities, thereafter many years may go by before it will reappear again in a particular locality.

LARVAL FOOD PLANTS

Capparis sepiaria var. *citrifolia, Capparis* sp. (Capparaceae).

DISTRIBUTION

South Africa, from KwaZulu-Natal to Mpumalanga and Northern Province, into Swaziland, Moçambique and eastern Zimbabwe.

CONSERVATION

D. spilleri is a widespread species and is under no threat.

Dixeia spilleri male underside

Dixeia spilleri male upperside

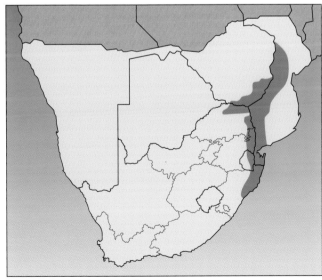

Distribution map of *Dixeia spilleri*

Genus *Appias* Hübner

Appias Hübner, 1819. *Verz. bek. Schmett.* (6): 91. Type species: *Papilio zelmira* Stoll, 1780, by selection by Butler, 1870.

Moderately-sized species with white, yellow or orange wings, generally with dotted margins. The males have very pointed forewings and long antennae, with a rather abrupt club. Forewing with veins R_1 and R_2 well separated from cell before upper angle; R_3 on a long stalk with R_{4+5}; M_1 from stalk of R_3 and R_{4+5} nearer to upper angle than to origin of R_{4+5}; MDC much shorter than LDC and curved so as to form a right angle with the stalk of M_1 and radials. Hindwing with precostal spur long and curved outwards from base; Rs, M_1 and M_2 separate from cell; LDC distinctly longer than either MDC or UDC. Abdomen with a hair-pencil in male beneath the eighth segment in front of the genitalia (van Son, 1949: 199).

Early stages: eggs elongate conical, with a rather small number of longitudinal ribs. Larvae cylindrical, almost smooth in the final instar. Pupae with a rather long upcurved cephalic projection and with a pair of rather long spreading basal abdominal projections; thoracic keel high and laterally compressed (van Son, 1949: 200).

Food plants are species of Euphorbiaceae and Capparaceae.

There are five species in Africa. Only *A. epaphia* and *A. sabina* occur in Southern Africa.

Subgenus *Glutophrissa* Butler

Glutophrissa Butler, 1887. *Entomologist's mon. Mag.* **23**: 249. Type species: *Appias poeyi* Butler, by original designation.

Subgenus *Glutophrissa* Butler has been associated with the African species of this genus.

KEY TO THE GENUS *APPIAS*

1. Hindwing with distinct dots at ends of veins .... *A. sabina*

   Hindwing without distinct dots at ends of veins .... *A. epaphia*

Appias (Glutophrissa) sabina (Felder)

ALBATROSS RAINFOREST WHITE

Pieris sabina Felder, 1865. *Reise Novara, Lep.* **II**: 167.

This species with its diverse female forms has four subspecies. The nominate is West African, two are from the Indian Ocean islands and *phoebe* is from Kenya to South Africa.

Appias (G.) sabina phoebe (Butler)

Phrissura phoebe Butler, 1901. *Proc. zool. Soc. Lond.* **1901**: 936. Type locality: Nairobi Forest, Kenya.

IDENTIFICATION

Adult. Male. Upperside: white with black apex and well developed black marginal spots at the ends of veins. Underside: white with creamy white to pale yellow hindwing and forewing apex; hindwing with costa basally yellowish-orange; base of forewing may be deep yellow. Female. Upperside: white, forewing with black apex and black marginal spots much larger than in male; pale areas within apex may be white or yellow; base, particularly forewing, may be orange to dark grey; hindwing may be white to pale yellow to orange-yellow. Underside: white with pale yellow to orange-yellow hindwing and forewing apex; black marginal spots smaller than upperside; basal area of forewing orange.

Forewing lengths: male 30-34 mm; female 25-34 mm.

Early stages. Unrecorded.

Appias sabina phoebe male underside

HABITAT AND ECOLOGY

A. (G.) sabina is an inhabitant of montane and riverine forest. The males are fast-flying, usually keeping fairly high above the ground. They will often be found only in one particular area of a forest. This is the case at Woodbush/De Hoek forest where it apparently flies only in an area about 500 m long along the road. The females keep to the undergrowth, coming out only to bask in the sunshine or to feed at flowers. The species can be found on damp patches and even on monkey or civet dung (Larsen, 1991). It has also been recorded migrating in East Africa (Stoneham, 1958).

Males appear to be almost communally territorial. They fly a particular course through the forest which is followed by many males. The only interaction is a brief circling, in most cases other males being ignored. Some of the area patrolled will be along a forest margin but specimens disappear into the forest only to suddenly appear again much later.

The females fly at random in the undergrowth in search of suitable food plants on which to oviposit. The laying behaviour has been recorded as a brief fluttering among the branches of the food plant followed by swift ovipositing.

It has been recorded on the wing in South Africa from March to May only, with occasional records for June.

Appias sabina phoebe female upperside

Appias sabina phoebe male upperside

Appias sabina phoebe female underside

LARVAL FOOD PLANTS

Drypetes gerrardii, Phyllanthus sp. (Euphorbiaceae), *Ritchiea* sp. and *Boscia* sp. (Capparaceae).

DISTRIBUTION

South Africa, in the forests of the Wolkberg in the Northern Province, Dhlinza forest and Ngoye forest in KwaZulu-Natal, Moçambique and eastern Zimbabwe.

CONSERVATION

A. (G.) sabina phoebe is classified as **rare** in the *South African Red Data Book – Butterflies* by S.F. & G.A. Henning (1989: 146). The forests of the Wolkberg are now under the protection of the provincial Department of Nature Conservation. It has also been found in the Dhlinza forest at Eshowe and the Ngoye forest. A rare species in South Africa, more commonly found to the north.

Appias (Glutophrissa) epaphia (Cramer)

DIVERSE RAINFOREST WHITE

Papilio epaphia Cramer, 1779. *Uitl. Kapellen* **III**: 26.

A widely distributed forest species divided into three subspecies. The nominate occurs in the western Afrotropical region, *contracta* (Butler, 1888) the eastern region and *orbona* (Boisduval, 1833) in Madagascar.

Appias (G.) epaphia contracta (Butler)

Glutophrissa contracta Butler, 1888. *Proc. zool. Soc. Lond.* **1888**: 75. Type locality: Eastern Sudan.

IDENTIFICATION

Adult. Male. Upperside: creamy-white with black apex; hindwing with marginal spots very small and diffuse. Underside: creamy-white, pale yellowish white at apex of forewing and on hindwing; marginal spots small and diffuse, if present; base of forewing yellow. Female. Upperside: white to yellow with broad black marginal borders; forewing basal area and cell may be entirely black. Underside: white with broad brown borders and a yellow base to forewing; cell may be distally dark brown; hindwing and apex of forewing may be creamy-white to pale yellow and there are no spots at ends of veins.

The dry-season form has been named *albida* (Mabille, 1885, in Grandidier's *Hist. Phys. Natur. et Polit. Madag.* **1**: 262).

Forewing lengths: male 25-32 mm; female 23-31 mm.

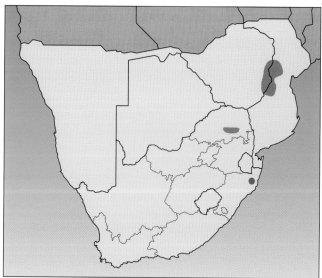

Distribution map of *Appias sabina*

Appias epaphia contracta female

Early stages. Egg: white when laid, changing to amber yellow later; diameter 0,5 mm, height 1,0 mm; with 12 longitudinal ribs and about 30 cross ribs. Larva: first instar light yellow; second to fourth instars increasingly darker green; fifth (final) instar dark green with a narrow yellow dorsal stripe. Pupa: about 22 mm long; almost straight ventrally, with a long upcurved cephalic projection, there is a pair of large and acute lateral abdominal processes which are curved slightly forward, and a fairly prominent, rectangular dorsothoracic keel; colour light green, margins of abdominal processes and upper edge of cephalic projection dark brown (Clark, 1949: 205; Clark, 1994: 388).

HABITAT AND ECOLOGY

A. (G.) epaphia contracta is a forest inhabitant, sometimes recorded in woodland and along rivers. The males are not very fast and flit along the forest margins, stopping to rest on a sunny patch of vegetation or to feed on flowers. Both sexes feed at flowers and on damp places.

The males appear to patrol a short territory along the forest edge. Here they fly about and over the bushes and around the trees.

The females fly at random through the undergrowth in search of suitable food plants on which to oviposit. She will flutter slowly around the food plant, flying within the shrub between the leaves and twigs. She settles on a young shoot and curls her abdomen around to lay an egg under the growing tip. Females frequently select growing tips of the food plant which are already decimated by previous generations of larvae, even though other similar but undamaged food plants are available nearby. Although the female lays only a single egg at a time she may lay a dozen or more eggs at the same site. The benefit of communal laying in this way is difficult to understand. The eggs take from 7 to 10 days to hatch. The five larval instars take about a month. The pupa is attached by the cremaster to a silken pad and held upright by a silken girdle around the middle. The pupal stage lasts about 2 weeks (Clark, 1949: 205; Clark, 1994: 388).

This species is on the wing in most months of the year, the dry-season forms can often be found commonly during winter.

Appias epaphia contracta male upperside

Appias epaphia contracta form *albida* female upperside

Appias epaphia contracta final instar larva (After G.C. Clark, 1994)

Appias epaphia contracta pupa (After G.C. Clark, 1994)

LARVAL FOOD PLANTS

Capparis sepiaria var. *citrifolia, Capparis* sp. *Maerua kirkii, M. racemulosa, Boscia albitrunca, Cadaba* sp. (Capparaceae). Mr R. Paré observed a female ovipositing on *Salvadora persica* (Salvadoraceae) at Watamu, Kenyan coast in August 1993.

DISTRIBUTION

South Africa, from the coastal bush of the Eastern Cape through KwaZulu-Natal to Mpumalanga and Northern Province, into Swaziland, Moçambique and Zimbabwe to northern Botswana.

CONSERVATION

A. (G.) epaphia contracta is a widely distributed woodland and forest species and is under no threat.

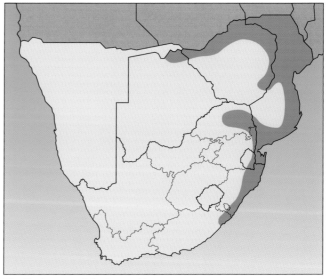

Distribution map of *Appias epaphia*

Genus *Mylothris* Hübner

Mylothris Hübner, 1819. *Verz. bek. Schmett.* (6): 90. Type species: *Papilio poppea* Cramer, 1777, by selection by Butler, 1870.

Wings broad with black dots along outer margins. Antennae with a rather short, broad, flattened club. Forewing triangular, with outer margin slightly convex and oblique; apex subacute; R_1 and R_2 arise from cell rather close to each other and to upper angle; R_3 completely fused with R_{4+5} in all Southern African species, M_1 on a fairly long stalk with R_{3+4+5}; LDC much longer than MDC. Hindwing with precostal spur moderately strong, curved distad about middle (van Son, 1949: 213).

This genus is apparently unpalatable to birds. Swynnerton's studies undertaken in Zimbabwe indicated that the *Mylothris* were consistently rejected by birds (Carpenter, 1941).

Early stages: eggs elongate barrel-shaped, with numerous longitudinal ribs connected by transverse ridges, and are laid in clusters. Larvae elongate-cylindrical, sparsely setose in the first instar, some of the primary setae being forked at tip, pubescent in later stages, the hairs being longer than in most other genera. They are gregarious, and cluster together between meals, and when moving, follow each other in procession. Pupae with a long upcurved cephalic projection, a mid-dorsal series of irregular tubercles along thorax and abdomen, and several pairs of lateral claw-like processes on the first few abdominal segments (van Son, 1949: 215).

Food plants: species of Loranthaceae and Santalaceae.

There are seven species in Southern Africa, namely *M. agathina* (Cramer), *M. carcassoni* van Son, *M. rubricosta* (Mabille), *M. rueppellii* (Koch), *M. sagala* Grose-Smith, *M. trimenia* Butler and *M. yulei* Butler. Only three species come from the Republic of South Africa, *M. rueppellii*, *M. agathina* and *M. trimenia*.

KEY TO THE GENUS *MYLOTHRIS*

1 UHW yellow .... *M. trimenia*

   UHW not yellow 2

2. Base of UFW orange .... *M. rueppellii*

   Base of UFW not orange .... *M. agathina*

Mylothris rueppellii (Koch)

TWIN DOTTED BORDER

Pieris rueppellii Koch, 1865. *Indo-Austral. Lep. Fauna*: 88.

There are six subspecies through the eastern Afrotropical region. The nominate comes from Ethiopia and one subspecies occurs in Southern Africa.

Mylothris rueppellii haemus (Trimen)

Pieris haemus Trimen, 1879. *Trans. ent. Soc. Lond.* **1879**: 342. Type locality: Cape Colony.

IDENTIFICATION

Adult. Male. Upperside: white with small black apex and distinctly dotted border; forewing base broadly orange. Underside: similar to upperside. Female. Upperside: similar to male but with orange basal areas more extensive and diffusing across wings almost to outer margin. Underside: similar to upperside.

Forewing lengths: male 24-33 mm; female 24-33 mm.

Early stages. Egg: yellowish-white coated with a sticky yellow substance; diameter 0,7 mm, height 1,1 mm; with 28 longitudinal ribs and about 26 cross ribs. Larva: greenish-brown to green; setose in early instars. Mid-dorsal dark green line from fourth instar; first instar 2 mm long on hatching and grows to 4 mm; second instar grows to 5,5 mm; third instar grows to 9,5 mm; fourth instar grows to 17 mm and fifth (final) instar grows to 30 mm. Pupa: 18 mm long; white with variable yellow, brown and black markings (Clark, 1994: 392).

HABITAT AND ECOLOGY

M. rueppellii is an inhabitant of woodland and savannah on the highveld and in coastal forest. Both sexes exhibit a slow floating flight which is typical of many species in this genus. Males usually flutter and glide around trees, ever on the lookout for females. The females generally fly somewhat lower down and may be seen fluttering about the branches of trees searching for food plant on which to lay their eggs. Both sexes can be found feeding at flowers.

Males sometimes appear to establish a territory around a stand of high trees where the larval food plant is growing and remain there through the warmer hours of the day and may even be found on subsequent days.

The females fly at random through the branches of the trees in search of suitable food plants on which to lay. They lay their eggs in clusters of about fifty on the leaves of the food plant and they take about 6 days to hatch. The first instar larva emerges from the side of the egg, near the top and eats the eggshell as its first meal. The larvae are gregarious throughout their larval stages. They sit close-

Mylothris rueppellii haemus male underside

Mylothris rueppellii haemus female upperside

Mylothris rueppellii haemus male upperside

ly aligned on the leaves of the food plant. When they moult the larvae eat the discarded skin. When the time comes to pupate the larvae drop to the ground on a silken thread and then find a suitable place to pupate. All the larvae scatter in different directions to pupate. The duration of the larval stage is about 40 days. The pupa is attached by the cremaster and held firmly in place by the silken girdle. They pupate on a leaf or against a flat surface and do not project out from the substrate as do other pierids. This also enhances their resemblance to bird dropping from which they gain protection from predators. Some pupae also resemble their surroundings and the pupa is not solely reliant on the bird dropping resemblance for protection. All *Mylothris* pupae, when disturbed, wriggle vigorously. The pupal stage lasts about 16 days (Clark, 1994: 392).

This species is on the wing throughout the year and often has a stronger winter brood than the summer one.

LARVAL FOOD PLANTS

Tapinanthus oleifolius, T. rubromarginatus (Loranthaceae).

DISTRIBUTION

South Africa, from the Eastern and Western Cape from as far south as George, KwaZulu-Natal, to Gauteng, North-West Province, Northern Province and Mpumalanga, into Swaziland, Moçambique and Zimbabwe.

CONSERVATION

M. rueppellii haemus is a fairly plentiful species which can also be found in many gardens and is under no threat.

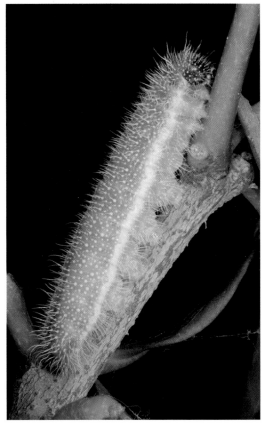

Mylothris rueppellii haemus final instar larva on its food plant *Tapinanthus rubromarginatus*

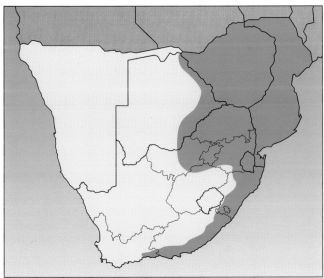

Distribution map of *Mylothris rueppellii*

Mylothris rueppellii haemus pupa

Mylothris agathina (Cramer)

COMMON DOTTED BORDER

Papilio agathina Cramer, 1779. *Uitl. Kapellen* **3**: 76.

A widespread species throughout the eastern and central Afrotropical region. There are two subspecies with nominate *agathina* in Southern Africa.

Mylothris agathina agathina (Cramer)

Papilio agathina Cramer, 1779. *Uitl. Kapellen* **3**: 76. Type locality: "Java" = *patria falsa*.

IDENTIFICATION

Adult. Male. Upperside: white with small black apex and black dots at ends of veins. Underside: white with deep yellow on hindwing and apex of forewing; base of forewing broadly reddish-orange. Female. Upperside: white to creamy-yellow to orange-yellow with or without reddish-orange dusting at base; forewing with small black apex; both wings with large distinct marginal dots at ends of veins. Underside: similar to upperside with broad reddish-orange basal area on forewing.

Forewing lengths: male 29-34 mm; female 28-37 mm.

Early stages. Egg: creamy-yellow with a coating of a sticky yellow substance; barrel-shaped, diameter 0,75 mm, height 1,0 mm; with about 27-30 longitudinal ribs, nearly every second one stopping short of micropyle, the remainder coalesce in pairs and terminate in white prominences (seven to nine in number) around the micropyle. Larva: first instar yellow, becoming greenish once it starts to feed; second and third instars brownish-yellow with white spots, darkening between instars and taking on a greenish tinge with ingestion of food; fourth instar generally brown but as it feeds, changes to dull green; fifth (final) instar dark chocolate brown with reddish-brown bands and attains a length of 32 mm. In the pre-pupal stage it turns yellow-brown and shrinks slightly. Pupa: about 22 mm long; with long, upcurved, finely granulated cephalic projection, a series of mid-dorsal granulate blackish tubercles and three pairs of lateral abdominal spines curved forwards; yellow with pale markings which darken later to brown or black; wing-cases occasionally quite black; ground colour can also fade with time to whitish-yellow (Clark, 1949: 225; S.F. Henning, 1984b: 43; Clark, 1994: 394).

HABITAT AND ECOLOGY

M. agathina is widespread through most wooded habitats from bushveld to forest. Both sexes fly slowly and leisurely around the trees of their habitat. They glide and flutter, rising to the treetops and then fluttering down to a metre or so above the ground. The males tend to fly higher than the females. They can be found in numbers on

Mylothris agathina male upperside

Mylothris agathina male underside

particular flowering trees, such as *Poinsettias*, and often visit gardens.

The males usually establish their territories around a small stand of trees with growths of larval food plants. They remain in this area during the warmer hours of the day. They keep to the higher branches of the trees where they can be seen floating around and perching frequently on the leaves.

The females are most often seen flying among the tree branches, searching for food plants on which to lay their eggs. They will flutter slowly around the food plant before selecting a particular leaf and will then painstakingly lay her eggs in a very orderly fashion on its underside. The eggs are laid in clusters of 45 to 70 and take about 6 days to hatch. The first instar larva hatches from the side of the egg near the top and eats the eggshell as its first meal. The larvae are gregarious throughout the larval instars which take about 40 days to complete. The newly emerged larvae cluster together and feed on the surface of the leaf. When resting they lie close together and appear as a yellow patch on the leaf surface. After feeding, the green food shows through the body and gives it a greenish appearance. The larvae also cluster close together and moult in unison and devour their discarded skins. The brownish-yellow to brown older larvae cluster together and feed at intervals on the edge of leaves, crawling away from their resting mat in procession. When the larvae are ready to pupate they drop to the ground on silken thread. They do not pupate together but scatter in different directions. The pupa is attached by the cremaster to a silken pad and is held in place by a silken girdle around the middle. The pupa resembles a bird dropping in some instances or a piece of bark in other cases. The pupal stage lasts about 2 weeks (Clark, 1949: 225; S.F. Henning, 1984b: 43; Clark, 1994: 394).

This species is on the wing throughout the year, often with a good winter brood.

Mylothris agathina female upperside

Mylothris agathina female underside

LARVAL FOOD PLANTS

Tapinanthus kraussianus, T. oleifolius, T. rubromarginatus, Erianthemum dregei, Tieghemia quinquenervia (Loranthaceae); *Ximenia caffra* (Olacaceae); *Osyris lanceolata, Colpoon compressum* (Santalaceae).

DISTRIBUTION

South Africa, from the Western Cape from as far west as George through the Eastern Cape to KwaZulu-Natal, to the North-West Province, Gauteng, Northern Province and Mpumalanga. A number of records were made from the Western Cape during the 1980's and much speculation was made as to the migratory habits of this butterfly. It would appear that this is more likely immigration as popula-

Mylothris agathina final instar larvae on their food plant *Ximenia caffra*

tions extend their range slowly through adjacent habitats during favourable climatic conditions. Common in Swaziland, Moçambique, Zimbabwe, Botswana and northern Namibia.

CONSERVATION

M. agathina is a common and widespread species and is under no threat.

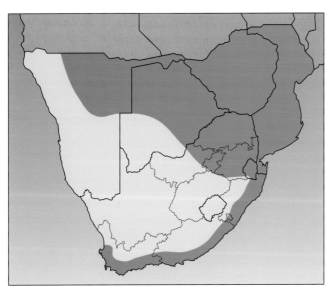

Distribution map of *Mylothris agathina*

Mylothris agathina pupa

Mylothris trimenia Butler

TRIMEN'S DOTTED BORDER

Mylothris trimenia Butler, 1869. *Cist. Ent.* **1**: 13. Type locality: KwaZulu-Natal.

An endemic South African forest species.

IDENTIFICATION

Adult. Male. Upperside: forewing white with small black apex, hindwing lemon-yellow; large distinct marginal dots at ends of veins of both wings. Underside: similar to upperside, hindwing and apical area of forewing chrome-yellow; margins with black dots. Female. Upperside: hindwing ochreous-yellow. Underside: as in male.

Forewing lengths: male 26-30 mm; female 23-30 mm.

Early stages. Egg: white with a coating of a yellow sticky substance; diameter 0,7 mm, height 1,1 mm; with 22 to 24 longitudinal ribs and about 26 cross ribs. Larva: first instar pale yellow with a black head; second instar pale green with a black head; third instar green with two pale yellow glands visible under the skin of ninth segment, head black; fourth instar green with greenish-white lateral line; fifth (final) instar dull green with a broken black dorsal stripe and

whitish lateral line. It attains a length of 32 mm. In the pre-pupal stage it turns pale green and shrinks to 21 mm. Pupa: 20-22 mm long; pale green at first, darkening later; tip of cephalic projection turns white (Clark, 1949: 227; Clark, 1994: 396).

HABITAT AND ECOLOGY

M. trimenia is a montane forest species. It flies faster than the other members of the genus, gliding smoothly around the treetops. Males keep to the canopy of the forest, only making forays down to the forest margins in search of females or to feed at flowers. The females can also be seen feeding on flowers, often high up in the canopy of the forest. They are often encountered along the forest edge where they come out to flutter in the sunshine before disappearing again into the depths of the forest.

Males appear to establish territories around the tops of tall trees. They remain there, swooping and gliding or basking in the sun, during the warmer hours of the day.

The females generally fly high up within the forest or along the margins where the food plants are likely to be found. They lay their eggs in clusters of about fifty on the undersides of the leaves of the food plant. The eggs take about 5 days in summer and up to 10 days in winter to hatch. The first instar larva hatches from the side of the egg near the top and eats the eggshell as its first meal. The larvae are gregarious throughout the larval instars. There are 5 larval instars which take about 24 days to complete in summer and

Mylothris trimenia male underside

up to 3 times as long during winter. The larvae, as they feed on the leaves of the food plant, keep close together, side by side. When the larva moults it devours the discarded skin. When the larva is ready to pupate it drops to the ground on a silken thread. They do not pupate together, each larva going in a different direction. The pupa is attached by the cremaster and is held in place by a silken girdle around the middle. The pupa resembles a curled leaf. The pupal stage lasts about 2 weeks in summer and 3 weeks in winter. There appears to be a continuous succession of broods throughout the year in the Eastern Cape (Clark, 1949: 227; Clark, 1994: 396).

This species is on the wing throughout the year in the warmer parts of South Africa but in more temperate areas it generally flies from October to April.

LARVAL FOOD PLANTS

Tieghemia quinquenervia; Tapinanthus kraussianus (Loranthaceae).

DISTRIBUTION

South Africa, from the Eastern Cape as far south as the Bedford district, through KwaZulu-Natal and Swaziland to Mpumalanga and Northern Province.

CONSERVATION

M. trimenia is an endemic South African species whose populations in its forest habitats should be monitored. However, at the present time it is under no threat.

Mylothris trimenia male upperside

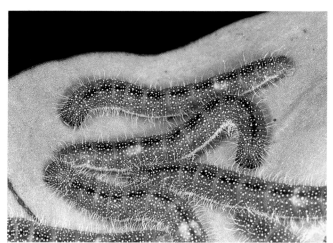

Mylothris trimenia final instar larvae

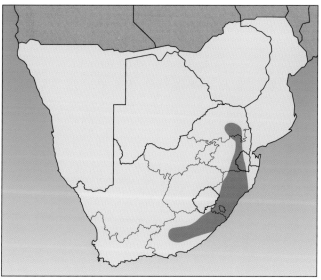

Distribution map of *Mylothris trimenia*

Mylothris trimenia pupa

Genus *Leptosia* Hübner

Leptosia Hübner, 1818. *Zuträge Samml. exot. Schmetterl.* **1**: 13. Type species: *Leptosia chlorographa* Hübner, 1818, selected by Scudder, 1875.

Forewing with apex and outer margin strongly rounded; veins R_1 and R_2 from cell, well separated; R_3 completely fused with R_{4+5}; M_1 on a fairly long stalk with R_{3+4+5}; MDC very short, LDC very long, incurved. Hindwing with precostal spur strong, with the proximal half inclined inwards, distal half sharply bent outwards; MDC very short, LDC very long and incurved. Antennae fairly long, with a gradual club, last joint much longer than broad, acute (van Son, 1949: 211).

Early stages: egg very elongate, tapering towards micropyle, with about 10 longitudinal ribs connected by about 30 transverse ridges; laid singly. Larvae cylindrical, slightly tapering near bifid posterior end. Pupae laterally compressed; head conically produced; thorax convex dorsally; wing-cases extending ventrally.

Food plants Capparaceae.

Leptosia alcesta (Stoll)

AFRICAN WOOD WHITE

Papilio alcesta Stoll, 1780. *Uitl. Kapellen.* **4**: 175.

This wood white is separated into five subspecies: *sylvicola* (Boisduval, 1833) in Madagascar, the nominate in West Africa, *inalcesta* from Sudan to South Africa and two in central Africa.

Leptosia alcesta inalcesta male underside

Leptosia alcesta inalcesta Bernardi

Leptosia alcesta inalcesta Bernardi, 1959. *Bull. Soc. ent. Fr.* **64**: 35. Type locality: Neeu Moschi, Kilimanjaro, Tanzania.

IDENTIFICATION

Adult. Male. Upperside: white with a small black apical patch on forewing and a black postdiscal spot in CuA_2. Underside: white with fine striations on hindwing, base and apex of forewing; black postdiscal spot as on upperside. Female. Similar to male.

Forewing lengths: male 16-23 mm; female 22-24 mm.

Early stages. Egg: pure white; elongate, diameter 0,4 mm, height 1,5 mm; with 10 longitudinal ribs, only six reach the micropyle and 28-30 fine cross ridges. Larva: first instar transparent watery-white until it consumes the green leaf and becomes pale green; second instar pale green above and whitish below; third and fourth instars pure green; fifth (final) instar a shade darker with a faint whitish lateral line. It attains a length of 23 mm. Pupa: about 16 mm long; pale green in colour (Clark & Dickson, 1967: 38).

HABITAT AND ECOLOGY

L. alcesta is an inhabitant of forest and heavy woodland, particularly along rivers. It usually keeps to the deep shade of the understorey. Its flight has been likened to a classical ballet as it bounces up and down like a ballerina's tutu in the sunbeams that shine down from the canopy into its forest haunts. It flies slowly with a bouncing action and settles frequently on flowers or on the ground. It keeps low down on the forest floor and can be seen feeding at small insignificant flowers in sunny clearings in the forest.

Males appear to establish their territory among the boles of the big forest trees and patrol this area for most of the warmer hours of the day. Interaction between males is difficult to assess as specimens have been seen chasing each other at quite a speed, but whether these were both males or a male and female was not determined.

The females fly at random through the undergrowth in search of suitable ffood plantplants on which to oviposit. They lay their eggs singly on young shoots of the food plant. The eggs take 4-6 days to hatch. The first instar larva eats its way out of the top of the egg. It feeds on the edge of a leaf. Several keep to one resting place, although they are not gregarious, and move away independently to feed. The larval stage lasts some 25 days. The pupa resembles a twig or an old curled leaf. The pupa is attached to a silken pad on a twig and is held upright by a silken girdle. The pupal stage lasts about 10 days (Clark & Dickson, 1967: 38).

This species is on the wing throughout the year but is generally more plentiful in late summer and autumn.

Leptosia alcesta inalcesta male upperside

Leptosia alcesta inalcesta final instar larva

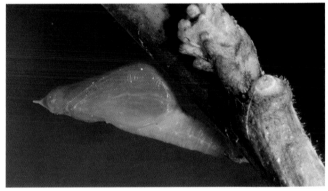

Leptosia alcesta inalcesta pupa

LARVAL FOOD PLANTS

Capparis brassii, C. fascicularis var. *zeyheri, C. tomentosa, Maerua juncea* (Capparaceae).

DISTRIBUTION

South Africa, from KwaZulu-Natal to Mpumalanga and Northern Province, northwards into Swaziland, Moçambique and eastern Zimbabwe.

CONSERVATION

L. alcesta inalcesta is a widespread forest species and is under no threat.

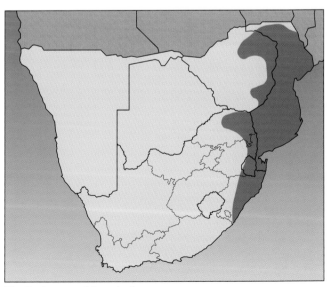

Distribution map of *Leptosia alcesta*

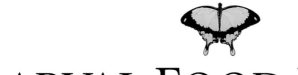

LARVAL FOOD PLANTS

Borassus aethiopum (Photo: Adrian van Rensen)

ANGIOSPERMAE: MONOCOTYLEDONAE

ARECACEAE – PALMAE

Borassus sp. – *Zophopetes dysmephila*
Chrysalidocarpus lutescens H. Wendl. – *Zophopetes dysmephila*
Cocos sp. – *Zophopetes dysmephila*
Phoenix canariensis Chabaud – *Zophopetes dysmephila*
Phoenix dactylifera L. – *Zophopetes dysmephila*
Phoenix reclinata Jacq. – *Zophopetes dysmephila*
Raphia sp. – *Zophopetes dysmephila*

DIOSCOREACEAE

Dioscorea cotinifolia Kunth. – *Tagiades flesus*

DRACAENACEAE

Dracaena afromontana Mildbr. – *Artitropa erinnys*
Dracaena fragrans (L.) Ker-Gawl. – *Artitropa erinnys*
Dracaena hookeriana Koch. – *Artitropa erinnys*
Dracaena angustifolia Roxb. – *Artitropa erinnys*
Dracaena steudneri Schweinf. ex Engl. – *Artitropa erinnys*

POACEAE – GRAMINEAE

Andropogon sp. – *Pelopidas mathias*
Cynodon sp. – *Gegenes pumilio gambica*
Ehrharta erecta Lam. – *Borbo borbonica, B. detecta, B. fallax, B. fatuellus, B. gemella, B. lugens, Gegenes niso, G. hottentota, Metisella malgacha, M. metis, Pelopidas mathias, P. thrax inconspicua*

Ehrharta sp. – *Borbo borbonica, Gegenes pumilio gambica*
Imperata cylindrica (L.) Raeuschel – *Astictopterus inornatus,*
    Kedestes barberae, K. lenis, K. lepenula, K. macomo, K.
    niveostriga, Pelopidas thrax inconspicua
    Merxmuellera sp. – *Tsitana tulbagha*
Oryza sp. – *Borbo borbonica*
Panicum deustum Thunb. – *Metisella metis, Borbo lugens*
Panicum sp. – *Pelopidas mathias*
Pennisetum clandestinum Chiov. – *Gegenes niso, G. hottentota, G.*
    pumilio gambica
Pennisetum sp. – *Borbo borbonica, B. lugens*
Pseudopentameris macrantha (Schrad.) Conert – *Tsitana dicksoni*
Saccharum sp. – *Borbo fallax, B. gemella, Parnara monasi*
Setaria megaphylla (Steud.) Dur. & Schinz. – *Borbo fatuellus, B.*
    lugens, Metisella metis

Setaria sp. – *Metisella willemi*
Sorghum sp. – *Zenonia zeno*
Stenotaphrum dimidiatum (L.) Brongn. – *Metisella metis*
Stenotaphrum glabrum Trin. – *Metisella metis*
Stipa dregeana Steud. – *Metisella metis, Tsitana tsita, T. uitenhaga*
Stipa sp. – *Borbo lugens*
Themeda triandra Forssk. – *Gegenes niso*
Themeda sp. – *Gegenes hottentota*
Thamnocalamus tessellatus (Nees) Sod. & Ellis – *Metisella syrinx*
Triticum sativum Lam. – *Borbo gemella*
Zea sp. – *Borbo borbonica, B. gemella, Pelopidas mathias*

STRELITZIACEAE

Strelitzia nicolai Regel & Koern. – *Moltena fiara*

ANGIOSPERMAE: DICOTYLEDONAE

ACANTHACEAE

Asystasia schimperi T. Anders – *Eretis umbra*
Barleria sp. – *Alenia sandaster, Sarangesa phidyle, S. motozi*
Blepharis capensis (L.f.) Pers. – *Alenia sandaster*
Chaetacanthus setiger (Pers.) Lindl. – *Eretis djaelaelae, E. umbra*
Dyschoriste sp. – *Eretis djaelaelae, E. umbra*
Isoglossa woodii C.B.Cl. – *Celaenorrhinus mokeezi*
Justica protracta (Nees) T. Anders. – *Eretis djaelaelae*
Justica sp. – *Eretis djaelaelae, E. umbra, Sarangesa motozi*
Peristrophe hensii (Lindau) C.B.Cl. – *Sarangesa motozi,*
    S. phidyle, S. seineri
Phaulopsis imbricata (Forssk.) Sweet – *Eretis djaelaelae*
Phaulopsis sp. – *Eretis umbra*

ANACARDIACEAE

Rhus coriarius L. – *Acleros mackenii*

ANNONACEAE

Annona reticulata L. – *Graphium antheus*
Annona senegalensis Pers. – *Graphium angolanus*
Annona sp. – *Abantis paradisea*
Artobotrys cinerea – *Graphium leonidas*
Artobotrys monteiroae Oliv. – *Graphium antheus, G. colonna,*
    G. policenes, G. porthaon, G. morania
Artobotrys brachypetalus Benth. – *Graphium morania, G. antheus*
Artobotrys senegalensis Pers. – *Graphium morania*
Artobotrys sp. – *Graphium colonna*
Cleistochlamys kirkii (Benth.) Oliv. – *Graphium antheus,*
    G. porthaon
Friesodielsia obovata (Benth.) Verdc. – *Graphium leonidas,*
    G. porthaon
Hexalobus monopetalus (A. Rich.) Engl. & Diels. – *Graphium*
    antheus, G. morania

Monanthotaxis caffra (Sond.) Verdc. – *Graphium leonidas*
Monodora junodii Engl. & Diels – *Graphium porthaon*
Uvaria caffra E. Mey. ex Sond. – *Graphium antheus, G. morania,*
    G. policenes, G. colonna, G. leonidas
Xylopia parviflora (A. Rich.) Benth. – *Abantis paradisea*

APIACEAE

Deverra burchellii (DC.) Eckl. & Zeyh. – *Papilio demodocus*
Foeniculum vulgare Mill. – *Papilio demodocus*
Peucedanum galbanum (L.) Drude – *Papilio demodocus*
Peucedanum gummiferum (L.) Wijnands – *Papilio demodocus*

ASCLEPIADACEAE

Dregea angolensis – *Coeliades anchises*
Dregea sp. – *Coeliades forestan, C. keithloa, C. pisistratus*

BRASSICACEAE

Heliophila linearis (Thunb.) DC. – *Pontia helice*
Heliophila sp. – *Pontia helice*
Lepidum capense Thunb. – *Pontia helice*
Lobularia maritima (L.) Desv. – *Pontia helice*
Sisymbrium officinale (L.) Scop. – *Pontia helice*

CAESALPINIOIDEAE – FABACEAE

Brachystegia boehmii Taub. – *Andronymus neander*
Julbernardia globiflora (Benth.) Troupin – *Fresna nyassae,*
    Andronymus caesar philander
Macrolobium coeruleum (Taub.) Harms. – *Andronymus*
    caesar philander
Pericopsis angolensis (Bak.) van Meeuwen – *Andronymus*
    caesar philander
Senna abbreviata Oliver – *Catopsilia florella*

Senna didymobotryia (Fresen.) Irwin & Barnaby – *Catopsilia florella*

Senna italica Mill. – *Catopsilia florella*

Senna mimosoides L. – *Catopsilia florella, Eurema brigitta, E. hecabe solifera, E. desjardinsii marshalli*

Senna occidentalis (L.) Link – *Catopsilia florella*

Senna petersiana (Bolle) Lock – *Catopsilia florella*

Senna septemtrionalis (Viv.) Irwin & Barnaby – *Catopsilia florella*

Senna singueana (Delile) Lock – *Catopsilia florella*

CAPPARACEAE

Boscia albitrunca (Burch.) Gilg. & Ben. – *Appias epaphia contracta, Belenois aurota, B. creona severina, Colotis agoye bowkeri, C. antevippe gavisa, C. celimene amina, C. evenina, C. eris, C. regina, C. subfasciatus, Pinacopteryx eriphia*

Boscia oleoides (Burch. ex DC.) Tölken – *Belenois aurota, B. creona severina, B. zochalia, Colotis antevippe gavisa, C. eris, C. euippe omphale, Pinacopteryx eriphia*

Boscia salicifolia Oliver – *Colotis celimene amina, C. evenina, C. regina, Pinacopteryx eriphia*

Boscia sp. – *Appias epaphia contracta, A. sabina phoebe, Belenois thysa, Colotis agoye agoye, C. ione, C. regina, C. vesta argillaceus*

Cadaba aphylla (Thunb.) Wild. – *Colotis euippe omphale, C. evagore antigone*

Cadaba natalensis Sond. – *Colotis danae annae, C. auxo*

Cadaba termitaria N.E. Br. – *Colotis auxo, C. danae annae, Dixeia doxo parva*

Cadaba sp. – *Appias epaphia contracta, Colotis agoye agoye, C. ione, Eronia leda*

Capparis brassii DC. – *Leptosia alcesta inalcesta*

Capparis fascicularis DC. – *Belenois aurota, B. creona severina, Eronia cleodora, Leptosia alcesta inalcesta*

Capparis sepiaria var. *citrifolia* (Lam.) Tölken – *Appias epaphia contracta, Belenois aurota, B. creona severina, B. gidica, Colotis antevippe gavisa, C. euippe omphale, C. evagore antigone, Dixeia charina, D. pigea, D. spilleri, Eronia leda*

Capparis tomentosa Lam. – *Belenois aurota, B. creona severina, B. gidica, Dixeia pigea, Eronia cleodora, E. leda, Leptosia alcesta inalcesta*

Capparis sp. – *Appias epaphia contracta, Belenois aurota, B. creona severina, B. thysa, B. zochalia, Colotis celimene amina, C. evenina, C. ione, C. pallene, C. regina, C. vesta argillaceus, Dixeia doxo parva, D. pigea, D. spilleri, Eronia leda, Nepheronia buquetii*

Maerua angolensis DC. – *Belenois aurota, B. creona severina, Colotis danae annae, C. vesta argillaceus*

Maerua cafra (DC.) Pax – *Belenois aurota, B. zochalia, B. creona severina, Colotis antevippe gavisa, C. euippe omphale, C. evagore antigone, Pinacopteryx eriphia*

Maerua juncea Pax. – *Belenois aurota, Colotis antevippe gavisa, C. evagore antigone, C. euippe omphale, C. ione, Leptosia alcesta inalcesta*

Maerua kirkii (Oliver) F. White – *Appias epaphia contracta*

Maerua racemulosa (DC.) Gilg. & Ben. – *Appias epaphia contracta, Belenois creona severina, B. thysa, B. zochalia, Colotis erone, C. ione*

Maerua rosmarinoides (Sond.) Gilg. & Ben. – *Colotis euippe omphale, C. ione*

Maerua schinzii Pax -*Colotis doubledayi flavulus*

Ritchiea sp. – *Appias sabina phoebe, Colotis ione, C. vesta argillaceus, Nepheronia argia mhondana*

CELASTRACEAE

Hippocratea africana (Willd.) Loes. – *Nepheronia thalassina sinalata*

Hippocratea longipetiolata Oliv. – *Nepheronia argia variegata, N. argia mhondana, N. thalassina sinalata*

CHRYSOBALANACEAE

Parinari capensis Harv. – *Platylesches ayresii, P. neba*

Parinari curatellifolia Planch. ex. Benth. – *Coeliades forestan, Platylesches moritili, P. picanini, P. tina*

Parinari sp. – *Platylesches galesa*

CLUSIACEAE

Hypericum aethiopicum subsp. *sonderi* (Bredell) N. Robson – *Eurema brigitta, E. desjardinsii marshalli, E. hecabe solifera*

COMBRETACEAE

Combretum apiculatum Sond. – *Coeliades forestan*

Combretum bracteosum (Hochst.) Brandis – *Coeliades forestan*

Combretum molle R.Br ex G. Don. – *Parosmodes morantii*

Combretum sp. – *Coeliades keithloa, C. pisistratus*

Quisqualis sp. – *Coeliades forestan, Parosmodes morantii*

Terminalia sp. – *Coeliades forestan, Parosmodes morantii*

CONNARACEAE

Byrsocarpus sp. – *Coeliades keithloa*

ERYTHROXYLACEAE

Erythroxylum emarginatum Thonn – *Eagris nottoana knysna*

EUPHORBIACEAE

Bridelia cathartica Bertol. – *Abantis paradisea*

Bridelia micrantha (Hochst.) Baill. – *Abantis paradisea, Parosmodes morantii*

Drypetes gerrardii Hutch. – *Appias sabina phoebe, Coeliades libeon*

Phyllanthus sp. – *Appias sabina phoebe*

Pseudolachnostylis maprouneifolia Pax. – *Abantis paradisea*

FABACEAE

(see Caesalpinioideae, Mimosoideae, Papilionoideae)

GERANIACEAE

Geranium sp. – *Coeliades forestan*

LAURACEAE

Cryptocarya woodii Engl. – *Papilio euphranor*

LECYTHIDACEAE

Barringtonia racemosa (L.) Roxb. – *Coeliades keithloa*

LORANTHACEAE

Erianthemum dregei (Eckl. & Zeyh.) V. Tiegh. – *Mylothris agathina*
Tapinanthus kraussianus (Meisn.) V. Tiegh. – *Mylothris agathina, M. trimenia*
Tapinanthus oleifolius (Wendl.) Danser – *Mylothris agathina, M. rueppellii haemus*
Tapinanthus rubromarginatus (Engl.) Danser – *Mylothris agathina, M. rueppellii haemus*
Tieghemia quinquenervia (Hochst.) S. Balle – *Mylothris agathina, M. trimenia*

MALPIGHIACEAE

Acridocarpus glaucescens Engl. – *Coeliades keithloa*
Acridocarpus natalitius A. Juss. – *Coeliades keithloa, C. lorenzo*
Acridocarpus smeathmanni (DC.) Guill. & Perr. – *Acleros mackenii*
Acridocarpus zanzibaricus A. Juss. – *Coeliades keithloa*
Acridocarpus sp. – *Coeliades pisistratus*
Sphedamnocarpus pruriens subsp. *galphimiifolius* (A. Juss.) De Villiers & Botha – *Coeliades forestan*
Sphedamnocarpus pruriens (A. Juss.) Szyszyl. – *Coeliades pisistratus, Graphium angolanus*
Triaspis glaucophylla Engl. – *Coeliades anchises*
Triaspis macropteron Oliver – *Coeliades pisistratus*

MALVACEAE

Abutilon grandiflorum G. Don. – *Gomalia elma*
Abutilon grantii Meeuse – *Gomalia elma*
Abutilon guineense (K. Schum.) Bak. f. & Exell. – *Gomalia elma*
Abutilon intermedium Hochst. ex Schweinf. – *Gomalia elma*
Abutilon sonneratianum (Cav.) Sweet – *Gomalia elma*
Gossypium sp. – *Coeliades forestan*
Hibiscus aethiopicus L. – *Spialia diomus ferax, S. mafa, S. nanus, S. sataspes, S. spio*
Hibiscus fuscus Garcke – *Spialia colotes transvaaliae*
Hibiscus pusillus Thunb. – *Spialia spio*

Hibiscus tiliaceus L. – *Abantis paradisea*
Hibiscus sp. – *Spialia asterodia*
Lavatera arborea L. – *Spialia spio*
Pavonia burchellii (DC.) R. A. Dyer – *Netrobalane canopus, Spialia agylla, S. asterodia, S. diomus ferax, S. sataspes, S. spio*
Pavonia columella Cav. – *Spialia spio*
Pavonia sp. – *Spialia mafa*
Sida sp. – *Spialia diomus ferax, S. spio*

MYRTACEAE

Syzygium cordatum Hochst. – *Parosmodes morantii*

OLACACEAE

Ximenia caffra Sond. – *Mylothris agathina*

OLEACEAE

Jasminum sp. – *Nepheronia thalassina*

PAPILIONOIDEAE – FABACEAE

Canavalia sp. – *Coeliades forestan*
Cassia sp. – *Coeliades libeon, C. forestan*
Craibia brevicaudata (Vatke) Dunn – *Coeliades libeon*
Crotalaria sp. – *Coeliades forestan*
Indigofera sp. – *Coeliades pisistratus, C. forestan*
Lonchocarpus capassa Rolfe – *Abantis paradisea, Coeliades forestan*
Medicago sativa L. – *Colias electo*
Millettia sutherlandii Harv. – *Coeliades forestan*
Millettia sp. – *Coeliades libeon*
Phaseolus sp. – *Coeliades forestan*
Pterocarpus brenanii Barbosa & Torre. – *Abantis venosa*
Pterocarpus rotundifolius (Sond.) Druce – *Abantis venosa*
Robinia pseudoacacia L. – *Coeliades forestan, Colias electo*
Sesbania sp. – *Coeliades forestan*
Trifolium africanum Ser. – *Colias electo*
Vicia sativa L. – *Colias electo*

PTAEROXYLACEAE

Ptaeroxylon obliquum (Thunb.) Radlk. – *Papilio demodocus*

RESEDACEAE

Reseda odorata L. – *Pontia helice*

RHAMNACEAE

Scutia myrtina (Burm. f.) Kurz. – *Eagris nottoana*

RHIZOPHORACEAE

Cassipourea ruwensorensis (Engl.) Alston – *Nepheronia argia*

RUTACEAE

Archangelica officinalis Hoffm. – *Papilio demodocus*

Calodendrum capense (L. f.) Thunb. – *Papilio demodocus, P. nireus lyaeus, P. ophidicephalus*

Citrus (various cultivated species) – *Papilio dardanus cenea, P. demodocus, P. echerioides, P. nireus lyaeus, P. ophidicephalus*

Clausena anisata (Willd.) Hook. f. ex Benth. – *Papilio dardanus cenea, P. constantinus, P. demodocus, P. echerioides, P. nireus lyaeus, P. ophidicephalus*

Oricia bachmannii (Bak. f.) Verdoorn – *Papilio dardanus cenea, P. demodocus, P. nireus lyaeus*

Teclea natalensis (Sond.) Engl. – *Papilio dardanus cenea, P. demodocus, P. nireus lyaeus*

Teclea nobilis Del. – *Papilio constantinus, P. dardanus cenea*

Teclea sp. – *Papilio constantinus*

Toddalia asiatica (L.) Lam. – *Papilio dardanus cenea, P. demodocus, P. nireus lyaeus*

Vepris lanceolata (Lam.) G. Don. – *Papilio constantinus, P. dardanus cenea, P. demodocus, P. echerioides, P. nireus lyaeus*

Vepris reflexa Verdoorn. – *Papilio constantinus*

Zanthoxylum capense (Thunb.) Harv. – *Papilio demodocus, P. echerioides, P. nireus lyaeus, P. ophidicephalus*

Zanthoxylum delagoense Waterm. – *Papilio echerioides, P. demodocus, P. nireus lyaeus, P. ophidicephalus*

SALVADORACEAE

Azima tetracantha Lam. – *Nepheronia buquetii*

Salvadora persica L. – *Appias epaphia contracta, Colotis amata calais, Nepheronia buquetii*

Salvadora sp. – *Colotis vesta argillaceus, Eronia cleodora, E. leda*

SANTALACEAE

Colpoon compressum Berg. – *Mylothris agathina*

Osyris lanceolata Hochst. & Steud. – *Mylothris agathina*

SAPINDACEAE

Blighia unijugata Bak. – *Andronymus caesar philander*

Deinbollia sp. – *Andronymus caesar philander*

Hippobromus pauciflorus (L.f.) Radlk. – *Papilio demodocus*

Lecaniodiscus fraxinifolius Baker – *Abantis paradisea*

Phialodiscus zambesiacus (Bak.) Radlk. – *Andronymus caesar philander*

SOLANACEAE

Solanum mauritianum Scop. – *Coeliades forestan*

STERCULIACEAE

Cola natalensis Oliv. – *Abantis paradisea*

Dombeya burgessiae Gerr. ex Harvey – *Caprona pillaana*

Dombeya calantha K. Schum. – *Netrobalane canopus*

Dombeya cymosa Harv. – *Netrobalane canopus, Eagris nottoana*

Dombeya rotundifolia (Hochst.) Planch. – *Caprona pillaana*

Hermannia coccocarpa (Eckl. & Zeyh.) Kuntze – *Spialia spio*

Hermannia comosa Burch. ex DC. – *Spialia diomus ferax, S. nanus, S. spio*

Hermannia cuneifolia Jacq. – *Spialia diomus ferax, S. nanus, S. spio*

Hermannia depressa N.E. Br. – *Spialia mafa*

Hermannia diffusa L. f. – *Spialia asterodia, S. diomus ferax, S. nanus, S. spio*

Hermannia incana Cav. – *Spialia asterodia, S. diomus ferax, S. nanus, S. spio*

Hermannia pulverata Andr. – *Spialia nanus*

Hermannia sp. – *Spialia agylla, S. sataspes*

Melhania sp. – *Spialia confusa, S. dromus, S. depauperata australis*

Sterculia quinqueloba (Garcke) K. Schum. – *Caprona pillaana*

Waltheria sp. – *Spialia diomus ferax, S. dromus*

TILIACEAE

Grewia flava DC. – *Abantis tettensis, Caprona pillaana, Leucochitonea levubu*

Grewia flavescens A. Juss. – *Netrobalane canopus*

Grewia monticola Sonder – *Abantis tettensis, Caprona pillaana*

Grewia occidentalis L. – *Netrobalane canopus, Eagris nottoana*

Grewia similis K. Schum. – *Netrobalane canopus*

Triumfetta rhomboidea Jacq. – *Spialia dromus*

Triumfetta tomentosa Boj. – *Spialia dromus*

Triumfetta sp. – *Spialia confusa, S. spio*

TRIMENIACEAE

Xymalos monospora (Harv.) Baill. – *Papilio dardanus cenea*

VIOLACEAE

Rinorea arborea (Thou.) Baill. – *Eagris nottoana knysna*

GLOSSARY

Aberration: A relatively rare shape or colour variation that can be distinguished from the normal in any species

Aedeagus: Sclerosed tube in male Lepidoptera through which the vesica or penis passes

Aestivate: Pass the dry season in a state of dormancy or diapause to ensure survival (see also hibernation)

Allele: Any of the alternative expressions (states) of a gene (locus)

Allopatric: Occurring in different geographical areas

Allotype: A designated paratype of the opposite sex to the holotype

Anal angle: The outer angle of the hindwing between the outer and inner margins (= tornus of hindwing)

Anal lobes: See **papillae anales**

Anal veins: One to three longitudinal wing veins (1A to 3A) situated posterior to the cubitus or cubital vein

Androconia: Specialised wing scales in male butterflies which are adapted to produce pheromones

Antennae: Feelers on the head which are sensitive to hearing and smell; club-tipped in butterflies

Anther: Upper free end of the stamen of a flower which produces pollen

Arthropods (Arthropoda): The phylum of jointed-legged invertebrate animals. The insects, including the butterflies and moths, constitute the largest class in this phylum.

Antrum: The posterior part of the ductus bursae often heavily sclerosed and connected with the sclerites of the sterigma

Apex: Tip of the wing

Apical: Area at or adjacent to the tip of a wing or other structure

Apiculus: Tapering apical portion (hooked tip) of the antennal club in Hesperiidae

Apodeme: Infolded projection of the insect exoskeleton to which muscles are attached

Basal: Area at or adjacent to the base of the wing or other structure

Batesian mimicry: The mimicking of a species distasteful or poisonous to a predator by an unrelated edible species

Bifid: Forked

Binomial nomenclature: Giving two names to animals and plants, a generic name and a specific name to denote the genus and species respectively

Bursa copulatrix: The copulatory ducts and sac in adult female Lepidoptera, consisting of the ostium bursae, ductus bursae and corpus bursae

Carinae: Ridge or keel on body or leg

Catalepsis (catalepsy): State of immobility of the body

Caterpillar: See **larva**

Character: An attribute of a member of a population or taxon by which it differs from a member of a different group or taxon

Chemoreception: Perception of chemical compounds by the sense of smell or taste

Chitin: A horn-like, non-living substance made of nitrogen containing polysaccharide (multiple sugar). It consists of long fibrous molecules of great strength and resistance to chemicals. It occurs in the cuticle of insects and other arthropods

Chorion: The egg-shell

Chromosomes: Strands of genetic material in the cell nucleus carrying the genes

Claspers: Paired terminal part of the male genitalia used to hold the female butterfly's terminal segment during mating. Also a pair of prolegs situated on the last abdominal segment of the caterpillar and used to grasp the food-plant

Cline: A gradual and essentially continuous change of character in a series of contiguous populations; a character gradient

Club: Thickened or swollen apical end of the antenna

Cocoon: Protective covering of silk spun by the larvae of many insects inside which they pupate

Compound eye: The eye of an insect and certain other invertebrates. It consists of hundreds or even thousands of tiny, separate elements, called ommatidia (singular – ommatidium) each with its own visual cells

Congeneric: Belonging to the same genus

Conspecific: Belonging to the same species

Convergence: Morphological similarity in distantly related forms

Corema: Ventral, eversible scent processes on segments 7 to 9 in some male Lepidoptera

Corpus bursae (bursa): The membranous sac of the female genitalia in which is deposited the male spermatophore during copulation

Costa: (costal margin): The front edge of the fore- or hindwing

Coxa: The first or basal segment of the leg

Cremaster: Constricted anal segments of the pupa bearing hooked hairs used for attaching the posterior end of the pupa to the silk pad spun by the larva

Cremastral hooks: Minute hooks beneath the anal segment of the pupa in most Lycaenidae, or on the cremaster in other families, attaching it to a pad of silk spun by the larva

Crepuscular: Active during twilight, i.e. during dusk or dawn. See also **nocturnal** and **diurnal**

Crochets: A series of terminal sclerosed hooks on larval proleg

Cryptic: A term used to indicate that the colour and pattern tend to conceal an animal by matching it to the background against which it lives, i.e. camouflaged

Cubitus: The fifth main longitudinal vein (Cu) of the wing

Cuticle: The non-cellular skin of insects consisting of chitin and protein; it is cast at moulting to allow increase in size

Dentate: Toothed

Description: In taxonomy, more or less a complete statement of the characters of a taxon without special emphasis on those which set limits to the taxon or distinguish it from related species

Diagnosis: In taxonomy, a formal statement of the characters which distinguish a taxon from other similar or closely related taxa

Diapause: A period when growth and development are suspended, usually accompanied by a greatly decreased metabolism, permitting survival during unfavourable periods, such as winter or adverse weather

Dimorphic: The occurrence of a butterfly in two different forms. When the sexes are different they are called sexually dimorphic.

Disc: The central area of the wing

Discal cell: The large central area of the wing partly or completely bounded by veins

Discocellulars: The short and weak transverse veins which form the distal margin of the discal cell in the wing

Distal (distad): Farthest from the base or centre

Diurnal: Active during the day. See also **nocturnal** and **crepuscular**

Dormancy: Resting or dormant phase accompanied by cessation of growth and development (diapause)

Dorsal: Upper surface

Dorso-lateral: Area between the dorsal and lateral surfaces

Ductus bursae: The duct joining the corpus bursae in the female genitalia to the copulatory aperture or ostium bursae

Ductus seminalis: The duct leading from the ductus bursae to the vestibulum or vagina of the female

Ecdysis: Moulting. In insects it is the periodic shedding of the skin of the larva to allow for growth

Eclosion: Emergence of a larva from an egg or an adult from a pupa

Ecology: The relationship between animals and plants and their living and non-living environment. Also the study of the relationships between plants and animals and their living (biotic) and non-living (abiotic) environment

Ecosystem: A community of animals and plants, interacting with one another and with their non-living environment, e.g. a forest, a mountain, a river bed

Elaiosome: An oily structure attached to seeds of certain indigenous plants, e.g. Proteas, which attracts ants so that the seeds may be dispersed by them

Endemic: Confined to a given region, e.g. a country

Entomology: Study of insects

Environment: The totality of physical, chemical and biotic conditions surrounding an organism

Epidermal glands: Secreting glands of the cuticle

Epidermis: Outermost layer of cells. One cell thick in invertebrates and often secreting a cuticle, e.g. in insects

Epiphysis: A movable lobe of the fore tibia found in Hesperiidae, Papilionidae and most moths

Evolution: A cumulative inheritable change in a population

Exoskeleton: External hardened integument in Arthropoda

Exuvium: Moulted or cast cuticle of the larva or pupa

Eye spot: A coloured spot, ringed with a contrasting colour

Falcate: When the apex of the wing is produced to a point that extends well beyond the level of the outer margin

Family: An assemblage or group of related subfamilies, tribes or genera below the superfamily rank but above the subfamily

Family group: In the hierarchy of classification, the highest-ranking group of taxa; includes taxa at the ranks of superfamily, family, family, subfamily, tribe, subtribe

Femur: The third segment of the leg between the trochanter and the tibia

Flagellum: That portion of the antenna distal to the two basal segments, the scape and pedicel

Forewing length: Measured from centre of mesonotum of thorax to apex of forewing

Form: Those individuals of a species differing, in a stated way, from other individuals within the species (e.g. larval and adult forms, male and female forms, ecological forms and seasonal forms)

Formicarium: Ants' nest. Usually applied to an artificial ants' nest used for observation of ants and their guests

Frenulum: A strong bristle or bristles at the base of the hindwing which hooks into a structure called a retinaculum on the forewing of many moths. The arrangement helps to keep the two wings together during flight

Frons: Forehead; upper part of head

Furca: Median structure between bases of the valvae in male genitalia; used to guide and support aedeagus during copulation

Gene: The unit of inheritance carried in a chromosome which is responsible for transmitting the inherited characters of the parents to the offspring

Gene pool: The totality of the genes of a given population existing at a given time

Genital capsule: External sclerosed genitalia; usually what is meant when the term "male genitalia" is used in taxonomic studies

Genitalia: Organs used for either mating or oviposition

Genotype: The totality of genetic factors that make up the genetic constitution of an individual

Genus (plural – genera): A species or group of related species below family group rank and above subgenus rank

Gnathos: A single or paired structure of the male genitalia beneath the anus

Girdle: A supporting strand of silk wrapped around the caterpillar prior to finally changing into a pupa. It occurs in the so-called "primitive" butterflies such as the Hesperiidae, Pieridae, Papilionidae and some Lycaenidae. It is not found in the subfamilies of the Nymphalidae

Ground colour: The dominant colour of the wing contrasted to that of the pattern

Haemolymph: Circulatory fluid of invertebrate animals such as insects; equivalent to blood and lymph of vertebrate animals

Hair-pencil: A dense tuft of long hairs on the wings or bodies of male butterflies which are displayed during courtship and may carry pheromones from the androconia towards the female (also see **androconia**)

Harpe: Stiff bristles on valvae of male genitalia; or part of the valvae themselves

Haustellum: Coiled proboscis in insects

Heterocera: Moths, i.e. those Lepidoptera in which the antennae do not end in a knob, but have various other shapes, e.g. pointed or feather-like. The term Heterocera is no longer used officially as the order of Lepidoptera is now classified according to the wing venation (also see **Rhopalocera**)

Hibernate (hibernation): Spending the winter in a dormant state. The caterpillars of certain species of butterfly and many pupae hibernate. Certain butterflies hibernate as adults, especially in countries in the northern hemisphere with protracted, definitely cold winters (also see **aestivate**)

Hilltopping: Behaviour exhibited by certain insects whereby they fly to hilltops or elevated points. In butterflies the behaviour is linked to mate-location

Holotype: The single specimens selected and labelled as the name-bearing specimen for each species or subspecies

Honey-dew: A sugary substance excreted by aphids and certain plant bugs. It is much sought after by ants which therefore attend these insects. The term is also used to refer to the secretion of the honey-gland of lycaenid larvae

Honey-gland: A shallow, usually transverse, slit or depression on the top of the 7th abdominal segment, into which several glands discharge a fluid which is imbibed by ants attending to lycaenid larvae

Hormone: The product of a ductless gland which is discharged directly into the blood stream and transported by the blood to a part of the body where it carries out its function, e.g. stimulating growth or moulting in insect larvae

Humeral lobe: A projection of the basal part of the costa of the hindwing which fits over the inner margin of the forewing. It helps to keep the two wings together during flight by increasing the overlap between them. In moths this function is performed by the frenulum and retinaculum

Humeral vein: A short vein arising near the base of the hindwing and running towards the base of the costa; also known as the precostal spur

Hyaline: Clear, transparent or translucent. In some butterflies e.g. Acraeinae, parts of the wings are translucent due to the absence of scales

Hybrid: The progeny of two individuals belonging to different species

Hyperparasite: An organism, e.g. wasp, parasitising another parasite. Hyperparasites may also be parasitised

Imago: Adult, sexually mature insect

Incubation period – with reference to the egg: the time between the laying of an egg and hatching (emergence) of the larva

Indigenous: Native to a particular area (not introduced)

Inflorescence: A flowering shoot, bearing more than one flower

Inner margin (anal margin): Posterior or rear edge of the fore- and hindwing

Instar: The larval stages between the hatching of the egg and the first larval moult, and between each successive moult until pupation

Integument: Outer protective covering of an insect, e.g. cuticle

Juxta: A sclerosed plate beneath the aedeagus of the male genitalia

Labial palpi: Paired appendages arising from the insect labium; three-segmented in butterflies

Labium: Fused mouth-parts forming the posterior (ventral) wall of the mouth

Larva: Caterpillar; the feeding, sexually immature, developmental stage of an insect with a complete metamorphosis

Lectotype: One of a series of syntypes which subsequent to the publication of the original description, is selected and designated through publication to serve as the name-bearing type specimen

Legumes: Legume or pod-bearing plants of the family Fabaceae = Leguminosae which includes the subfamilies Papilionoideae, Caesalpinioideae and Mimosoideae

Lepidoptera: Order of scale winged insects comprising butterflies and moths

Lepidopterist: Student of Lepidoptera. Lepidopterology is the study of Lepidoptera

Lunule: Crescent-shaped spot

Mandible: Sclerosed dentate jaws of the larva

Marginal: Along the outer margin

Maxillae: Paired mouth-parts situated between the mandibles and labium, serving as accessory jaws and assisting in the selection of food by touch and taste

Meconium: Waste products accumulated during the pupal stage and expelled as a coloured liquid from the anus of the newly emerged adult insect

Media: The fourth main longitudinal vein (M) of the wing; the basal half is lost in butterflies

Median: Applying to the media; the central area of the wing or other structure

Mesoseries: The arrangement of the crochets of the proleg in a single longitudinal band

Metamorphosis: The transformation from larval to adult form; referred to as complete in those insects, including butterflies, in which there is a non-feeding pupal stage

Micropyle: Tiny opening in the chitinous shell of an insect egg through which a sperm cell can enter and fertilise it. It is also the respiratory opening of the egg

Middens: Refuse heap or dung hill of ants

Migration: The mass movement of butterflies, or other animals, in one direction at any one time

Mimic: An organism that superficially resembles another of a different species so that one or both benefit

Mimicry: The resemblance of one species to another occurring in the same area

Monotypy: When an author establishes a genus or subgenus name for a single taxonomic species

Morphology: The description and study of the structural characteristics, particularly those on the surface of the body

Model: An unpalatable organism resembled by a mimic

Moulting (ecdysis): Replacing of non-living chitinous cuticle of the immature stage of an insect, often accompanied by change in colour, markings and organs

Mullerian mimicry: Similarity among several species that are distasteful or poisonous to a predator

Multiordinal: Of many sizes, referring to the crochets

Myrmecochore: Seed adapted for dispersal by ants (also see **elaiosome**)

Myrmecochory: Seed dispersal by ants

Myrmecophilous: Associated with ants

Neotype: A specimen selected as the name-bearing type subsequent to the original description in cases where the original types are known to be destroyed or were suppressed by the International Commission on Zoological Nomenclature

Niche: The particular environment in which an organism lives

Nocturnal: Active by night, e.g. many moths (also see **diurnal** and **crepuscular**)

Nominate (nominotypical): The taxon at a lower rank that contains the name-bearing type of a divided taxonomic taxon and bears the same name as the rank above it but with an amended suffix in the family group (e.g. Papilio, Papilionini, Papilioninae, Papilionidae, Papilionoidea)

Ocellate: Resembling ocelli, or small eyes

Ocellus (plural – ocelli): Simple eye. Butterfly caterpillars have three pairs of ocelli on the head. They are used mainly to perceive differences between light and dark and perhaps at very close quarters. The term ocellus is also used to denote a so-called eye-like spot on the wing of a butterfly

Osmeterium: A forked eversible scent-producing organ arising from the anterior margin of the prothorax in larvae of the Papilionidae

Ostium bursae: The copulatory aperture at the entrance to the bursa copulatrix

Oviposit: To lay an egg

Ovum: An egg

Palpus (plural – palpi): Paired segmented mouth-parts (labial palpi) projecting forwards from the head

Papillae anales: A pair of hairy lobes at the posterior end of the female abdomen, used in oviposition

Parasite: An animal or plant completely dependent on the tissues of another for its food; in insects usually internal and causing the ultimate death of its host, and then known as a 'parasitoid'

Paratype: A specimen other than the holotype in the type series

Paronychia: Bristle-like appendages on tarsus

Patagia: A pair of anterior sclerites of the prothorax

Patrolling: Mate-location behaviour in which males fly along a selected route in search of females

Pedicel: The second segment of the antenna

Perennial: Lasting more than two years. Usually applied to plants

Perching: Mate-locating behaviour in which males sit at characteristic prominent sites and dart off towards passing objects, in search of females

Perforated cupolas: Tiny epidermal glands in the epidermis of some lycaenid butterfly larvae. They secrete a substance, possibly a pheromone, which may appease potential predatory ants, or even mimic the brood pheromone of the host ants

Pheromone: A chemical substance secreted by an individual which produces a response in other individuals of the same species, or, as in the case of myrmecophilous butterflies, to produce a response in other insects

Phytophagous: Plant-eating

Phyto-predacious: First plant-eating then changing to a predatory diet of other insects

Pleural: Referring to the lateral surfaces of the body

Polymorphism: Existence of more than two forms in the same interbreeding population

Population: A group of organisms of the same species living together in the same locality

Postdiscal: Distal to the middle or discal area of the wing

Precostal spur: See **humeral vein**

Predator: An animal that uses two or more other animals for food

Primary forest: Forest that has not been altered by human activities

Proboscis: The coiled tubular organ of insects used for sucking in liquid food; in Lepidoptera it is called the haustellum. Often referred to as a tongue

Processes: Outgrowths or appendages on the bodies of insects

Procrypsis: Protective coloration

Prolegs: Fleshy leg-like organs of abdominal segments 3 to 6 and 10 in butterfly larvae

Proximal: Nearest to the base or centre

Pulvilli: Two lateral/ventral lobes beneath the tarsus. If there is only one lobe it is called an arolium

Pupa: (chrysalid, chrysalis). Non-feeding stage occurring between the larva and adult, during which metamorphosis into adult takes place

Race: See **subspecies**

Radius: The third main longitudinal wing vein (R), usually with three to five branches in the forewing

Rank: The level of a taxon in the zoological hierarchy, e.g. in descending rank: Superfamily, family, subfamily, tribe, subtribe, genus, subgenus, species and subspecies

Retinaculum: An apparatus occurring on the underside of the forewing of a moth into which fits the so-called frenulum of the hindwing. The combination of the two structures holds the fore- and hindwings together during flight (also see **frenulum** and **humeral lobe**)

Saccus: Part of the male genitalia. A usually hollow apodeme directed anteriorly midventrally from the vinculum into the body cavity of the male body

Savannah: Open grassy country with scattered trees or clumps of bushes

Scale: A flattened hair forming the characteristic clothing of Lepidoptera

Scape: The basal segment of the antenna

Scent brush: See **hair pencil**

Scent patch (sex brand, sex mark): A patch of dense androconia or specialised scent scales on the wings of certain male butterflies (also see **androconia**)

Sclerite: A sclerosed plate, forming part of the exoskeleton or body wall of an insect, and surrounded by membrane

Sclerotin: The brown substance produced by tanning of protein, deposited in certain areas of the exoskeleton producing hard, often thickened, plates or sclerites

Sclerosed (sclerotized): Hardened by the formation of sclerotin

Secondary forest: A forest that has been altered by human activity and subsequently allowed to regenerate

Seasonal dimorphism: Different colour forms (sometimes also shape and size) in a species depending on the season (winter or dry-season forms and summer or wet-season forms)

Segment: A ring-like or tubular section of the body or its appendages

Seta (plural – setae): A hair, arising from a socket

Sex-brand, sex-patch: A patch of dense androconia scales on the male wing

Sexual dimorphism: Differences in the outward appearance of the sexes of any species of butterfly

Shaft: That part of the flagellum of the antenna between the pedicel and the club

Signum (plural – signa): A sclerosed patch or structure on the internal surface of the corpus bursae. Presumed to be used to puncture the spermatophore

Solarium: Place for sunning or sun-bathing. Ants often bring their brood under flat stones warmed by the sun during the day

Species (singular and plural): A population of interbreeding organisms sharing a common mate recognition system. The basic rank of zoological classification

Species-group: A group of closely related species

Spermatheca: A storage sac for sperms, opening into the vagina of the female

Spermatophore: A membranous sac containing sperms, deposited by the male in the bursa copulatrix of the female during mating

Sphragis: A hardened male secretion deposited around the ostium bursae (female copulatory opening) during mating in certain butterflies, e.g. Acraeinae, and preventing mating by other males

Spinneret: A tubular organ beneath the larval head through which silk is extruded from the silk glands

Spiracle: Paired openings on the sides of insects, leading into the tracheal tubes

Spur: A movable spine-like structure found on the mid- and hind tibiae

Sternite: The sclerosed plates on the ventral surface of the abdomen

Sternum: The lower surface of the body

Striated: Covered with striae or minute lines

Subapical: Before the apex

Subbasal: Near the base

Subcosta: The second main longitudinal vein (Sc) of the wing

Subcostal: Near the costa of the wing

Subfamily: A group of related genera below the rank of family or a grouping of tribes

Subgenus (plural – subgenera): A species or group of related species below the rank of genus

Submarginal: Near the outer margin

Submedian: Before the middle or central area of the wing

Subspecies: One or more taxonomically distinct populations within a species, occurring in different geographical areas to each other (also see **nominate race**)

Subtribe: A group of related genera below the rank of tribe

Superfamily: A group of related families

Symbiosis: Association between different organisms, e.g. between ants and lycaenid larvae

Sympatry: The occurrence of two or more populations in the same area

Symplesiomorphic: Ancestral characteristics

Synapomorphic: Derived characteristics

Synonym: Each of two or more names that have been applied to one species

Syntype: Every specimen in a type series in which no holotype was designated

Tail: An outgrowth from the outer margin of the hindwing

Tarsus (plural – tarsi): Foot, typically of 5 joints in butterflies, but reduced in some, especially in the first pair of legs

Taxon (plural – taxa): A taxonomic group that is sufficiently distinct to be worthy of being distinguished by a name and to be ranked in a definite category

Taxonomist: One who classifies animals or plants

Taxonomy: Science of classification of organisms

Tegumen: The upper basal section of the male genitalia, the modified ninth tergite of the abdomen

Tergite: The sclerosed plates on the dorsal surface of the abdomen

Tergum: The upper surface of the body, joined by the membranous lateral pleuron to the sternum

Termen: The outer margin of the wing joining the apex and the tornus

Termitary (termitarium): Mound or nest of termites

Territoriality: Mate-location behaviour in which males remain in an area, which they defend against intruding males, while waiting for the arrival of a female with which to mate

Territory: The area defended by an animal against other members of its species and occasionally members of other species

Tibia: The fourth segment of the leg

Thorax: The body division between the head and abdomen of an insect, bearing the wings and legs

Tornus: The outer angle of the wing between the outer and the inner margins; on the hindwing often called the anal angle

Trachea: Respiratory tubes leading from the spiracles to supply air to the various internal organs

Translucent: Semi-transparent (also see **hyaline**)

Tribe: A group of related genera below the rank of subfamily

Trinomial nomenclature: Giving three names to an organism: a generic name, a specific name and a subspecific name to denote the genus, species and subspecies respectively

Trochanter: The small second segment of the leg, between the coxa and the femur

Tubercles: Paired, eversible organs on the eighth abdominal segment of many lycaenid larvae, and functioning in ant association

Type: A zoological or botanical object which serves as the base for the name of the taxon

Type-locality: The locality at which the holotype, lectotype or neotype was collected

Type series: A series of specimens upon which a species or subspecies name was based

Type species: The species that is the name-bearing type of a genus or subgenus

Uncus: The upper structure of the male genitalia

Valva or valve (plural – valvae): The paired lateral claspers of the male genitalia

Vein: A structural strut of the wing, usually tubular and containing a trachea and blood

Venation (neuration): The arrangement of veins in the wings of an insect. An important characteristic in classification

Vernacular names: Names in the language spoken by the people

Ventral: The lower or undersurface of the body or other structure

Vesica: The penis, a membranous eversible organ partly or wholly contained in the tubular aedeagus

Vinculum: The ventral U-shaped body of the male genitalia; the modified ninth sternite of the abdomen

Wing-span (wing-expanse): The greatest width of an insect measured across the forewings from apex to apex, including the fringes or cilia

Wing expansion: The wings of a newly emerged butterfly consist of an upper and a lower membrane kept apart by strands or fibres. Blood (haemolymph) is forced between the two membranes as well as in the hollow veins so that they expand and reach full size. Soon the fluid in the wings and veins harden and the butterfly is ready to fly. The stiff hollow veins form a supporting framework and strengthen the wings

REFERENCES AND SUGGESTED FURTHER READING

ACKERY, P.R. 1984. Systematic and Faunistic Studies on Butterflies. In, *The Biology of Butterflies*, edited by R.I. Vane Wright & P.R. Ackery. Academic Press, London.

ACKERY, P.R., SMITH, C.R. & VANE-WRIGHT, R.I. 1995. *Carcasson's African Butterflies*. CSIRO, Australia.

ACOCKS, J.P.H. 1975. Veld types of South Africa, 2nd. ed.. *Memoirs of the Bot. Survey of S. Africa*, No. 40

ARNOLD, R.A. 1983. *Ecological Studies of Six Endangered Butterflies (Lepidoptera, Lycaenidae): Island Biogeography, Patch Dynamics, and the Design of Habitat Preserves*. University of California Publications, Entomology, **99**: 1-161.

AURIVILLIUS, C. 1925. In Seitz, A., *The Macro Lepidoptera of the World*. **13**. Stuttgart.

BARNES, R.S.K., CALOW, P. & OLIVE, P.J.W. 1988. *The Invertebrates: a new synthesis*. Blackwell Scientific Publications, Oxford.

BERGER, L.A. 1950a. Catalogues raisonnés de la faune entomologique du Congo Belge: Lépidoptères – Rhopalocères. I Fam. Papilionidae. *Annls. Mus. r. Congo belge, Sér. Zool.* **8**(30): 1-104.

_____ 1950b. Systématique des Papilionidae de la faune éthiopienne (Lepidoptera – Rhopalocera). *III Congres National des Sciences* **8**: 47-50.

_____ 1980. Mission entomologique du Musée royal de l'Afrique Centrale aux Monts Uluguru, Tanzanie. 25. Lepidoptera Papilionidae et Pieridae. *Rev. Zool. afr.* **94**: 861-880.

_____ 1981. *Les papillons du Zaire*. 323 pp., 213 pls. Weissenbruch, Bruxelles.

BERNARDI, G. 1962. Missions Ph. Bruneau de Mire au Tibesti: Lépidoptères, Pieridae, Nymphalidae et Danaidae. *Bull. I.F.A.N.*, Ser. A **25**(3): 813-851.

BOND, W. & SLINGSBY, P. 1982. Collapse of an ant-plant mutualism – the Argentine ant, *Tridomyrmex humilis*, and myrmecochorous Cape Proteaceae. *Veld & Flora* **19**(4): 102-104.

BROCK, J.P. 1971. A contribution towards an understanding of the morphology and phylogeny of the ditrysian Lepidoptera. *J. nat. Hist.* **5**: 29-102.

CARCASSON, R.H. 1960. The Swallowtail Butterflies of East Africa (Lepidoptera, Papilionidae). *J. E. Afr. nat. Hist. Soc.*, supplement, No 6.

_____ 1964. A preliminary survey of the Zoogeography of African Butterflies. *E. Afr. Wildlife. J.* **2**: 122-157.

_____ 1981. *Butterflies of Africa*. Collins, London.

CARPENTER, G.D.H. 1935. The Rhopalocera of Abyssinia. A faunistic study. *Trans. R. ent. Soc. Lond.*, **83**: 313-348.

_____ 1941. The relative frequency of beak-marks on butterflies of different edibility to birds. *Proc. zool. Soc. Lond.* (A) III: 223-231.

CHIBA, H. & ELIOT, J.N. 1991. A revision of the Genus *Parnara* Moore (Lepidoptera, Hesperiidae), with Special Reference to the Asian Species. *Tyô to Ga* **42**(3): 179-194.

CLAASSENS, A.J.M. 1974. Methods employed in the successful rearing, under artificial conditions, of two Cape species of *Lepidochrysops* (Lepidoptera: Lycaenidae). *J. ent. Soc. sth. Afr.* **37**(2): 387-392. Text figure.

_____ 1976. Observations on the myrmecophilous relationships and the parasites of *Lepidochrysops methymna methymna* (Trimen) and *L. trimeni* (Bethune-Baker) (Lepidoptera: Lycaenidae). *J. ent. Soc. sth. Afr.* **35**(2): 279-289.

CLAASSENS, A.J.M. & DICKSON, C.G.C. 1974. The early stages of *Aloeides thyra* (L.) (Lep. Lycaenidae) with notes on ant association, distribution and general ecology of the species. *Entomologist's Rec. J. Var.* **86**: 253-258.

_____ 1977. A study of the myrmecophilous behaviour of the immature stages of *Aloeides thyra* (L.) (Lep. Lycaenidae) with special reference to the function of the retractile tubercles and with additional notes on the general biology of the species. *Entomologist's Rec. J. Var.* **89**: 225-231.

_____ 1980. *The Butterflies of the Table Mountain Range*. C. Struik Publishers, Cape Town.

_____ 1984. Butterfly migrations in the South Western Cape. *Metamorphosis* **1**(8): 4

_____ 1986a. *Mylothris chloris agathina* (Cramer) (Lepidoptera: Pieridae), a species which has extended its range of distribution from the easterly part of South Africa to the extreme Western Cape. *Entomologist's Rec. J. Var.* **98**: 1-4. 1 pl., 1 map.

_____ 1986b. *Zophopetes dysmephila dysmephila* (Trimen), a butterfly introduced into the extreme Western Cape on palms. *Entomologist's Rec. J. Var.* **98**: 4-6.

CLARK, G.C. 1940. On the life-histories of some South African Lepidoptera. Part 1. *J. ent. Soc. sth. Afr.* **3**: 42-56.

_____ 1949. Life histories of Papilionidae and Pieridae. In, *The Butterflies of Southern Africa. Part 1. Papilionidae and Pieridae*, by G. van Son. Transvaal Museum Memoir No. 3.

_____ 1978. Life histories of South African Hesperiid butterflies. In, *Pennington's Butterflies of Southern Africa*, edited by C.G.C. Dickson & D.M. Kroon. Ad. Donker, Johannesburg, pp. 205-281.

_____ 1994. Life histories of South African Papilionid butterflies. In, *Pennington's Butterflies of Southern Africa*, revised by G.A. Henning, E.L. Pringle & J. Ball. C. Struik Publishers, Cape Town.

CLARK, G.C. & DICKSON, C.G.C. 1952. *Some South African Butterflies*. Longmans Green and Co., Cape Town.

_____ 1956. The Honey Gland and Tubercles of Larvae of the Lycaenidae. *Lepid. News.* **10**: 37-40.

_____ 1965. The life-histories of two species of South African *Eurema*. *J. Res. Lepid.* **4**: 252-257.

_____ 1967. The life-histories of South African *Colotis erone, C. ione, C. vesta* and *Leptosia alcesta*. *J. Res. Lepid.* **6**: 31-42.

_____ 1971. *Life Histories of the South African Lycaenid Butterflies*. Purnell and Sons, Cape Town.

CLARKE, C.A., CLARKE, F.M.M. & GILL, A.C.L. 1987. Race crosses between two Kenyan mimetic forms of *Papilio dardanus* Brown 1776 and the non-mimetic *Dardanus humbloti* Obth. 1888 from the Comoros. *Papilio Int.* **3**(3): 199-201.

CLARKE, C.A., CLARKE, F.M.M. COLLINS, S.C., GILL, A.C.L. & TURNER, J.R.G. 1985. Male-like females, mimicry and transvestism in butterflies (Lepidoptera: Papilionidae). *Systematic Entomology* **10** : 257-283.

CLENCH, H.K. 1975. Introduction. In, *The Butterflies of North America*, edited by W.H. How. Doubleday & Co., New York. pp 1-72.

COLERIDGE, P.L. 1916. The life history of *Papilio pylades angolanus* Goeze (Lepidoptera: Papilionidae).*J. E. Afr. and Uganda Nat. Hist. Soc.* **5** : 91-93.

COLLINS, N.M. & MORRIS, M.G. 1985. *Threatened Swallowtail Butterflies of the World*. The IUCN Red Data Book. IUCN, Gland, Switzerland.

COMMON, I.F.B. & WATERHOUSE, D.F. 1972. *Butterflies of Australia*. Angus and Robertson, Sidney.

COOPER, R. 1973. *Butterflies of Rhodesia*. Longman Rhodesia, Salisbury, Rhodesia.

CORBET, P.S. 1983. *A Biology of Dragonflies*. Facsimile reprint by E.W. Classey Ltd.

COTTRELL, C.B. 1965. A study of the *methymna*-group of the genus *Lepidochrysops* Hedicke (Lepidoptera: Lycaenidae). *Mem. ent. Soc. sth. Afr.* **9**: 1-110. 3pls., text figures.

_____ 1978. *Aspects of the biogeography of southern African butterflies*. 100 pp. Supplement to *Zambezia* (the Journal of the University of Zimbabwe, Harare).

_____ 1984. Aphytophagy in butterflies: its relationship to myrmecophily. *Zoological Journal of the Linnaean Society* **79**: 1-57.

_____ 1985. The absence of co-evolutional association with Capensis floral element plants in the larval/plant relationships of southwestern Cape butterflies. In Vrba, E.S., ed., *Species and speciation* pp. 115-124. Transvaal Museum Monograph No. 4. Transvaal Museum, Pretoria.

D'ABRERA, B. 1980. *Butterflies of the Afrotropical Region*. 593 pp., 576 col. pls. Lansdowne Editions, East Melbourne.

DE JONG, R. 1976. Affinities between the West Palaearctic and Ethiopian butterfly faunas. *Tijdschr. Ent.* **119**(6): 165-215.

_____ 1978. Monograph of the genus *Spialia* Swinhoe (Lepidoptera, Hesperiidae). *Tijdschr. Ent.* **121**(3): 23-145.

DICKSON, C.G.C. 1972. *What Butterfly is That?* Purnell and Sons, Cape Town.

DICKSON, C.G.C. & KROON, D.M. (eds.) 1978. *Pennington's Butterflies of Southern Africa*. Ad. Donker, Johannesburg.

EHRLICH, P.R. 1958. The comparative morphology, physiology and higher classification of the butterflies (Lepidoptera: Papilionoidea). *Kans. Univ. Sci. Bull.* **39**: 305-370.

ELIOT, J.N. 1973. The higher classification of the Lycaenidae (Lepidoptera): a tentative arrangement. *Bull. Brit. Mus. nat. Hist.* (Ent.) **28**: 371-505.

EVANS, W.H. 1937. *A catalogue of the African Hesperiidae in the British Museum (Natural History)*. Oxford University Press.

_____ 1946. Revisional notes on *African Hesperiidae*. *Ann. Mag. nat. Hist.* (11) **13**: 641-648.

_____ 1949. *A catalogue of the Hesperiidae from Europe, Asia and Australia in the British Museum (Natural History)*. London.

FOX, R.M., et al., 1965. The butterflies of Liberia. *Mem. Am. ent. Soc.* **19**: 1-438.

GERMISHUYS, H. 1982. *Butterflies of southern Africa*. Chris van Rensburg Publications, Johannesburg.

GIFFORD, D. 1965. *A list of the Butterflies of Malawi*. The Society of Malawi. 155 pp., 9 pls in colour.

HANCOCK, D.L. 1983. Classification of the Papilionidae (Lepidoptera): phylogenetic approach. *Smithersia* **2**: 1-48.

_____ 1984. The *Princeps nireus* group of Swallowtails (Lepidoptera: Papilionidae) systematics, phylogeny and biogeography. *Arnoldia Zimbabwe* **9**(12): 181-215.

HANCOCK, D.L. & GARDINER, A.J. 1982. The *Kedestes nerva* group of species (Lepidoptera: Hesperiidae). *Arnoldia Zimbabwe* **9**(8): 105-124.

HEMMING, F. 1967. The generic names of the butterflies and their type species (Lepidoptera: Rhopalocera). *Bull. Brit. Mus. nat. Hist.* (Ent.). Suppl. 9: 1-509.

HENNING, G.A. 1991. Effective Lepidoptera Conservation. *Metamorphosis* **2**(4): 34-35.

_____ 1993. Survival strategies in the Acraeinae (Lepidoptera: Nymphalidae). *Metamorphosis* **4**(3): 100-106.

HENNING, G.A. & HENNING, S.F. 1992. Conservation of Lepidoptera in Southern Africa. In, *A Practical Guide to Butterflies and Moths*, edited by S.E. Woodhall *et al*. The Lepidopterists' Society of Southern Africa, Florida Hills. pp 29-42.

HENNING, G.A., PRINGLE, E.L. & BALL, J. (Revisors) 1994. *Pennington's Butterflies of Southern Africa*. Edited by E.L. Pringle, G.A. Henning & J.B. Ball. C. Struik Publishers, Cape Town.

HENNING, S.F. 1979. Butterflies. In, *African Insect Life*, by S.H. Skaife, revised by J. Ledger. C. Struik Publishers, Cape Town. pp 190-208.

_____ 1982. Moths and butterflies. In *The Sandton Fieldbook*, edited by V. Carruthers. the Sandton Nature Conservation Society. pp. 162-175.

_____ 1983a. Biological groups within the Lycaenidae (Lepidoptera). *J. ent. Soc. sth. Afr.* **46**(1): 65-85.

_____ 1983b. Chemical communication between lycaenid larvae (Lepidoptera: Lycaenidae) and ants (Hymenoptera: Formicidae). *J. ent. Soc. sth. Afr.* **46**(2): 341-366.

_____ 1984a. The effect of ant association on lycaenid larval duration (Lepidoptera Lycaenidae). *Entomologist's Rec. J. Var.* **96**: 99-102.

_____ 1984b. *Southern African Butterflies* with illustrations by Clare Abbott. Macmillan, South Africa, 24 colour plates.

_____ 1984c. Life history and behaviour of *Erikssonia acraeina* Trimen (Lepidoptera: Lycaenidae). *J. ent. Soc. sth. Afr.* **47**(2): 337-342.

_____ 1985. Lepidoptera: Hesperioidea and Papilionoidea. In, *Insects of Southern Africa*, edited by C.H. Scholtz & E. Holm. Butterworths, Durban. pp 366-376.

_____ 1987a. Myrmecophilous Lycaenidae (or how ants help butterflies). *S. Afr. J. Sci.* **83**: 8-9.

_____ 1987b. Myrmecophily in lycaenid butterflies (Lepidoptera: Lycaenidae). *Entomologist's Rec. J. Var.* **99**: 215-222, 261-267.

_____ 1987c. Outline of Lepidoptera Conservation with Special Reference to ant associated Lycaenidae. *Proceedings of the first Lepidoptera Conservation Symposium of the Lepidopterists' Society of Southern Africa*.

_____ 1987d. Dragonflies migrating with *Belenois aurota* in January 1986. *Metamorphosis* **1**(19): 9-14.

_____ 1988. Communication in ants (Hymenoptera: Formicidae). *Entomologist's Rec. J. Var.* **100**: 109-114.

_____ 1989a. *The Charaxinae Butterflies of Africa*. Aloe and Frandsen Publishers, Johannesburg. 472 pages.

_____ 1989b. Observations on butterfly and dragonfly migration in Southern Africa. *Abstract, Zoological Society of Southern Africa: International Symposium on Savanna Movements and Migrations*. p. 20

_____ 1990. Courtship and mating of butterflies. *Entomologist's Rec. J. Var.* **102**: 205-213.

HENNING, S.F. & HENNING, G.A. 1985. South Africa's Endangered Butterflies. *Quagga* **10**: 16-17.

_____ 1989. *South African Red Data Book – Butterflies.* South African National Scientific Programmes Report No 158: 1-175. Council for Scientific and Industrial Research, Pretoria.

HINTON, H.F. 1949-1950. Myrmecophilous Lycaenidae and other Lepidoptera – a summary. *Proc. Trans. S. Lond. ent. Nat. Hist. Soc.* **1949-50**: 111-175.

HOLLAND, W.J. 1896. A preliminary review and synonymic catalogue of the Hesperiidae of Africa and the adjacent islands. *Proc. zool. Soc. Lond.* **1896**: 2-107.

_____ 1920. Lepidoptera of the Congo, being a systematic list of the butterflies and moths collected by the American Museum of Natural History, Congo Expedition, together with descriptions of some hitherto undescribed species. *Bull. Am. Mus. nat. Hist.* **43**(6): 109-369, pls 6-14.

JOANNOU, J.G. 1992. A comparative study of the immature stages of the Southern African species of *Papilio* Linnaeus and an account of the life history of *Papilio constantinus* (Ward), 1871 (Lepidoptera: Papilionidae). *Metamorphosis* **3**(3): 89-94.

KIELLAND, J. 1990. *Butterflies of Tanzania,* Antiquariat Goecke & Evers, Germany.

KINGSOLVER, J.G. 1985. Butterfly engineering. *Scient. Am.,* **253**(2): 90-97.

KLOPPERS, J & VAN SON, G. 1978. *The Butterflies of the Kruger National Park.* National Parks Board of Trustees, Pretoria.

KLOTS, A.B. 1970. Lepidoptera, in *Taxonomists' glossary of insect genitalia,* S.L. Tuxen (ed.), 2nd edition. Munksgaard, Copenhagen. 115-130.

KRISTENSEN, N.P. 1976. Remarks on the family-level phylogeny of butterflies. *Z. Zool. Syst. Evol. Forsch.* **14**: 25-33.

LARSEN, T.B. 1991. *Butterflies of Kenya and their Natural History.* Oxford University Press, Oxford.

_____ 1992a. Migration of *Catopsilia florella* in Botswana (Lepidoptera: Pieridae). *Tropical Lepidoptera,* **3**(1): 2-11.

_____ 1992b. On the status of *Colotis agoye* (Wallengren, 1857) and its subspecies. *Metamorphosis* **3**(1): 5-10.

MARSHALL, G.A.K. 1897. On the synonymy of the butterflies of the genus *Teracolus. Proc. zool. Soc. Lond.* **1897**: 3-36.

MIGDOLL, I. 1987. *Field Guide to the butterflies of Southern Africa.* C. Struik, Cape Town.

MILLER, J.G. 1987. Phylogenetic studies in the Papilioninae (Lepidoptera: Papilionidae). *Bull. Am. Mus. Nat. Hist.* **186**: 365-512.

MONTEIRO, R. 1891. *Delagoa Bay: Its Natives and Natural History.* XI, 274 pp.

MOREAU, R.E. 1966. *The bird faunas of Africa and its islands.* Academic Press, London and New York

MURRAY, D.P. 1932. The early stages of some South African Hesperids. *S. Afr. J. Sci.* **29**: 584-588.

_____ 1935. *South African Butterflies: A Monograph of the Family Lycaenidae.* John Bale, Sons and Danielsson, Ltd., London. 195 pages.

NORRIS, K.R. 1970. General Biology. In: *Insects of Australia.* Melbourne University Press, Carlton, Victoria, 107-140.

OWEN, D.F. 1971. *Tropical Butterflies.* Clarendon Press, Oxford.

PENNINGTON, K.M. 1978. see Dickson, C.G.C. & Kroon, D.M., 1978.

PENNINGTON, K.M. 1994. see Henning, G.A., Pringle, E.L. & Ball, J. 1994.

PETERS, W. 1952. *A provisional check-list of the butterflies of the Ethiopian Region.* Feltham, Middlesex, E.W. Classey.

PICKER, M. & GRIFFITHS, C. 1989. Insects within insects. Parasites of the Garden Acraea. *Sagittarius* **4**(1): 12-15. South African Museum.

PINHEY, E. 1949. *Butterflies of Rhodesia.* Rhodesia Scientific Association, Salisbury, Rhodesia.

_____ 1965. *Butterflies of Southern Africa.* Nelson, Cape Town.

_____ 1968. Check list of the Butterflies (Lepidoptera: Rhopalocera) of Botswana: Part 1. *Botswana Notes and Records* **1**: 85-92.

_____ 1971. Check list of the Butterflies (Lepidoptera: Rhopalocera) of Botswana: Part 2. *Botswana Notes and Records* **3**: 148-152.

_____ 1974. Check list of the Butterflies (Lepidoptera: Rhopalocera) of Botswana: Part 3. *Botswana Notes and Records* **6**: 197-200.

_____ 1976. Check list of the Butterflies (Lepidoptera: Rhopalocera) of Botswana: Part 4. *Botswana Notes and Records* **8**: 269-288.

PRINGLE, E.L., HENNING, G.A. & BALL, J.B. (eds.) 1994. *Pennington's Butterflies of Southern Africa.* Revised by G.A. Henning, E.L. Pringle & J.B. Ball. C. Struik Publishers, Cape Town.

PYLE, R.M., BENTZEN, M.M., & OPLER, P.A. 1981. Insect Conservation. *Ann. Rev. Entomol.* **26**: 233-258.

PYLE, R.M. & OPLER, P.A. 1975. Interview on the rôle of the Office of Endangered Species in insect conservation. *Atala* **3**: 2-3.

QUICKELBERGE, C.D. 1976. A re-assessment of the status of the forms of the *Dixeia doxo* (Godart) complex. *Durban Mus. Novit.* **11**: 107-114.

_____ 1982. Systematic notes on Southern African butterflies – 6. *Durban Mus. Novit.* **13**(11): 139-148.

_____ 1986. *Familiar South African Butterflies.* Natal Branch of the Wildlife Society of Southern Africa, Durban.

ROBBINS, R.K. 1980. The lycaenid "False Head" hypothesis: historical review and quantitative analysis. *J. Lepid. Soc.* **34**(2): 194-208.

_____ 1981. The "False Head" hypothesis: predation and wing pattern variation of lycaenid butterflies. *Am. Nat.* **118**: 770-775.

_____ 1988. Comparative morphology of the butterfly foreleg coxa and trochanter (Lepidoptera) and its systematic implications. *Proc. Entomol. Soc. Wash.* **90**(2): 133-154.

ROBBINS, R.K. & SMALL, G.B. 1981. Wind dispersal of Panamanian Hairstreak Butterflies (Lepidoptera: Lycaenidae) and its Evolutionary Significance. *Biotropica* **13**(4): 308-315.

SCHOLTZ, C.H. & HOLM, E. (Editors) 1985. *Insects of Southern Africa.* Butterworths, Durban.

SCOTT, J.A. 1968. Hilltopping as a mating mechanism to aid in the survival of low density species. *J. Res. Lepid.* **7**(4): 191-204.

_____ 1973. Mating of butterflies. *J. Res. Lepid.* **11**(2): 99-127.

_____ 1974. Mate-locating behaviour of butterflies. *Amer. Midl. Nat.* **91**: 103-117.

SEITZ, A. 1925. *Macrolepidoptera of the World* Vol. XIII. Stuttgart, Alfred Kernen.

SHIELDS, A.O. 1967. Hilltopping. *J. Res. Lepid.* **6**(2): 69-178.

SKAIFE, S.H. 1955. *Dwellers in darkness, An introduction to the study of termites.* Longmans Green, London.

_____ 1961. *The study of ants.* Longmans Green, London

SLINGSBY, P. 1982. The Argentine Ant – How much of a threat. *Veld & Flora,* **69**(4): 102-104.

_____ & BOND, W. 1981. Ants – friends of the fynbos. *Veld & Flora,* **68**(4): 102-104.

STONEHAM, H.F. 1951 – 1965. *The Butterflies of Western Kenya with Notes on Allied forms.* Stoneham Museum Publications, Nairobi. (11 parts, published in a limited edition of 5 fascicles).

STUCKENBERG, B. 1962. The Distributions of the Montane Palaeogenic Element in the South Africa Invertebrate Fauna. *Ann. Cape Prov. Mus.* **II**: 190-205.

SWANEPOEL, D.A. 1953. *Butterflies of South Africa: Where, when and how they fly.* Maskew Miller Ltd., Cape Town.

TALBOT, G. 1939. Revisional notes on the genus *Colotis* Hübn. (Lepidoptera: Pieridae). *Trans. R. ent. Soc. Lond.* **88**: 173-246.

_____ 1943a. Revisional notes on *Anaphaeis* Hübn. and *Belenois* Hübn., with descriptions of new forms. *Ann. Mag. nat. Hist.* (11)**10**: 305-366.

_____ 1943b. Notes on the genus *Dixeia* Talbot, with descriptions of new forms (Lepidoptera, Rhopalocera, Pieridae). *Proc. R. ent. Soc. Lond.* (B) **12**: 102-112.

_____ 1944. A preliminary review of the genus *Mylothris* Hübn. (1819) (Lepidoptera: Rhopalocera, Pieridae). *Trans. R. ent. Soc. Lond.* **94**: 155-185.

TRIMEN, R. 1862-1866. *Rhopalocera Africae Australis,* Parts 1-2, iv + 353 numbered pages.

_____ 1887-1889. *South African Butterflies,* Vols. 1-3. Truber and Co., London.

TURNER, J.R.G. 1963. Geographical variation and evolution in the males of the butterfly *Papilio dardanus* Brown (Lepidoptera: Papilionidae). *Trans. R. ent. Soc. Lond.* **115**(9): 239-259.

USHER, M.B. 1980. The *Andronymus caesar* complex of species (Hesperiidae). *Systematic Entomology* **5**: 291-302.

VAN SON, G. 1939. Notes on the *menestheus* group of *Papilio* L. and the South African races of *Papilio ophidicephalus* Oberthür. *Ann. Transv. Mus.* **20**: 52-64.

_____ 1949. The Butterflies of Southern Africa. Part 1. Papilionidae and Pieridae. *Transv. Mus. Mem.* **3**: 1-237, 47 plates.

_____ 1955. The Butterflies of Southern Africa. Part 2. Nymphalidae: Danainae and Satyrinae. *Transv. Mus. Mem.* **8**: 1-166, 37 plates.

_____ 1963. The Butterflies of Southern Africa. Part 3. Nymphalidae: Acraeinae. *Transv. Mus. Mem.* **14**: 1-130, 29 plates.

_____ 1979. The Butterflies of Southern Africa. Part 4. Nymphalidae: Nymphalinae. Edited by L. Vári. *Trans. Mus. Mem.* **22**: 1-286, 76 plates.

VANE-WRIGHT, R.I. & ACKERY, P.R. 1984. *The Biology of Butterflies,* Published for The Royal Entomological Society, London, by Academic Press, pp. 429.

VANE-WRIGHT, R.I. & SMITH, C.R. 1991. Phylogenetic relationships of three African swallowtail butterflies, *Papilio dardanus, P. phorcas* and *P. constantinus*: a cladistic analysis (Lepidoptera: Papilionidae). *Systematic Entomology* **16**: 275-291.

VÁRI, L. 1976. South African Lepidoptera, 7. Descriptions and notes on new taxa of Rhopalocera. *Ann. Transv. Mus.* **30**: 121-143.

VÁRI, L. & KROON, D.M. 1986. *Southern African Lepidoptera: A series of cross-referenced indices.* The Lepidopterists' Society of Southern Africa & The Transvaal Museum, Pretoria.

VIETTE, P. 1956. Faune de Madagascar. III Insectes, Lépidoptères: Hesperiidae. *Pub. Inst. Rech. Scient. Tananarive.*

VILLIERS, A. 1957. Les Lépidoptères de l'Afrique Noire Francaise. Fasc. 2, Papilionides. *Initiations Africaines, Dakar, I.F.A.N.,* **I**: 1-49.

VRBA, E.S. (Editor) 1985. *Species and Speciation.* Transvaal Museum Monograph No 4, pp. 176.

WEIS-FOGH, T. 1975. Unusual mechanisms for the generation of lift in flying animals. *Scient. Am.,* **233**(5): 81-87.

WELLS, R.W. 1957. The life-history of *Papilio euphranor* Trimen (Lepidoptera: Papilionidae). *J. ent. Soc. sth. Afr.* **20**: 117-119.

WILLIAMS, J.G. 1969. *A field guide to the butterflies of Africa.* Collins, London.

WILLIAMS, M.C. 1985. Breeding butterflies in captivity. Part 1. Introduction. *Metamorphosis* **13**: 1.

_____ 1986. Breeding butterflies in captivity. Part 2. Danaidae. *Metamorphosis* **17**: 6.

_____ 1987. Basic Techniques in Butterfly and Moth rearing. *Proceedings of the first Lepidoptera Conservation Symposium, Lepidopterists' Society of Southern Africa.* p. 32.

_____ 1994. *Butterflies of Southern Africa, A Field Guide.* Southern Book Publishers, Halfway House.

WOODHALL, S. (Editor) 1992. *How to collect and study Lepidoptera.* The Lepidopterists' Society of Southern Africa.

_____ 1994. Notes on the early stages of three species of *Platylesches* Holland (Lepidoptera: Hesperiidae). *Metamorphosis* **5**(3): 127-131.

ABBREVIATIONS

Explanation of abbreviations and other matters concerning the references.

Am. ent. Soc. = American Entomological Society

Amer. Midl. Nat. = American Midlands Naturalist

Am. Nat. = American Naturalist

Amoen. Acad. = Amoenitates seu Dissertationes variae

Ann. Cape Prov. Mus. = Annals of the Cape Provincial Museums

Ann. ent. Soc. Amer. = Annals of the Entomological Society of America

Ann. Mag. nat. Hist. = Annals and Magazine of Natural History

Annls. Mus. r. Congo belge = Annales du Musée royaume du Congo belge

Ann. Transv. Mus. = Annals of the Transvaal Museum

Arch. Naturgesch. = Archiv für Naturgeschichte

Atti. Accad. Sci. Ist. Bologna. Mem. = Atti dell'Accademia dellae scienze dell'Instituto di Bologna. Memorie

Ausland. Schmetterl. = Die ausländischen Schmetterlinge

Bibl. Zoologica = Bibliotheca Zoologica

Bull. Am. Mus. nat. Hist. = Bulletin of the American Museum of Natural History

Bull. Brit. Mus. nat. Hist. (Ent.) = Bulletin of the British Museum (Natural History), Entomology

Bull. Hill Mus., Witley = Bulletin of the Hill Museum, Witley

Bull. I.F.A.N. = Bulletin de l'Institut Française d'Afrique

Bull. Soc. ent. Fr. = Bulletin de la Société entomologique de France

Cat. Afr. Hesper. = A Catalogue of the African Hesperiidae in the British Museum (Natural History)

Cat. Hesp. Europe, Asia, Australia = Catalogue of the Hesperiidae of Europe, Asia, Australia

Cist. Ent. = Cistula Entomologica

C. r. Soc. ent. Belg. = Compte Rendu de la Société entomologique de Belgique

Dt. ent. Z. Iris. = Deutsche entomologische Zeitschrift, Iris

Durban Mus. Novit. = Durban Museum Novitates

E. Afr. Wildlife. J. = East African Wildlife Journal

Encycl. Méth. d'Hist. Nat. (Zool.) = Encyclopédie Méthodique d'Histoire naturelle, etc.

Ent. Beyträge = Entomologische Beyträge zu des Ritter, Linné, Zwölften Ausgabe des Natursystems

Ent. Rdsch. = Entomologische Rundschau

Entomologist's mon. Mag. = Entomologist's Monthly Magazine

Entomologist's Rec. J. Var. = Entomologist's Record and Journal of Variation

Ent. Z., Frankf. a. M. = Entomologische Zeitschrift, Frankfurt am Main

Étud. d'Ent. = Études d'Entomologie (Lépidoptères) de l'Afrique orientale et d'Algérie

Exot. Butterfl. = Illustrations of new species of Exotic Butterflies

Faune ent. de Madag. = Faune entomologique de Madagascar etc. Lépidoptères

Ferr. Gal. Voy. Abyss. Ent. = Les Insectes dans le voyage en Abyssinie par Ferret et Galliner

Genera Insect. = Genera Insectorum

Hist. Phys. Natur. et Polit. Madag. = Histoire physique, naturelle et politique de Madagascar: Histoire naturelle des Lépidoptères

Illustr. zool. = Illustrations of Zoology

Initiations Africaines, Dakar, I.F.A.N. = Initiations Africaines, Dakar, Institut Française d'Afrique

Indo-Austral. Lep. Fauna = Die Indo-Australische Lepidopteren-Fauna

Int. ent. Z.= Internationale entomologische Zeitschrift

Introd. Hist. Nat. = Introduction to Natural History

J. E. Afr. and Uganda Nat. Hist. Soc. = Journal of the East Africa and Uganda Natural History Society

J. E. Afr. nat. Hist. Soc. = Journal of the East Africa Natural History Society

J. ent. Soc. sth. Afr. = Journal of the Entomological Society of Southern Africa.

J. Lepid. Soc. = Journal of the Lepidopterists' Society

J. nat. Hist. = Journal of Natural History

J. Res. Lepid. = Journal of Research in the Lepidoptera

Kafirs Illustr. = The Kafirs illustrated in a series of drawings taken among the Amazulu, Amapondo, and Amakosa tribes, etc.

Kans. Univ. Sci. Bull. = Kansas University Science Bulletin

K. svenska VetenskAkad. Handl. (N.F.) = Kungliga Svenska vetenskapsakademiens handlingar (Ny Följd)

Lepid. Ceylon. = Lepidoptera of Ceylon

Lepid. Indica = Lepidoptera Indica

Lepid. News = Lepidopterists' News

Macrolep. of World = The Macrolepidoptera of the World

Mag. f. Insektenk. (Illiger) = Magazin für Insektenkunde. Herausgegeben von K. Illiger

Mber. dt. Akad. Wiss. Berl. = Monatsbericht der Deutschen Akademie der Wissenschaften zu Berlin

Mem. Am. ent. Soc. = Memoirs of the American Entomological Society

Mem. ent. Soc. sth. Afr. = Memoirs of the Entomological Society of Southern Africa

Memoirs of the Bot. Survey of S. Africa = Memoirs of the Botanical Survey of South Africa

Mitt. nat. Ver. Greifsw. = Mitteilungen des Naturwissenschaftlichen Vereins für Neu-Vorpommern u. Rugen in Greifswald

Mitt. zool. Mus. Berl. = Mitteilungen aus dem Zoologischen Museum in Berlin

Mus. Lud. Ulr. Reg. = Museum Ludovicae Ulricae Reginae

Ofvers. K. VetenskAkad. Forh. = Öfversigt af K. Vetenskapsakademiens förhandlingar. Stockholm

Papilio Int. = Papilio International

Petites Nouvelles. = Catalogue des Hespérides du Musée Royal d'Histoire Naturelle des Bruxelles in Petites Nouvelles

Proc. Entomol. Soc. Wash. = Proceedings of the Entomological Society of Washington

Proc. R. Dublin Soc. = Proceedings of the Royal Dublin Society

Proc. R. ent. Soc. Lond. = Proceedings of the Royal Entomological Society of London

Proc. Trans. S. Lond. ent. Nat. Hist. Soc. = Proceedings and Transactions of the South London Entomological and Natural History Society

Proc. zool. Soc. Lond. = Proceedings of the Zoological Society of London

Pub. Inst. Rech. Scient. Tananarive = Publications de l'Institut de Recherche Scientifique Tananarive - Tsimbazaza

Reise Mossamb. Ins. = Naturwissenschaftliche Reise nach Mossambique

Reise Novara = Reise der Östereichischen Fregatte 'Novara' um de Erde

Rev. franc. Ent. = Revue française d'Entomologie

Rev. Mag. Zool. = Revue et Magasin de Zoologie

Rev. Zool. afr. = Revue de Zoologie et de Botanique Africaines

Rhop. Caffr. = Rhopalocera Africae Australis

S. Afr. Butterfl. = South African Butterflies

S. Afr. J. Sci. = South African Journal of Science.

Samml. exot. Schmetterl. = Sammlung exotischer Schmetterlinge

Scient. Am. = Scientific American

Spéc. gén. Lépid. = Spécies génerales des Lépidoptères

Stettin. ent. Ztg. = Stettiner entomologische Zeitung

Stylops = A Journal of Taxonomic Entomology. London

Suppl. Syst. Ent. = Supplement of Systematic Entomology

Symb. Phys. = Symbolae Physicae

Syst. Ent. = Systema Entomologiae

Syst. Nat. = Systema Naturae

Tijdschr. Ent. = Tijdschrift voor Entomologie. Holland.

Trans. ent. Soc. Lond. = Transactions of the Entomological Society of London

Trans. R. ent. Soc. Lond. = Transactions of the Royal Entomological Society of London

Transv. Mus. Mem. = Transvaal Museum Memoirs

Uitl. Kapellen = De Uitlandsche Kapellen

Verh. zool.-bot. Ges. Wien = Verhandlungen der Zoologisch-botanischen Gesellschaft in Wien

Verz. bek. Schmett. = Verzeichniss bekannter Schmetterlinge

Voy. Afr. austr. = Voyage dans l'Afrique australe

Wien. ent. Mschr. = Wiener entomologische Monatsschrift

Zool. Ill. Ins. = Zoological Illustrations Insects

Zool. Misc. = The Zoological Miscellany by J.E. Gray

Zuträge Samml. exot. Schmetterl. = Zuträge zur Sammlung exotischer Schmetterlinge

Z. Zool. Syst. Evol. Forsch. = Zeitschrift für Zoologische Systematik und Evolutionforschung, Frankfurt

pl (s) = plate, plates

17 in bold print = volume 17

17(2) = volume 17, No. 2

17(3): 111-123 = Volume 17, No.3, pages 111 to 123.

PRINTING IN ITALICS

Title of publication in italics = The publication is in book form.

Title of publication in normal print and reference in italics = The publication is in the form of an article in a journal or a special edition of a journal such as a memoir or bulletin.

INDEX TO COMMON AND SCIENTIFIC NAMES

SUBSCRIBERS

Sponsors' Edition

Steve Bales
B•O•E NatWest
The Brenthurst Library
Steve Collins
First National Bank
Doreen Read
Walter Becker SA (Pty) Ltd
Ken Whyte

Collectors' Edition

5th Avenue Properties
Carolynn & Jonathan Ball
Alex Barrell
Viv & Lori Bartlett
Michel Beaurain
John E Bishop
Howard & Di Blight
Paul Brink
N R G Brunette
John & Brenda Collett

The Curle Trust
Elmi & Roger Dixon
Mr J P du Plessis
F G Eckl
Shigeru Eda
Liz & Alex Fick
Eugene & Lalie Fourie
Robert Gee
Alec & Cathy Grant
R G Jeffery

W Harry Lange
Allen & Carol Miller
Takuhei Murase
Dr Kiyoshi Okubo
Arda & Kotie Retief
Alan Stanley
François Steffens
Sean Swarts & Arnia van Vuuren
Dave & Andrew Upshon
Derric H Wilson

Standard Edition

A B C Bookshop	R J Clinton	Dr & Mrs J E & Miss K E M Granger
Albertus Delport Biblioteek	Jan & Jerine Coetzee	Marie Hanni
Antiquariat Goecke & Evers	André J Coetzer	Harry Molteno Library, National Botanical
Daphne Arfanotti	Steve Collins	Institute
Andrew Atkinds	T C E Congdon	Mrs J E Haynes
Paoletta Baker	Pietro Corgatelli	Peggy Heard
Dr A Ballantine	Mr Alistair Cowan	Hugh D C Heron
Ivan Bampton	Jack Crutchley	Anton Hirsiger
K Baragwanath	Andrew Crutchley	R W Hornabrook, New Zealand
David B Batchelor	Raymond Danowski	Doug & Jane Hutson
Bauer & Sato, Japan	Peter & Dyanne de Vos	Infor. South Africa
Stephen Baytopp	J I de Wet	Jennifer Kim Jager
Michel Beaurain	N J S Duke	Inez Jordan
J & J P Bello	Vincent Faiella	Simon Joubert
T Bodbijl	Prof Dr Konrad Fiedler	Mrs P J Kenny-Gibon
John Bridgeman	Richard Fisher	K D Kirkman
Ernst Brockmann	Malcolm G Foster	Johan Kloppers
Margaret Brooks	Eugene & Lalie Fourie	Mr D P Knoop
Nino & Karin Burelli	M D Frudd	Andy & Shirley Krajewski
Marius Burger	Dr A J Gardiner	A Kreulen
Cape Nature Conservation, Stellenbosch	M W Gardiner	Fanie Kriel
Dr Dario Cappelli	Dr H Geertsema	David C Lees
Gregory Chantler	F W Gess	Jean Pierre Lequeux
Dr A J M Claassens	Jan Giliomee	Oscar Lockwood

Henk & André Loots

John David Loren

Martin W and Dean K Lunderstedt

Peter & Yvonne MacQuilkan

Dr Ralph W Macy

Amy, Sue & Don Marshall

P G Mavros

Gordon McCallum

Clive McDowell

Mrs A W McQueen

Rob (W R G) Millar

Roy Miller

Doug Morton

Peter & Hester Müller

Cornelia Naude

Juliet Nixon-Hollis

Rolf Oberprieler, Pretoria

Dr P P E Oosthuizen

B W J O'Keeffe

Gavin Paulsen

Mark & Charlie Paxton

Dr R M Pelteret

Renzo & Glennell Perissinotto

Antonitus Marius & Harriet Potgieter

Rand Afrikaans University Library

Marion & Malcolm Read

Liezl Retief

R K Richmond

Douglas Stuart Roberts

P J Roestorf

Peter & Keith Roos

Mrs A Salusbury

J N E Scott

H E T Selb

Dr R Sevin

Sylvia & Barnard Shull

Dennis & Ansie Slotow

Smithsonian Institution Libraries

Keith & Dorothy Smith

Prof Sir Richard Southwood DL, FRS

Kobus Spies

Bill & Christina Steele

Johannes Lodewyk Steenekamp

James D Stewart

D P J Steyn

Susan Strauss

Mr R J Symmonds

Colin & Sarah Tilbury

Roy Trendler

Bernard Turlin

James W D Turner

University of Florida

University of Stellenbosch Library Service

University of Stellenbosch

University of Toronto Library

Prof C J Uys

M & M A van Rijswijck

Lenie van Schalkwyk

Henri & Maureen Viljoen

Peter, Matthew & Sarah Ward

Richard Warren

Steven E Whitebread

Michael Whitley

William R Perkins Library, Duke
   University

Jürgen Witt

Dr C S Wood-Baker

G W Woodland

James John Young